PAN-AFRICAN CONGRESS ON PREHISTORY

THE PROCEEDINGS OF THE THIRD CONGRESS
LIVINGSTONE 1955

THIRD PAN-AFRICAN CONGRESS ON

PREHISTORY

LIVINGSTONE 1955

Edited by
J. DESMOND CLARK

Assisted by
SONIA COLE

LONDON
CHATTO & WINDUS
1957

Printed in Scotland at the University Press, Glasgow
by Robert MacLehose and Company Limited

Preface

THE PAN-AFRICAN CONGRESS ON PREHISTORY, which meets approximately every four years, enables workers in the fields of Prehistory, Quaternary Geology and Palaeontology, to meet and discuss mutual problems and obtain up-to-date information on the research projects that are being carried out in the various parts of the African Continent. In addition, excursions that are arranged enable delegates to see some of the more important prehistoric sites in the area of the host country.

The idea of holding such a Congress was first conceived by Dr L. S. B. Leakey, shortly after the war, and the first Congress, organized by him, met in 1947 in Nairobi at the invitation of the Kenya Government. (The Proceedings of this Congress were published in 1952 and are obtainable from Basil Blackwell, Oxford.) The Second Congress met in 1952 in Algiers, by invitation of the three Governments of French North Africa. (The Proceedings of this Congress were published in 1955 and are obtainable from Arts et Métiers Graphiques, 18 rue Seguier, Paris 6e.)

In 1955 the Third Congress was invited by the Northern Rhodesia Government to meet in Livingstone in connection with the celebrations to commemorate the centenary of the discovery of the Victoria Falls by Dr David Livingstone, and the beginning of the systematic exploration of the interior parts of the continent north of the Zambezi River.

The Congress met in session from July 22 to July 28 and there were various excursions before and after the sessions.

Generous grants from the Governments of Northern and Southern Rhodesia, the Southern Rhodesia State Lotteries, and the four Copper Companies—Rhokana Corporation, Limited, Roan Antelope Copper Mines, Limited, Mufulira Copper Mine Ltd. and Nchanga Mines Limited —made this meeting possible and went a long way to enable these Proceedings to be published so expeditiously. The excursion to the Katanga Province of the Belgian Congo was sponsored and financially assisted by the Minister for the Colonies, the Union Minière du Haut-Katanga and the Comité Spécial du Katanga. The Wenner-Gren Foundation of New York for Anthropological Research has also made a generous grant towards the cost of publishing the Proceedings, while Mr A. L. Wilkie, sponsor of the Wilkie Foundation, Illinois, has borne the full cost of the colour blocks.

For all these generous donations, which speak eloquently of the interest of their donors in furthering prehistoric research in this continent, our most grateful thanks must be recorded.

Not a few discoveries, some of the greatest importance, have been made in Africa since the Algiers Congress in 1952. The Livingstone Congress, therefore, enabled workers to present the results of their researches to their colleagues—in not a few instances for the first time—and much valuable discussion followed from the reading of papers. This present volume provides an up-to-date record of the progress of investigations in the various inter-related fields of Quaternary research in the African Continent and as such it is hoped will prove of value not only to workers in Africa, but also to all who seek a concise and up-to-date record of research there.

Owing to printing costs and the need to cut our coat according to our cloth, it has unfortunately been necessary to return to the authors some of the communications submitted by non-participating delegates; this has been done only where papers were of indirect interest to workers in Africa, or where the subject matter had already been published in materially the same form elsewhere. It has also proved necessary in some cases to reduce the number of illustrations and to redraw certain tables and diagrams, but this has only been done with the author's consent.

Preface

To Mr John Easton of Robert MacLehose & Co. Ltd, the printers, I am indebted for much helpful advice on the printing of this book.

Finally I should like to place on record my most grateful thanks to Mrs Sonia Cole for her careful and time-consuming work in the later stages of editing the papers and preparing these for the printers. Her help has made the task of editing this book far less onerous than it otherwise would have been and I gratefully acknowledge her valuable assistance.

J. DESMOND CLARK
General Secretary

Contents

SECTION I

QUATERNARY GEOLOGY, GENERAL PALAEONTOLOGY AND CLIMATOLOGY

*In addition to the above, the following paper
was read but not submitted for publication:*

SYMPOSIUM ON KALAHARI SANDS

Contents

Contents

In addition to the above, the following papers were read but not submitted for publication:

PUBLIC LECTURES

Contents

The following Public Lectures were also given:

COLOURED PLATES

THIRD PAN-AFRICAN CONGRESS

ON

PREHISTORY

LIVINGSTONE, JULY 22-28, 1955

PATRON-IN-CHIEF

THE RIGHT HON. THE LORD LLEWELLIN, G.B.E., M.C., T.D.

Governor-General of the Federation of Rhodesia and Nyasaland

PATRONS

VICE-ADMIRAL SIR PEVERIL WILLIAM-POWLETT, K.C.B., C.B.E., D.S.O.

Governor of Southern Rhodesia

SIR ARTHUR BENSON, K.C.M.G.

Governor of Northern Rhodesia

SIR GEOFFREY COLBY, K.C.M.G.

Governor of Nyasaland

COMMITTEE ELECTED AT THE OPENING PLENARY SESSION OF THE THIRD PAN-AFRICAN CONGRESS AT LIVINGSTONE ON JULY 22, 1955

President	DR L. S. B. LEAKEY (Kenya)
Vice-Presidents	PROF. C. VAN RIET LOWE (South Africa)
	PROF. C. ARAMBOURG (France)
General Secretary	DR J. DESMOND CLARK (N. Rhodesia)
Assistant Secretaries	PROF. G. MORTELMANS (Belgium)
	MRS SONIA COLE (Kenya)

Section I—QUATERNARY GEOLOGY, Etc.

President	PROF. G. MORTELMANS (Belgium)
Vice-Presidents	DR K. P. OAKLEY (Great Britain)
	DR H. B. S. Cooke (South Africa)

Section II—HUMAN PALAEONTOLOGY

President	PROF. G. H. R. VON KOENIGSWALD (Holland)
Vice-Presidents	PROF. S. L. WASHBURN (U.S.A.)
	PROF. S. ALCOBE (Spain)

Section III—PREHISTORIC ARCHAEOLOGY

President	PROF. L. PERICOT GARCIA (Spain)
Vice-Presidents	M. C. BURKITT, ESQ. (Great Britain)
	DR R. MAUNY (French West Africa)

List of Delegates

Name	Country	Representing	Present Address
ALCOBÉ, Prof. S.	Spain	Universidad, Barcelona	Universidad, Barcelona, Spain
ANCIAUX DE FAVEAUX, Dr Dom Adalbert, Docteur ès Sciences	Congo Belge	Musée Léopold II	B.P. 212, Jadotville, Katanga, Belgian Congo
ARAMBOURG, Prof. C.	France	(i) Museum National d'Histoire Naturelle (ii) Société Géologique de France	Laboratoire de Paléontologie, 3, Place Valhubert, Paris 5e
BAKKER, Dr E. M. van Zinderen	South Africa	University of the Orange Free State	University of the Orange Free State, Bloemfontein, S. Africa
BARBOUR, Prof. G.B., Ph.D., F.R.S.E., F.G.S.A.	U.S.A.	(i) University of Cincinnati (ii) Ohio Academy of Science (iii) Cincinnati Museum of Natural History	3521 Cornell Place, Cincinnati 20, Ohio, U.S.A.
BLANKOFF, B.	Congo Belge	Private	B.P. 245, Luluabourg, Kasai, Belgian Congo
BOND, Dr G., F.G.S.	Southern Rhodesia	National Museum of Southern Rhodesia	P.O. Box 240, Bulawayo, S. Rhodesia
BONÉ, Dr E. L.	Belgium	University of Louvain	Dept. des Sciences, Collège Philosophique St Albert, 23 Route de Mont St Jean, Louvain, Belgium
BOSTON, D.	Great Britain	Private	86 Crane St., Salisbury, Wilts., England
BRAIN, C. K., B.Sc.	South Africa	Transvaal Museum	P.O. Box 413, Pretoria, S. Africa
BRIGGS, Dr L. Cabot, A.B., A.M., Diploma in Anthropology (Oxon.)	U.S.A.	(i) American Association of Physical Anthropologists (ii) Peabody Museum of Harvard University	7, Rue Pierre Viala, Algiers
BURKITT, M. C., M.A., F.S.A.	Great Britain	(i) Cambridge University (ii) The British Association	Merton House, Grantchester, Cambridge, England
CATON-THOMPSON, Miss G., Litt.D., F.B.A.	Great Britain	Private	Conduit Rise, Conduit Head Rd., Cambridge, England
CHITTICK, N., M.A.	Sudan	Sudan Government Antiquities Service	Highfield, Levylsdene, Merrow, Guildford, Surrey
CLARK, J. D., O.B.E., M.A., Ph.D., F.S.A.	Northern Rhodesia	(i) Northern Rhodesia Government	P.O. Box 124, Livingstone, Northern Rhodesia

List of Delegates

Name	Country	Representing	Present Address
		(ii) Rhodes-Livingstone Museum (iii) National Monuments Commission	
CLARK, Sir Wilfred Le Gros, M.A., M.D., B.Sc., LL.D., F.R.C.S., F.R.S.	Great Britain	(i) Oxford University (ii) The Royal Society	Dept. of Anatomy, University Museum, Oxford
COLE, Mrs S., F.G.S.	Great Britain	Kenya Government	Flat 6, 11 the Paragon, Blackheath, London S.E. 3
COOK, A. M. SPENCER	Southern Rhodesia	Private	P.O. Box 121, Que Que, Southern Rhodesia
COOKE, C. K.	Southern Rhodesia	National Monuments Commission of Southern Rhodesia	P.O. Box 240, Bulawayo, Southern Rhodesia
COOKE, Dr H. B. S., F.R.S.S.	South Africa	University of the Witwatersrand	Dept. of Geology, University of the Witwatersrand, Milner Park, Johannesburg
COON, Prof. C. S.	U.S.A.	University of Penna	University of Penna, 33rd and Spruce Street, Philadelphia, U.S.A.
DART, Prof. R. A., M.D., CH.M., M.Sc.	South Africa	University of the Witwatersrand	25 Park St., Oaklands, Johannesburg
DAVIES, Dr O.	Gold Coast	University College of the Gold Coast	University College, Achimota, Gold Coast
DRENNAN, Prof. M. R., M.A., M.B., F.R.C.S.E.	South Africa	(i) Government of the Union of South Africa (ii) Royal Society of South Africa	Dept. of Anatomy, University of Cape Town, Mowbray, Cape
EWER, Mrs R. F., Ph.D.	South Africa	Private	Zoology Dept. Rhodes University, Grahamstown, S. Africa
FAGG, B. E. B., M.A.	Nigeria	Jos Museum	Jos Museum, Nigeria
FEJOS, Prof. P., M.D. Sc.D.	U.S.A.	Wenner-Gren Foundation for Anthropological Research	Wenner-Gren Foundation for Anthropological Research, 14 East 71st St., New York 21, N.Y.
FOCK, Dr G. J.	South West Africa	(i) Swakopmund Museum (ii) Hugo Obermaier Gesellschaft and its journal *Quartär*	P.O. Box 256, Swakopmund, S.W. Africa
FOSBROOKE, H. A., M.A.	Tanganyika	Tanganyika Government	P.O. Box 900, Lusaka, Northern Rhodesia
GALLOWAY, Prof. A., M.B.E., D.Sc., F.R.S.	Uganda	The University College of East Africa (Makerere College)	Makerere College Medical School, P.O. Box 2072, Kampala, Uganda
GODFREY, Prof. W. S., A.B., A.M., Ph.D.	U.S.A.	(i) The Wilkie Foundation (ii) The American Anthropological Association	Beloit College, Beloit, Wisconsin, U.S.A.

List of Delegates

Name	Country	Representing	Present Address
GOODALL, Mrs E., F.R.A.I.	Southern Rhodesia	(iii) Logan Museum of Anthropology, Beloit College Queen Victoria Memorial Museum	51a Montagu Avenue, Salisbury, Southern Rhodesia
GROBBELAAR, Dr C. S.	South Africa	Stellenbosch University	University of Stellenbosch, Stellenbosch
HAUGHTON, Dr S. H.	South Africa	Commission de Coopération technique en Afrique au Sud du Sahara	P.O. Box 401, Pretoria
HIERNAUX, Dr J.	Ruanda Urundi	Institut pour la Recherche scientifique en Afrique Centrale	I.R.S.A.C. Astrida, Ruanda-Urundi, via Belgian Congo
HOFFMAN, Dr A. C.	South Africa	National Museum, Bloemfontein	National Museum, Bloemfontein, South Africa
HOWELLS, Prof. W. W., S.B., A.M., PH.D.	U.S.A.	(i) Peabody Museum, Harvard University (ii) American Anthropological Association	Peabody Museum, Harvard University, Cambridge 38, Mass., U.S.A.
JEAN, Mlle S.	France	Private	Women's Residence, University of the Witwatersrand, Milner Park, Johannesburg
JEFFREYS, Dr M. D. W.	South Africa	Private	University of the Witwatersrand, Johannesburg
JOKL, Dr A.	South Africa	Schweizer Institut für Kunstforschung (Zürich)	80 Lister Building, Jeppe Street, Johannesburg
JOLLY, K., B.A.	South Africa	Private	Reinet House, Newlands Ave., Newlands, Cape Town
KARVE, Dr I.	India	Deccan College	Deccan College Research Institute, Poona 6, India
KOENIGSWALD, Prof. G. H. R. von	Holland	University of Utrecht	320, Oude Gracht, Utrecht, Holland
LANNING, E. C., F.R.A.I.	Uganda	Protectorate of Uganda	P.O. Box 19, Masaka, Uganda
LAWRENCE, Prof. A. W., M.A., F.S.A.	Gold Coast	(i) University College of the Gold Coast (ii) National Museum of the Gold Coast	University College of the Gold Coast, Achimota
LEAKEY, Dr L. S. B.	Kenya	(i) Kenya Government (ii) Coryndon Memorial Museum	P.O. Box 658, Nairobi, Kenya
LECOINTRE, Dr G.	France	Bureau des Recherches Géologiques	17, Avenue de Saxe, Paris 7e

List of Delegates

Name	Country	Representing	Present Address
*LOWE, Prof. C. VAN RIET, D.SC., F.S.A., F.R.S. (S.A.)	South Africa	(i) The Government of the Union of South Africa (ii) University of the Witwatersrand	c/o P.O. Box 207, Windhoek, S.W.A.
LÜCK, Dr H.	South West Africa	Private	
McCONNELL, Dr R. B.	Bechuanaland Protectorate	Government of Bechuanaland Protectorate	Geological Survey, Lobatsi, Bechuanaland Protectorate
MABBUTT, J. A., M.A.	South Africa	University of Cape Town	c/o Land Research and Regional Survey, C.S.I.R.O., Box 109, Canberra City, A.C.T., Australia
MALAN, B. D., B.A.	South Africa	(i) South African Archaeological Society (ii) South African Association for the Advancement of Science	Archaeological Survey, University of the Witwatersrand, Milner Park, Johannesburg
MARTIN, Dr M. H.	South West Africa	South West Africa Scientific Society	P.O. Box 207, Windhoek, South West Africa
MASON, R. J., B.A., B.Com.	South Africa	Private	Archaeological Survey, University of the Witwatersrand, Milner Park, Johannesburg
MAUNY, Dr R.	French West Africa	Institut Français d'Afrique Noire, Dakar	L'IFAN, Place de l'Étoile, Dakar, French Sénégal
MEIRING, Dr A. J. D.	South Africa	National Museum, Bloemfontein	National Museum, Bloemfontein, South Africa
MORTELMANS, Prof. G., D.Sc.	Belgium	(i) Government of Belgian Congo (ii) Université Libre de Bruxelles (ii) Société Royale Belge d'Anthropologie et de Préhistoire	Faculté des Sciences, Université Libre de Bruxelles, 50, avenue F. D. Roosevelt, Brussels
OAKLEY, Dr K. P., F.G.S., F.S.A.	Great Britain	British Museum (Natural History)	British Museum (Natural History) Cromwell Road, London S.W. 7
PERICOT GARCIA, Prof. L.	Spain	Instituto de Estudios Africanos (Consejo Superior de Investigaciones Cientificas), Madrid	The University of Barcelona, Spain
REEVE, W. H., M.Sc., F.G.S.	Northern Rhodesia	Geological Survey, Northern Rhodesia	P.O. Box 671, Lusaka, Northern Rhodesia
RICHARDS, Dr H. G.	U.S.A.	Academy of Natural Sciences, Philadelphia	Academy of Natural Sciences, Philadelphia 3, Pa., U.S.A.

* Deceased.

Name	Country	Representing	Present Address
RIZKANA, Prof. I.	Egypt	(i) The Egyptian Government (ii) King Fuad I University, Cairo	3, Rue Misaha, Dokki, Cairo
ROBINSON, Dr J. T.	South Africa	Transvaal Museum, Pretoria	P.O. Box 413, Pretoria, South Africa
ROBINSON, K. RADCLIFFE	Southern Rhodesia	National Historical Monuments Commision, Southern Rhodesia	P.O. Box 240, Bulawayo, Southern Rhodesia
SADIQ EN NUR, F.R.A.I., A.M.A.	Sudan	Sudan Government Antiquities Service	P.O. Box 178, Khartoum, Sudan
SCHAPERA, Prof. I., M.A., D.Sc.	Great Britain	University of London	London School of Economics, Aldwych, London W.C.2
SCHERZ, Mrs	South West Africa	Private	P.O. Box 207, Windhoek, South West Africa
SINGER, Dr R.	South Africa	University of Cape Town	Medical School, University of Cape Town, Mowbray, Cape
SMOLLA, Dr G.	Germany	Tübingen University and Institut für Vor- und Frühgeschichte	Institut für Vor- und Frühgeschichte, Tübingen Schloss, Western Germany
STREY, R. G.	South Africa	Private	P.O. Silverton, Near Pretoria
SUMMERS, R. F. H., F.S.A.	Southern Rhodesia	National Museum of Southern Rhodesia	P.O. Box 240, Bulawayo, S. Rhodesia
TOERIEN, Dr M. J., M.Sc.	South Africa	University of the Witwatersrand	Dept. of Anatomy, Medical School, Hospital St., Johannesburg
VALLOIS, Dr H. V.	France	(i) Museum National d'Histoire Naturelle (ii) Institut de Paléontologie Humaine	1, Rue Réné Panhard, Paris 13e
WALTON, J., F.S.A., B.Sc.	Basutoland	(i) Basutoland Government (ii) Basutoland Scientific Association	P.O. Box 16, Maseru, Basutoland
WASHBURN, Prof. S.	U.S.A.	(i) Wenner-Gren Foundation (ii) University of Chicago	University of Chicago, Chicago 37, Illinois, U.S.A.
WAYLAND, E. J.	Uganda	Private	P.O. Box 9, Entebbe, Uganda
WELLS, Dr L. H., D.Sc., M.B., B.Ch., F.R.S.E., F.R.S.S.	Great Britain	University of Edinburgh	Dept. of Anatomy, Medical School, University of Cape Town, Rondebosch, Cape, South Africa
WHITTY, A.	Southern Rhodesia	Private	9 Enterprise Rd., Newlands, Salisbury, S. Rhodesia
WILKIE, L. A.	U.S.A.	The Wilkie Foundation	Des Plaines, Illinois, U.S.A.

xvii

List of non-participating Members

ALIMEN, Mlle M. H., 12, rue Achille Garnon, Sceaux, Seine, France
AMER BEY, Professor Manstafa, Director General, Antiquity Dept., Cairo
ANDERSON, M. M., Dept. of Geology, University College, Achimota, Gold Coast, W. Africa
BIBERSON, M. P., Controleur Civil, Chef du Bureau du Territoire des Chaonia, Casablanca, Morocco
BOSAZZA, V. L., D.Sc., F.R.G.S., F.G.S., A.I.M.M., 39, Barkly Rd., Parktown, Johannesburg
BOSCH-GIMPERA, Professor, Privada de Olivo, 84-4, Mexico 20, D.F.
BRÜCKNER, Dr W. D., University College of the Gold Coast, Achimota, Gold Coast, W. Africa
BUTCHER, A. M., Highway, Oxford Rd., Hillside, Bulawayo
CARVALHO, Dr G. Soares de, C.P. 1260, Luanda, Angola
GEOLOGICAL SOCIETY OF LONDON, Burlington House, London W.1, England
HEANLEY, C. M., M.B., B.Sc., D.Ph., D.T.M.H., P.O. Box 169, Salisbury, Southern Rhodesia
INSTITUT ROYAL DES SCIENCES NATURELLES DE BELGIQUE, 31, rue Vantier, Bruxelles 4, Belgium
LAVOCAT, Abbé R., Museum National d'Histoire Naturelle, Laboratoire de Paléontologie, 3 Place
    Valhubert, Paris 5e
MALSON, A. Conserv. M.R.C.B., P.R. Mwanza, Katanga, Congo Belge
MARTIN, A.R.H., Ph.D., Botany School, University of Sydney, Sydney, N.S.W., Australia
MAZURCZAK, Dr L., P.O. Box 413, Lusaka, N. Rhodesia
MINES AND GEOLOGICAL DEPT., P.O. Box 339, Nairobi, Kenya
MOUTA, Dr F., c/o Reparticae Tecnica de Industria e Geologica, C.P. 217, Lourenço Marques, Mozam-
    bique
MUSÊE ROYAL DU CONGO BELGE, Tervuren, Belgium
PÈRE, M. Claude, c/o Dr L. Cabot Briggs, 7, rue Pierre Viala, Algiers, Algeria
POLDERVAART, Prof. A., Dept. of Geology, Columbia University, New York 27, N.Y., U.S.A.
POWER, Dr J. H., Alexander McGregor Memorial Museum, P.O. Box 316, Kimberley, S. Africa
ROCHE, Abbé J., 13, rue Coli, Rabat, Morocco
SANKALIA, Dr H. D., Deccan College, Poona 6, India
SANTOS JUNIOR, Professor dos, Instituto de Antropologia, Universidade do Porto, Porto, Portugal
SMITH, G. D., Box 413, Lusaka, N. Rhodesia
SOUVILLE, M. G., 13, rue Coli, Rabat, Morocco
STEKELIS, Dr M., Dept. of Prehistoric Archaeology, The Hebrew University, Jerusalem, Israel
VLCEK, M. E., Archeologicky ustav S.A.V., Nitra-Hrad, Czechoslovakia

List of persons accompanying Members

Name	Country
ANDERSON, W. T.	U.S.A.
BARBOUR, Mrs G. B.	U.S.A.
BRAIN, Mrs C. K.	S. Africa
BRIGGS, Mrs L. Cabot	U.S.A.
BURKITT, Mrs M. C.	Great Britain
BURKITT, Miss J.	Great Britain
COETZEE, Miss J. A.	S. Africa
DART, Mrs R. A.	S. Africa
FOCK, Mrs G. J.	S. W. Africa
HAUGHTON, Mrs S. H.	S. Africa
HOWELLS, Mrs W. W.	U.S.A.
HOWELLS, Miss G.	U.S.A.
JOKL, Mrs A.	S. Africa
LAWRENCE, Mrs A. W.	Gold Coast
LÜCK, Mrs H.	Germany
McCONNELL, Mrs R. B.	Bechuanaland
MARTIN, Mrs M. H.	S. W. Africa
MELICK, W.	U.S.A.
MORTELMANS, Mme G.	Belgium
RUHLE, J.	U.S.A.
STREY, R. W.,	S. Africa
TREDGOLD, Miss M. P.	S. Africa
VALLOIS, Mme H. V.	France
VANDERVOODT, Mlle M.	Belgian Congo
WALTON, Mrs J.	Basutoland
WASHBURN, Mrs S.	U.S.A.

Rules and Constitution

IN view of the imperative need to ensure that collaboration in the fields of prehistory, Tertiary and Quaternary geology and palaeontology should be permanently established, the following Rules and Constitution were drawn up at the First Pan-African Congress on Prehistory in 1947, and with the amendments incorporated by the Second Congress in 1952, are set out below.

(1) The Pan-African Congress on Prehistory shall meet every four years or at such other interval as circumstances shall dictate.

(2) The Office-Bearers elected at any Meeting shall hold office until the succeeding meeting.

(3) The Organizing Secretary of any particular Meeting shall act as General Secretary during the interval between one Congress and the next.

(4) It shall be left to the Authorities of the inviting Country to appoint in advance the Organizing Secretary for the Congress to be held in their Territory.

(5) The Office-Bearers to be appointed by Congress shall consist of a President, one or more Vice-Presidents and three Chairmen (with necessary Vice-Chairmen) of the following sections:
   (*a*) Prehistoric Archaeology
   (*b*) Geology, General Palaeontology and Climatology
   (*c*) Human Palaeontology
   (*d*) Any other Sections deemed necessary

(6) The Organizing Secretary shall be an *ex-officio* member of the General Committee which shall consist of President, Vice-President, or Vice-Presidents, and the Chairmen of the several Sections.

(7) Such Sub-Committees as may be deemed necessary shall be nominated by the General Committee and the names submitted to Congress for approval.

(8) One or more Standing Sub-Committees on various subjects may be appointed to hold office from one Congress until the next.

(9) The General Committee shall deal with all recommendations and resolutions passed to them by individual members of the Congress, by Sub-Committees or by resolutions from the General Sessions and shall present such recommendations and resolutions to Congress in plenary session for ratification.

(10) The Proceedings of the Congress shall be published as soon as possible after the Congress is over in such detail as financial circumstances shall allow.

(11) All languages currently used in Africa by prehistorians may be employed for oral communications, but as far as possible members should use either English or French for drafting all documents destined to be printed, or, if they should choose some other language they should enclose with their manuscripts a substantial précis in French or English and not merely a brief summary.

(12) Papers that are not directly concerned with African prehistory, Pleistocene geology or palaeontology, including human palaeontology, cannot be accepted for presentation at a Congress or for publication in the Proceedings.

Opening Session, Friday, July 22, 1955

THE opening session was held in the Victoria Hall, Livingstone, at 2.30 p.m. in the presence of His Excellency the Right Hon. The Lord Llewellin, G.B.E., M.C., T.D., Governor-General and Commander-in-Chief of the Federation of Rhodesia and Nyasaland, who attended to open the Congress.

The first Vice-President, Dr. L.S.B. Leakey (Kenya) took the chair and presided in the absence of the President, Monsieur l'Abbé H. Breuil (France).

The following message which had been received from the President was then read to the meeting:

Your Excellency and my dear Colleagues,

Today you open your third Pan-African Congress on Prehistory. My advanced age obliged me to give up the idea of being with you, as your colleagues of Algiers so much desired that they elected me your President. I very much appreciate their kindness and consideration.

Though I am still writing, doing some moderate field work and a little visiting of the caves and painted rocks, I must avoid long tiring days of discussions and group excursions.

Thanks to Dr Desmond Clark I had a chance in 1948 to see, or else revisit, some of the sites to which he is leading you. A quarter of a century has passed since I took part in the travelling Congress of the joint meeting of the British and South African Associations for the Advancement of Science between Capetown, Johannesburg, Salisbury and Livingstone. Professor Dart had just discovered (and was well aware of the importance of his discovery), the first Australopithecus skull. John Goodwin and C. van Riet Lowe, had just published a first volume setting forth in a satisfactory manner what was known of your Stone Age epoch; these outlines still remain.

More and more the scientific world tends to turn towards southern Africa, the cradle of production of the human type, if we must, as is probable, consider the Australopithecus as, if not our ancestor, at least a very close relation of his.

It was apparently from your very ancient Pebble Culture that chipped stone tools began to develop and spread through the world as did, a little later, the techniques and civilizations of the Lower Palaeolithic. It seems that after that the movement went into reverse and that it was from North Africa that the first breath of our Mediterranean Upper Palaeolithic reached you, bringing with it artistic elements developed in our Western Europe; these elements came, I think, to strengthen the dawn of your art, born parallel to the northern art. The inspiration came in waves, continuously through the ancient historical ages.

It is for you, gentlemen, to carry on the work which had been more than sketched out, to pursue it without heeding childish scruples or prejudices unsupported by solid facts.

H. BREUIL
de l'Institut de France

His Excellency the Governor-General was then invited to address the delegates and said:

I would first like to welcome, on behalf of everyone in the Federation of the Rhodesias and Nyasaland, all who come to this Congress from outside our boundaries. This is, I believe, the first International Congress ever to have been held within the territories of Northern Rhodesia,

xxiii

Southern Rhodesia and Nyasaland, and is, within my own knowledge, the first to be held here since we became the Federation. I think we will all agree that thanks are due to one of our members, Dr Desmond Clark, for his energy and organization in helping to arrange that you should all come here.

We are privileged to have with us here today, representatives of some twenty-five nations, and we are delighted to have you with us. You may be prehistorians, Mr Chairman, but you are making history—just as Livingstone made history when he discovered the Victoria Falls— the most remarkable falls in the world. I say this without fear of contradiction from any of the delegates here. A hundred years ago these Falls were discovered by a most remarkable observer and recorder of all he saw—a trait which must obviously commend itself to all of you.

You are making history, just as Professor Darwin made history when he opened the Victoria Falls Bridge fifty years ago this year. That bridge is the main link for all heavy freight between Northern Rhodesia with its great copper industries and the other countries of Southern Africa.

I know nothing of prehistory. It rests upon your discoveries, and the books which you may write to instruct me, and the like of me, upon that. Those of you who write will make history by writing it, and the sad thing to me is, that as you write that history you will, each of you, lose your status as a prehistorian. No doubt you will make that history by more authentic and less reprehensible methods than those used by the manufacturer of the Piltdown Skull! There was a time when I thought that I lived in a part of England where the first *Homo sapiens* had lived, but when I migrated from Wessex it would seem that I was, in fact, coming to the country where the first true man had his home. How disillusioned one can be, unless a whole Congress of wise men, such as yourselves, give a combined judgment on a matter.

You are, however, in a very different position than that of the manufacturer of the Piltdown Skull. You have little or nothing to gain by falsifying or inventing such facts about the past as you may discover. Unlike the atomic scientists of today who may, at any time, be the means of blowing all history sky-high, you, Mr Chairman, are, I understand, mild and modest men. You try to discover the past rather than destroy the future.

I hope, during your stay here, that you will not discover that our Broken Hill man is also a fake. When I mentioned recently to Lord Malvern that you might be the means of discovering at last the authentic date of the Zimbabwe and Khami ruins, he replied that he hoped you would not, as then many more such eminent men would be persuaded to come to this country to study the problem.

You are wise to come here in mid-winter, which is one of the pleasantest winters in the world, and when all the flowers are in full bloom. You are also wise to come here where our earliest history is only a hundred years old. It would be a very much more formidable task were you investigating prehistory in Egypt or China.

We shall be sad when you leave us, and we hope that you will come back again.

His Excellency then declared the Congress officially open.

Dr Leakey then replied to the address of welcome and thanked His Excellency. He said that it was most fitting that the Pan-African Congress should be held in Livingstone, which owed its name to the greatest of all African explorers and on this, the occasion of his centenary celebrations. We are extremely grateful to those early explorers, such as David Livingstone and the work they did. It is fit that we should be holding our meeting here in Livingstone in this centenary year, because we feel we represent the successors of those early explorers. We are trying our best to continue the exploration of this continent. We are confident too, that we shall find the coming of Man's evolution in the African Continent.

Dr Leakey went on to say that a vast amount of exploration remained to be done today; not geographical exploration such as that of David Livingstone, but into the prehistoric aspects of man's life in the African Continent. It was the task of prehistorians to study the geography, animals and men of those days.

Professor G. B. Barbour, (U.S.A.) then spoke on behalf of the delegates from America. He was followed by Professor H. V. Vallois (France) who replied on behalf of the delegates from Europe and Asia and by Professor C. van Riet Lowe (South Africa) who expressed to His Excellency the thanks of the delegates from Africa.

His Excellency Lord Llewellin and the members of the public then left the Hall.

IN MEMORIAM

The Vice-President and Chairman, Dr Leakey, said that he regretted to inform delegates that since the Second Congress they had had the misfortune to lose four distinguished colleagues—Professor T. F. Dreyer of South Africa, Monsieur J. P. Janmart of Angola, Dr Neville Jones of Southern Rhodesia and R. P. Teilhard de Chardin of France. Delegates stood for a moment in silence after which the following In Memoriam Notices were read:

THOMAS FREDERIK DREYER was born in 1886 at Malmesbury in the Cape Province. He was a brilliant student both at school and at University. After obtaining his M.Sc. in the first class at the University of Cape Town he went to Halle where he graduated Ph.D. He then proceeded to Naples and from there to the Cornell University for further studies on the Neudobranchs. After completion of these studies he went to Australia to investigate certain agricultural problems.

On his return to South Africa he accepted an appointment in the Department of Agriculture as Entomologist and was stationed at Oudtshoorn.

In 1912 he was appointed to the Chair of Zoology and Geology at the Grey University College in Bloemfontein and this post he occupied until his retirement in 1949, whereafter he was prevailed upon to accept the honorary curatorship of Archaeology and Anthropology at the National Museum in Bloemfontein in which capacity he served Science until his death on July 13, 1954.

Dr Dreyer was a brilliant professor of Zoology and a capable administrator, proved by the fact that for many years he served as chairman of the Senate of the University of South Africa, but his main interest, for which he became such a well-known personality, started in 1917 when he visited the Florisbad Site for the first time. Since then, archaeology and anthropology became his main lines of thought.

At his own expense and sometimes with a great deal of self-sacrifice, Dreyer gathered and collected some of the most valuable material in the fields of archaeology and anthropology. To his credit stand such outstanding discoveries as thousands of stone artefacts and Pleistocene fossils; the Kakamas-Upington Hottentots; the Matjes River Shelter with its mass of human material; but the most outstanding of all was the discovery of the Florisbad Skull and its associated implements and fossil fauna. All this splendid material, which he collected over many years and from all parts of Southern Africa and at very great cost to himself, he presented to the National Museum to be available for further studies to the scientists of the world.

Dreyer himself published many papers on the material he collected. Some of these papers may have been controversial, but the fact remains that he was always sure of himself and that he was prepared to stand or fall by his own convictions.

In the beginning of 1954 the University of the Witwatersrand conferred upon him an honorary Doctor's Degree in recognition of his contributions to our knowledge of primitive man in South Africa.

Dreyer was a most pleasant character and was very well liked by all his colleagues. To us in Bloemfontein his untimely death came as a severe shock, when on the morning of July 13, 1954 he walked into my office a dying man. While discussing certain Florisbad problems with Professor Meiring and myself his head suddenly dropped and Dreyer passed away.

To Bloemfontein, to the Free State, in fact, to the whole of South Africa, he will always be remembered as 'the Dear Old Man of Science'.

A. C. HOFFMAN

JEAN PAUL JANMART was born in Roeulx, Belgium, on June 30, 1894, and died on March 28, 1955, at Elisabethville, Belgian Congo.

He had the following Belgian studies' certificates: Certificat homologué d'humanités latines-scientifiques; Certificat d'admission aux écoles préparatoires au grade légal d'Ingénieur de constructions civiles (Université de Gand).

He served in the Great War, as a volunteer, throughout the whole of the 1914-1918 campaign, and was taken prisoner by the Germans. He was recommended for the Belgian War Cross— Médaille Commémorative Belge.

He joined the staff of the Angola Diamond Company (Diamang) on July 7, 1920. From 1920 to 1923 he was a member of Grant's Prospecting Mission working for the Company in Southern Angola.

From 1928 to 1937 he prospected widely in Central Africa, in particular in the Great Lakes region, returning to the Angola Diamond Company on March 3, 1937, where he occupied the post of Head of the Prospecting Department from that date up to December 4, 1954, when he retired.

In the course of his duties, he displayed intelligence and courage, and endeavoured, on all occasions, to extend the technical and scientific scope of the services under his charge.

In 1942 he undertook the systematic geological survey of the Lunda region, simultaneously with his studies on prehistory.

In pursuit of his aim and always anxious to enlarge his knowledge, he spent a few months in South Africa in 1943, where he frequented Museums and Institutions, and contacted many well-known South African archaeologists and geologists.

In 1947, he attended on behalf of the Dundo Museum, the First Pan-African Congress on Prehistory, held at Nairobi, Kenya.

In Diamang's Cultural Publications Series *Contributions to the History, Archaeology and Ethnography of the Peoples of Lunda* he published the following papers:

'Stations Préhistoriques de l'Angola du Nord-Est' (1946)

'Analyse géologique, climatologique et préhistorique d'un sondage fait en bordure de la rivière Luembe (Angola du Nord-Est)' (1946)

'La Station préhistorique de Candala (District de la Lunda, Angola du Nord-Est') (avec d'autres études sur la préhistoire de la Lunda) (1948)

'Les limons et graviers de l'Angola du Nord-Est et leur contenu archéologique', en collaboration avec l'Abbé Henri Breuil (1950)

'The Kalahari Sands of the Lunda (N.-E. Angola), their earlier Redistributions and the Sangoan Culture' (1953)

He had retired from his professional activities and was devoting all his time to new studies, one of them to be presented at the Third Pan-African Congress on Prehistory, when he suddenly died.

M. Janmart's pioneer work in N.E. Angola has provided a very important link in correlating the prehistoric succession in Equatoria with that in South and East Africa; his enthusiasm and careful attention to stratigraphical detail enabled him to make a major contribution to African prehistory.

G. MORTELMANS

THOMAS FREDERIK DREYER

JEAN PAUL JANMART

Photo. by C. K. Brain

NEVILLE JONES

PIERRE TEILHARD DE CHARDIN

Opening Session

NEVILLE JONES died in October 1954 at the age of seventy-four at Bulawayo, in the heart of a country which he had served as a missionary and as a scientist for over forty years.

Jones always considered himself an amateur prehistorian and indeed prehistory was but the chief of several hobbies until he joined the Museum Staff when he was over fifty-five years old. Despite his claim to amateur status Jones' field work was always careful and his publications are models of clarity. He hated pomposity and intellectual pomposity most of all so that he insisted that papers must be clear, quite free from jargon and as brief as possible. 'It sounds so easy when Neville Jones writes it up' is a remark I have heard, but this apparent simplicity was never a mask for slipshod field work or careless interpretation.

His greatest work for Rhodesian prehistory was the unravelling of the Stone Age cultural succession in Matabeleland which he started in his missionary days, publishing his first tentative succession in 1926. A much more detailed work appeared in 1933 when he applied the term 'Middle Stone Age' to cultures that had previously been termed 'Mousterian' and made the first attempt to link Southern Rhodesia MSA cultures with those of the Union. Later publications fitted in more and more detail and in 1948 the succession as we now know it was published.

Jones was always ready to share his knowledge and unpublished material with other prehistorians especially if they were younger than he was. Although his field work lay in a somewhat restricted geographical area his influence has been a very wide one and every prehistorian working in the Federation today is the richer, not only for his scientific work but also for having known and worked with a man whose human qualities set him above other people.

PIERRE TEILHARD DE CHARDIN was born in Auvergne on May 1, 1881, fifth of the eleven children of Emanuel Teilhard who was descended directly from the father of François-Marie Arouet, better known as Voltaire. Pierre grew up on the family farm on the vine-clad slopes beneath the Puys de Dôme. At the age of eighteen he entered the Jesuit Order and underwent the severe intellectual discipline required of all members of the Society of Jesus. After a thorough grounding in physical and biological science, he found his interest concentrating on vertebrate palaeontology and for his doctoral dissertation presented a masterly study of the Lower Eocene primates of the Paris Basin. During the first world war he served as stretcher-bearer with a battalion of French Colonial troops. On demobilization he was appointed to the teaching faculty of the Catholic University of Paris and to the research staff of the Institute of Human Palaeontology, first under Marcelin Boule, and then with Henri Breuil, the previous President of this Congress. Some of Teilhard's ideas regarding *transformisme* (evolution) brought him under criticism and he was advised to confine his work to strictly palaeontological and stratigraphical studies. In 1923 he went to China and for the next two decades devoted himself to field and laboratory research in Tientsin and Peking. The seventy titles from his pen during that period attest to the surprising range of his interests—studies on the tectonic, stratigraphic and igneous history of south-east Asia, reconnaisance reports from half-a-dozen provinces of China, palaeontological descriptions ranging from the late Palaeozoic, through the Mesozoic of Jehol and the Cenozoic of Mongolia to the Pontian of Nihowan, and the Pleistocene of Chou-kou-tien. He took part in half-a-dozen expeditions including the American Museum's Central Asiatic Expedition, the Citroen's Croisière Jaune, de Terra's expedition to the Siwaliks. He also did field work in Java and Abyssinia. He was attached to the Rockefeller Foundation's Cenozoic Laboratory of the Chinese Geological Survey working with the team responsible for the Peking Man (Sinanthropus) discoveries. His keenest interest remained in the primate field and the problem of human evolution. It is here that his thinking outstripped that of his contemporaries. He extended the common concept of the biosphere to allow place for the evolution of consciousness or noösphere and to look into the future direction of evolutionary advance—including what Piveteau has aptly termed 'la paléontologie de l'avenir'.

Some of his conclusions were written down tentatively during the months of the Japanese occupation of North China, when his movements were restricted and he had ample time to develop these dawning ideas. These draft statements—'comment je crois'—were sent to his more intimate friends in Paris and elsewhere for their thoughtful criticism, with no thought of wider dissemination. They came however at a critical moment when the youth of France, disillusioned by the privations of war and the failures of peace, were looking for some ray of hope in the prevailing gloom of cynicism and materialism of the time. Teilhard's writing were avidly seized upon and quoted from, in unauthorized form, and undoubtedly exerted a profound influence on the thinking of thousands.

But these essays were to his mind only a by-product of an uninterrupted enquiry into the origins, nature and future of Man, and he took every opportunity that offered of securing more facts. He was already familiar with the main European and Asiatic sites of hominid and pre-hominid discovery and welcomed an invitation to join the University of California's South African Expedition in 1947. On the eve of departure, a heart-attack forced him to abandon the idea. Two years later, however, he had recovered so completely that he was able to visit the Transvaal and Central Africa as an emissary of the Wenner-Gren Foundation for Anthropological Research. Appointed Research Associate under the Viking Fund of that organization, he returned to New York where he contributed to the seminars and symposia of the Foundation. On Easter Sunday, 1955, he had attended mass and gone for a walk in a nearby park where special music was being played. After lunch, he was pacing the floor in a friend's room, describing the fresh beauty of that spring day, when suddenly he stumbled, and his spirit was gone.

Among the many letters of sympathy received during the weeks following, the outstanding impression was that everyone who had met Pierre Teilhard, even if only casually for the briefest period, felt as if he had lost a personal friend of long-standing—one who had a specially sympathetic understanding of his particular problems. As was written in another connection, 'It is personal influence that determines the size of life—not words, or even deeds'. Through the death of Pierre Teilhard, African Prehistory has lost a true friend.

GEORGE BARBOUR

The Organizing Secretary then read to the meeting messages of welcome and greetings from the three Patrons, Governments, Institutions and individuals. He followed this by his report giving an account of events which led up to the holding of the Third Congress in Livingstone and the assistance both financial and otherwise that had made this possible. Livingstone had been chosen as the *venue* as it is in the centre of the main sites in the Upper Zambezi Valley on which the Rhodesian cultural and climatic succession has been mainly built up, because most of the collections from Northern Rhodesia are housed in the Museum there, and because it was the centre for the Centenary Celebrations.

Appointment of Office Bearers and Sub-Committees

Delegates then proceeded to hear nominations and elect the new Council which would hold office until the next Congress. The officers elected are as set out on page xii of these Proceedings.

At the Nairobi Congress there were formed three Sub-Committees to deal with specific matters requiring discussion by each of the three sections and to consider the draft Resolutions to be submitted to the Council. The following nominations to these Sub-Committees were then approved.

Appointments to the Sub-Committee on Geology, General Palaeontology and Climatology.

Chairman: Prof. G. Mortelmans (Belgium)
Members: Prof. C. Arambourg (France)

Opening Session

Dr Geoffrey Bond (Southern Rhodesia)
Dr H. B. S. Cooke (South Africa)
Mr J. A. Mabbutt (South Africa)
Dr K. P. Oakley (Great Britain)

Appointments to the Sub-Committee on Human Palaeontology

Chairman: Prof. G. H. R. von Koenigswald (Holland)
Members: Prof. S. Alcobe (Spain)
Prof. R. A. Dart (South Africa)
Prof. H. V. Vallois (France)
Prof. S. Washburn (U.S.A.)
Dr L. H. Wells (United Kingdom)

Appointments to the Sub-Committee on Prehistoric Archaeology

Chairman: Prof. L. Pericot Garcia (Spain)
Members: Mr M. C. Burkitt (United Kingdom)
Dr G. Caton-Thompson (United Kingdom)
Mr B. D. Malan (South Africa)
Dr R. Mauny (French West Africa)
Prof. C. van Riet Lowe (South Africa)

The President and General Secretary to be ex-officio members of all three Sub-Committees.

Minutes and Resolutions of the Algiers Congress

The meeting then proceeded to consider the Minutes of the closing session of the Algiers Congress and what action had been taken on the Resolutions passed by that meeting.

Delegates noted with satisfaction that the majority of these Resolutions had had favourable results, but regret was expressed that there still remained some African territories in which there was no provision made for prehistoric research. (Resolutions Nos. 6 and 7 refer.)

Venue for the Fourth Congress

Professor G. Mortelmans (Belgium) read an official invitation from the Government of the Belgian Congo for the Fourth Congress to be held in Léopoldville in 1959.

The President thanked Professor Mortelmans and said that this invitation would be gratefully considered by the Council and a reply given at the closing session.

An invitation was also extended on behalf of the Government of French West Africa by Dr R. Mauny, inviting the next Congress to meet in Dakar.

Professor Pericot Garcia, on behalf of the Spanish Government, also invited the Congress to meet in the Canary Islands.

The President thanked these two delegates and said that it would be a hard matter to decide the *venue* for the next Congress.

General

Delegates were then invited by the Organizing Secretary to put forward any suggestions they might have that would further the deliberations of the Congress, or that they wished to have discussed by the Section Committees.

Mr Walton (Basutoland) proposed that a new Section devoted to proto-history should be introduced. Mr Fosbrooke (Tanganyika) said that he considered that a dividing line should be drawn between proto- and prehistory. After discussion it was agreed by the delegates that it would be too difficult a matter at this stage to define the dividing line and that it would serve no useful purpose at present to set up a new Section for proto-historic studies.

Dr Cabot Briggs (United States) spoke of the difficulties that he and several of his colleagues encountered from time to time over the differences in terminology employed by the various disciplines. These differences complicated correlation work and he considered that there was a real and urgent need to standardize terminology, especially that applying to stone implements. Mr Miles Burkitt (United Kingdom) supported this proposal and said he hoped that this suggestion of simplifying cultural terminology would receive careful consideration.

The President replied that this question had occupied the attention of previous Congresses. The first thing to be done, in his opinion, was to put the matter before a special Committee which would formulate proposals to be laid before a plenary session.

A decision on this matter had previously been taken at the Nairobi Congress, but he agreed that the matter should again be brought up before a special Committee.

Delegates approved this suggestion.

Following the reading of Notices and particulars of excursions by the Organizing Secretary the President then declared the opening plenary session closed at 4.50 p.m.

RESOLUTIONS

RESOLUTION 1

1. This Third Pan-African Congress on Prehistory endorses clauses 1 and 2 of Resolution XIV of the First Pan-African Congress, namely that:

    (i) Africa should be treated for the time being as a geological unit distinct from Europe for the Pleistocene period and an African nomenclature should be used for the deposits and faunas of this period in the continent, excluding the North African littoral.

    (ii) The established succession of deposits and faunas in East Africa should be used as a basis for the development of the African terminology.

2. Since 1947 the classification proposed in clause 3 of Resolution XIV has been modified by the XVIIIth International Geological Congress of 1948, when the term KANJERAN was introduced to define the upper part of the Kamasian stage, the term Kamasian itself being retained for the lower part. This is confirmed.

3. The present Congress considers that the terms proposed in 1947 (and 1948) have not been used consistently in the purely stratigraphic sense intended by the original resolution; it is therefore proposed that henceforth the application of these terms should be modified as set out below in clauses 4, 5 and 6.

4. It is recommended that Kageran, Kamasian, Kanjeran, Gamblian, Makalian and Nakuran should be recognized as stratigraphic climatic divisions only in the East African region, and that these terms should not be applied in other parts of Africa except where correlation is firmly attested by at least two of the three lines of evidence: palaeontological, archaeological or the geological setting.

5. The original definitions did not take account of the position to be assigned to interpluvial phases in the East African sequence, and therefore it is recommended that each division should have its upper limit defined by the onset of the next pluvial period or phase.

6. It is recommended that in the description of Pleistocene faunas throughout Africa this period be regarded as divided into four faunal stages, namely Omo-Kanam, Lower Olduvai, Upper Olduvai and Post-Olduvai.

In East Africa these stages are equated as follows:

Nakuran	
Makalian	}—Post-Olduvai
Gamblian	
Kanjeran	—Upper Olduvai (Beds III, IV)
Kamasian	—Lower Olduvai (Beds I and II)
Kageran	—Omo-Kanam

7. Since there is general agreement that the Omo-Kanam faunal stage is equivalent to the Villafranchian of Europe, it is recognized as forming the lowest division of the Pleistocene as defined by the XVIIIth International Geological Congress.

8. Until general agreement has been reached on correlation with Eurasia and America, it is recommended that in Africa, excluding the North African Littoral, the terms Lower, Middle and Upper Pleistocene should be avoided.

9. It is recommended that the above resolutions should be communicated to the Terminology Committee of INQUA, with the request that they be circulated.

10. It is recommended that it should be communicated for information to the C.C.T.A. and the XXth International Geological Congress.

RESOLUTION 2

1. It is recognized that in Central and Southern Africa there is clear evidence for the existence of more than one phase of distribution of red wind-blown sand in Pleistocene times, these sands being generally of similar character and not at present readily distinguishable.

2. This Congress accordingly recommends that, until the position is clarified, such sands should not be described as 'Kalahari Sand' (thereby implying correlation and contemporaneity) but should be referred to simply as 'sand of Kalahari type'.

RESOLUTION 3

This Congress wishes to urge the geological committee of C.C.T.A. to take such steps as it can to assist in the promotion of research on Quaternary correlation problems in Africa, particularly through the application of the important techniques developed by Mr C. K. Brain of the Transvaal Museum, Pretoria.

RESOLUTION 4

This Congress reaffirms its resolution that papers that are not directly concerned with matters of African Prehistory, Pleistocene Geology, or Palaeontology, including human palaeontology, will not be accepted.

RESOLUTION 5

The Congress recommends that a catalogue of skeletal and cranial material belonging to the following population groups and housed in Institutions and Museums not only in Africa but also outside this Continent, should be prepared:

(i) Bushmen and Hottentots;
(ii) Guanches and Canary Island Peoples;
(iii) Pygmies;
(iv) Early Ethiopian and earlier African groups;
(v) North African Mesolithic and Neo-Mesolithic.

RESOLUTION 6

The Congress recommends to workers in Prehistory in the African Continent that they should endeavour, in the interval before the next Congress, to fit their Stone Age Culture sequences into a frame which provides for:

> Earlier Stone Age
> First Intermediate
> Middle Stone Age
> Second Intermediate
> Later Stone Age

with a view to an endeavour to achieve a wider measure of correlation and understanding; the First Intermediate to include Fauresmith, Sangoan Acheul-Levallois and comparable material. The Second Intermediate to include the Magosians and comparable material.

RESOLUTION 7

The Congress recommends that the workers in Prehistory in each territory in Africa should prepare on cyclostyled sheets of paper a brief statement of each of the cultures and/or culture stages of importance in their country, along the lines of the specimen format which will be distributed. The object of this is to enable workers in other countries to see at a glance the essential elements of any culture or industry in Africa of which they have not personal knowledge. The Congress requests the President and the Secretary to take the necessary action to secure co-operation in this matter.

RESOLUTION 8

The Congress has taken account of the very great development that has taken place in the fields of Prehistory, Pleistocene Palaeontology, Human Palaeontology, and Geology in the last ten years and of the outstanding discoveries that have been made. The Congress feels that there is a very urgent need now for leading workers to travel and visit the sites of other workers and see something of the field and laboratory evidence in detail. To this end the Congress strongly urges on individuals, Universities and Foundations and Governments to do all in their power to make travel grants for this purpose available to selected workers.

RESOLUTION 9

The Congress appoints a sub-comittee consisting of the President, General Secretary, Dr H. B. S. Cooke and Mr B. D. Malan to consider the whole question of the preparation and presentation of papers at future Congresses, and to take all necessary action in this connection without referring back to the Council.

RESOLUTION 10

The Congress in plenary session recommends that until an Archaeological Survey is established a Prehistorian be immediately appointed to the staff of the Coryndon Memorial Museum not only to assist the Curator in his duties relating to Prehistory but also to enjoy the privilege of being introduced to his field and being trained by him.

RESOLUTION 11

The Congress in plenary session recommends that until an Archaeological Survey is established a Prehistorian be immediately appointed to the staff of the Rhodes-Livingstone Museum not only to assist the Curator in his duties relating to Prehistory but also to enjoy the privilege of being introduced to his field and being trained by him.

Opening Session

RESOLUTION 12

The Congress in plenary session confirms the following persons chosen by Council to serve on the standing committee on Terminology:

Dr E. G. Gobert (North West Africa)
Dr G. Caton-Thompson (North East Africa)
Prof. G. Mortelmans (West Africa)
Dr L. S. B. Leakey (East Africa)
Prof. C. van Riet Lowe (South Africa)

RESOLUTION 13

The Congress in plenary session unanimously confirms the recommendation of the Council that the invitation of the Belgian Government to hold the Fourth Pan-African Congress on Prehistory in the Belgian Congo in 1959 be accepted. Congress expresses its gratitude to the Governments of France and Spain for their invitations to meet respectively in Dakar and the Canary Islands and expresses the hope that these Governments will explore the possibility of a joint invitation for the Fifth Congress which will enable the delegates to visit both French West Africa and the Canary Islands.

RESOLUTION 14: VOTES OF THANKS

Votes of Thanks were unanimously passed by the Congress in respect of the following:

1. Hosts in Bulawayo, Livingstone, Lusaka, Broken Hill and Abercorn.
2. The Northern Rhodesia Government, the Southern Rhodesia Government, the Rhokana Corporation, Ltd., Roan Antelope Copper Mines Ltd., Mufulira Mines Ltd., Nchanga Mine, Ltd., The Southern Rhodesia State Lotteries and other subscribers.
3. The Trustees of the National Museum of Southern Rhodesia.
4. The Trustees of the Rhodes-Livingstone Museum.
5. The National Monuments Commissions of Southern and Northern Rhodesia.
6. The Mayor and Council of Bulawayo.
7. The Mayor and Council of Livingstone.
8. The Mayor and Council of Broken Hill.
9. The Rhodesia Broken Hill Development Company.
10. The Women's Institute, Livingstone.
11. Mrs R. F. H. Summers and Mrs C. K. Cooke and their helpers with picnic lunches in Bulawayo.
12. The Government of the Belgian Congo, Le Comité Special du Katanga, L'Union Minière du Katanga, and other co-operating Societies and individuals in the Belgian Congo.
13. Prof. Mortelmans for organizing the Katanga Excursion.
14. Mr Summers and his associates for organizing the Southern Rhodesia Excursion.
15. Mrs Slade for the flowers in the Victoria Hall.
16. Mr A. J. Johnson for arranging the Victoria Hall and for the loan of equipment and Mr Davis for setting up the lanterns and the other equipment in the Hall and Library.
17. The Evelyn High School, Bulawayo.
18. Mr Garlick for operating the projector in the Evelyn High School.
19. The Irish Capuchin Mission, Maramba, Livingstone.
20. The Organizing Secretary and Congress Office Staff.
21. The President.

Closing Session, Thursday, July 28, at 8.30 p.m.

Delegates met in the Victoria Hall and were addressed by the President, Dr L. S. B. Leakey:

This is our closing session and we have, this evening, a total of fourteen Resolutions to come before this plenary session for ratification or rejection. These Resolutions have been very carefully examined, both by the relative sub-Committees and by the Council itself. I would, therefore, ask delegates either to reject or accept these Resolutions as laid before you and not to suggest minor amendments in details of wording.

Dr R. Mauny, (French West Africa) then translated for the benefit of the French-speaking delegates.

The General Secretary (Dr J. D. Clark), then read the Resolutions which were also translated into French by Dr Mauny.

RESOLUTION 1: The definition of African stratigraphical terms to be universally adopted by workers in the continent—carried unanimously.

RESOLUTION 2: Definition of Kalahari sand to be universally adopted in Africa—carried unanimously.

RESOLUTION 3: Promotion of Quaternary Geological Research. Mr C. K. Brain's paper describing new techniques for determining climatic deductions from Pleistocene dolomitic soils had greatly impressed the Council and the Committee of Section I, and they had taken steps to frame a Resolution that would help promote research along those lines—carried unanimously.

RESOLUTION 4: Only papers of African interest will be accepted by the Congress. This Resolution reaffirms an early decision of the Congress—carried unanimously.

RESOLUTION 5: Catalogue of Skeletal and Cranial Material—carried unanimously with an amendment proposed by Dr Cabot Briggs (U.S.A.) that a category covering Neo-mesolithic material should be included.

RESOLUTION 6: A Simplication of African Stone Age Terminology. Over three hours' discussion had gone into the framing of this Resolution. Dr Leakey referred to the difficulty expressed by the West African Delegates and the question of overlapping. After discussion this Resolution was carried with two against.

RESOLUTION 7: Compilation of Reference Book of African Prehistoric Cultures—carried unanimously.

RESOLUTION 8: Travelling Grants—carried unanimously.

RESOLUTION 9: Preparation and presentation of papers at future Congresses—carried unanimously.

RESOLUTIONS 10 and 11: Need to appoint Assistant Prehistorians at the Coryndon Museum, Nairobi and the Rhodes-Livingstone Museum, Livingstone. Professor van Riet Lowe explained the need to ensure continuity in the work of Dr Leakey and Dr Clark and that there should be trained research workers to take over from them when they retire. Mr Summers pointed out that such continuity was assured so far as Southern Rhodesia was concerned as the National Museum there, for the past twenty years, has had a Keeper of Antiquities on its staff.

Mr Fosbrooke raised the question of finance to enable these Resolutions to be passed.

The President replied that there was good reason to believe that the Governments concerned would not be unwilling to provide the necessary funds and if the Resolution was supported there was a reasonable chance of these appointments being made. The Resolutions were then carried unanimously.

RESOLUTION 12: Appointment of the Standing Committee on Terminology—carried unanimously.

RESOLUTION 13: Venue for the next Congress. The President said that the important question as to where the next Congress on Prehistory should be held had been discussed and considered at length by the Council. One Congress had already been held in North West Africa and it would therefore be fitting to accept the invitation of another great country—namely that of the Belgian Government and hold the next Congress in Léopoldville. The Council suggested that at some future date the respective Governments of France and Spain might like to combine their invitations, and thus enable the Congress to hold its meetings in both Dakar and the Canary Islands. It was unanimously decided that the Fourth Pan-African Congress on Prehistory should be held in the Belgian Congo.

RESOLUTION 14: Votes of Thanks. The President then expressed, on behalf of the Congress, thanks to Dr Clark, the Organizing Secretary, and his wife and to the staff of the Museum, for the great amount of preparation and organization which had gone into this most successful Congress —the most successful Pan-African Congress on Prehistory that had yet been held.

Dr Clark thanked the President and said how enjoyable he and Mrs Clark and all members of the office administration of the Congress had found the occasion. They had enjoyed every moment of it. Dr Clark then went on to express votes of thanks to the office staff and various commercial enterprises, to hosts and to all who had helped to make the Congress a success.

Professor van Riet Lowe then expressed a warm vote of thanks to Dr Leakey for his efforts as President of the Congress. He could not recall a Congress where everything had gone so smothly and well and so pleasantly. Professor van Riet Lowe said that Dr Leakey had himself thanked Dr Clark and his staff, but behind it all they had been inspired by Dr Leakey's example, by his purposefulness and single-mindedness and he was to be congratulated on his manner, his personality, and the manner in which he gave all of himself. Regret was also expressed at the necessary absence of Mrs Leakey. Dr Leakey then replied:

LADIES AND GENTLEMEN,

I thank you very deeply and warmly for what you have been so kind to say and to express about the little I have been able to do, and also for the mention you have made of Mary—as she is known to most of you. Had she been here with me, she would have helped me to do what I have been trying to do, and that is to serve the cause of Prehistory in this country. And if I have succeeded a little bit, then I am grateful. Thank you very much.

The President then declared the effective business of the Third Congress closed at 10.25 p.m., with the exception of the Northern Rhodesian and Katanga Excursions.

EXCURSIONS

EXCURSION A

To Prehistoric Sites in Southern Rhodesia. July 14 *to* 21 (*distance approximately* 1,200 *miles*)

The Excursion Handbook was compiled by Dr Geoffrey Bond and Messrs R. F. H. Summers, C. K. Cooke and K. R. Robinson, who also organized this excursion.

Delegates were transported in cars and some fifty-six delegates and their friends took part in this excursion. There are some five hundred archaeological sites in Southern Rhodesia and delegates were able to visit a good cross-section of the more important ones on which the chronological and cultural succession for both the Stone and Iron Ages has been built up. Representative collections of the material from these sites and of the rock art in the territory were displayed in the National Museum of Southern Rhodesia in Bulawayo.

The excursion was based on Bulawayo, where delegates were accommodated privately and in hotels. Visits were made to the early Upper Pleistocene site at Chelmer Spruit, which has yielded one of the best faunal assemblages of this date from the territory, and to the impressive Later Iron Age settlement at Khami Ruins, which has been the scene of recent excavations by K. R. Robinson. Also at Khami the excursion examined new sections exposed by C. K. Cooke at his important Magosian site and were privileged to handle a large collection of the material recovered.

A very enjoyable day was spent in the Matopos Hills, visiting two of the painted rock shelters excavated by the late Dr Neville Jones—Bambata which forms the type-site for the proto-Still Bay and Still Bay cultures, and Nswatugi, with its fine bichrome paintings, which also forms the type-site for the Wilton culture in Southern Rhodesia. The very interesting outline drawings in the small White Rhino Shelter were also visited.

The main event was a visit to the Zimbabwe area, near Fort Victoria, made all the more eventful by the presence of Dr G. Caton-Thompson, who had carried out the excavations there in 1929.

On the return journey to Bulawayo, some of the delegates were able to pay a quick visit to the Earlier Stone Age site at Lochard, where erosion has exposed a series of Acheulian and later living floors.

Travelling north again to Livingstone, the delegates saw one of the gravel-pits in the Bembesi River Valley, where evidence was first found of the Sangoan Culture (Bembesi variant) in Southern Rhodesia.

In a quick visit to the Wankie Game Reserve it was possible to show the excursion a good example of the savannah/grassland fauna indigenous to this type of country in Central Africa.

On the last day of the journey north the delegates were shown the rock engravings or carvings at Sunga Road (Chinobi) which were done by Late Stone Age Wilton peoples.

EXCURSION B

To Sites in the Zambezi Valley in the vicinity of Livingstone and the Victoria Falls, July 26 *and* 28
    (*approximate distance* 40 *miles*)

The Northern Rhodesian Excursion Guidebook gives details of the sites visited. Approximately 120 delegates and friends visited some twenty-one sites in the Zambezi and Maramba Valleys under the guidance of Dr J. D. Clark. A number of clean sections were excavated for this excursion and these showed the Congress the evidence on which the foundations of Northern Rhodesian prehistory are based.

Delegates saw the main fluviatile and other deposits in the river valleys and were able to make collections of cultural material from these. These deposits and their contents were also examined in relation to the regression of the Zambezi River through its gorge below the Victoria Falls. The corresponding sections on the flanks of the valleys were also examined where the rubble beds, on which rest floors of the Sangoan culture, are overlain by redeposited Kalahari sands.

Excursions

EXCURSION C

To Sites in Northern Rhodesia north of Livingstone, July 29 to August 6 (approximate distance 1,500 miles)

The Excursion Handbook was compiled by Dr J. D. Clark who also organized the excursion. Fifty-four Delegates joined this excursion, travelling in cars, and were shown some of the more important prehistoric sites in the south-eastern and northern parts of Northern Rhodesia. Pleistocene gravels were examined in the Kalomo River valley, where delegates collected pre-Chelles-Acheul and Middle Stone Age material. A quick visit was also paid to an interesting Middle Stone Age factory site at Magoye where outcrops of chert had formed the raw material. Some open station sites of early Upper Pleistocene age were examined in the Kafue river valley as well as excavations in the bone-bearing breccia at Twin Rivers kopje, near Lusaka. These breccias, believed to be contemporary with that which filled the Broken Hill cave, have thrown fresh light on the industry of *Homo rhodesiensis*. Some Iron Age rock engravings were also seen in this area.

Moving north to Broken Hill, a visit was paid to the site of the discovery of the human remains, and to the excavation close by, where in the clays overlying the dolomite have been found industries ranging from one of Hope Fountain type, through Acheulian to Sangoan and proto-Still Bay.

In the high country of the Muchinga Escarpment, visits were made to the painted caves of Nsalu and Nachikufu; the latter, which contains nearly 13 feet of Late Stone Age deposits, being the type-site for the Nachikufan culture, the savannah woodland equivalent of the contemporary Wilton culture in the grasslands. These caves contain good examples of the schematic rock paintings which post-date the naturalistic paintings north of the Zambezi. The Carbon 14 date for the earliest stage of the Nachikufan is approximately 4000 B.C.

After a visit to another group of painted rock shelters near Kasama, where delegates were able to see a few of the earlier naturalistic paintings, the excursion moved north to Abercorn, near the south end of Lake Tanganyika and the Kalambo Falls, close to which is one of the most important sites in the territory. Sections in the former lake beds show five living-floors, giving the succession from final Chelles-Acheul through a Fauresmith/Sangoan phase into the Middle Stone Age. Besides a richness of fine artefacts, the site in its lower levels is waterlogged, so that in peaty clays have been preserved pollens, leaves, and other organic material, including a quantity of wood in a partially carbonized state. A Carbon 14 reading for wood from one of the lower floors has given a date of more than 36,000 years before the present, which puts the earlier occupation at this site largely outside the range of the C. 14 method.

Visiting Lake Tanganyika the following day, the excursion was able to see high level beaches and erosion surfaces, an excavation yielding an early microlithic industry in the low-level beach at Mpulungu and a later shell midden in which occurred a degenerate stone industry, together with a burial which showed a physical type combining pre-Negro characteristics with those of an East African 'Caucasoid' strain.

From Abercorn the excursion returned to Kasama and then travelled due west to the Luapula river, visiting sites of schematic rock engravings, pecked into a coarse, gritty sandstone on the Munwa Stream, near Johnstone Falls. The majority of the delegates then made the crossing of the Luapula to Kasenga where the Katanga Excursion commenced.

EXCURSION D

To Prehistoric Sites in the Katanga Province of the Belgian Congo, August 7 to 14 (approximate distance 1,000 miles)

The Excursion Handbook was compiled by Professor G. Mortelmans who was also responsible for the organization and direction of this excursion. Approximately thirty-eight delegates took part. Transport was by motor-bus and special train. The excursion visited most of the main prehistoric sites in the Katanga Province.

From Kasenga a visit was made to Johnstone Falls on the Luapula River to see the lenticular grooves on flat outcrops of sandstone, believed to have been worn as a result of grinding and polishing stone axes. A number of such sites are known, stretching from Northern Rhodesia through the Congo to West Africa, having, as might be expected, much the same distribution as that of the polished axe in the western half of the continent.

The delegates were conveyed in buses to Elisabethville, stopping *en route* to examine the plateau gravel exposures at Site II at Mulundwa, where pebble tools of both Oldowan and Kafuan form occur, rolled in the basal gravels and ferricrete. The quantity of flaked pebbles at this site, in sharp contrast to their absence at other sites in these gravels was striking, and is a strong point in favour of their human origin.

At Elisabethville the excursion boarded a special train and proceeded north to the Kansenia region, where Dom Anciaux de Faveaux's sites at Kansenia Mission and at Katentenia have yielded what is known as the Kansenia industries. Some of these are vast workshop sites around outcrops of *grès polymorphes*; the greater part must date to post- or late Middle Stone Age times, the artefacts taking the form of picks and heavy scrapers.

From Lubudi delegates went to see the engravings at the cave of Kiantapo. Around the entrance to a sink-hole in the limestone occur a number of interesting schematic engravings, executed both by direct incision and *pointillé* technique. The similarity of many of the engravings to the tattoo marks of the surrounding tribes suggests that Kiantapo may have been a sacred place where ceremonial tattooing was carried out by the Bantu.

Proceeding to Luena, delegates were able to examine and collect from the gravels overlying the open cast workings. These gravels contained numerous tools and debris of Early Sangoan affinities.

Some 60 km. west of Kolwezi, a pit in a low terrace of the Kamoa stream has yielded quantities of fine late or final Acheulian implements, together with *ciseaux* of Katanga Sangoan (Kalinian) type.

At Kolwezi delegates were conducted by M. Paul du Ry on a day's excursion to sites in the vicinity, including a sand-pit section in which wood and charcoal were apparently associated with a Kalinian industry. At Kakontwe they visited the breccia where a late Gamblian fauna was found in association with a unifaced Middle Stone Age point. The excursion ended at Jadotville, where Iron Age copper-smelting furnaces were examined.

SECTION I

QUATERNARY GEOLOGY, GENERAL PALAEONTOLOGY AND CLIMATOLOGY

1

The Climatic and Cultural Sequence in the late Pleistocene of the Gold Coast

by O. DAVIES

THIS paper outlines the late Quaternary sequence in the Gold Coast, as revealed in river-terraces and gravels and associated artefacts. It deals almost entirely with the inland region, comprising the basins of the Black Volta, White Volta and Oti. The forest being far more difficult to explore than the savannah, a detailed sequence has not been worked out and may be discoverable only by digging numerous trenches. Moreover, it seems that intensifications of the Benguela Current have subjected the coastal area to the climatic rhythm of the southern hemisphere. Near Accra an arid period with soil-denudation was contemporary with or just anterior to the first Sangoan tools; up the coastal rivers Sangoan remains occur on the lowest terraces, usually at 30–40 feet, in what is now forest but was probably open country.[1] A section at Achimota failed to reveal climatic variations since the arid phase. Higher terraces and gravels are known on the Rivers Ankobra Pra and Birim; but the rarity of associated artefacts makes it impossible to date them; the topmost lateritized peneplain is probably Pliocene, and corresponds to the 160-foot marine terrace.

The arid phase near the coast may have thinned but hardly destroyed the forest. The present drier region, near the Volta, will have become orchard-bush; but the absence, to date, of Sangoan remains in the central and northern marginal forest, comprising most of Ashanti, though partly due to lack of exploration and political difficulties, suggests that the pre-Gamblian interpluvial was not severe between Lat. 6 and $7\frac{1}{2}°$. The forest-belt probably separates the northern and southern climatic sequences. Thus while the coast is more or less southern, according to the strength of the Benguela Current, the middle Volta basin should follow a straightforward northern rhythm.

I am assuming that in orchard-bush and savannah aridity will stabilize valleys and deposit gravel, while increased rainfall will deepen valleys by scouring, at least in the early stages before advancing forest hinders erosion. On the open plains of our Northern Territories erosion will have proceeded regularly; nor apparently did fluctuating sea-levels affect the Volta north of the gorge and of the forest-margin. Just above the gorge, between Dukludja and Kete Krachi, low water is now at 120–140 feet S.L.; but the old peneplain is at least 100 feet higher, and so well above the highest sea-level. The rapids down which the northern rivers descend are seldom as much as 20 feet high; over 60 feet on the Daka at Wiae is exceptional; all seem to be at ribs of harder rock in the horizontally bedded shales and sandstones.

The laterite-capped peneplain is at 100–150 feet above the Oti and White Volta, nearly 200 feet above the Black Volta; the scarp is usually several miles inland. It is clearly seen not only in the

A   1

Silurian rocks near Kete Krachi and Yapei, but on the comparatively level granite around Burufu and Wa. On the Silurian, laterite up to 10 feet thick may seal pebble-gravels which seem derived from the erosion of local conglomerates. These pebbles were seldom discovered by early man save where they were eroded down slopes or were redeposited in lower river-terraces.

On the rivers there are probably two rock-cut terraces containing occasional human artefacts, at 60–75 and 30–40 feet. It is however rare that both occur on the same traverse. At Yapei the 75-foot gravel contains rolled cores flakes and choppers, nondescript of pre-Chellean types. In an erosion-gravel sealed by laterite at the back of this gravel were found also formless unrolled artefacts which might be Middle Stone Age; this erosion probably belongs to the last rejuvenation of the valleys in the Gamblian pluvial. On the 30-foot terrace are unrolled microliths and probably quasi-Magosian tools. Nondescript rolled artefacts of vaguely pre-Chellean type occur on what seems to be the higher terrace at Lungbunga and Jakasi on White Volta, Mamata, and Ayrafie on Oti; there are occasionally unrolled Middle Stone Age objects on the lower terrace and on the rejuvenated rock-slopes below it.

If these two terraces indicate dry periods, it may be inferred that they correspond to the second and third interglacials usually recognized in Europe. The upper terrace with its possibly pre-Chellean artefacts is unlikely to be older than the second; the lower must be older than the late Middle Stone Age; on it at Buafori Konkomba is unrolled late Sangoan and atypical rolled flakes and choppers, which have been found also at Morago Bridge and Bato. Unrolled Sangoan material is uncommon beside rivers; where it occurs, near Kete Krachi and at Kaura, it is on a higher terrace about 100 feet. That the climate was dry though hardly arid is shewn by sand-blasting of several picks from north of Kete Krachi; but the level valleys of large rivers may have been marshy, or it was advantageous to settle well above them, whence game descending to water could be watched from a safe distance.

Yet unrolled Sangoan tools are not uncommon along streams, on the lateritized floors of the old mature valleys and even in the laterite-covering of rejuvenation-slopes. No stream has an upper terrace; the valleys are wide and mature, and in their bases narrow troughs have been cut to a depth usually of 20 feet.* On clean sections at Ypala and Furu, Sangoan material lay near the surface of the laterite, so maturity had been attained long before Sangoan man arrived. Rolled pieces in the terrace-laterite at Kamba Bridge are atypical flakes, like those from the upper terraces of the rivers.

Sangoan man was dependent on suitable material. He disliked the ubiquitous quartz, and went for greenstone, good quartzite and hornstone. This explains the patchy distribution of remains; so far as any conclusion is permissible, their rarity and developed forms near the Black Volta preclude this as a route of entry. There is a little developed Sangoan from the middle Oti, but none from the wide upper valley. So penetration near the Red Volta, past an important group of Sangoan sites in the Nangodi hills, is probable.

Deepening of the valleys took place during the Gamblian pluvial. Most modern streams have incised the rock-floors of the troughs through their silt-filling; but larger rivers have generally not reached the base of the silt, and the rock-floor may be up to 70 feet deeper (at Pwalagu). The troughs of the larger rivers are wide except at nickpoints. The meanders of the lower Oti seem to have formed before microlithic times in the silt filling a valley up to three miles wide. Rejuvenation of the rivers was terminated by the deposition of basal gravel, which may be seen at rapids and beneath the inner edge of inner silt-terraces. The gravel is usually sealed by water-laid grits, ferruginized but seldom compact as block-laterite; they are overlaid unconformably by the greyer silt of the silt-terraces. Only at Kwayasi have I seen erosion of the basal gravel before the formation of the inner silt-terrace.

The basal gravel often contains artefacts, rolled and unrolled, which I would describe as quasi-

---

* The Volta has eroded more deeply towards its gorge, so all depths are greater. On the Pru the height of the lowest terrace is 35 feet.

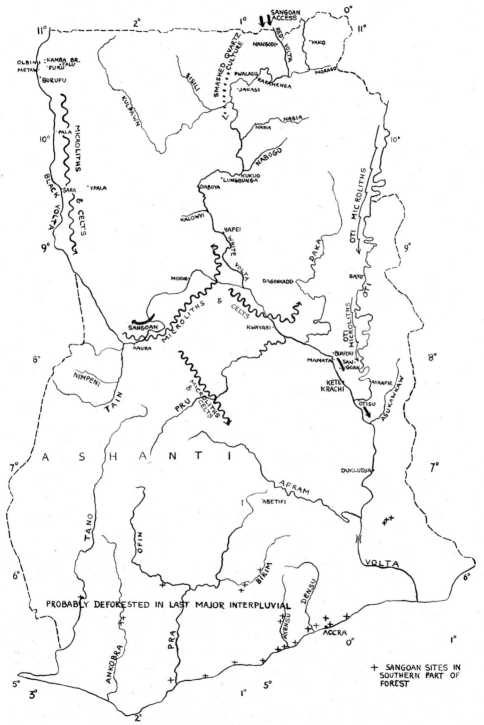

The Sangoan and Microlithic Colonisations of the Gold Coast

Magosian. There is a fair number of faceted butts and bipolar striking, and a mixture of forms which in other parts of Africa could be described as developed Middle Stone Age and Late Stone Age. Further exploration may reveal several stages in the industry. Similar artefacts unrolled can be found on the lower rock-terraces. The Gamblian pluvial probably drove men out of the Gold Coast, except perhaps from the coast where quasi-Magosian forms hardly occur. The basal river-gravels do not contain tools of Sangoan tradition, save possibly crude pieces from Karamenga and Sara. Quasi-Magosian sites are frequent along the Black and White Volta, but not on the Oti; no single route of recolonization can be postulated. Man came south owing to desiccation and probably the retreat of the forest; at Lungbunga some pebbles and artefacts are sand-blasted,* implying strong dry winds and a less sheltered valley before the deposition of the silt-terraces. The rejuvenated valleys of many streams are covered with block-laterite, proving that there was at best seasonal flow for a long period.

The rejuvenated valleys of both rivers and streams were filled with silt in what must have been a wetter phase when floods were high but scouring negligible. Inner silt-terraces are recognizable by laterite-nodules just below the surface, becoming biscuity in depth and towards the inner edge, as at Naga. There is sometimes calcrete about 5 feet down. One might call the inner silt-terraces Makalian; but it is unwise to correlate minor climatic fluctuations across the width of Africa.

Mere surface-exploration and absence of clean sections makes it impossible to date the build-up of the inner silt-terraces. A fine chert flake with faceted butt from Pala had probably lain well down in the silt. A chert scraper and other flakes from a gravel included in the silt at Kukuo are atypical. Some artefacts from dongas in the silt look large to be microlithic and may have faceted butts; I suspect that these had lain below the normal microlithic horizon and continued the quasi-Magosian tradition after the sealing of the basal gravel.

A rich collection of microliths has been made from many sites on the inner silt-terraces, both of rivers and streams. Where clean sections invite examination, these occur on or just below the top of the laterite nodules. The nodules generally extend into the soil covering the rock-slope above the silt-terrace; and microliths often are found a short way up the slope. We are not yet in a position to make a detailed report on industries, or to determine the length of the dry phase, when floods no longer reached and aggraded the top of the silt.

Most microliths on the Black Volta and tributaries are struck from small quartz pebbles. Chert was not available save at Morno; greenstone flakes and choppers are found near Burufu. The microliths are associated with polished axes, probably not with pottery, which seems to lie at a higher level. The main types are scrapers (thumbnails, rounded scrapers, end-scrapers, hollow scrapers rare), blades and backed blades, crescents and tranchets, points very rarely biface, angle-burins, burins made by obliquely slicing a triangular point, becs-de-flute, and some microburins. This industry may be ancestral to the microliths of North Ashanti and of Abetifi.[2]

Along the White Volta developed quasi-Magosian sites are known at Vako, Nasia, etc. Struck quartz flakes are very rare except below Daboya and on the lower tributaries like the Boinya and Kalowvi, whither they probably penetrated along with most of the tool-types from the Black Volta. North of Daboya smashed quartz chips are found; they may be artificial, but are not recognizable tools. Microliths occur on the Gambaga scarp, mostly of chert.

Below the confluence of the Voltas and up the Daka sites with struck microliths are rare and few tools have been found, mostly blades and points. No celts or sherds are associated. At Dagonkade on the Daka there is a concentration of microliths on what seems to be the biscuity laterite-cap of an old lake-silt. Perhaps a tongue of marginal forest extended up the Volta to the confluence, as it still does up the Oti to the same latitude.

On the Oti struck microliths of quartz, with usually some chert, are common on the inner silt-terrace. There are many blades and thumbnails; other types, points burins hollow scrapers and fabricators, are rare. Large spherical mullers and quartzite choppers are associated, but no celts or

* Identified by Dr Brückner of the Department of Geology, Achimota.

pottery. The only celt found was on a surface-site far above the silt, associated with smashed quartz chips.

Presumably an increased but irregular rainfall incised the inner silt-terraces of all the rivers to a width two or three times the present beds. A section at Bato on Oti shews that the banks were steep. The silt-fillings of the stream-troughs also have been incised, usually into the rock. Since this incision, outer terraces of silt or sand have been building up to contract the river-beds. They are probably still aggrading, and are often embanked above the level of the inner silt-terrace; on smaller rivers like the Daka they may overlie it. They never contain lateritic nodules. Clean sections at Pwalagu shew two main turf-lines, probably the result of low floods for several years, and many small turf-lines, perhaps due to annual flooding. At Nabogo a bank of red sand, perhaps initially lateritized in a dry period, is covered with grey silt which may still be aggrading. As the outer silt-terrace is a flood-plain, finds in it are rare and pretty modern, unweathered oyster-shells at Metaw, sherds at Olbini and Falu, small quartz flakes unlike the usual microliths at Bui, and pottery at Otisu.*

The sequence I have described is normal for the northern hemisphere, two pluvials when the Gold Coast was probably uninhabited and two interpluvials, of which the second does not seem to have been severe. There is no trace of the arid conditions which may have prevailed on the coast, a phenomenon of southern and central Africa. After the second pluvial (Gamblian) a dry period is followed by minor oscillations, which it is dangerous yet to equate with those of the East African and Mediterranean Holocene.

* Discovered by my colleague, Mr D. Collings.

REFERENCES

1. See *Notes africaines*, 1954, p. 65.
2. Shaw, C. T., *Proc. Prehistoric Soc.*, 1944, pp. 1–67.

2

Some Quaternary Events in the Winter Rainfall Area of the Cape Province

by J. A. MABBUTT

[ABSTRACT]

THE Pleistocene climatic cycles of the winter rainfall area as revealed in the terraces of the Olifants River resemble those of the Vaal in the summer rainfall region. Four pluvial periods occur, with a notable arid phase separating the third and fourth and following the excavation of a buried channel. Fauresmith sites occur on the red sands of this arid valley fill. Longitudinal terrace profiles and raised marine deposits indicate that periods of increased rainfall coincide with falling sea-levels. The raised beach succession in this region is effectively eustatic and marks a steadily falling sea-level upon which transgressional phases have been superposed. Levels of 100, 60, 45, 23–28, 18, 6–8 and 2 m. are recognized, with periods of lower sea-level preceding and following the 6–8 m. beach. The geomorphological connotations of the periods Lower, Middle and Upper Pleistocene are given and their potential value in comparative dating is discussed.

THIS is a preliminary sketch of the changing environment of Prehistoric Man in the Winter Rainfall area of the South-West Cape Province (Fig. 1), an examination of those avenues of research for which this region offers unique opportunities. These are, firstly a comparison of its Pleistocene climatic changes, as revealed in river terraces, with those of the Summer Rainfall region, secondly the relationship of these fluctuations to the contemporaneous movements of sea-level, thirdly the nature and chronology of the raised beach succession and lastly the potential contribution of geomorphology to the correlation of Pleistocene events in widely separated regions.

Events in the river valleys

Much of the area has remained semi-arid, with an annual rainfall below 25 cm., and the response of rivers and of weathering processes to past climatic fluctuations has accordingly been sensitive. Its major streams, such as the Olifants and the Great Berg Rivers, are perennial, however, and are sufficiently evolved to have recorded these fluctuations as terraces, the records fortunately being particularly rich in the lower courses across the drier coastal lowlands where the grading is thalassostatic. Surveys have already been carried out in the lower valleys of the Olifants and Great Berg and I shall refer to the former as typical of the area and as illustrative of its potentialities.

Flowing through a truly arid region, the lower Olifants receives no important tributary, and the coarse quartzite gravels derived from the headwater or 'montane' area are clearly differentiated from the finer gravels of vein quartz and argillaceous rocks coming from the adjoining plain and which may be distinguished as a 'lateral' facies. During exceptional drought, the drainage has been choked by red silty sands, partly aeolian in origin and characteristic of the even drier regions to the north-west. The terrace deposits are thus sensitive indicators of climatically induced changes in the discharge-load balance of the river.

6

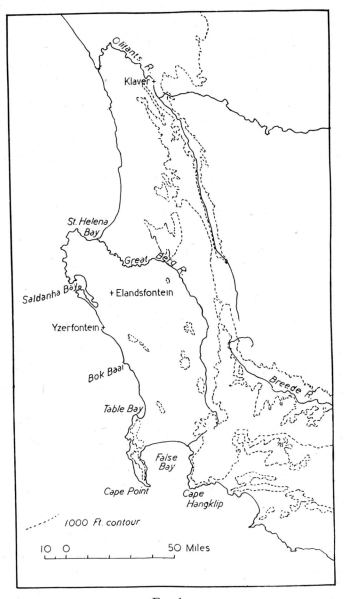

FIG. 1

A composite cross-section of the lower Olifants valley is given in Fig. 2. The river is incised below a plain of considerable perfection developed across soft phyllites of the Malmesbury Series. This plain descends southwards and abuts against the river valley at an altitude of 110 m. Below its even surface the Olifants initially formed a broad valley in a composite cycle revealed in its High Terraces at heights of 60 and 45 m. above the present valley floor. The gravels, which grade laterally into surface quartzites, have subsequently been calcified, with gypsum horizons locally present; they are predominantly of 'lateral' facies.

In two succeeding cycles, gravel terraces were formed at lower levels, and these are encased

7

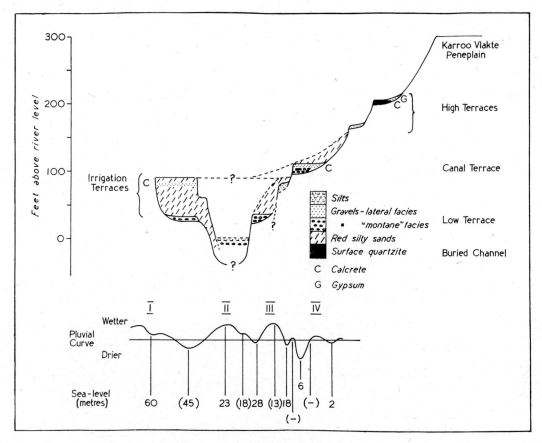

Fig. 2

within a more narrowly incised valley. The upper, or Canal Terrace gravels are well exposed in irrigation canal sections, whereas the Low Terrace is more locally developed. Both consist mainly of gravels of 'montane' facies overlying planed rock shelves graded to 23 and 10 m. above sea-level respectively, while the depositional surfaces reflect base-levels approximately 30 and 18 m. above the present. The base of the Canal gravels in the lowest reaches is composite, however, ranging between 23 and 18 m. above river level. Both sets of gravels have undergone surface calcification.

Deep channelling followed. No bedrock outcrops in the river below Klaver; sections to a depth of 6 m. in the floodplain in the lower valley have revealed only sand and gravel, and a quarry face in the Hol River exposes a channel fill 12 m. deep. In its possession of a buried channel the Olifants resembles most South African rivers, but there is evidence that the low sea-level cycle has regressed further upstream than normal, as borings for the National Road bridge above Klaver, where the river is 15 m. above sea-level, have penetrated 27 m. without striking the rock bed!

There ensued the deposition within the valley of fine gravels and of red silty sands indicative of an arid climate. The gravel terraces were covered and the valley filled locally to a depth of 20 m. at least. This fill has been excavated in two stages in a subsequent cycle of erosion, forming the Irrigation Terraces, and apparently proceeding to below the present valley floor. The final event has been the deposition of silts to form the flood plain of today.

8

Some Quaternary Events in the Winter Rainfall Area of the Cape Province

Climatic events

The climatic interpretation of this terrace sequence is given in Fig. 2 as fluctuations about a norm showing progressive regional desiccation as evidenced by the diminishing size of the mainstream, the decreasing importance of the lateral facies in the terrace deposits and the invasion of the valley by red sands. There is a striking resemblance between the history outlined and that of the Vaal River (Van Riet Lowe, 1952); the fourfold pluvial rhythm with the intervention of extreme aridity between the first and second and the third and fourth phases is present in both. Furthermore, the archaeological evidence from the Olifants valley suggests that the changes have been not only parallel but synchronous in the two areas. Numerous sites on the red sands along the valley margins have yielded implements which may be related to the Fauresmith culture from the association of small pick-like hand-axes of Sangoan affinity with cordates and with miniature biface hand-axes on obliquely struck flakes. Together with these occur fine biface hand-axes, cleavers and smallish blades showing convergent flaking and occasional facetting of the striking platform. One may recall the similar association of the Fauresmith with 'Kalaharian' deposits in the Vaal River valley. The significance of this assemblage, transitional to the evolved Middle Stone Age cultures, is increased by its affinity with the implement collection from the fossil horizon at Elandsfontein.

Evidence of the ages of the earlier cycles is provided by heavily rolled and patinated implements, collectively and broadly defined as African Chelles-Acheul, which occur reworked in the assemblage described. Since these are manufactured in the surface quartzite which is characteristic of the High Terrace they must emanate from the Canal or Low Terraces. Professor Oliver Davies has reported the discovery of 'a moderately evolved hand-axe' in the calcified crust of the Canal Terrace.

The evidence of the Olifants River terraces suggests that the Pleistocene climatic changes of the interior of South Africa are paralleled by those of the winter rainfall area. This carries with it the important corollary that in the Southern Hemisphere, at least, we may regard these pluvial periods

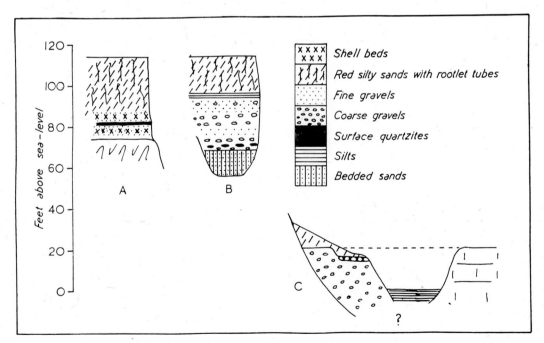

FIG. 3

9

as due not merely to latitudinal shifts of climatic boundaries, but also to increased precipitation within existing zones, possibly consequent upon changes in the intensity of atmospheric circulation. Additional evidence is found in the relationship of these climatic changes to the fluctuating sea-level of the Pleistocene as given by the relations of river terraces to beach lines and by the lithology of high and low sea-level deposits respectively.

Only if we assume a correspondence of pluvial climate and falling sea-level can we account for the fact that the ability and the tendency of the river to deepen its bed have coincided and that base-level changes have been effectively transmitted upstream with the formation of thalassostatic terraces. In the lowest reaches the terrace base should tend to 'plunge', due to rejuvenation, with resultant thickening of the gravel overburden; the terrace deposits should thin upstream until the effect of down-valley rejuvenation is more than counterbalanced by the need for increased gradient with heavier load during the depositional phase. This is notably demonstrated by the Canal Terrace in the Olifants valley. Upstream, a thickness of 6–8 m. of gravel is normal, decreasing to 4 m. in the middle course and increasing to 9 m. in the lowest reaches where the base is composite, a well-marked shelf at 23 m. above river level being locally eroded down to 18 m. The Canal Terrace can be linked with raised deltaic gravels above the present mouth and laterally with the marine deposits revealed in the cliffs 5 km. to the north and described by Reuning (1931).

A wave-cut surface at 23 m. above present sea-level is overlain by 2 m. of marine deposits which fall into two strata (Fig. 3*A*), a lower grit with *Kraussina lata* being separated by a hard surface quartzite from an upper bed containing boulders of the quartzite and characterized by *Ostrea prismatica*. These beds pass into bedded sands and gravels reaching to within 18 m. of sea-level near the Olifants River mouth (Fig. 3*B*), the basal gravels containing fragments of surface quartzite. This is seen as evidence of a marine stillstand at 23 m. followed by regression to 18 m. and recovery to 28 m., the upper level of the marine gravels, and the composite base of the Canal Terrace indicates corresponding fluvial regrading. It is noteworthy that both sets of marine deposits are terminated upwards by arid facies, namely surface quartzites and red sands with lime rootlet horizons. The Canal Terrace likewise reveals an upward change to 'lateral' facies, false-bedded sands and fine gravels of torrential character being prominent towards the top of terrace sections in the lower part of the valley.

The most diagnostic markers of former pluvial conditions in this semi-arid area are ferruginous horizons, or *ferricretes*, which are no longer forming, and the relationship of such deposits to the coastal sequence is best seen at Bok Baai (Fig. 1). Sinuous ferricrete ridges and platforms which outcrop through the sand dunes descend between headlands planed by the 6–8 m. sea to within 5 m. of present sea-level, and bear an assemblage of artefacts which, although ranging into the Middle Stone Age, yet includes forms characteristic of the Elandsfontein series, notably the small hand-axes (Mabbutt *et al.*, 1955). Corroborative evidence of humid conditions during part of the regression from the 6–8 m. level is seen at the base of the Dorcasia Limestones overlying the raised beach and formerly continuous beyond the present shoreline at Yzerfontein. Ferruginous silcretes occur at the base of delta terraces in a former estuary of the Great Berg River. Finally, one may cite the extension of vlei deposits with the freshwater gasteropod *Bulinus tropicus* down to H.W.M. on the False Bay coast, where they overlie typical Dorcasia dune sands.

Coincidence of falling sea-level and pluvial conditions may be presumed to imply rough coincidence of glacial advances and pluvial periods, and to this extent, therefore, the Recent marine deposits of the winter rainfall area support the conclusion from the river terraces that pluvial rhythms have been shared in common by regions of differing rainfall régime.

Coastal events

The raised beaches of the west coast have been classified by Haughton (1931) into 5 zones, partly on what is now regarded as untrustworthy palaeontological data, in particular the fossil oyster content. His Zone D, the *Ostrea prismatica* horizon, which includes the deposits in Fig. 3*A*, has a wider altitudinal range than the lower, younger raised beaches, and Haughton has postulated transverse warping which, he claims, has controlled the positions and levels of many of the major river outlets, including the Olifants and Saldanha estuaries. It is important that the extent of warping be ascertained prior to any attempt at long range beach correlation on an altitude basis.

If we accept the above evidence of a marine cycle between 18 and 28 m., the height range of the *Ostrea prismatica* zone in our area is largely accounted for. That little or no warping has subsequently occurred near the Olifants mouth is proved by the constant altitude of the 23 m. wave-cut surface, which can be traced from 5 km. north of the mouth to Strandfontein, 8 km. south of the outlet. Surface quartzites at lower levels within the valley, which Haughton would correlate with those of the marine sections in Fig. 6a, are on distinctly younger surfaces.

The Saldanha-Langebaan estuary has been claimed as an area of downwarping from the occurrence in its head reaches and near to sea-level of oyster beds with *Ostrea atherstonei*, regarded as being older than the fauna of the 6–8 m. terrace nearby. Palaeontological uncertainty apart, the conformity of these shell beds to the contours and water level of the modern estuary and their survival on a former drainage line render such antiquity unlikely. The vindication by recent survey of Du Toit's view that the Dorcasia Limestones, which largely frame the estuary, are *wholly* terrestrial and younger than the 6–8 m. terrace allows reconsideration of the origin and age of the Saldanha estuary. Its *ria* outline would appear to be largely fortuitous and due to the linking to the mainland by dune and shore deposits of granite islands planed at the *Ostrea prismatica* level, and to the drowning, during the final eustatic recovery of sea-level, of drainage channels deepened during the preceding regression.

South of Namaqualand, sea-levels above the *Ostrea prismatica* cycle have as yet been traced only in higher river terraces and in the older marine planation surfaces of the littoral belt. The High Terraces of the Olifants River have been tentatively interpreted as indicative of 60 and 45 m. sea-levels and the peneplain into which they are incised is graded approximately to the 100 m. level. The *Ostrea prismatica* terraces would seem to embrace the Major Emergence of Krige (1929), albeit somewhat higher than normal, for there is no other feature comparable with the 18 m. strand line elsewhere. Haughton (1931) distinguishes a 10 m. level (his Zone B), and a boulder beach exposed in cliff gulleys near Strandfontein and ranging from 11 to 15 m. above H.W.M. may represent this zone and the base level of the Low Terrace of the Olifants River. The 6–8 m. beach occurs at constant altitude everywhere and is distinguished by its cold-water fauna of more modern character, indicative of the onset of the ocean currents associated with present-day aridity.

The overall picture is one of falling sea-level during the Pleistocene, broken by successive transgressional phases. The strand lines would not appear to have undergone sufficient subsequent warping to disqualify their use in correlation with eustatic beaches elsewhere.

At least one period of lower sea-level has been interposed in the above succession, as shown by the drowned mouths and buried channels of the rivers in this area. On geomorphological evidence the major regression must certainly be placed later than the Major Emergence, for strand lines and terraces at this altitude are truncated by the estuaries. The main evidence of regression is even younger than the Minor Emergence beach, for the latter is extensively masked by terrestrial deposits, such as the Dorcasia Limestones, which formerly continued out beyond the present shoreline. No important transgression has taken place since the emplacement of this Formation and its equivalents such as the dune sands of the False Bay coast and the sandy limestones around Table Bay. Recent borings have shown that much of the Cape Flats originated during this regressional phase, no evidence of marine deposition at the higher levels having been forthcoming. Wood found at a depth of 6 m. at Epping, and therefore within 6 m. of present sea-level has recently been dated at 38,000 years, throwing important evidence on the age of the phase, and setting a lower limit to the age of the Minor Emergence.*

* I am indebted to Mr S. Amdurer for this information.

There is, however, physiographical evidence for an earlier period of lower sea-level, between the Major and Minor Emergence, although probably of lesser importance, for the latter beach frequently extends into the estuary mouths and is found to be emplaced within the rock lips of the deep channels. That this is so in the Olifants is shown in Fig. 3C. Also shown here is a shell bank at 4 m. above present sea-level, equivalent to the resting stage claimed by Krige to have followed the Minor Emergence. Its relationship to the major regression is not yet clear, but it is physiographically closely linked with the 6–8 m. shoreline (Mabbutt, 1954a).

At many points in the area under consideration there are signs that recovery from the low sea-level continued to approximately 2 m. above the present shore. 'Dead' shingle beaches and backshore terraces occur at this altitude at Cape Hangklip (Mabbutt, 1954b), and the prominent shingle beach north of Cape Point is also overgrown and beyond the present range of storm waves. A raised shell beach at this altitude was formerly exposed near Hout Bay harbour. The point is one which hinges upon accurate levels, such as are unfortunately rarely available.

Archaeological evidence from coastal sites and river terraces gives some time markers in the above succession. The Major Emergence must certainly antedate the later stages of the Chelles-Acheul as developed in the Winter Rainfall area, for unworn implements of a relatively advanced stage of this culture overlie an abrasion platform of this marine stage and extend to within 8 m. of present sea-level at Cape Hangklip. The equivalent terrace cycle in the Olifants valley may also be attributed to the Earlier Stone Age. Goodwin* has emphasized the correspondence of Still Bay sites near Noordhoek with the 6–8 m. strand line in the same area, but we may reasonably place the Minor Emergence somewhat earlier, probably as Fauresmith from the evidence at Bok Baai and its corroboration at Elandsfontein and in the Olifants valley. Terrestrial sands above the 6–8 m. beach at Yzerfontein have yielded flakes of Middle Stone Age affinity, while the calcareous sands which mask the corresponding cliff line near Cape Point have buried Still Bay as well as earlier sites. Still Bay-type flakes have been found in the upper levels of delta terraces around a former estuary of the Great Berg River enclosed by and therefore younger than the 6–8 m. shell beach. The evolved Middle Stone Age cultures would seem to equate with an advanced stage of the Minor Emergence. The beach ridges attributed to the 2 m. sea at Cape Hangklip are overlain by middens with Wilton implements (Rudner, 1954).

To summarize: the raised beaches described above are staged below the outer edge of a marked erosion bevel at 100 m. which borders the Atlantic coast. Part sub-aerial and part marine in origin, its relationship to the higher river terraces sets its upper age limit as Lower Pleistocene, but it represents a period of stable base level probably extending back into the Tertiary. Marked littoral rejuvenation sets in with the Middle Pleistocene, the descending sequence of river terraces being matched by the raised beach succession outlined above. A major regression would appear to mark the boundary between the Earlier and Middle Stone Age and, by definition, that between Middle and Upper Pleistocene. The Upper Pleistocene sees the recovery of sea-level, probably to 2 m. above the present, and the final movement is one of slight regression.

Given that these variations in sea-level reflect glacial advance and retreat, and accepting the Mediterranean beaches as being satisfactorily linked with the glacial chronology of Europe, we would seem to have, in our raised beach record, an invaluable means of linking our prehistoric chronology with that of the Palaearctic region. To attempt this solely on the basis of altitude may lead to confusion in the measure that our Pleistocene beaches are not wholly eustatic; the bases of correlation must be wider and must rest upon stratigraphic and geomorphological principles.

Quaternary events in the geomorphological setting

The homotaxial problems encountered in defining and sub-dividing such a short geological episode as the Quaternary on faunal grounds are particularly real in a refuge area such as Africa.

* Quoted in Haughton (1933).

The same difficulty is met with definition on an archaeological basis, for the broad similarity of the African Chelles-Acheul gives place to regional differentiation of cultures of unequal duration which become increasingly inadequate as 'zone fossils'.

The similarity between the Pleistocene climatic succession in the two contrasting rainfall provinces is paralleled and emphasized in the geomorphological sequence. In both Summer and Winter Rainfall areas extensive 'high-level' terraces of Lower Pleistocene age give place to the more narrowly incised gravel terraces of the Middle Pleistocene. The latter are demarcated physically from the arid deposits which characterize the Upper Pleistocene, a demarcation seemingly emphasized in the winter rainfall area by the interpolation of a deep channel phase. The breaks in the terrace sequence of the winter rainfall area are also found in the coastal succession. Terraces and planation levels above the Major Emergence pertain to the Lower Pleistocene, the two defined raised beach levels are Middle Pleistocene and the succeeding regression and recovery of sea-level and associated terrestrial deposits are Upper Pleistocene.

The geomorphological connotation of the divisions of the Quaternary period is stressed for two reasons. Firstly, if found valid over the whole sub-continent, it could serve as a time scale independent of and therefore capable of dating the regionally differing culture changes which characterize the latter part of the Prehistoric period. Secondly, the physiographical setting, if given such chronological significance, would assist in unravelling Quaternary events where palaeontological and archaeological evidence is lacking or indecisive.

REFERENCES

Haughton, S. H. (1931), 'The Late Tertiary and Recent Deposits of the West Coast of South Africa', *Trans. Geol. Soc. S. Afr.*, XXXIV, pp. 19–57.

Haughton, S. H. (1933), 'The Geology of Capetown and Adjoining Country', Expln. to Sheet 247, *Geol. Surv. S. Afr.*, Pretoria.

Mabbutt, J. A. (1954a), 'The Physiography of an Area adjoining Cape Maclear', *Trans. Roy. Soc. S. Afr.*, XXXIV, pp. 61–7.

Mabbutt, J. A. (1954b), 'Cape Hangklip—A study in coastal geomorphology', *Trans. Roy. Soc. S. Afr.*, XXXIV, pp. 17–24.

Mabbutt, J., J. Rudner and R. Singer (1955), 'Geomorphology, Archaeology and Anthropology from Bok Baai, Darling District, C.P.', *S. Afr. Archaeol. Bull.*, X, pp. 85–93.

Reuning, E. (1931), 'The Pomona-Quartzite and Oyster-Horizon on the West Coast north of the Mouth of the Olifants River, Cape Province', *Trans. Roy. Soc. S. Afr.*, XIX, pp. 205–14.

Rudner, I. and J. (1954), 'A Local Late Stone Age Development', *S. Afr. Archaeol. Bull.*, IX, pp. 103–7.

van Riet Lowe, C. (1952), 'The Vaal River Chronology', *S. Afr. Archaeol. Bull.*, VII, pp. 135–49.

3

The Pleistocene in South-West Africa

by H. KORN* and H. MARTIN

Published by permission of the South-West African Administration

[ABSTRACT]

TOWARDS the end of the Tertiary a period of extreme aridity must have brought river action to a stillstand, whilst the upwarping of the continent created a big potential of erosion for the Early Pleistocene pluvials. These pluvials are therefore represented by an incision of all the major rivers. The first Pleistocene gravels, present in all the river systems, belong to the Kanjeran pluvial. The terraces of this stage are always calcified and have yielded abundant Late Chelles-Acheul tools. Fauresmith assemblages are rare. It is not yet certain whether this is due to climatic circumstances or to the comparatively short duration of this transition culture, or both. The Late Pleistocene pluvial is well represented by non-calcified gravel terraces containing South African Middle Stone Age implements. Later M.S.A. assemblages are rare and confined to the neighbourhood of springs showing thus the approach of a new arid phase, during which the Kalahari dunes were on the move again. The latest phase of the M.S.A. seems to be completely lacking. When climatic conditions became more favourable again the country was occupied by people practising a Smithfield culture. Typical Wilton seems to be confined to the Kalahari fringe.

The Tertiary

The Tertiary seems, on the whole, to have been a time of quiet. Sediments, reaching thicknesses of up to 800 feet, accumulated in the Etosha-Ovamboland basin and in the bigger river systems of the Kalahari. Even the rivers leading from the inland plateaus directly down to the Atlantic Ocean show aggradations of up to 400 feet. The sediments range from wind-blown sands to very coarse, ill-sorted, calcareous conglomerates. Climate, as deduced from the nature of the sediments, seems to have varied from extreme aridity to periods with a considerably higher rainfall than today. But even then a torrential rainy season and a long dry winter seem to have been the rule. The end of the Tertiary brought again a period of extreme aridity with the deposition of enormous volumes of aeolian Kalahari sand. River action must have come to a complete stillstand. During this time the continent rose at least 2,000 feet, bequeathing to the Pleistocene a big, unused potential of erosion.

The Early Pleistocene Pluvials

The return of pluvial conditions led to a rapid incision of all the bigger rivers. In the Auob and Nossob valleys (southern Kalahari) maximum incision reached 150 feet (45 m.), in the valleys running westwards to the Atlantic Ocean 400 feet (120 m.). The Omuramba Omatako, a tributary of the Okawango (see Map), is the only bigger river showing only a very slight incision into the broad Tertiary valley plain.

Though the incised valleys show often well preserved rock benches, no gravel terraces attributable to the Early Pleistocene pluvials have yet been discovered. From the fact that older as well as

* Deceased.

14

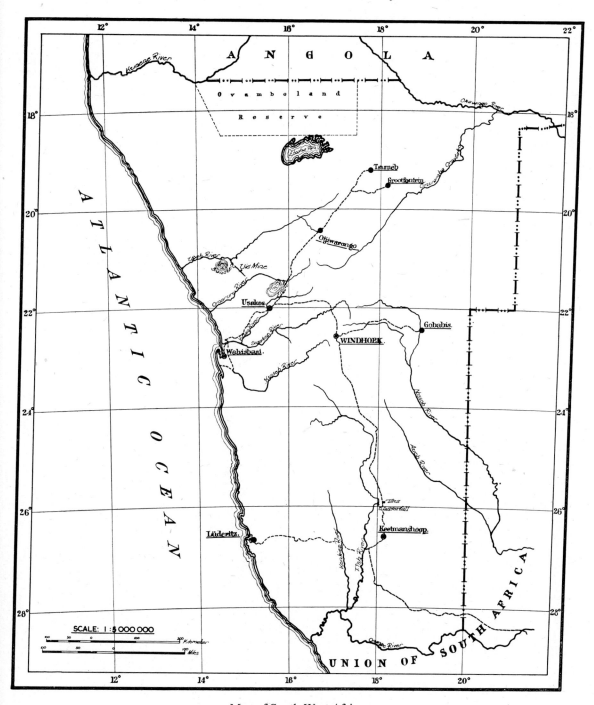

Map of South-West Africa

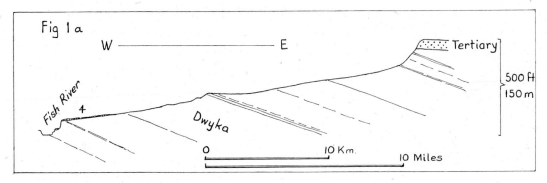

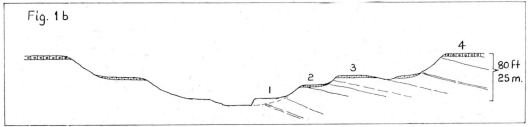

FIG. 1*a*. Section of Fish river valley at Wasserfall. 4 calcified Chelles-Acheul gravels (Kanjeran)

FIG. 1*b*. The Pleistocene terraces at Wasserfall. 1 flood plain, 2 and 3 non-calcified gravels, 4 calcified Kanjeran gravels

younger calcified gravels have been well preserved, it can perhaps be deduced that the Lower Pleistocene had a more uniformly humid climate, unfavourable to calcification. But the general distribution of the rainfall must have followed a pattern resembling the present one. This is indicated by the fact that not one of the rivers between the Kuiseb and the Orange River was able to cut through the Tertiary deposits, proving that the area with the lowest rainfall today had a lower rainfall than the rest of the country already during the Early Pleistocene.

The Middle Pleistocene Pluvial

The Middle Pleistocene is in all the river systems represented by calcareous gravels. These gravels, having at numerous localities yielded Chelles-Acheul implements, can safely be attributed to the Kanjeran pluvial.

The calcified gravels form conspicuous terraces along many rivers. Along the middle course of the Fish river, between Gibeon and Tses, the Kanjeran terrace has a height of 60–80 feet (20–25 m.). At other rivers it is much lower, for instance at the Auob and Nossob rivers in the Kalahari only 15 feet (5 m.).

Fossils have so far only been found in the terrace of the Khan river at Usakos (Gevers, 1933). The fossils support the conclusion that these deposits correspond to the Chelles-Acheul gravels of the Vaal river (Haughton).

In the canyon stretches with which the rivers Kuiseb, Swakop, Omaruru and Ugab traverse the Namib desert a calcified gravel terrace of 100–200 feet height is present. It is probable, though not proved by finds of implements, that this is the Kanjeran terrace. The narrow, flood-swept canyons were probably unfit as living sites.

At the Fish river, the rivers Auob and Nossob and many of the smaller rivers, the gravels form a layer, only 3–6 feet thick, capping a platform of older rocks. Fig. 1*a* shows a typical section of the

Fish river valley at Wasserfall, 10 miles to the west of Tses. The calcified gravel is simply packed with Chelles-Acheul implements representing stages III–V of the Vaal river. Tools of stages III and IV are found everywhere and are always slightly rolled. Stage V is usually confined to distinct localities (living sites) and is never rolled. A high percentage of cleavers is characteristic for these sites. Fig. 2 shows implements from a site just south of Tses, collected on the corresponding terrace of a small tributary of the Fish river.

The thin gravels, spread over broad, well graded valley floors seem to indicate very stable climatic conditions for the whole later part of the development of the Chelles-Acheul culture (stages III–V of the Vaal river). The gravels can hardly be called aggradations, they make far more the impression of gravels left and reworked by shifting river channels on a stable flood plain.

In South-West Africa no sediments have been observed which could be correlated with the calcified sands overlying the younger gravels in the Vaal river basin (Söhnge, Visser and van Riet Lowe, 1937). There is therefore no geological evidence for an arid period following the deposition

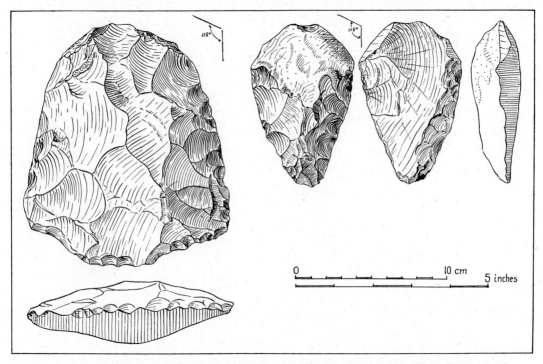

FIG. 2. Unrolled Stellenbosch V tools from the top of the calcified gravels at Tses. Cleaver made from flake (indurated shale). Small hand-axe made from flake (quartzite)

of the Middle Pleistocene gravels. But there can be little doubt that, as elsewhere on the continent, a dry period intervened between the deposition of the calcified gravels and the phase of erosion which is the next recognizable event.

In the country as a whole open Chelles-Acheul sites are numerous and they occur occasionally at spots which, today, are miles removed from even the nearest temporary water hole.

The End-Pleistocene Pluvial

This pluvial is well represented by an erosion into the Kanjeran gravels and by ubiquitous non-calcified gravels accompanying all the rivers as low terraces. Only some of the rivers ending in pans in the Namib dunes have not been able to cut a channel into these youngest gravels. Their rare floods are still using an End-Pleistocene flood plain.

For the earlier part of this pluvial the archaeological evidence is still inconclusive. Only 3 or 4 Fauresmith sites have so far been found in South-West Africa, a fact suggesting that climatic conditions may have become too dry for human occupation or that the Fauresmith period was too short to have left plentiful relics.

Future work will perhaps reveal a Fauresmith terrace. This is indicated by a collection made on the 40-feet (12 m.) terrace of the Fish river at Wasserfall (Fig. 1*b*). This collection though consisting of only 20 implements, has a strong Fauresmith flavour (Fig. 3). There is of course no proof that

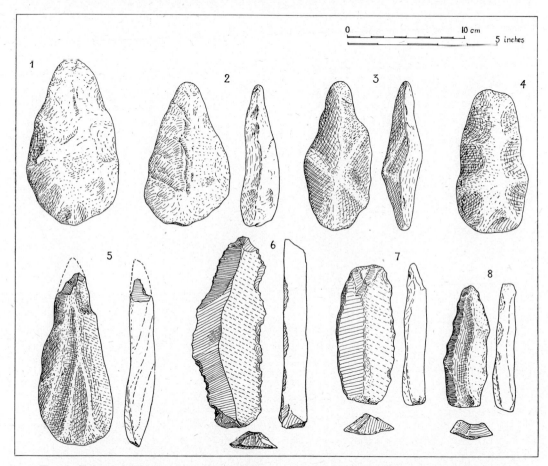

FIG. 3. Fauresmith? Implements from 40-feet terrace at Wasserfall. Note rough workmanship of No. 3 compared with tools in Fig. 2. All implements made from quartzite

the small hand-axes, all heavily rolled, are not derived from the higher terrace, where the late Chelles-Acheul sites already contain a fair proportion of small hand-axes. But even discounting the hand-axes, the heavy, rolled and unrolled blades are more suggestive of the Fauresmith than of the South African Middle Stone Age.

That water may have been not too plentiful during Fauresmith times is suggested by the fact that the only Fauresmith living site, discovered so far, is situated at the mouth of the Orabes gorge at the Brandberg, where there is a spring even today. At this site the implements are weathering out of a sandy tufa.

All evidence regarding the Fauresmith is still very inconclusive.

It is not yet clear whether the End-Pleistocene pluvial consists of one or of two wet phases. Fig. 1b suggests that the lowest terrace, on which no implements were found, represents a second wet phase. It is not impossible that along the smaller rivers the two terraces practically merge into one another. If this should be the case then the second wet phase was probably the more pronounced one, as implements, rolled and unrolled, belonging to the South African Middle Stone Age have been found at numerous localities in the unconsolidated gravels.

The existence of pluvial conditions during this period is further proved by the wide-spread occurrence of M.S.A. implements in the driest parts of the Namib desert.

M.S.A. implements from open sites are usually characterized by a red patina. Such a patina was never observed on the younger Smithfield assemblages.

Towards the end of the M.S.A. period the climate seems to have become drier again. Whilst the earlier stages of the M.S.A. are to be found everywhere, the final stage, characterized by retouched and bifaced points, is rare and always confined to the neighbourhood of springs or to old spring deposits. Fig. 4 shows implements weathering out of a tufa hill at the homestead of farm Doornkom No. 173, Otjiwarongo District. The tufa hill rises about 10–15 feet above the sand covered plain. Its origin as a spring deposit is clearly revealed by numerous, silicified reed stalks. A borehole sunk on the hill struck hot water at a depth of 108 feet, proving that a hot spring must have existed here during Late M.S.A. times.

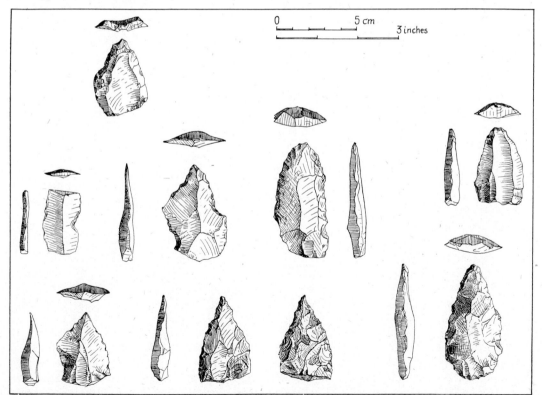

FIG. 4. Late Middle Stone Age implements from tufa hill on Farm Doornkom. All the implements are made from indurated shale

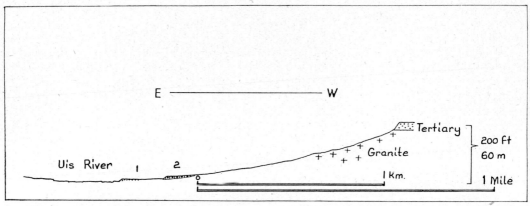

FIG. 5. The terraces of the Uis river near Tsisab Bank. 1 non-calcified terrace with M.S.A. implements. 2 calcified gravels with Late Chelles-Acheul implements

In the Namib too a Late M.S.A. culture was found in a spring deposit on farm Sukses No. 133, Maltahöhe district, at a spot where the water table is today 70 feet deep. On the whole the distribution of the Late M.S.A. seems to indicate a climate slightly wetter than the present one.

The Epi-Pleistocene

The latest stage of the M.S.A. seems not to be represented in South-West Africa. The climate seems to have become too arid for human occupation. During this period the Kalahari dunes were probably heaped up to their present shapes.

The return of more favourable conditions brought a renewed erosion of the rivers down to their present levels and the occupation of the country by people practising a Smithfield culture. The famous rock paintings of the Brandberg and Erongo mountains seem to be connected with the Smithfield culture. This is indicated by the fact that three excavations in painted shelters in the Tsisab gorge (Brandberg) and one in Phillip's cave (Erongo) have yielded only Smithfield implements. Although M.S.A. is plentiful in front of the shelters and in the neighbourhood, none was found in the excavations right down to bed-rock, and the only younger cultural elements on the surface were a few potsherds (Mason, 1954). More excavations are of course necessary before certainty can be reached on this point. An approximate age of 3,300 years for the earlier (?) stage of the Smithfield culture is indicated by a C14 date, obtained by Prof. Libby, for charcoal from layer II of the Phillips cave excavation (Breuil, 1954; Martin and Mason, 1954).

Wilton, characterized by crescents, has so far only been found at two localities, at Haruchas in the Auob valley on top of a small dune and on the banks of the Okavango river at Sambio.

The microlithic sites of the Namib seem to belong to the Smithfield.

Climatic Changes during the Pleistocene

The climatic changes which affected the western rim of the subcontinent during the Pleistocene are well exhibited by the terraces of the Uis river.

The Uis river is a 25-mile long tributary of the Ugab river, joining the latter to the east of Brandberg. It runs parallel to the 4-inch (100 mm.) isohyet. This means that river action cannot have been influenced by climatic changes affecting only part of the river system, a conclusion justified by observations in other parts of the country which indicate that the general distribution pattern of the rainfall has remained unaffected by the gross variations of precipitation. The river not only runs parallel to the isohyets but parallel to the coast too. Its gradient can therefore not have been altered by the upwarping of the continental margin. Neither was the river system affected by tectonic movements or by the loss or capture of tributaries. Everything seems to justify the conclusion that the varying gravel sizes of the different terraces are a direct expression of the variations of rainfall.

Fig. 5 shows the terraces in the neighbourhood of Tsisab Bank. The calcified Chelles-Acheul gravels, containing numerous rolled and unrolled late Acheulian tools (Stellenbosch III–IV), are composed of pebbles with maximum diameters of 20–25 cm. The non-calcified 5-foot terrace, containing rolled and unrolled Middle Stone Age tools, shows pebbles with maximum diameters of 8–10 cm. The present day river bed shows only sand.

The smaller tributaries have not everywhere been able to cut through the calcified gravels. At Uis Mine one deposit was worked successfully for alluvial tin. The same deposit contains an abundance of Victoria West cores, speaking eloquently of Mid-Pleistocene quarrying operations (Collection Alice Bolitho, mentioned by Mason, 1955, and Collection Abbé Breuil). No alluvial tin deposits are formed under today's climatic conditions anywhere in the country, because alluvial ore deposits can only be formed under a far more humid climate with rivers flowing for a considerable part of the year. The occurrence of tin concentrations in the Mid-Pleistocene deposits thus corroborates the conclusion drawn from the size of the gravels.

Summing up the evidence, the following sequence of climatic changes emerges. For the early-Pleistocene pluvials a high precipitation and a generally humid climate must be assumed (absence of calcification).

The Kanjeran pluvial was, compared with today, characterized by a far higher and better distributed rainfall.

During the last stage of the Chelles-Acheul culture the climate became dry approaching today's conditions and it probably passed into an even drier phase during the height of the interpluvial.

There are indications that the End-Pleistocene pluvial consisted of two wet phases. The position of the Fauresmith culture is not yet certain, but there is little doubt that the main development of the Middle Stone Age industries took place during the last phase of the pluvial. The climate of this time was considerably wetter than today but not nearly as humid as during the Kanjeran pluvial.

A period of great aridity, followed by a minor wet phase, characterizes the Epi-Pleistocene.

The whole sequence seems to show, right through the Pleistocene, a decline of the rainfall on which the pluvial and interpluvial fluctuations are superimposed.

The rainfall curve for the Pleistocene of South-West Africa will probably, after elimination of the uncertainties, be very similar to the curve deduced by Cooke, 1946, for the Vaal river basin. The cultural sequence is closer related to the development in the Union of South Africa than to any other part of the continent.

The Coast

Very little is known about the Pleistocene deposits of the coastal belt.

All the bigger rivers reaching the coast show a well developed terrace of non-calcified gravels. At both the Swakop and the Omaruru rivers rolled M.S.A. implements have been found in these gravels. The terrace of the Omaruru river ends at the coast at a height of 63 feet, but the corresponding beach is probably lower.

Observations at the coast are made very difficult by the extremes of the desert climate. Sand-blast and insolation have destroyed the pebbles on all the older surfaces to such an extent that it is difficult even to recognize a raised beach. Stone implements have of course had the same fate.

REFERENCES

Breuil, Abbé H., 'Carbon Test and South-West African Paintings', *S. Afr. Archaeol. Bull.*, June 1954.
Cooke, H. B. S., 'The Development of the Vaal River and its Deposits', *Trans. Geol. Soc. S.A.*, XLIX, 1946.

Section One

Haughton, S. H., 'The Fossil Equidae of South Africa', *Annals S.A. Museum*, XXVIII (4).

Gevers, T. W., 'Über ein vermeintliches Eocänkonglomerat bei Usakos in Südwestafrika', *Centralblatt f.Min.* etc., 1934, Abt. B. No. 7.

Martin, H. and Mason R., 'The test Trench in the Phillips Cave, Ameib, Erongo Mountains, South-West Africa', *S. Afr. Archaeol. Bull.*, IX, December 1954.

Mason, R., 'Notes on the later Stone Age in South-West Africa', *S. Afr. Archaeol. Bull.*, IX, December 1954.

Brain, C. K. and Mason R., 'A Later African Chelles-Acheul Site near Nakop, South Kalahari', *S. Afr. Archaeol. Bull.*, X, March 1955.

Söhnge, P. G., Visser, D. J. L. and van Riet Lowe, C., *The Geology and Archaeology of the Vaal River Basin*, Geol. Survey, Memoir No. 35, 1937.

4

Le Cénozoïque du Congo Belge[*]

par G. MORTELMANS

I Introduction

Ces dernières années ont été marquées, dans l'étude du Cénozoïque du Congo Belge, par la parution d'une série d'importants travaux dûs, en ordre principal, à L. Cahen,[2] L. Cahen et J. Lepersonne,[3, 4] J. de Heinzelin de Braucourt[6 à 9] et G. Mortelmans.[15, 16] Ces travaux ont grandement contribué à préciser l'histoire géologique de cette portion de l'Afrique centrale au point de vue stratigraphique, tectonique, morphologique, faunique et climatique et permis d'asseoir sur des bases plus sûres les comparaisons et les corrélations avec les contrées avoisinantes. C'est en nous inspirant de ces travaux et plus particulièrement de la *Géologie du Congo Belge* de L. Cahen dont la préparation a fourni à son auteur l'occasion d'une critique serrée de toutes les données et interprétations existantes que nous avons rédigé cette note. Nous y avons intégré, en outre, diverses données nouvelles recueillies pendant une mission en cours au Katanga, mission effectuée sous les auspices du Centre Scientifique et Médical de l'Université de Bruxelles en Afrique Centrale (CEMUBAC).

Le Cénozoïque du Congo Belge peut être scindé en deux grands ensembles continentaux, le 'système du Kalahari' à la base, le 'système Plio-Pléistocène' au sommet. Tous deux présentent des équivalents marins et lacustres. Ces grands systèmes continentaux peuvent, à leur tour, être subdivisés en ensembles moins importants dont les limites correspondent au déclenchement de 'cycles géographiques' successifs. Il existera par conséquent une relation approchée entre le relief du Congo et la distribution de ces ensembles successifs.

On sait, et L. Cahen l'a récemment rappelé et précisé, qu'une des caractéristiques essentielles du relief du Congo est l'extension considérable qu'y prennent les plaines et les plateaux. Ceux-ci notamment forment un bourrelet annulaire entourant une dépression appelée 'cuvette centrale'. Bourrelet périphérique et cuvette centrale se raccordent l'un à l'autre par une série de paliers successifs dont les plus élevés sont d'une remarquable régularité, tandis que les autres sont, en général, d'une moindre perfection. D'autres paliers s'étagent entre l'Océan Atlantique et la portion occidentale du bourrelet. Enfin certaines régions du Congo, rajeunies tectoniquement, ont subi l'effet d'une dissection plus poussée : c'est notamment le cas du Mayumbe à l'ouest et, à l'est, celui du grand fossé tectonique où se situent les volcans.

Aussi l'étude et la description du Cénozoïque du Congo Belge sera-t-elle facilitée par une division du territoire en trois grandes unités paléogéographiques qui correspondent à cette distribution en grand du relief. L. Cahen en a fourni la définition suivante (Fig. 1) :

1. *La région centrale*, avec ses plateaux et ses plaines bien conservés, régulièrement étagés ; elle est limitée à l'ouest par le Stanley-Pool et la vallée de la Nsele, à l'est par une ligne suivant d'abord la crête Congo-Nil, puis celle du Haut Lomami-Lubilash. Au nord comme au sud, cette région se poursuit au delà des frontières.

[*] Le texte de cette note unique reprend, en les développant quelque peu, ceux de mes contributions au symposium sur les Kalahari Sands et à la Section I du congrès auxquelles correspondent respectivement les chapitres II et III de ce travail.

23

On y peut distinguer des *zones de surélévation* soumises à l'érosion et caractérisées par l'embôitement de surfaces morphologiques successives (nord-est du Congo par exemple) et des *dépressions synclinales* où s'accumulent, en superposition ou non, les matériaux détritiques dérivés des premières (sud du Congo par exemple).

2. *La région du Bas-Congo*, comprise entre le Stanley-Pool et la Nsele d'une part, l'Océan Atlantique d'autre part. Cette région comprend une *zone orientale*, à l'est de Boma, où se retrouvent certains au moins des traits de la région centrale, et une *zone occidentale*, à l'ouest de Boma, où peut être étudiée la relation de ceux-ci avec des formations marines fossilifères.

3. *La région orientale*, à l'est et au sud-est de la région centrale, affectée de faillages d'âge varié, souvent récents. Cette région peut, à son tour, se subdiviser en deux zones : au sud-est, une *importante portion du Katanga* où, malgré le rajeunissement tectonique, la continuité avec la région centrale reste facile à établir ; à l'est, la *zone du fossé tectonique* où cette continuité devient beaucoup moins évidente et parfois même douteuse.

II LE 'SYSTÈME DU KALAHARI' ET SES ÉQUIVALENTS MORPHOLOGIQUES, MARINS ET LACUSTRES*

Le problème de la stratigraphie et de l'âge des formations rangées par les géologues du Congo Belge dans leur 'système du Kalahari' et, en particulier, celui des 'Kalahari Sands' a, contrairement à d'autres parties de l'Afrique centrale, été rapidement et aisément résolu grâce, d'une part, aux conditions géomorphologiques idéales qui existent au Congo méridional et, d'autre part, aux données paléontologiques fournies par les équivalents marins à la côte atlantique et lacustres dans le fossé tectonique.

A. LE 'SYSTÈME DU KALAHARI'

1. *Le 'Système du Kalahari' dans les dépressions synclinales*

On a signalé plus haut que c'était dans les aires d'ennoyage que s'étaient accumulées les formations terrigènes qui constituent le 'système du Kalahari'. C'est donc à ces régions qu'il faut s'adresser pour établir la stratigraphie de ces dépôts et plus particulièrement à la *cuvette du Kwango* où sont conservées les puissances maxima.[2, 4]

Primitivement divisé en trois étages, dits 'de Kamina', des 'grès polymorphes' et des 'sables ocres', le système du Kalahari a récemment été amputé de son terme inférieur dont a été reconnu l'âge mésozoïque.[2] Sa composition actuelle est, par conséquent, la suivante :

(*a*). Étage des 'sables ocres'
(*b*). Étage des 'grès polymorphes'

(*a*) *L'étage des 'grès polymorphes'*

Le terme de 'grès polymorphes' a été attribué par J. Cornet, en 1893, à un ensemble de roches silicifiées, parfois fossilifères, analogues aux 'silcretes' et 'surface quartzites' des auteurs de langue anglaise. Ces roches occupent une situation stratigraphique et morphologique parfaitement définie.

Stratigraphie

Leur stratigraphie est variable, de même que l'intensité et le niveau des phénomènes de silicification. En général elle est, de haut en bas, la suivante :

> grès blancs non silicifiés
> roches silicifiées
> grès tendres avec silicifications locales vers le sommet
> couches de base, conglomératiques ou non

La puissance maxima de l'étage est de 60 à 80 m.

* Cette partie du travail a été présentée dans le cadre du 'Symposium sur les Kalahari Sands'.

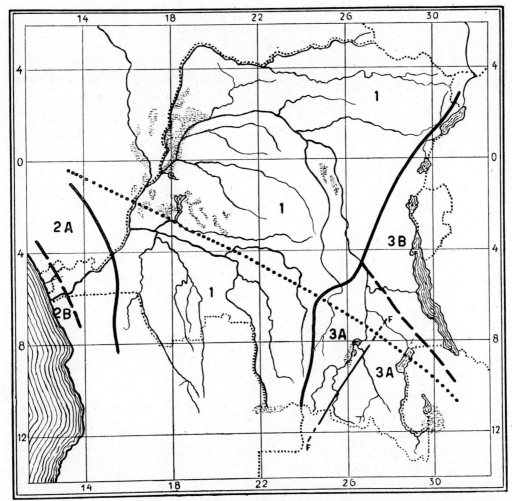

Fig. 1. Localisation des grandes régions morphologiques du bassin du Congo. (1) Région centrale ; (2) région du Bas-Congo avec (2A) sous-région du Congo occidental et (2B) sous-région côtière ; (3) région orientale avec (3A) sous-région du Katanga coupée en deux par la faille de l'Upemba (FF) et (3B) région de bordure du fossé tectonique. La ligne de points figure la limite nord des témoins du Système du Kalahari
(d'après L. Cahen)

Les roches silicifiées comprennent des *grès*, anciennement à ciment calcaire, riches en grains éoliens souvent recouverts d'une pellicule ferrugineuse les isolant de leur ciment calcédonieux, des *calcaires* et des *marnes* d'eau douce transformés en calcédonilites et opalites, des *brèches* à plaquettes de calcaire et marnes silicifiés—disposées sans ordre dans un grès silicifié—'edgewise conglomerates' formés par dessiccation de dépôts de pans.

Les *grès tendres* sont, comme les grès silicifiés, à prédominance éolienne.

Quant au *conglomérat de base*, il est local et pas toujours silicifié ; les eléments grossiers en sont tantôt arrondis et d'origine fluviatile, tantôt anguleux et, dans ce cas, souvent éolisés. On a comparé la surface qui le porte à un reg. A l'ouest du Kwango ces couches de base sont absentes et les 'grès polymorphes' reposent sur un substratum latéritisé.

De même, le sommet de l'étage a été érodé et latéritisé avant le dépôt de l'étage supérieur.

Section One

Données paléontologiques

Les calcaires et marnes silicifiés, plus rarement les grès silicifiés, renferment de nombreux gîtes fossilifères qui ont fourni une faune et flore lacustres : ostracodes du genre *Cypris*, gastéropodes pulmonés des genres *Physa*, *Pyrgophysa* et *Planorbis*, axes et oogones de *Chara*. Cet ensemble n'a pas, pour l'instant, de grande signification chronologique et indique, au plus, un âge éogène. Aussi les limites entre lesquelles vient se placer l'étage des 'grès polymorphes' sont-elles mieux définies par des considérations d'ordre morphologique.

Age des 'grès polymorphes'

L'étage des 'grès polymorphes' repose sur un aplanissement d'extension et de régularité remarquables qui recoupe toutes les formations allant du Précambrien au Crétacé supérieur. Les observations effectuées près de la côte atlantique montrent que cet aplanissement est le produit d'un cycle géographique ayant agi entre l'Albien et le Maestrichtien. Ce cycle fut interrompu, entre le Maestrichtien et le Paléocène, par les mouvements laramides qui, en déformant l'aplanissement fin-crétacé, engendrèrent un nouveau cycle géographique. Les 'grès polymorphes' apparaissent, par conséquent, comme les produits sédimentaires dûs à l'activité de ce nouveau cycle, érodant les zones surélevées et comblant les aires synclinales.

Les 'grès polymorphes' sont tronqués à leur sommet par un nouvel aplanissement, aussi parfait que le 'fin-crétacé', et souligné par un faible gravier, des grenailles ou une cuirasse latéritique. Cet aplanissement, qui déborde les 'grès polymorphes' pour venir entailler les formations plus anciennes, est recouvert, à la côte et dans le fossé tectonique du lac Albert-Semliki-lac Edouard, par des dépôts fossilifères d'âge burdigalien inférieur. Ce fait a conduit à lui attribuer un âge mi-tertiaire.

Compris entre une surface fin-crétacée et une surface mi-tertiaire, l'étage des 'grès polymorphes' ne peut être que paléogène et, si l'on tient compte de l'érosion de son sommet, fruit d'une phase de déformation paléogène, essentiellement paléocène et éocène.

Conditions de dépôt et environnement climatique

Les caractères de l'aplanissement fin-crétacé, tant dans les zones où il est enfoui sous les 'grès polymorphes' que dans celles de surélévation où il est exposé, sont d'avantage ceux d'une pédiplaine que d'une pénéplaine davisienne : rareté des reliefs adoucis, maintien de l'angle des escarpements, présence fréquente de pédiments, etc. Il en est de même pour l'aplanissement mi-tertiaire.

On en peut déduire que, d'une façon générale, les conditions climatiques ayant régné pendant les cycles géographiques leur ayant donné naissance sont de type semi-aride à aride. Il a dû exister pourtant, à certaines époques, des conditions plus humides et même franchement pluviales, dont témoignent, par exemple, les graviers fluviatiles et les latérites rencontrées localement sous ou à la base des 'grès polymorphes'. De même, ces derniers sont coupés par des horizons de marnes et calcaires de pans, à faune et flore d'eau douce, qui témoignent d'interruptions momentanées des conditions d'aridité contemporaines du dépôt du reste de l'étage. On peut donc se représenter comme suit la succession des climats :

aplanissement mi-tertiaire
phase relativement humide : érosion et latéritisation
phase d'aridité désertique : grès éoliens
phase semi-aride oscillante : marnes et calcaires d'eau douce
phase d'aridité désertique : grès éoliens
phase relativement humide : conglomérats et latéritisation
aplanissement fin-crétacé

(b) L'étage des 'sables ocres'

Dans les zones déprimées où l'aplanissement mi-tertiaire n'est pas exposé, cette surface est enfouie sous une épaisseur variable, d'un maximum de 120 m. au Kwango, de sables fins, peu argileux, non stratifiés, de teinte ocre, d'origine éolienne. Plus clairs en surface, par lessivage des particules argileuses, plus rouges en profondeur, par concentration de celles-ci, ces sables ne renferment pas le moindre fossile. Ils reposent parfois, ainsi qu'on l'a vu, sur un horizon conglomératique comportant de petits galets de quartz, des grenailles ou des blocs provenant du démantellement d'une cuirasse latéritique.

Age des 'sables ocres'

En l'absence de toute donnée paléontologique, l'âge des sables ocres ne peut être établi qu'indirectement, en se basant sur des considérations d'ordre géomorphologique et sédimentologique.

Ces sables sont compris entre deux surfaces morphologiques. L'inférieure, sculpturale, est, on l'a vu, d'âge mi-tertiaire. La supérieure, structurale, est déterminée par la surface même des sables ; d'âge indéterminé, elle forme la surface des hauts plateaux du Kwango.

Ces plateaux, avec leurs sables ocres, dominent des surfaces sculpturales plus récentes, dites 'fin-tertiaires', qui possèdent leur propre couverture sableuse dont la distribution et la lithologie sont différentes de celles des 'sables ocres' et ne montrent aucun passage à ceux-ci.

Enfin, des tronçons de cours d'eau appartenant au cycle géographique fin-tertiaire entaillent les 'sables ocres'. Ceux-ci sont, par conséquent, antérieurs au début de ce cycle et totalement indépendants des dépôts sableux, très postérieurs, qui recouvrent les surfaces morphologiques produites par ce cycle.

Compris entre un aplanissement mi-tertiaire et des aplanissements fin-tertiaires, l'étage des 'sables ocres' ne peut être que néogène et, puisque antérieur à la formation des premières surfaces du groupe fin-tertiaire, plutôt miocène que pliocène.

Conditions de dépôt et environnement climatique

Entièrement formé de sables éoliens, l'étage des 'sables ocres' témoigne d'un environnement désertique, au moins en ce qui concerne leur aire de formation. Leur finesse plus grande que celle des 'grès polymorphes', la présence d'un peu d'argile qui les rapprochent des limons font penser à de fins sables et poussières déposés par le vent hors du désert générateur, soit en bordure de celui-ci, soit même dans une zone de steppes. Ces sables enfin ont subi une oxydation au cours d'une phase plus humide, phénomène comparable à la rubéfaction des dunes des 'grands ergs' sahariens pendant les pluviaux quaternaires.

Il semble par conséquent que, dans l'ensemble, l'environnement climatique ait été moins nettement aride que pendant le dépôt des 'grès polymorphes' sous-jacents, mais sans permettre toutefois le développement de mares temporaires où auraient pu se former des calcaires et marnes d'eau douce.

2. Le 'Système du Kalahari' dans les zones de surélévation

On vient de voir que dans les zones d'ennoyage se sont formés, du Crétacé supérieur au Pliocène inférieur, les deux étages du 'système du Kalahari', séparés l'un de l'autre par un intervalle plus ou moins long correspondant à la formation de l'aplanissement mi-tertiaire. Les deux surfaces fin-crétacée et mi-tertiaire y sont déprimées et enfouies sous les dépôts respectifs des deux étages du système. C'est ce que montre, en général, le sud du Bassin du Congo. L'aire déprimée principale est celle du Kwango où sont conservées les puissances maxima ; une seconde est celle du Lomami tandis que le Bas Congo, le Kasai et le Katanga correspondent à des cuvettes moins profondes et plus érodées.

Lorsque l'on sort de cette vaste aire d'ennoyage, on passe aux zones de surélévation dont l'érosion a fourni les matériaux du 'système du Kalahari' accumulés dans la première. Ici, les aplanissements fin-crétacé et mi-tertiaire sont actuels en ce qu'ils sont nus et constituent une part importante du paysage. Leurs relations sont inverses de celles observées dans la première zone : l'aplanissement mi-tertiaire est entaillé en contrebas de l'aplanissement fin-crétacé.

Entre les zones de surélévation et les aires d'ennoyage se trace une ligne le long de laquelle ces deux surfaces morphologiques se croisent ; parfois visible sur le terrain, la position de cette ligne est toujours aisément déductible des profils (Fig. 2). Les relations montrées dans les zones de surélévation se voient surtout dans le nord-est du Congo, ainsi qu'à sa frontière sud, au voisinage du bourrelet limitant la cuvette.

B. Les Équivalents marins du Système du Kalahari

Lorsqu'on passe de la cuvette du Kwango aux monts du Mayumbe on retrouve, entre deux, des témoins des deux étages du système du Kalahari et des aplanissements fin-crétacé et mi-tertiaire qui les supportent. Près des monts du Mayumbe se produit le croisement de ceux-ci dont les relations deviennent celles des aires de surélévation.

Au delà du bourrelet du Mayumbe on entre, entre Boma et l'océan atlantique, dans une zone particulièrement intéressante, car elle permet d'établir les relations entre les aplanissements susmentionnés et des couches marines datées (Fig. 3).

Le long du fleuve Congo ces couches sont souvent détruites et leur existence primitive n'est plus prouvée que par leur présence, sous forme de galets, dans le Quaternaire. Au nord, dans l'enclave de Cabinda, et au sud, en Angola, elles sont conservées, ce qui permet de contrôler les hypothèses élaborées au Congo.

(*a*) Le début du cycle géographique qui, à l'intérieur du bassin du Congo, a donné naissance à l'aplanissement fin-crétacé, correspond aux mouvements pré-albiens qui provoquèrent la transgression du Crétacé supérieur sur les 'grès sublittoraux'. La fin de ce cycle est produite par les mouvements laramides qui séparent le Maestrichtien du Paléocène, avec lacune du Danien. Entre la surface pré-albienne et la discontinuité fin-crétacée, parfois soulignée par une faible discordance angulaire, existe, le long de la côte, un biseau de dépôts marins fossilifères allant de l'Albien ou du Cénomanien au Maestrichtien. Ces dépôts apparaissent, en tout ou partie, comme l'équivalent sédimentaire de la période pendant laquelle a agi le 'cycle fin-crétacé', générateur de l'aplanissement fin-crétacé. Les deux surfaces qui les encadrent à la côte doivent, théoriquement, s'unir plus à l'est pour venir se confondre avec la surface fin-crétacée. Effectivement, leur inclinaison divergente vers le large permet de les raccorder sans peine à cette surface qui passe au dessus des monts du Mayumbe pour se raccorder à l'aplanissement conservé plus à l'est.

(*b*) Les mouvements laramides se traduisent, dans le milieu marin, par une discontinuité ou une faible discordance séparant Maestrichtien et Paléocène. Cette coupure—et lacune—stratigraphique correspond à l'amorce du 'cycle géographique mi-tertiaire' au cours duquel s'est formé, sur les aires de surélévation, l'aplanissement mi-tertiaire et, dans les zones déprimées, a eu lieu le dépôt de l'étage des 'grès polymorphes'. Le fait que la surface mi-tertiaire érode le sommet de ceux-ci permet de supposer que ce cycle a été interrompu par des mouvements qui en ont modifié le développement, interrompant notamment le dépôt des 'grès polymorphes' et provoquant leur plus ou moins grande ablation.

Effectivement on rencontre le long de la côte, au dessus de la discontinuité post-Maestrichtienne, un ensemble de formations marines paléocènes ('couches de Landana') et éocènes ('couches de Sasa Zao') qui vont du Montien au Lutétien. L'Éocène final et l'Oligocène sont absents, absence qui paraît correspondre à une grande régression marine, bien connue sur la côte ouest africaine. On peut supposer que cette régression est le fait des mouvements fin-éocènes qui, à l'intérieur des terres, ont modifié le cycle géographique en cours. Si ces vues sont fondées, l'étage des 'grès polymorphes' serait d'âge exclusivement éocène.

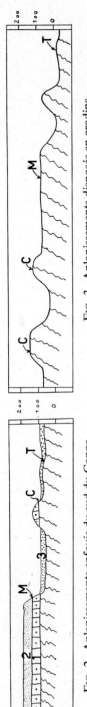

FIG. 2. Aplanissements enfouis du sud du Congo

FIG. 3. Aplanissements disposés en gradins

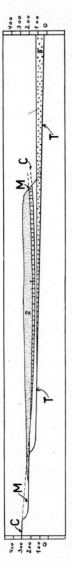

FIG. 4. Profil schématique dirigé de la crête Congo-Zambèse (à gauche) vers la cuvette congolaise (à droite)

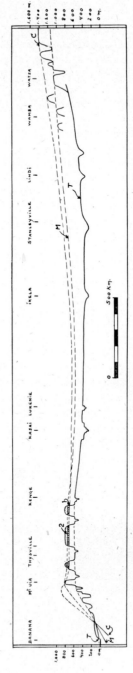

FIG. 5. Profil schématique SO-NE depuis Banana (Océan Atlantique) jusqu'à Watsa (Ituri) (toutes d'après L. Cahen)

(C) aplanissement fin-crétacé; (M) aplanissement mi-tertiaire; (T) aplanissements fin-tertiaires

(1) étage des 'grès polymorphes' (Kalahari inférieur)
(2) étage des 'sables ocres' (Kalahari supérieur)
(3) sables plio-pléistocènes

(*c*) Au dessus de cet Éocène marin on observe une nouvelle surface d'érosion que soulignent des lambeaux d'une cuirasse latéritique plus ou moins graveleuse. Cette surface, qui érode tous les dépôts antérieurs, est enfouie sous de nouvelles formations marines appartenant au Burdigalien inférieur et est donc, en gros, d'âge mi-tertiaire. Moins inclinée vers le large que les surfaces plus anciennes, elle s'élève vers les monts du Mayumbe dont elle constitue la courbe enveloppe pour rejoindre, plus à l'est, l'aplanissement mi-Tertiaire. On constate par conséquent que, de part et d'autre du Mayumbe, cet aplanissement vient croiser la surface fin-Crétacée qui s'y établit au-dessus d'elle, témoignant de la surélévation répétée et accentuée de cette portion du bourrelet périphérique. Celui-ci apparaît donc comme un trait permanent de la morphologie de bordure du continent africain, séparant zone côtière et cuvette centrale.

(*d*) Sur cette surface mi-Tertiaire repose un ensemble de dépôts marins terrigènes, grès et calcaires gréseux avec conglomérats,—les 'couches de Malembe'; à la base on observe un conglomérat à éléments arrachés aux couches éocènes. Ces dépôts renferment des vertébrés marins mais aussi terrestres, ces derniers fortement roulés. Faune marine et faune terrestre concordent pour leur faire attribuer un âge burdigalien inférieur. La faune terrestre notamment, qui comporte les genres *Mastodon*, *Chalicotherium*, etc., est, d'après un examen préliminaire de C. Arambourg, très proche de celle du Miocène inférieur du Kenya. Le caractère grossier des couches témoigne de la proximité de la côte et d'une érosion continentale puissante. Sur ces 'couches de Malembe' viennent des argiles de teinte claire renfermant des lentilles sableuses qui, vers le continent, se développent aux dépens des argiles et semblent peu à peu les remplacer. Reposant en discordance sur ces argiles par l'intermédiaire d'une surface d'érosion on a la 'série des cirques' d'âge plio-pléistocène. Tout ce qu'on peut dire de ces argiles c'est, par conséquent, qu'elles sont d'âge néogène. On les a, par ailleurs, rapprochées des argiles à septaria de Luanda qui appartiennent à la fin du Burdigalien inférieur.

(*e*) Lorsqu'on suit la surface pré-burdigalienne vers l'est on entre dans le domaine continental où l'on voit cette surface bien développée niveler tous les terrains, du Cristallin au Paléocène. Elle est soulignée par un horizon latéritique ou un gravier, cimenté ou non, qui surmontent une profonde zone d'altération. Sur cette 'zone de base' reposent quelque 60 m. de sables argileux ocres, analogues aux 'sables ocres' de l'étage supérieur du système du Kalahari, mais moins franchement éoliens, semble-t-il. De même que les argiles et sables de la zone marine, ces sables argileux ocres sont recouverts en discordance par la 'série des cirques', plio-pléistocène. Il semble par conséquent qu'au moins leur base corresponde aux argiles marines d'âge Burdigalien probable; leur lithologie conduit d'autre part à les paralléliser avec les 'sables ocres' de l'intérieur, les vrais 'Kalahari Sands'.

Le sommet des argiles marines porte des traces d'une émersion qui témoignent d'une grande régression, connue partout en Afrique, celle du Mio-Pliocène. A cette régression doivent correspondre des déformations tectoniques qui ont arrêté le dépôt de l'étage des sables ocres et, en créant des cuvettes et des surélévations autrement disposées, avoir mis en action un nouveau cycle géographique, celui des 'aplanissements fin-Tertiaires'.

Tels sont, par conséquent, les enseignements, corrélations et parallélismes qui se dégagent d'une étude comparative de la région côtière et des hauts plateaux du sud du Congo. Il reste à examiner à présent ceux que peut apporter l'étude du fossé des Grands Lacs.

C. Les Équivalents lacustres du Système du Kalahari

Le grand fossé tectonique où se situent le lac Albert, la Semliki et le lac Edouard a un remplissage lacustre qui a fait l'objet d'études poussées, tant en Uganda qu'au Congo Belge. Ces études, auxquelles sont attachés notamment les noms de E. J. Wayland et J. Lepersonne,[14] et plus récemment J. de Heinzelin de Braucourt,[8] avaient conduit à définir un ensemble de dépôts d'âge pléistocène ancien, les 'couches de Kaiso'. Il y a assez peu de temps, l'examen par A. T.

Hopwood de l'abondant matériel recueilli par J. Lepersonne, a fait apparaître qu'il existait, sous les 'couches de Kaiso', d'autres formations lacustres à vertébrés, d'âge miocène inférieur, fort analogues aux 'couches de Rusinga' du lac Victoria.[11] Ces dépôts se rencontrent au sud-ouest du lac Albert et dans la basse vallée de la Semliki. Ils consistent essentiellement en grès tendres, de teinte claire, argileux, conglomératiques ou non, à passées argileuses et 'bone-bed', épais de 80 à plus de 100 m., à caractère grossier s'atténuant vers le large. Leur faune comporte plusieurs mammifères dont un *Mastodonte trilophodonte* dont le degré d'évolution est intermédiaire entre les deux espèces décrites de Rusinga, un *Rhinoceros* de type Miocène, etc. Les reptiles, de leur côté, sont identiques à ceux de Rusinga. Il n'y a donc pas de doute que l'on ait à faire à des formations équivalentes, d'âge très voisin. On sait que celui des 'couches de Rusinga' est considéré comme burdigalien-helvétien. Il semble enfin que les dépôts du lac Albert congolais se poursuivent sur la rive ugandaise par les 'Kisegi Beds' de E. J. Wayland sous-jacents, eux-aussi, aux couches de Kaiso.

Les couches miocènes congolaises reposent, par un contact ravinant, sur une 'formation de base' consistant en grès grossiers, argileux et tendres, surmontant une carapace limonitique. Cette formation de base, qui atteint 8 à 10 m. de puissance, repose à son tour en discordance sur le socle précambrien. On a émis l'hypothèse qu'il s'agissait soit de formations terrestres latéritiques, correspondant à un dépôt en surface de l'aplanissement mi-tertiaire, soit d'un biseau de couches lacustres limonitisées, d'âge identique ou plus ancien. La première hypothèse paraît, pour l'instant, plus plausible. Un autre intérêt de ces formations albertines réside dans le fait qu'elles montrent la naissance d'un tronçon au moins du grand fossé tectonique occidental dès avant le Miocène par le jeu de grandes failles. Ces couches montrent encore qu'un léger basculement s'est produit entre leur dépôt et celui des couches de Kaiso.

D. Le Système du Kalahari au delà du Congo

Les recherches de L. Cahen et J. Lepersonne sur le 'système du Kalahari' leur ont permis, par la réinterprétation de nombreuses sections situées au sud du Congo, notamment dans le Kalahari, la région des Victoria Falls, etc., d'établir des corrélations précises entre ces régions et le Bassin du Congo.[4]

De leurs conclusions on retiendra surtout :

(*a*) qu'il existe une identité générale de stratigraphie entre le 'système du Kalahari', tel qu'il est défini au Congo Belge, et les 'Kalahari Beds' de la région type ;

(*b*) que les aplanissements anciens définis au Congo se poursuivent à travers les Rhodésies pour se rattacher aux surfaces correspondantes reconnues par L. C. King : sa 'Gondwana surface' est l'aplanissement fin-crétacé, son 'African surface' l'aplanissement mi-tertiaire du Congo Belge ;

(*c*) que les aplanissements anciens du bassin du Congo et les dépôts qu'ils supportent peuvent se suivre à travers le nord-est de l'Angola jusqu'à la vallée du Zambèze à l'amont des rapides de Katima Molilo et de là dans le Kalahari septentrional ;

(*d*) que les 'Kalahari Beds' des Rhodésies et du Bechuanaland sont, comme ceux du Congo Belge, conservés dans des dépressions tectoniques affectant les surfaces fin-crétacée et mi-tertiaire et, comme au Congo, absents des portions surélevées de ces surfaces ;

(*e*) les régions des Batekes (Afrique Equatoriale Française), du Kwango (Congo Belge), de la Lunda (Angola), du Haut Zambèze et du Kalahari septentrional constituent un ensemble de cuvettes tectoniques se distribuant le long d'un axe synclinal unique de direction nord-ouest—sud-est. Des surélévations transverses orientées grossièrement sud-ouest—nord-est coupent cet axe principal. On peut donc, avec L. Cahen et J. Lepersonne, parler d'un seul grand bassin Kalahari, conservant son identité entre les parallèles de 1° nord et 20° sud.

E. Conclusions

De l'exposé critique des données congolaises et centre-africaines se dégage clairement, pensons-nous, l'existence d'un système du Kalahari d'âge cénozoïque couvrant de vastes portions de l'Afrique centrale et comprenant deux étages reposant sur de vastes surfaces d'aplanissement continental. Les relations existant entre ces étages et ces aplanissements et les surfaces et dépôts marins d'une part, lacustres d'autre part, permettent de définir, avec une approximation satisfaisante, l'âge de ces dépôts et surfaces. On en retiendra surtout l'âge éogène de l'étage inférieur du système et celui, miocène ou pliocène ancien de l'étage supérieur, celui des 'sables ocres' ou 'Kalahari Sands'. Cette détermination de l'âge des 'Kalahari Sands' montre que l'emploi de ce terme pour désigner des redistributions plus récentes et notamment pléistocènes est à proscrire sévèrement si l'on veut mettre un terme à la confusion déjà grande qui règne en ce domaine.

Au point de vue paléoclimatique on notera que, pendant cette longue période, les climats furent à prédominance désertique, excepté vers la mi-Tertiaire, où des conditions tropicales de plus grande humidité favorisaient le développement de latérites sur l'aplanissement mi-tertiaire et le dépôt, pendant le Burdigalien, à la côte et au lac Albert, de couches à mammifères. La corrélation des climats et des facies fait ressortir qu'en Afrique centrale, du Paléocène au Pliocène inférieur, ce ne sera qu'au seul Miocène inférieur, et uniquement à la côte et dans le fossé tectonique qu'auront régné des conditions favorisant le développement et la conservation de grands vertébrés. Ailleurs existaient soit une érosion tropicale, soit des conditions désertiques ou péridésertiques. Si l'on examine la distribution des zones de facies et de climat au Miocène inférieur, on observe une distribution curieuse, non équatoriale, avec les différentes bandes grossièrement parallèles à la côte atlantique, et montrant une orientation générale nord-ouest—sud-est. A la côte règnait un climat subtropical, favorisant le développement des grands mammifères; à l'intérieur se rencontraient des conditions plus arides passant rapidement à un environnement désertique; au nord-est du Congo par contre, dans l'Ituri notamment, on revenait à des conditions semi-arides de savane controlant le développement d'une topographie à inselberge; enfin, en atteignant le fossé occidental des grands lacs, en voie de formation, on trouvait des conditions d'humidité plus grande permettant la formation de lacs et de rivières permanents peuplés de reptiles et visités par des grands mammifères. C'est là une distribution climatique dont le moins qu'on puisse en dire est qu'elle est bien curieuse.

III Le Système Plio-Pléistocène*

Dans la description des évènements géologiques qui se sont produits, au Congo Belge, pendant le Plio-Pléistocène, il est utile de conserver une division du territoire en les grandes unités géographiques définies dans l'introduction.

C'est sur des bases morphologiques analogues à celles qui ont fourni les fils directeurs de l'étude du système du Kalahari qu'ont été fondées les recherches sur le système Plio-Pléistocène à l'intérieur du Bassin du Congo. La région côtière a, de son côté, apporté quelques éléments qui n'ont toutefois qu'une valeur assez limitée. Le grand fossé tectonique par contre contient des séries sédimentaires fossilifères renfermant, parfois aussi, des industries préhistoriques et des fossiles humains. La mise en œuvre de toutes ces données permet de se faire, déjà, une idée assez claire de l'enchaînement des évènements qui se sont produits, au Congo Belge, au cours du Plio-Pléistocène.

* Partie du travail présentée à la Section I du Congrès sous le titre 'Outlines of the Geology of the Congo Basin during late Tertiary and Quaternary Times'.

Le Cénozoïque du Congo Belge

A. Le 'Système Plio-Pléistocène' dans l'intérieur du Congo

On se propose de décrire sous ce titre l'essentiel de ce qui est connu sur cette période en dehors de la zone côtière et de la région orientale — Katanga et fossé des grands lacs.

1. Le Système Plio-Pléistocène dans la région centrale

Les recherches de L. Cahen et J. Lepersonne, et l'interprétation par eux de tout un ensemble de données anciennes ou récentes (F. Delhaye et G. Borgniez, J. de Heinzelin de Braucourt, etc.), leur ont permis de montrer que l'évolution morphologique et sédimentologique de cette vaste région était le produit de l'action de trois cycles géographiques successifs, qui sont:

(*a*) Le cycle pliocène supérieur;
(*b*) Le cycle pliocène final à pléistocène inférieur;
(*c*) Le cycle récent.

Suivant la région considérée, ces différents cycles ont eu une action d'érosion ou de déposition prépondérante.

Comme pour le système du Kalahari, c'est dans les portions les plus méridionales du Congo que leurs relations sont les plus évidentes.

(*a*) Le Cycle géographique du Pliocène supérieur (*Cycle I*)

L'action essentielle du cycle géographique du Pliocène supérieur a, tout autour de la cuvette centrale, consisté en le dégagement d'une série d'aplanissements dits 'aplanissements fin-tertiaires' dont le nombre et les caractéristiques varient de région à région. Il s'agit tantôt de pédiplaines d'extension considérable, quoique moindre que celle des aplanissements fin-crétacé et mi-tertiaire tantôt de simples aplanissements locaux, sans grande continuité. Leur façonnement a manifestement été interrompu plus d'une fois par la tectonique, sinon par des fluctuations climatiques. C'est dans le sud du Bassin du Congo, de part et d'autre de la frontière angolaise, que les relations entre ces surfaces fin-tertiaires et les aplanissements et recouvrements plus anciens sont le mieux définis; ces surfaces constituent en effet, dans la plus grande partie du Kasai, un plateau assez bas auquel A. C. Veatch[17] avait donné le nom de 'pénéplaine fin-tertiaire' mais dont les études ultérieures ont montré la complexité. L. Cahen[2, 4] a pu distinguer en effet trois ou quatre aplanissements fin-tertiaires dont le plus récent est bien développé, les autres moins. Ces aplanissements ont une faible pente nord et sont entaillés fort en contrebas des aplanissements plus anciens et des dépôts du système du Kalahari. Le groupe morphologique auxquels ils appartiennent a été initié par des déformations qui ont affecté ceux-ci postérieurement au dépôt des 'sables ocres' ou 'Kalahari sands' du Kalahari supérieur. L. Cahen a pu montrer qu'il était l'œuvre d'un réseau hydrographique au cours sud-nord dont les restes se retrouvent dans le cours supérieur de l'actuel réseau hydrographique du sud du Congo. Il apparaît vraisemblable que ce réseau pliocène supérieur se poursuivait vers le nord en direction du Tchad, bien au delà des actuelles frontières du Congo. Ces divers aplanissements fin-tertiaires du sud du Congo portent des graviers fluviatiles ou éluviaux dont l'étude systématique reste à faire. Tout au plus peut-on signaler une diminution progressive des blocs dérivés de 'grès polymorphes' lorsqu'on passe du plus ancien au plus récent. Aucune industrie lithique n'y a jamais été rencontrée, pas plus que dans les sables sus-jacents. Sur ces graviers reposent des nappes sablo-argileuses rouges qui passent vers l'aval, en continuité, à la partie supérieure au moins des 'sables de la Salonga' de la cuvette centrale. Leur âge, encore incertain, peut être très postérieur à celui de l'aplanissement et de son gravier. Les plus anciens, fluviatiles, semblent bien pliocènes.

Au Kwango se retrouve, dans les mêmes conditions morphologiques, un groupe de surfaces qui se rattachent, sans difficultés, aux aplanissements fin-tertiaires du Kasai.

Section One

Dans le nord du Congo on ne peut distinguer qu'une seule surface fin-tertiaire assez plane, souvent recouverte d'une cuirasse latéritique ; vers l'est, cette surface est dominée par les aplanissements mi-tertiaire et fin-crétacé. Selon J. de Heinzelin de Braucourt la formation de cette surface aurait été contrôlée par une altération latéritique *in situ*, fruit d'un climat chaud et humide de longue durée.[6] Cette conception semble en opposition, au moins en apparence, avec le caractère aride décelé en d'autres régions.

Lorsqu'on passe à la cuvette centrale, encore peu étudiée, on rencontre un certain nombre de dépôts qui sont, soit antérieurs aux aplanissements fin-tertiaires, soit contemporains de leur formation. Ce sont, à l'aval de Stanleyville, la 'série de Yangambi', sur le Bas-Lomami les 'couches d'Opala' et, dans la région comprise entre les cours supérieurs de la Lukenie et de la Tshuapa, les 'couches de Lodja'.

La 'série de Yangambi', étudiée par J. Henry[10] puis par J. de Heinzelin de Braucourt,[6] débute par un poudingue quartzeux à ciment ferrugineux associé à des bancs d'argiles latéritiques (bauxites sédimentaires) que surmontent des sables jaune-roux. Cet ensemble a été déposé dans un bassin de sédimentation lacustre par des apports fluviaux torrentiels, par des écoulements en nappe vers des playas alternativement noyés et desséchés, par des apports éoliens enfin dont l'importance est prépondérante vers le bas et le sommet. Le climat paraît avoir été aride à semi-aride. Les écoulements torrentiels se sont faits vers l'ouest, parallèlement au cours actuel du fleuve. La puissance de la formation semble voisine de 35 à 40 m. Sur la série de Yangambi repose une nappe de concrétions limonitiques qui semblent liées à celle-ci et s'être formées dans une topographie semi-immergée, sous un climat oscillant, et pouvoir être parallélisée avec la 'surface fin-tertiaire' du nord-est. Les 'couches d'Opala' sur le Bas-Lomami sont faites de grès, d'arkoses et de conglomérats à peine consolidés, peu puissants, compris entre le Mésozoïque et une terrasse de 10 m.[2]

Quant aux 'couches de Lodja', qui ont été rencontrées dans les bassins de la Lukenie, de la Lomela et de la Tshuapa, régions qui se raccordent à celle du Kasai, elles consistent essentiellement en sables et grès clairs, avec niveaux graveleux, compris entre le Mésozoïque et le gravier de base des 'couches de la Salonga'. Leur puissance atteint localement 30 m. Ils comportent des formations fluviatiles surmontées ou non de dépôts lacustres.[5]

Toutes ces formations semblent en relation avec des écoulements fermés, independants sans doute—au moins initialement—du grand réseau sud-nord du Kasai et du Kwango. On a vu que les surfaces fin-tertiaires qui appartiennent à ce dernier sont recouvertes de sables argileux ocre, de type fluviatile, qui sont en continuité avec les 'couches de la Salonga' de la région de la Lukenie-Lomela-Tshuapa, qui reposent elles-mêmes sur les 'couches de Lodja'. En réalité ces 'couches de la Salonga', qui comprennent une centaine de mètres de sables argileux grossiers reposant sur un gravier parfois fort épais semblent complexes et comporter des dépôts d'âge varié : seule la partie des 'couches de la Salonga' qui recouvre les replats supérieurs serait Pliocène.[2]

(b) *Le Cycle géographique du Pliocène final et du Pléistocène inférieur (Cycle II)*

C'est encore à la région des bas-plateaux du Kasai qu'il faut faire appel pour saisir la suite des évènements. On y observe un nouveau groupe de six à sept surfaces assez rapprochées—écart de 20 à 30 m. en général—étagées entre les aplanissements fin-tertiaires et les terrasses situées sur les flancs des vallées actuelles. Ces surfaces sont l'œuvre d'un nouveau cycle d'érosion chevauchant la limite Plio-Pléistocène. Ce Cycle II a lui-même été initié par des déformations de la fin du Pliocène qui en surélevant la région nord-ouest du Congo et en affaissant ses parties centrales a créé la 'cuvette centrale congolaise'. De ce fait l'écoulement vers le bassin du Tchad du réseau hydrographique fin-tertiaire a été interrompu et il s'est formé un nouveau réseau centripète dont le niveau de base devait se situer un peu au sud de Coquilhatville.[2] Les aplanissements du Cycle II se développent dans les tronçons moyens et inférieurs des grandes rivières, à cours dirigé vers le nord-ouest. Leur inclinaison est faible. Leur nombre est variable suivant l'éloignement du niveau de base.

En Angola, dans la Lunda, une de ces surfaces, formant les interfluves mineurs—de direction équatoriale—est recouverte de graviers ondulés, latéritisés, très différents de ceux qui surmontent les surfaces fin-tertiaires des interfluves majeurs. Ces graviers sont stériles et, par conséquent, encore pliocènes. A leur surface et à la base des sables ocres qui les recouvrent existent des industries acheuléennes tardives et sangoennes qui datent ces sables de la grande dessication de la fin du Pléistocène moyen. [12]

Plus à l'aval, à Luebo, on a reconnu six aplanissements, respectivement situés à 280, 230, 200, 155, 95 et 76 m. au dessus de la rivière. Plus bas s'étagent quatre terrasses. Le plus inférieur de ces aplanissements porte un gravier à gros blocs empâtés dans des sables argileux et surmonté par une argile rouge. L'abbé H. Breuil y a décelé, outre les traces d'un minage des blocs de 'grès polymorphes' par les Sangoens, l'existence d'une industrie à galets taillés, d'affinités oldowayennes. Cette découverte montre que l'introduction du cycle géographique actuel s'est produite au début du Kamasien, peu après les 'Pebble Cultures'. Ce fait suggère que si cet aplanissement est pré-kamasien ou kamasien le plus inférieur, les autres aplanissements du groupe II sont, au moins pour les plus anciens, encore pliocènes.

Dans la région de la Lunda, où l'évolution morphologique est moins poussée, les équivalents des aplanissements pléistocènes anciens (Kagérien) de Luebo, sont représentés par des terrasses de 40 m., à Kafuen frais, et de 20 m., à Kafuen roulé; cette dernière a été latéritisée au moment de la dessication fin-kagérienne (Latérite I de L.S.B. Leakey). [13]

Au point de vue climatique, il est permis de penser que les plus anciens aplanissements du cycle ont été controlés par un climat semi-aride favorisant la pédiplanation, climat passant progressivement aux conditions plus humides du début du Pléistocène, dont témoignent notamment les dépôts du fossé des grands lacs.

En dehors des régions du Kasai et du Kwango on ne dispose guère, pour le reste de la région centrale, que de données fort incertaines. Dans le nord-est, le cycle Pliocène final-Pléistocène inférieur semble n'avoir conduit qu'au dégagement, en climat oscillant, d'un plateau de 25 m. à surface latéritique, antérieur à la phase érosive du Pléistocène inférieur qui a donné des graviers à galets taillés. Ceux-ci sont à leur tour surmontés d'une carapace latéritique qui pourrait correspondre à la dessication fin-kagérienne. [6, 9] De même dans le Bas-Uele et l'Ubangi n'existe qu'un groupe unique de surfaces se rattachant à l'ouest comme à l'est au groupe fin-tertiaire.

(c) *Le Cycle géographique du Pléistocène moyen à actuel* (*Cycle III*)

On a dit que sous les aplanissements du groupe Pliocène final à Pléistocène inférieur existait une nouvelle série de surfaces d'érosion et de sédimentation. Elles ont le caractère de terrasses localisées dans les vallées actuelles beaucoup plus étroites que celles du cycle précédent dont elles ne constituent d'ailleurs qu'un rajeunissement généralisé. Ce rajeunissement est dû au rattachement du réseau précédent à celui du Bas-Fleuve, avec renversement de l'écoulement dans le chenal entre Léopoldville et Bolobo. Le niveau de base controlant l'évolution du réseau récent est à présent le Stanley-Pool, ce qui a donné aux terrasses une inclinaison vers l'aval bien plus forte que celle des aplanissements antérieurs. C'est ainsi que pour un tronçon du Sankuru la pente des aplanissements est de 0·02 m./km., celle des terrasses de 0·10 m./km. et celle de la rivière de 0·16 m./km. Il existe par conséquent une véritable discordance angulaire entre les terrasses et les aplanissements. [2]

On avait cru jadis, en s'appuyant sur des données trop sporadiques, que les terrasses de la partie régularisée du bassin du Congo se trouvaient à des altitudes bien définies et constantes. En réalité, les pentes de celles-ci varient de point en point le long d'un même cours d'eau, ce qui rend tout raccord éloigné aléatoire. Si, en un point donné, on ne rencontre que quelques terrasses, leur nombre total le long d'une grande rivière peut être considérable, 20 à 30 par exemple pour le

Kasai. Ces données nouvelles traduisent la nécessité d'une étude systématique de chaque cours d'eau, avec fouilles dans les dépôts de terrasse, en vue de déterminer leurs âges relatifs et, éventuellement, absolus. En attendant, on ne peut que fournir quelques exemples, qui permettent de comparer les successions géo-climatiques du bassin du Congo à celles d'autres régions, Est-Africain notamment.

On reprendra, pour la région classique du Kasai, les exemples de la Lunda (Angola) et de Luebo (Congo Belge). A la Lunda, on peut distinguer, à la suite des recherches de J. Janmart, H. Breuil et L. S. B. Leakey,[1, 12, 13] une succession qui peut schématiquement se résumer comme suit (L. Cahen).[2]

1. *Appartenant au Cycle II*

   (*a*) Graviers ante-pléistocènes 'des interfluves mineurs', sans industries lithiques (en surface, *Chelléo-Acheuléen tardif*);

   (*b*) Terrasse de 40 m. au graviers de pente dérivés de (*a*), avec *Kafuen* frais;

   (*c*) Terrasse de 20 m., avec *Kafuen* roulé;

   (*d*) Latérite I, reposant sur le gravier de la terrasse de 20 m. et affectant une partie de ce gravier.

2. *Appartenant au Cycle III*

   (*e*) Terrasse de 10 m., avec *Chelléo-Acheuléen ancien* frais, fortement patiné;

   (*f*) Latérite II, locale, reposant sur le gravier de la terrasse de 10 m. et affectant une partie de ce gravier;

   (*g*) Graviers inférieurs de thalweg (ou de terrasse de 3 m.), à *Chelléo-Acheuléen évolué* à peine usé;

   (*h*) Dépôt de sables rouges éoliens au dessus de (*a*), avec grenailles latéritiques à la base; *Sangoen à poignards*;*

   (*i*) Sables analogues, redéposés sur (*b*) et (*c*); *Sangoen*;*

   (*j*) Sables analogues, redéposés sur (*e*).

   (*k*) Remblayage du thalweg: sable argileux jaune le long du bord de la terrasse de 10 m.; *Lupembien ancien*;*

   (*l*) Gravier supérieur de thalweg (ou de terrasse de 3 m.); industries roulées dont la plus récente est du *Lupembien évolué** (14,503 ± 560 ans);

   (*m*) Latérite III;

   (*n*) Sable blanc sur graviers supérieurs de thalweg (adossés à (*k*)); *Lupembo-Tshitolien** (11,189 ± 490 ans);

   (*o*) Terre noire ou grise, alluviale; *Tshitolien*.*

De cette succession ressortent un ensemble de données qui font apparaître un parallélisme très satisfaisant avec les observations faites en Afrique orientale et en Rhodésie, tant au point de vue de la succession industrielle que des climats successifs sous lesquels s'est opérée cette succession. On reconnaît en effet dans la terrasse de 10 m. un dépôt kamasien, dans la latérite II, un témoin de la phase sèche qui termine cet étage, dans les graviers inférieurs de thalweg un dépôt kanjérien et dans les sables rouges éoliens avec Sangoen à la base, une nappe éolienne formée pendant la grande dessication de la fin du Kanjérien. On notera encore que c'est du Kanjérien que date, à la Lunda, le creusement du thalweg des grandes rivières sud-nord. Quant aux termes (*k*), (*l*) et (*m*), ils correspondent au Gamblien et à son déclin, tandis que les sables blancs à Lupembo-Tshitolien traduisent une diminution du pouvoir de transport des cours d'eau correspondant exactement à la phase chaude d'Alleröd-'Two Creeks' des régions glaciaires et périglaciaires septentrionales.

---

  * Cette modification de la nomenclature résulte d'une étude détaillée faite après le congrès, des sites et industries récoltées dans la plaine de Léopoldville par le R. F. H. van Moorsel. Cette étude sera publiée ultérieurement, conjointement.

Le Tshitolien enfin apparaît comme épi-pléistocène, Makalien sans doute. Cette succession fait encore ressortir que depuis le Kanjérien la rivière n'a plus connu que des vidanges et remblayements d'ordre climatique qui en rendent l'étude extrêmement précieuse.

Plus en aval, à Luebo, au Congo Belge, on a mis en évidence une groupe de quatre terrasses de 27, 15, 10 et 2 m., situées en contrebas de l'aplanissement de 60 m. (A7) à 'Pebble Culture'.[2] Les deux premières, renfermant des industries chelléo-acheuléennes, sont kamasienne et kanjérienne et peuvent être rapprochées des termes (*e*) et (*g*) de la succession précédente. De même que l'aplanissement A7 elles ont été minées par les Sangoens avant que les sables rouges éoliens du grand-aride fin-kanjérien ne viennent recouvrir celui-ci. La terrasse de 10 m., à Sangoen roulé et Lupembien à faciès kalinien, est du Gamblien ancien ; celle de 2 m., à Lupembien évolué et Tshitolien, est du Gamblien récent et postérieur. Il existe donc un décalage sensible entre le creusement des thalwegs des grandes rivières, fin-Kanjérien en Angola et mi-Gamblien au Congo Belge, décalage qui traduit la remontée régressive de l'érosion controlée par l'évolution du Stanley-Pool.

Il en est de même des tributaires, dont le creusement est lié à celui des lits majeurs : il est au Kasai, Lupembien ancien ou Lupembien évolué, voire, pour les petits ruisseaux, plus récent encore.

On notera l'absence à Luebo de la latérite fin-kamasienne. La comparaison de ces deux ensembles fait encore ressortir que l'introduction du cycle géographique récent semble devoir se placer pendant la phase d'aridité de la fin du Kagérien mais qu'elle s'est fait, suivant les régions, sentir plus ou moins tardivement, jusqu'après le Kamasien le plus inférieur. On a là un parallélisme très étroit avec ce que montrent d'autres régions d'Afrique, vallée du Vaal par exemple. Il s'agit par conséquent des mouvements fin-villafranchiens, de distribution très générale.

Dans le nord du Congo, c'est encore aux travaux de J. de Heinzelin de Braucourt que l'on est redevable des quelques données que l'on possède sur l'évolution du tronçon du fleuve compris entre Stanleyville et Yangambi :[6, 9]

(*a*) Sur les plateaux existe une nappe de sables ocre-jaunes, pouvant atteindre 50 m. de puissance, principalement d'origine éolienne, mais largement remaniés par l'eau ; ces sables sont attribués au Pléistocène inférieur (dessication fin-kagérienne ?) ;

(*b*) formation des terrasses de 20 m., à éléments cailouteux mats ;

(*c*) recouvrement sableux ocre-jaune sur (*b*), formant des replats de 30·35 m. ; caractère fluviatile prédominant ;

(*d*) formation des terrasses de 10 m., à galets luisants mieux usés ; industrie *Tayacoïde* roulée ;

(*e*) recouvrement sableux blancs ou ocres sur (*d*), formant des replats de 15–20 m. ; essentiellement fluviatiles ;

(*f*) sables ocre-jaunes de Stanleyville, sur (*d*) ; identiques à (*e*) ? ; à la base, *Epilevalloisien* frais ;

(*g*) basses terrasses ;

(*h*) îles 'vieilles', 'intermédiaires' et 'jeunes'.

Le terme (*a*) de la succession appartiendrait encore au Cycle II, les autres au Cycle III. En s'inspirant de l'auteur on pourrait attribuer le (*b*) et (*c*) au Kamasien s.l., l'apport des éléments siliceux de la terrasse de 10 m. à la dessication fin-kanjérienne, le (*d*) et (*e*) au Gamblien, le (*f*) à la phase aride fin-gamblienne (ou encore au Gamblien) ; les termes (*g*) et (*k*) à l'Epi-Pléistocène et à l'Holocène. Un décalage général de la succession vers le bas ne paraît toutefois pas impossible.

Enfin pour terminer avec la région centrale, il convient de rappeler que la partie des 'sables de la Salonga' qui couvrent les aplanissements les plus inférieurs pourrait représenter les 'sables rouges' de la grande dessication fin-kanjérienne.

Section One

Des équivalents des trois cycles géographiques reconnus dans la région centrale se retrouvent ici. Il importe de les considérer successivement dans la partie est de la région, entre le bourrelet du Mayumbe et le Stanley-Pool et la vallée de la Nsele, puis dans la région côtière, à l'ouest de la chaîne du Mayumbe.[2, 3]

(a) Le Cycle géographique du Pliocène supérieur (Cycle I)
1. *Zone orientale*

On a dit plus haut que la surface mi-tertiaire était connue au Congo occidental, où elle était enfouie sous les sables ocres de l'étage supérieur du 'système du Kalahari'. Dans la région de Léopoldville, cette surface est déprimée par failles.

En contrebas des plateaux restés en position normale s'étagent trois groupes de surfaces avec leurs recouvrements.

(*a*) Entre 600 et 800 m.; cuirasses limonitiques englobant des blocs de grès polymorphes; recouvrement sablo-argileux rouge atteignant 75 m.

(*b*) Entre 450 et 550 m.; cuirasse limonitique; recouvrement limoneux rougeâtre atteignant 25 m.

(*c*) Surfaces moins évoluées vers 375–400 m. et 225–275 m.; cuirasses limonitiques moins épaisses; mince recouvrement limoneux.

En outre s'observent des niveaux de terrasses entre (*b*) et (*c*), puis en contrebas de (*c*).

La chronologie de ces aplanissements reste incertaine: (*a*) et (*b*) sont sans doute pliocènes de même que le recouvrement de (*a*). Ils pourraient correspondre respectivement au cycle fin-Tertiaire et au cycle Pliocène final-Pléistocène inférieur. Le recouvrement de (*b*) est pléistocène ainsi qu'en témoignent des découvertes archéologiques. Les surfaces du groupe (*c*) semblent pléistocènes. La chronologie du Quaternaire est précisée, quoique de façon encore imparfaite, par les observations effectuées au Stanley-Pool.

En contrebas d'un aplanissement de 155 m., appartenant au groupe (*b*) de surfaces s'observe une terrasse ou aplanissement moins parfait de 75 m., puis viennent les terrasses, avec leur sommet à 65 m. (T8), 45 m. (T7), 32 m. (T6), 23 m. (T5), 15 m. (T4), 9 m. (T3), 5 m. (T2), – 1 m. (T1).

Alors que la plupart de ces terrasses renferment des industries, seules T4, T3 et T2 ont fait l'objet de recherches systématiques. Les graviers de la terrasse de 15 m., situés à 10 m., renferment un *Acheuléen final* évoluant vers le Sangoen, et sont donc fin-kanjérien comme sur le Kasai. T3, T2 et T1 correspondent au reste de l'évolution, du Gamblien à l'époque actuelle. Il leur correspond, dans la plaine de Léopoldville—partie du Stanley-Pool remblayée—des remplissages variés de chenaux ou de marécages entre d'anciennes îles, ou encore des limons ocres éoliens, puis des sables blancs ou gris également éoliens. Dans ces dépôts variés s'observe toute l'évolution du complexe lupembien et tshitolien: *Lupembien ancien* à percussion (avec poignards = Djoko-cien; sans poignards = Kalinien), *Lupembien évolué* à pression (Lupembien typique), *Lupembo-Tshitolien* (perfection moindre de la retouche, apparition du micro-tranchet), *Tshitolien* (caractère 'mésolithique'). Des *éléments néolithiques* s'observent en surface à faible profondeur. La dessication fin-kanjérienne s'est traduite ici uniquement par une baisse des eaux exposant des îlots de grès polymorphes et de grès de l'Inkissi (Précambrien), ou des bancs de sable humifère durci ('grès tourbeux') sur lesquels se sont installés les Sangoens.*

Il y a par conséquent ici, à partir du Kanjérien tout ou moins, un parallélisme satisfaisant avec le bas et le haut-Kasai. On notera surtout le caractère plus atténué de la dessication fin-kanjérienne, puis la formation au Gamblien et après de dépôts éoliens limoneux ou sableux par

---

* Ces précisions diverses découlent d'une visite des sites et des collections du R. F. Henri van Moorsel, effectuée après le Congrès de Livingstone. Elles seront exposées en détail ultérieurement.

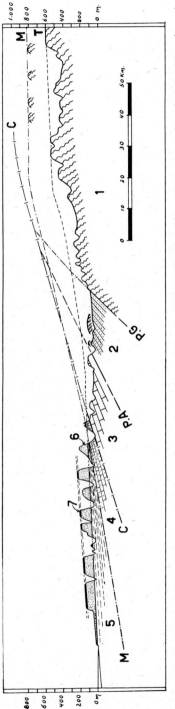

FIG. 6. Coupe schématique à travers le Mayumbe occidental et la région côtière (SSO-NNE). (1) socle précambrien; (2) grès sublittoraux; (3) Crétacé moyen et supérieur; (4) Eogène; (5) Néogène; (6) Série des Cirques; (7) sables du plateau de Tshikay. P.G, surface pré-grès sublittoraux; P.A, surface pré-albienne; C, surface pré-crétacée; M, surface mi-tertiaire; T, surface fin-tertiaire
(d'après L. Cahen, modifié)

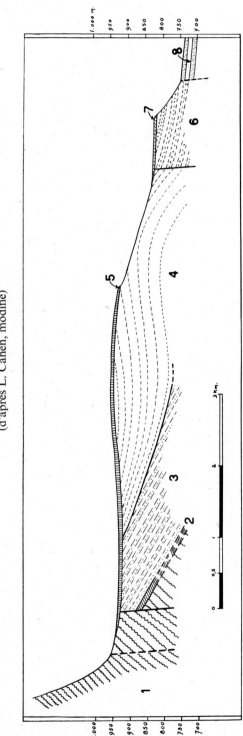

FIG. 7. Coupe schématique NO-SE à travers les séries lacustres du fossé tectonique du lac Albert (région Mohari-Sinda). (1) socle précambrien; (2) formation de base; (3) couches du Miocène inférieur; (4) série de Kaiso; (5) formations subaériennes post-Kaiso; (6) série de la Semliki; (7) formations subaériennes post-Semliki; (8) série lacustre récente. En trait fort les failles observées; en trait interrompu les failles probables ou déduites
(d'après J. Lepersonne)

vannage des alluvions exposées aux basses eaux. Comme en d'autres régions, le Gamblien paraît avoir été moins pluvial que les étages antérieurs du Pléistocène.

2. *Zone occidentale ou côtière*

On a vu précédemment comment s'établissait le raccord des formations cénozoïques (système du Kalahari) et des formations marines côtières.

(a) *Le Cycle géographique du Pliocène supérieur*

On se souviendra que les formations à caractère régressif du Miocène inférieur—argiles à lentilles sableuses et sables argileux ocres—étaient entaillées par une surface d'érosion que l'on peut voir, plus à l'est, s'élever vers les monts du Mayumbe en restant, toutefois, plus bas que les aplanissements plus anciens; cette surface fait partie du groupe des aplanissements fin-tertiaires. Bombée au dessus du Mayumbe, elle s'abaisse vers l'est pour rejoindre ce groupe. Près de la côte, cette surface fin-tertiaire disparait sous les dépôts de la 'série des cirques', d'âge plio-pléistocène. Il existe par conséquent une régression des mers pliocènes au cours de laquelle s'est opéré le façonnement de l'aplanissement côtier fin-tertiaire.

(b) *Le Cycle géographique du Pliocène final et du Pléistocène inférieur*

La 'série des cirques' débute par un puissant gravier de base ravinant, riche en bois silicifiés, appartenant à des genres actuels de savane. Aucun d'eux n'étant jamais perforé par les tarets, on est conduit à considérer le gravier comme continental et formant la base d'une série de remblayement dans la zone exondée par la continuation de la régression pliocène. Sur le gravier de base reposent, à la côte, des sables argileux rouges graveleux, à l'intérieur quelque 60 à 80 m. de grès tendres, de sables bariolés et d'argiles où l'on a décelé, au Gabon, des horizons latéritiques correspondant à des arrêts dans le remblayement, ainsi que des actions éoliennes. Vers l'océan, cette série est coupée par une falaise morte haute de 60 m. L'ensemble est probablement continental et est, au Gabon et au Congo Belge, considéré, par analogie avec la Nigérie, comme Plio-Pléistocène. Le fait que les bois appartiennent à des genres actuels suggère même un âge uniquement Pléistocène inférieur.

La série des cirques apparaît, par conséquent, comme un équivalent sédimentaire du cycle géographique du Pliocène final et du Pléistocène inférieur.

(c) *Le Cycle géographique récent*

A leur tour la série des cirques et les argiles miocènes sous-jacentes sont entaillées par des plages soulevées qui correspondent à des niveaux de base quaternaires.

1. *Plage de 100–120 m.*

En discordance légère sur la série des cirques qu'elle entaille s'observe une nappe de sables grossiers auxquelles correspondent, dans l'estuaire du Congo, des lambeaux de terrasses situés au même niveau. Cette nappe couronne le plateau de Senze-Tshikay et paraît correspondre à une transgression marine du Pléistocène ancien que nous rapprochons du Premier Interglaciaire (= Aride fin-Kagérien). Il lui succède une nouvelle régression qui pourrait correspondre à l'ensemble Kamasien-Kanjérien.

2. *Plage de 25–40 m.*

Le plateau de Moanda constitue une surface d'abrasion marine correspondant à une nouvelle transgression. Située à 20–25 m. à la côte, cette surface s'élève jusqu'à l'altitude de 40 m., atteinte au pied de sa falaise morte. On peut hypothétiquement la rapprocher du Troisième Interglaciaire (Grand Aride fin-kanjerien). Il lui succède une régression qui correspondrait alors au Gamblien.

3. *Plage de 2 m.*

A Vista existe une basse plage entaillée dans les argiles miocènes. Son sommet, situé à 2 m., est recouvert aux hautes-eaux. Elle renferme une faune d'invertébrés à caractère guinéen plus riche que l'actuelle. Cette basse terrasse pourrait être post-glaciaire.

4. *Plage actuelle*

Après une nouvelle régression, la mer s'établit au niveau actuel au cours d'un nouveau mouvement de transgression dont témoigne l'attaque des falaises et l'estuaire noyé du Congo. Il faut enfin rappeler l'existence de la vallée sous-marine du fleuve, entaillée dans les dépôts miocènes, dont la pente est celle de l'aplanissement fin-tertiaire et dont la formation est fin-tertiaire ou contemporaine du dépôt de la 'série des cirques'. Ainsi donc la région côtière témoigne d'oscillations répétées du niveau de la mer dont les plus anciennes sont sans doute d'origine tectonique, les autres d'ordre climatique.

C. LE SYSTÈME PLIO-PLÉISTOCÈNE DANS LA RÉGION ORIENTALE

On a vu dans l'introduction qu'il était légitime de distinguer, dans le relief du Congo, une région orientale comprenant le fossé des Grands Lacs et le Katanga, région séparée des portions centrales du bassin du Congo par une haute crête courant de Dilolo à Lubefu au sud, puis suivant la dorsale Congo-Nil. Cette région orientale est à diviser en deux : au sud le Katanga qui, bien qu'affecté par les mouvements récents du fossé tectonique, reste aisé à rattacher au reste du Congo ; au nord et à l'est, le fossé des Grands Lacs, aux bordures fortement morcelées.

1. *Le Katanga*

Si le Katanga a, plus que d'autres régions du Congo, fait l'objet de recherches parfois détaillées son étude est bien plus délicate. Il est en effet formé de bassins primitivement distincts, dont le rattachement au fleuve Congo ne s'est opéré que progressivement. Il a, à différentes époques sans doute, mais en tout cas à la fin du Kanjérien, été affecté par des bouleversements tectoniques qui en ont modifié la face et qui rendent plus aléatoire l'emploi des raccords géomorphologiques utilisés dans d'autres régions. Aussi les corrélations avec le reste du Congo reposent-elles en ordre principal sur la succession des industries préhistoriques récoltées et sur les considérations climatiques déduites de l'étude des dépôts et coupes naturelles. S'il est, comme pour les autres régions, possible de reconnaître l'action de plusieurs cycles géographiques successifs, il est, par contre, beaucoup plus difficile d'en fixer les limites. Aussi nous contenterons-nous d'énumérer l'un après l'autre les faits les mieux établis.

1. Le raccord avec le sud de la région centrale s'établit aisément pour les aplanissements fin-crétacé et mi-tertiaire qui se prolongent, avec leur recouvrements kalahariens, jusqu'au Lualaba. A l'est de celui-ci on entre dans un bloc surélevé et déformé où ne se retrouvent plus guère qu'à l'est du plateau de Kundelungu des témoins en place de ces recouvrements.

2. L'examen du réseau hydrographique du Lualaba et de ses affluents à l'amont de Kongolo a montré à L. Cahen que ce réseau de direction générale N.N.E. était primitivement séparé de celui de la région centrale. Une haute crête, allant de Dilolo à Lubefu, les sépare. Prolongé en direction, ce réseau atteint la région du fossé du lac Kivu, ce qui suggère des relations anciennes entre le Nil et le haut Lualaba. Cette hypothèse a trouvé une éclatante confirmation biologique : la faune ichtyologique du haut Lualaba renferme des éléments nilotiques absents du bas Lualaba. L. Cahen admet, pour diverses raisons, l'âge mi-tertiaire du réseau du haut-Lualaba qui faisait partie, avec le haut-Nil, d'un réseau dont le niveau de base se situait sur l'océan Indien ; ce réseau était un des agents du façonnement de la portion de la surface mi-tertiaire dépendant de ce niveau de base. La crête Dilolo-Lubefu serait donc un témoin de la ligne de séparation des eaux entre l'Atlantique et l'océan Indien. La date de la capture par le bas-Lualaba est encore inconnue.[2]

3. C'est encore à un réseau ayant cette orientation que semble dû le développement de plusieurs surfaces imparfaites, à couverture latéritique, dont la plus haute et la plus évoluée est, au sud du Katanga, la 'surface d'Elisabethville', située à 1250 m. Elle appartient probablement au 'groupe fin-tertiaire'.

D'autres aplanissements moins évolués, entaillés dans celle-ci, de même que la surface des plateaux du Kundelungu et des Biano, semblent le résultat de l'action du 'cycle Pliocène final-Pléistocène inférieur'. Les plus basses portent des industries de type Kafuen évolué qui pourraient les dater de la fin du Kagérien.

4. Des chenaux et des terrasses, qui correspondent dans certains cas à un renversement des écoulements fluviaux, renferment du Kafuen tardif, d'âge Kamasien le plus inférieur. Il semble, par conséquent, que le Kagérien final ait correspondu, au Katanga comme ailleurs, à des mouvements qui ont introduit un nouveau cycle géographique. Celui-ci toutefois est complexe et doit être scindé en deux.

Le Cycle IIIA correspond au Kamasien et au Kanjérien et a donné naissance, à l'ouest du Lualaba, à des aplanissements partiels étendus dont le plus inférieur est latéritisé (latérite fin-kanjérienne) et entaillé par des chenaux à Sangoen. Les réseaux qui leur ont donné naissance avaient encore l'orientation N.N.E. et leur niveau de base était celui des Portes d'Enfer à Kongolo. Par contre les terrasses situées plus bas, à partir de 60 m., sont gambliennes et plus récentes, et appartiennent à des cours d'eau dont le niveau de base est constitué par le graben de l'Upemba. L'introduction du Cycle actuel IIIB date par conséquent de la fin du Kanjérien, approximativement de la grande phase de dessication climatique. En effet, une dépression lacustre existait déjà vers ce moment ainsi qu'en témoigne le gisement à mammifères de la passe de Songwe, contenu dans une limonite compacte, unissant des éléments de la faune d'Olduvai aux premiers éléments de la faune gamblienne: *Loxodonta africana simplex*, Cooke.

Tels sont les faits essentiels auxquels conduit l'étude géomorphologique de quelques régions clefs du Katanga méridional et central. Ils font ressortir l'originalité de cette région.[2, 15, 16] Si l'on veut entrer dans de plus grands détails il faut faire appel aux données de l'archéologie préhistorique et de la paléopédologie pour tenter d'établir une succession détaillée qui puisse se comparer à celles du Kasai, du nord-est de l'Angola, des Rhodésies et de l'Est-Africain. Ces données fragmentaires et isolées suggèrent l'évolution suivante:

(*a*) Au Pliocène final ou au Pléistocène le plus inférieur, continuité des plateaux du Biano et du Kundelungu dont le réseau hydrographique s'écoulait vers la dépression du lac Bangweolo;

(*b*) Au Kagérien le plus ancien, formation, sur ces plateaux, de nappes de cailloutis de quartz et de quartzites dans un sable kaolineux; industries (?) du *Kafuen le plus ancien*; climat humide;

(*c*) Pendant le Kagérien, mouvements tectoniques, renversement des écoulements; façonnement des aplanissements les plus inférieurs (niveau de base des monts Koni) et de la plaine de la Lovoy; industries du *Kafuen typique*; climat humide de forêt ombrophile;

(*d*) Phase de dessiccation climatique: formation d'une cuirasse limonitique sur les aplanissements; industrie *Kafuenne typique*; dépôt de sables clairs sur les Biano (?); calcaires silicifiés de la Kampemba (?);

(*e*) Creusement, au Katanga méridional, de chenaux en contrebas de la cuirasse (*d*); industries du *Kafuen tardif*, équivalents de l'Oldowayen (Mulundwa II); climat humide;

(*f*) Phase de forte humidité, avec développement intense de forêt; évolution des industries *chelléo-acheuléennes*; plus de gisements *in situ*; possibilité d'une phase de dessiccation interne (concrétions limonitiques sur *Chelléo-Acheuléen* ancien roulé, puis dérivé; climat fort humide, avec possibilité d'une subdivision en deux phases pluviales séparées par un épisode plus sec;

(*g*) Terrasses, *in situ* ou solifluées, renfermant le matériel de (*f*), surmontées, quand *in situ*, d'un *Chelléo-Acheuléen final à tendances sangoennes*; ailleurs, terrasses et dépôts lacustres à industries *clactonoïdes* rappelant la 'Hope Fountain Culture'; climat progressivement moins humide, toujours sous forêt ombrophile;

(*h*) Augmentation de la sécheresse; formation d'une carapace limonitique généralisée; sur cette carapace, industrie *sangoenne typique*, à affinités rhodésiennes (bolas, etc.);

(*i*) Phase d'aridité intense; redistribution éolienne des sables ocres du Kalahari, sur les plateaux où ceux-ci existent encore; redistribution éolienne de sables clairs plus récents sur les Biano et la Manika; *rares pièces sangoennes*; mouvements tectoniques amenant le rajeunissement de la dépression de l'Upemba et la dislocation, par captures, du réseau hydrographique ancien; climat désertique;

(*j*) Accroissement de l'humidité; phénomènes de solifluxion sur les versants; terrasses ou thalwegs; industries *épilevalloisiennes anciennes* unissant les caractères du Proto-Stillbayen à ceux du Lupembien ancien;

(*k*) Suite de cette évolution; industries *épilevalloisiennes* unissant les caractères du Stillbayen au Lupembien typique (retouche par pression); brèches ossifères; climat humide oscillant;

(*l*) Phase de dessication climatique; formation allochtone des dépôts superficiels, roches mères des sols récents; remblayement des cirques de tête des cours d'eau avec formation de dembos; industries *épilevalloisiennes diminutives*, rares;

(*m*) Phase plus humide que l'actuelle; plaines alluviales; industries '*mésolithiques*' (Kansénien, Wiltonien, cf. Smithfieldien);

(*n*) Phase plus sèche; calcification des termitières anciennes; *mêmes industries*;

(*o*) Phase climatique récente, d'abord humide puis à tendance plus sèche; *mésolithique tardif, éléments néolithiques, âge du fer.*

Cette évolution climatique et industrielle fait ressortir qu'à l'est du Lualaba le Katanga appartient à l'aire rhodésienne, tandis que plus à l'ouest il établit la transition avec le sud du bassin du Congo.* On notera que cette succession fait ressortir un parallélisme satisfaisant avec l'Est-Africain, les Rhodésies et le nord-est de l'Angola, régions de hauts-plateaux et de savanes. Il existe toutefois un certain nombre de différences qui font que la succession, très satisfaisante vers le haut, ne l'est plus autant en dessous de la grande dessication fin-kanjérienne: pas plus qu'au Kasai belge, on ne trouve de trace certaine d'un interpluvial coupant en deux pluviaux kamasien et kanjérien, l'ancien grand pluvial kamasien; de même, le Kagérien paraît avoir eu une complexité plus grande que celle qui lui est attribuée dans l'Est-Africain.

2. *Le Fossé tectonique des Grands Lacs (région lac Albert-Semliki-lac Edouard-Ruindi)*

Si des dépôts d'âge pléistocène, caractérisés par leur sédimentologie, leur faune et leur contenu archéologique, existent en de nombreux points du grand fossé tectonique qui borde à l'est le bassin du Congo, seule la partie septentrionale — des lacs Albert et Edouard, de la Semliki et de la Ruindi — a fait l'objet d'études satisfaisantes. Aussi n'est-ce qu'à ces études, dues d'abord à J. Lepersonne, [14] plus récemment à J. de Heinzelin, [8] que nous nous adresserons pour tracer les grands traits de l'évolution géologique, climatique et culturelle de cette portion de l'Afrique centrale.

Dans la région étudiée, la bordure du fossé est constituée par des massifs de roches pré-cambriennes qui portent des témoins d'aplanissements dominant la plaine des lacs. Suivant les endroits il peut s'agir soit de l'aplanissement mi-tertiaire, soit du fin-tertiaire. Au sud du lac Albert et sur la basse Semliki la présence de couches du Miocène inférieur témoigne de l'âge pré-miocène de cette partie au moins du fossé tectonique. Celui-ci est encore caractérisé par la présence du massif culminant du Ruwenzori, horst basculé vers l'est, où se retrouvent les traces d'un aplanissement disséqué qui paraît être le mi-tertiaire. En plus des formations miocènes, très

---

* Esquissée dans nos travaux antérieurs, [15, 16] cette évolution a été précisée, sur plus d'un point, par notre récente mission CEMUBAC.

localisées, le fossé renferme trois séries sédimentaires qui, emboitées l'une dans l'autre, sont, de la plus ancienne à la plus récente :

1. Série de Kaiso ;
2. Série de la Semliki et couches de la Ruindi ;
3. Série lacustre récente du lac Albert ; terrasses d'Ishango
   et couche cendreuse du lac Edouard.

A. La Série de Kaiso

Découvertes d'abord sur la rive ugandaise du lac Albert, les couches de Kaiso furent retrouvées dès 1930 sur la rive congolaise ; leur stratigraphie et leur extension vers le sud furent établies en 1938–1940 par J. Lepersonne.[14] En 1955 J. de Heinzelin confirma ces données en les précisant.[9]

La série de Kaiso repose, au lac Albert et à la basse Semliki, soit sur les couches miocènes, soit sur leur formation de base. Au lac Edouard et sur la haute Semliki, sa base n'est pas exposée. Son épaisseur croit vers le centre de l'ancien lac, dépassant sans doute plusieurs centaines de mètres. On y peut distinguer un facies côtier, relativement grossier, et un facies profond, plus fin.

La série de Kaiso comporte trois termes superposés dont des exemples se présentent comme suit :

1. Région de la basse Semliki (facies littoral)

3 et 2. Alternances d'argiles, de sables, de grès tendres, de grès limonitiques et de lits lenticulaires de limonite. Teintes : brunes et blanches. Bone-beds vers la base et débris de végétaux dans les argiles. Épaisseur visible : environ 60 m.

1. Grès tendres et sables stratifiés à éléments fins ou grossiers, avec lits de petits galets et lits d'argile. Teinte blanche. Bone-bed à la base. Épaisseur maximum : 40 m.

Discordance sur les couches miocènes.

2. Même région (facies profond)

3. Sables et grès tendres avec rares niveaux argileux. Limonites gréseuses. Fossiles très rares. Épaisseur 40 m.

2. Argiles gris foncé avec quelques lits sableux. Diatomite au sommet. Nodules et lentilles limonitiques fossilifères nombreux. Épaisseur 125 m. Argiles du même type que les précédentes, à limonites fossilifères, constituant les niveaux les plus bas observés. Épaisseur 75 m.

1. Pas exposé.

3. Rive nord du lac Edouard

On observe un ensemble de marnes et de sables plus ou moins cohérents et concrétionnés, des bancs de limonite oolithique dont certains sont assez épais, des bancs de limonite concrétionnaire ; un horizon ou des lentilles gypsifères. Ces couches qui atteignent 50 m. environ semblent correspondre aux termes 3 et 2 de la succession établie au lac Albert.

Ces trois termes correspondent à deux groupes de formations lacustres encadrant des dépôts d'eau peu profonde avec dessiccations temporaires, paléosols de marais, précipitations ferrugineuses et gypseuses, grains éoliens[9] ; on peut les interpréter comme dépôts de phases pluviaies séparés par un épisode aride.

Les couches de Kaiso ont fourni, en Uganda surtout, une abondante faune de vertébrés comprenant des poissons, des reptiles et des mammifères de type kagérien-villafranchien. Les mammifères les plus caractéristiques sont *Archidiskodon griqua, Stegodon kaisensis, Anancus kenyensis*. De nombreux mollusques ont été récoltés ; ceux du terme moyen sont des viviparidés caractérisés par un test fortement caréné et épineux.

Sur la basse-Semliki cette faune de mammifères existe dès le bone-bed de base et est abondamment représentée dans le terme I ; elle est beaucoup plus rare dans le terme 2 où un seul bone-bed, situé à la limite des termes 2 et 3, a encore livré quelques éléments typiques de la faune de Kaiso.

Au bord nord du lac Edouard, J. de Heinzelin de Braucourt a relevé quatre groupes de bancs fossilifères dont l'inférieur, proche des horizons gypsifères, renferme, à côté des viviparidés épineux quelques restes de mammifères dont *Hippopotamus imaguncula* et *H. amphibius*. Les groupes II et III ont une forme de mollusques riche en Unionidés de type archaïque ; le groupe IV, encore mal défini, établirait le passage à la faune de la série de la Semliki.[9] Sur la base de ces éléments climatiques et fauniques, il avait généralement été admis la corrélation ci-après :

3. Phase pluviale : début Kamasien au moins.
2. Phase sèche : aride fin-Kagérien. Extinction de la faune kagérienne de mammifères.
1. Phase pluviale : Kagérien. Abondante faune de mammifères.

Constatant le caractère rélictuel de la faune de vertébrés et le caractère archaïque de celle de mollusques, J. de Heinzelin de Braucourt a proposé de placer toute la série de Kaiso dans le Kagérien, le terme 2 représentant alors un aride intra-kagérien. L'horizon IV à mollusques, au sommet du terme 3, où apparaissent des mollusques modernes, pourrait se rapprocher de l'aride fin-kagérien. Il est difficile, pour l'instant, de trancher entre ces deux hypothèses.

Une autre acquisition importante due aux recherches de J. de Heinzelin de Braucourt est la découverte dans le terme 2, chaque fois au voisinage d'un ancien horizon pédologique sub-aérien, d'une *industrie fraiche*, non roulée, isolée dans une masse de sédiments fins, consistant en éclats à bulbe de percussion très apparent, fort différente des autres industries villafranchiennes à galets ou blocs taillés ('Pebble Cultures').

B. Série de la Semliki et couches de la Ruindi

Discordante sur la série de Kaiso, la série de la Semliki y est souvent encastrée, colmatant alors des vallées creusées dans la première série. Ailleurs elle paraît déposée dans un fossé tectonique recoupant les couches de Kaiso.

Principalement représentée dans la région de la moyenne et de la haute-Semliki cette série est constituée par des graviers, des sables et des argiles en lits alternants, avec quelques horizons de grès tendres à ciment limonitique et des concrétions calcaires. La teinte est gris clair à blanc ou jaune brun. Cet ensemble atteint une centaine de mètres de puissance.

Considérée comme Pléistocène supérieur par J. Lepersonne,[14] la série de la Semliki appartient, sur la base de récoltes paléontologiques et archéologiques faites par J. de Heinzelin, au Pléistocène moyen. Celui-ci a en effet recueilli dans la partie moyenne de la série, *Palaeoloxodon recki*, forme caractéristique de la faune d'Olduvai. La faune de mollusques est moderne.

Les industries récoltées comportent, de la partie moyenne de la série, d'abord un *galet biseauté* rappelant l'Oldowayen puis des *industries atypiques et clactonoïdes* frustes à éclats épais. Plus haut, dans des couches qui correspondent à des oscillations climatiques préludant à une phase aride, s'observent des techniques très variées et apparemment contemporaines, les unes *atypiques*, les autres *levalloisiennes typiques*. Cet ensemble d'éléments conduit à paralléliser la série de la Semliki avec le pluvial kanjérien pour ses portions inférieure et moyenne, avec le déclin du pluvial pour le reste. Il lui a succédé une phase d'érosion correspondant, semble-t-il, au grand aride fin-kanjérien. En effet, les couches de base de la série récente renferment à l'état dérivé, un *Acheuléen final à bifaces et hachereaux* qui pourrait dater des débuts de cet aride qui n'a pas laissé de dépôts.

Au sud du lac Edouard, la série de la Semliki se retrouve dans les vallées de la Ruindi et de la Rutshuru où elle présente deux termes stratigraphiques, de sables avec lits de galets au sommet, d'argiles à la base. Ces couches ont le faciès de couches de Kaiso. Vers le sommet du terme supérieur existe un atelier préhistorique renfermant une variante à éclats prédominants de *l'Acheuléen évolué* (technique proto-levallois II) qui confirme l'attribution au Kanjérien. Le reste de la formation pourrait être plus ancien et établir le passage à la série de Kaiso; on n'y a malheureusement récolté aucun fossile.

C. *La Série lacustre récente et les couches d'Ishango*

Au lac Albert et sur la basse Semliki, J. Lepersonne a observé, remplissant une dépression en contrebas de la série de la Semliki, un nouvel ensemble sédimentaire auquel il a donné le nom de 'série lacustre récente'. Puissant de plus de 15 m., cet ensemble est formé de graviers, de sables, de limons et d'argiles parfois gypsifères, à concrétions calcaires. La teinte est grise, gris-vert ou blanche. Il n'existe ni limonites ni fossiles. Elle a fourni une industrie sur quartz de type 'méso-lithique'. Sur la rive nord du lac Edouard, près de son exutoire dans la Semliki, existent des terrasses lacustres dont les replats se situent à 40, 12 et 6 m. par rapport au niveau du lac. Ces terrasses ont récemment fait l'objet d'une étude approfondie et de fouilles dues à J. de Heinzelin.[9]

(*a*) Le groupe des 'terrasses supérieures', limonitisées, se situe à plus de 20 m. au dessus du cours actuel de la Semliki. Il s'emboîte dans les séries du Kaiso et de la Semliki. Il leur correspond des sols rouges profonds témoignant d'un climat chaud et humide similaire à celui qui règne actuellement dans la cuvette centrale. Les terrasses renferment, roulées, les industries reprises à la série de la Semliki, de l'Acheuléen final usé, datant sans doute des débuts du grand aride fin-kanjérien et, comme éléments de datation, du *Sangoen supérieur roulé* et des *industries épi-levalloisiennes* à faciès Middle Stone Age. La faune est gamblienne. Ces données concourent à faire attribuer à ces dépôts un âge gamblien et à les paralléliser au pluvial du même nom.

Au sommet de ces formations on observe parfois des accumulations de concrétions calcaires à aspect de kunkar qui témoignent d'une phase aride qui paraît bien correspondre à la phase sèche fin-gamblienne.

(*b*) Le groupe des 'terrasses moyennes' correspond au niveau d'Ishango et aux tufs volcaniques qui les couronnent. Il consiste en bancs épais, compacts, et bien classés, de cailloutis et de sables, contemporaines ou de peu antérieurs aux tufs volcaniques. Leur sommet s'établit entre 10 et 12 m. au dessus de la Semliki. Ces dépôts, qui traduisent un retour à des conditions plus humides et renferment une faune gamblienne de savane, sont le gisement de la civilisation et de l'Homme d'Ishango. *L'Ishangien* est une industrie originale, née et évoluant sur place, à quartz taillés de typologie mésolithique, avec meules et molettes, et surtout des harpons en os, d'abord à deux rangées puis à une rangée de barbelures.

Cette civilisation, de même que la formation de la terrasse d'Ishango, a été interrompue par la projection de tufs volcaniques qui ont recouvert toute la région.

D'autres cailloutis de terrasse, d'altitude à peine inférieure à celle de la terrasse d'Ishango, se sont déposés après cet épisode volcanique. Il leur correspond, sur les zones émergées, des habitats à *industrie à affinités smithfieldienne*.

Un épisode légèrement plus aride suit, qu'il est logique de paralléliser avec l'oscillation sèche post-makalienne. Au Makalien correspondrait alors l'ensemble des moyennes terrasses.

(*c*) Le groupe des 'basses terrasses', terreuses, situées à la côte de 3-5 m., s'est formé sous climat et faune actuelle. Il correspond au Nakurien. Il a vu se poursuivre, sur les rives de la rivière et du lac, des *cultures mésolithiques attardées*, à microlithes et poteries, qui n'ont disparu que récemment, avec l'arrivée des Bantous, peu avant celle des Européens sans doute.

Ces importantes recherches font ressortir que, malgré la proximité de l'Afrique orientale, il existe, à côté de corrélations évidentes, certains désaccords quant aux équivalences climatiques. Une équivalence satisfaisante peut être trouvée entre les séquences climatiques de l'Est Africain et des Rhodésies pour les phases humides nakurienne et makalienne et pour le pluvial gamblien. Les phases sèches qui séparent ces trois épisodes pluviaux sont moins évidentes, quoique probables. J. de Heinzelin n'a pu mettre en évidence, dans les dépôts gambliens, aucun des trois maxima postulés par L. S. B. Leakey et J. Desmond Clark dans leurs territoires de recherches.

Le grand aride fin-kanjérien, si bien caractérisé ailleurs par ses sables éoliens, ne semble pas avoir été extrêmement marqué ici. Il lui correspond les derniers dépôts de la série de la Semliki, à climat oscillant et surtout les érosions postérieures au dépôt de cette série.

Au delà de cet aride, les équivalences sont moins aisées à déterminer. Si la série de la Semliki ne représente que le Kanjérien, alors il existe une important lacune entre cette série et celle de Kaiso, lacune couvrant au minimum la phase aride post-kamasienne et le Kamasien. Si au contraire, la série de la Semliki représente, comme le suggère la coupe de la Ruindi, tout le Kamasien au sens large, alors il n'existe dans le fossé tectonique aucune trace de l'aride fin-kamasien (Bed III d'Olduvai).

De même la série de Kaiso soulève des problèmes provisoirement insolubles : si l'on admet que l'aride correspondant au terme moyen est l'aride post-kagérien on a, dans le terme supérieur, un témoin d'une partie au moins du Kamasien et, dans l'inférieur, un dépôt du pluvial kagérien ; si, au contraire, sur les évidences fauniques apportées par J. de Heinzelin on place l'ensemble de la série de Kaiso dans le Kagérien, alors le terme moyen doit représenter un nouvel aride intra-kagérien, correspondant à l'ancien interpluvial d' E. J. Wayland. Cette conception est loin d'être en opposition avec ce que montrent les Rhodésies et l'Afrique australe.

On ne saurait quitter le fossé tectonique sans rappeler les observations de glaciologie récente dues à J. de Heinzelin et qui font ressortir un parallélisme très satisfaisant entre les oscillations climatiques de l'hémisphère nord et de la zone équatoriale. [7]

Conclusions

De l'ensemble des données actuellement recueillies sur le système Plio-Pléistocène au Congo Belge et en Afrique Centrale se dégagent des vues d'ensemble déjà satisfaisantes, mais qui n'ont pas la simplicité des conclusions apportées par l'étude du Cénozoïque plus ancien. Cette complexité plus grande résulte d'une évolution moins poussée des trois cycles géographiques successifs que l'on a pu distinguer pour cette période et surtout aussi du fait que ces cycles n'ont pas, comme les fin-crétacé et mi-tertiaire, agi à partir d'un niveau de base unique, l'océan. Ici, au contraire, le territoire du Congo s'est trouvé scindé en une série de régions naturelles qui ont eu, chacune, son niveau de base propre. Ces conditions particulières font que les raccords de région à région sont plus difficiles à établir.

1. Le premier cycle géographique reconnu est le cycle du Pliocène supérieur dont l'action essentielle fut le dégagement des aplanissements du groupe fin-tertiaire. On a vu que suivant la région considérée, ces aplanissements pouvaient être plus ou moins nombreux, mais parfois unique, et plus ou moins évolués. Leurs caractères sont ceux de pédiplaines, formées théoriquement en climat semi-aride. Leur recouvrement toutefois, quand il est sablo-argileux, est de type fluviatile ; quand il est de caractère pédologique, il consiste en carapaces limonitiques couronnant des roches ayant subi une profonde altération latéritique.

Dans la future cuvette centrale existent un certain nombre de formations—série de Yangambi, couches d'Opala, couches de Lodja—qui semblent en relation avec des écoulements fermés ; la première au moins de ces formations revêt un caractère aride net. Par contre il n'existe aucun dépôt de cet âge dans la zone du fossé tectonique, ce qui donne à penser qu'à part la petite cuvette miocène du lac Albert entièrement comblée, ce fossé était encore inexistant. Pas d'avantage de dépôts à la côte d'où la mer s'est, au Miocène déjà, largement retirée.

Les données climatiques que l'on peut dégager de cet ensemble de faits sont contradictoires. Il semble bien que le climat sous lequel a été façonné l'essentiel des aplanissements ait encore été de type aride à semi-aride, mais qu'il ait évolué peu à peu vers un climat de savane—dégagement des inselberge—puis de forêt dense, avec altération latéritique profonde du sous-sol ; un retour à la savane ou à la steppe clot cette évolution, avec induration d'une cuirasse limonitique superficielle.

2. Le deuxième cycle géographique, ou cycle du Pliocène final et du Pléistocène inférieur, est initié par des mouvements qui créent la cuvette centrale congolaise, jusqu'alors zone d'érosion, et

déterminent la naissance d'un réseau centripète. En dehors de ce réseau existe à la côte une zone d'érosion suivie, vers le large, d'une aire de sédimentation où se dépose la 'série des cirques' continentale qui témoigne d'oscillations climatiques répétées. Plus à l'est existe toujours le réseau Lualaba-Nil. Enfin, c'est au cours de cette période que s'ouvre le fossé des grands lacs où se dépose la série de Kaiso.

Dans les zones d'érosion correspond à cette période un ou plusieurs aplanissements à surface généralement limonitisée.

Les industries humaines apparaissent, dans les plus inférieurs au moins de ces aplanissements; ce sont, au Kasai et au Katanga, des complexes rattachés au groupe de la Pebble Culture pré-abbevillienne et, dans l'aire de l'ancien lac Kaiso, des industries à éclats frustes.

Ce qu'on peut dégager de l'évolution corrélative des climats est encore assez contradictoire; comme pour le cycle précédent, il semble, qu'au début tout ou moins, le climat ait revêtu un caractère relativement aride: bois silicifiés du conglomérat de base de la 'série des cirques', caractère pédiplané des aplanissements; puis ce climat paraît avoir montré plusieurs oscillations allant jusqu'à des conditions de haute pluviosité, avec formation de sols latéritiques profonds, pour revenir, une ou plusieurs fois, à des conditions semi-arides ou arides. Le nombre et la hiérarchie de ces oscillations reste encore à établir, de même que la réalité de certaines. Dans les zones de plateaux, en tout cas, le cycle se clot à la fin du Kagérien, par une phase semi-aride à laquelle correspond la formation de cuirasses limonitiques (Latérite I de L. S. B. Leakey). Ce cycle paraît se clore d'autre part, par un retour de la mer qui découpe dans la 'série des cirques' une plage de 120 m.

Au point de vue faunique, il est caractérisé par le développement de la faune de Kaiso, à fort caractère relictuel.

3A. Le troisième cycle géographique distingué couvre le Pléistocène moyen, le Pléistocène supérieur et les temps post-pléistocènes. Il est initié par des mouvements qui rattachent le réseau de la cuvette centrale à l'exutoire du Congo, qui rattachent peut-être le réseau du haut-Lualaba à celui du Congo, qui approfondissent enfin le fossé des grands lacs (failles recoupant la série de Kaiso).

Ici encore il est difficile de dégager les traits d'une évolution commune à toutes les parties du bassin du Congo, car cette communauté d'évolution n'a pas existé. Si le réseau de la cuvette a eu pour niveau de base général le Stanley-Pool, le Congo occidental, le Katanga, etc., ont eu leurs propres niveaux de base; enfin la zone du fossé, plus ou moins fermée, échappe à ce mode d'évolution. On pourrait s'attendre à trouver dans des oscillations climatiques dont on a postulé la généralité le fil conducteur qui permette de rattacher l'une à l'autre les successions établies dans chaque région congolaise puis de les corréler aux successions d'autres régions péri-congolaises—Est-Africain, Rhodésies, Nord-Est de l'Angola. On s'aperçoit alors que s'il est bien possible de couper en deux ce vaste ensemble par un grand aride fin-kanjérien, on ne trouve en général pas trace de la phase d'aridité fin-kamasienne, soit qu'elle n'ait pas été enrégistrée, soit que son enrégistrement ait été détruit, soit enfin que le climat du Congo, au Pléistocène moyen, ait été systématiquement plus humide que celui des contrées avoisinantes. Il semble que cette dernière hypothèse soit la bonne: la dessication fin-kamasienne, bien marquée à Olduvai (Bed III), ne l'est déjà plus guère sur la Kagera. Dans ces conditions, les fils conducteurs auxquels on peut faire appel sont ceux fournis d'une part par les dépôts ou par les surfaces d'érosion qui les prolongent, d'autre part par les industries préhistoriques. Si les industries à galets taillés pré-abbevilliennes semblent abonder au début du Kamasien, il n'en est rien des stades abbevillien et acheuléen ancien dont aucun bon gisement en place n'est connu à ce jour; ce n'est qu'à l'Acheuléen évolué et final, et pendant le développement des industries clactonoïdes qui en tiennent localement la place, que reprend l'abondance. On en peut déduire, pensons-nous, que la majeure partie du Congo a été couverte, pendant la plus grande partie du Pléistocène moyen, par un intense développement de la grande forêt équatoriale, rejetant au delà de ses limites les humanités primitives.

Le Cénozoïque du Congo Belge

L'Acheuléen final correspond à une dessication qui provoque la formation, généralisée au Katanga, de concrétions ou de cuirasses limonitiques, témoignant par conséquent de l'existence de ces climats forestiers.

C'est sur ces cuirasses, ou sur les graviers kanjériens exposés, ou encore sur des îlots rocheux exondés (Stanley-Pool) que s'installent les populations sangoennes, au moment où la dessication kanjérienne devient sensible, avant de culminer, dans de vastes portions du Congo, en l'étalement des nappes sableuses éoliennes.

3B. C'est pendant cette phase d'intense aridité climatique que se produisent, dans l'est et le sud-est du Congo, des mouvements tectoniques qui rajeunissent le fossé des grands lacs et celui de l'Upemba. Cet épisode tectonique introduit, dans le Katanga méridional et central, un nouveau cycle géographique que caractérise la destruction du vieux réseau nilotique du haut-Lualaba.

A partir du Gamblien l'évolution climatique du bassin du Congo est plus conforme à ce que montrent les régions avoisinantes. Il faut noter toutefois que les trois maxima d'humidité décelés en Afrique orientale et en Rhodésie n'apparaissent pas ici, les conditions générales régnant au Congo ayant été plus humides qu'à présent. Une acquisition récente est la mise en évidence, au Katanga, d'importants phénomènes de solifluxion au début du Gamblien, remaniant les produits rocheux éclatés thermiquement et les dépôts fluviatiles de la fin du Kanjérien. Importante aussi fut la dessication fin-gamblienne, génératrice de 'kunkar' dans les aires d'épandage, de nappes éoliennes allochtones, support de la pédogénèse récente, dans les autres. La réalité d'une oscillation sèche post-makalienne reste à établir dans le bassin du Congo.

Cette longue période du Pléistocène supérieur et des temps post-pléistocènes correspond, pendant le Gamblien, à l'évolution, dans l'est du Congo, des civilisations épilevalloisiennes du type Middle Stone Age—Proto-Stillbayen, Stillbayen et Magosien ou affines—dans le reste du Congo à celles de type 'forestier' à gouges, ciseaux et pics—Lupembien ancien, Lupembien évolué, Lupembo-Tshitolien. Au Makalien correspondent respectivement, dans l'est et le sud-est, les civilisations 'mésolithiques' de l'Ishangien, du Kansénien, du Smithfieldien, du Wiltonien et affines, dans le sud et l'ouest du Congo, du Tshitolien et du Tshitolien final, à microlithes, de tradition 'forestière'.

Au Nakurien correspondent les survivances 'mésolithiques', le néolithique, localisé, et la pénétration des Bantous et du fer, contemporaine de ces derniers Ages de la Pierre.

Ces données font apparaître les liens qui, au point de vue géologique et culturel, unissent le Congo aux territoires environnants ou, à d'autres moments, lui donnent son originalité.

Elles font ressortir aussi que seules les phases climatiques les plus arides ont pu, au Quaternaire, s'enregistrer dans la succession des dépôts. Aux périodes plus humides, le développement intense de la forêt ne semble pas avoir permis l'inscription des oscillations arides moins marquées. Il en résulte un parallélisme moins satisfaisant que considéré antérieurement avec les régions 'classiques' de l'Afrique orientale. Ce fait, que nous avions mis en évidence dès 1950, montre que les arguments climatiques ne peuvent venir qu'en troisième ou quatrième rang dans l'établissement des corrélations intra-africaines, après les données convergentes apportées par la géologie et la géomorphologie, la paléontologie et les cultures préhistoriques.

BIBLIOGRAPHIE

1. Breuil, H. et Janmart, J., *Les limons et graviers de l'Angola du nord-est et leur contenu archéologique*, Lisbonne, 1949.
2. Cahen, L., *Géologie du Congo Belge*, Liége, 1954.
3. Cahen, L. et Lepersonne, J., 'Notes sur la géomorphologie du Congo occidental', *Ann. Mus. Congo belge*, 1948.
4. Cahen, L. et Lepersonne, J., 'Equivalence entre le Système du Kalahari du Congo belge et les Kalahari Beds d'Afrique australe', *Mem. Soc. Belge Géol.*, 1952.
5. Delhaye, F. et Borgniez, G., 'Contribution à la connaissance de la géographie et de la géologie de la région de la Lukenie et de la Tshuapa supérieures', *Ann. Mus. Congo belge*, 1948.

6. de Heinzelin de Braucourt, J., 'Sols, paléosols et désertifications anciennes dans le secteur nord oriental du bassin du Congo', *Publ. Inst. Nat. Et. Agron. du Congo* (INEAC), 1952.

7. de Heinzelin de Braucourt, J., 'Les stades de récession du glacier Stanley occidental (Ruwenzori, Congo Belge)', *Inst. Parcs Nat. Congo belge*, 1953.

8. de Heinzelin de Braucourt, J., 'Le fossé tectonique sous le parallèle d'Ishango', *Inst. Parcs Nat. Congo belge*, 1955.

9. de Heinzelin de Braucourt, J., 'Les horizons d'altération anciens, critères stratigraphiques en Afrique centrale', *Actes et C.R. Vme. Co. Int. Sc. Sol*, 1954.

10. Henry, J., 'Étude géologique du Congo belge dans la région comprise entre Basoko et Stanleyville à l'ouest, le lac Albert et la Semliki à l'est', *Ann. Soc. Géol. Belg.*, 1923.

11. Hopwood, A. T. et Lepersonne, J., 'Présence de formations d'âge Miocène inférieur dans le fossé tectonique du lac Albert et de la basse Semliki', *Ann. Soc. Géol. Belg.*, 1949.

12. Janmart, J., *The Kalahari Sands of the Lunda* (*N.E. Angola*), *their earlier redistributions and the Sangoan culture*, Lisbonne, 1955.

13. Leakey, L. S. B., *Tentative Study of the Pleistocene Climatic Changes and Stone Age Culture Sequence in N.E. Angola*, Lisbonne, 1949.

14. Lepersonne, J., 'Le fossé tectonique Lac Albert-Semliki-Lac Edouard. Résumé des observations géologiques effectuées en 1938, 1939, 1940, *Ann. Soc. Géol. Belg.*, 1949.

15. Mortelmans, G., 'Le Quaternaire de l'Afrique Sud-Equatoriale. Essai de corrélation', 3me. *Co. Nat. Sc.*, Bruxelles, 1950.

16. Mortelmans, G., 'Vue d'ensemble sur le Quaternaire du bassin du Congo', 3me. *Co. Int. Sc. Préhist. et Protohist.*, Zürich, 1950.

17. Veatch, A. C., 'Evolution of the Congo Basin', *Mem. Geol. Soc. America*, 1935.

5

The Problem of Quaternary Glacio-Pluvial Correlation in East and Southern Africa*

by H. B. S. COOKE

At the First Pan-African Congress on Prehistory, held in Nairobi in 1947, it was agreed that an African terminology should be developed for the subdivision of the Quaternary in this continent and it was recommended that the well-developed and well-studied East African sequence of deposits should be used as a starting point. The terms Kageran, Kamasian and Gamblian were adopted as *stratigraphic* subdivisions of the Quaternary, the responsibility for correlation with the known sequence being left to workers in different regions according to the evidence at their disposal. The Committee which formulated the relevant resolution made it clear that the terms were to be used in a geological sense and there was no implication that the climatic *interpretation* of the deposits was accepted or licensed for general adoption and use. Subsequently, the 'Kamasian' deposits were recognized as constituting two separable entities, divisible into a lower portion, or Kamasian *sensu stricto*, and an upper portion separated as the Kanjeran (Leakey, 1950).

It is, perhaps, unfortunate that in the East African field the terms Kageran, Kamasian, Kanjeran and Gamblian have been used also to name periods of rainfall apparently greater than that of the present-day climatic regime (so-called 'pluvials'). This appears to have led to a measure of confusion in the minds of some workers who have tended to emphasize the climatic factor in effecting or suggesting widespread correlations within the African continent. For example, references exist for deposits of the 'Gamblian Pluvial' in South Africa without due regard having been paid by the authors to the normal requirements for establishing geological correlations. It is true that fluctuations of climate have been shown to occur in various parts of Africa but the synchronous nature of these cycles cannot yet be regarded as satisfactorily proved either on geological or on meteorological grounds. That they may eventually prove to be contemporaneous cannot be denied but it is felt that the foundations for such an assumption require critical examination.

There is some evidence in the periglacial areas of ice-age Europe, America and Asia that periods of glacial maximum were also periods of higher rainfall. In East Africa there is some evidence of a similar relationship between advance of high mountain glaciers and increased rainfall. These indications have led some authorities to suggest that 'pluvial' periods in non-glaciated areas coincide closely (or even exactly) with 'glacial' periods; conversely dry periods ('interpluvials') are correlated with interglacials. A number of tables have been published in recent years in which the results of this assumed correspondence are set out for various parts of Africa and for Africa and Europe.

It was noted by the author that, with one exception (Oakley, 1949), these tables were type-set and not graphical; the time subdivision was indicated by ruled-off compartments separating pluvial and interpluvial, glacial and interglacial. The time scale was only very roughly represented, or ignored, and the suggested correlations of climate, fauna and culture appeared plausible or even

---

* Summary of the first part of the paper; the meteorological aspects will be considered in a separate publication.

TABLE I

CULTURE RELATIONSHIPS ASSUMING RIGID PLUVIAL - GLACIAL EQUIVALENCE

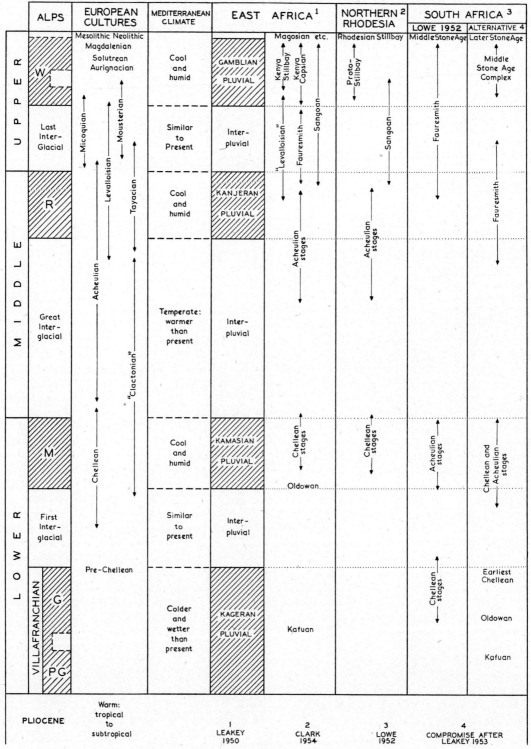

	ALPS	EUROPEAN CULTURES	MEDITERRANEAN CLIMATE	EAST AFRICA [1]			NORTHERN RHODESIA [2]	SOUTH AFRICA [3] LOWE 1952	SOUTH AFRICA [3] ALTERNATIVE [4]
UPPER	W	Mesolithic Neolithic Magdalenian Solutrean Aurignacian	Cool and humid	GAMBLIAN PLUVIAL	Magosian etc. Kenya Stillbay / Kenya Capsian	Sangoan	Rhodesian Stillbay Proto-Stillbay	Middle Stone Age	Middle Stone Age Complex
UPPER	Last Inter-Glacial	Micoquian / Levalloisian / Mousterian / Tayacian	Similar to Present	Inter-pluvial	"Levalloisian" / Fauresmith		Sangoan	Fauresmith	
MIDDLE	R	Acheulian	Cool and humid	KANJERAN PLUVIAL	Acheulian stages		Acheulian stages		Fauresmith
MIDDLE	Great Inter-glacial	"Clactonian" / Chellean	Temperate: warmer than present	Inter-pluvial					
LOWER	M		Cool and humid	KAMASIAN PLUVIAL	Chellean stages / Oldowan		Chellean stages	Acheulian stages	Chellean and Acheulian stages
LOWER	First Inter-glacial		Similar to present	Inter-pluvial					
LOWER	VILLAFRANCHIAN G / PG	Pre-Chellean	Colder and wetter than present	KAGERAN PLUVIAL	Kafuan			Chellean stages	Earliest Chellean / Oldowan / Kafuan
	PLIOCENE		Warm: tropical to subtropical	1 LEAKEY 1950	2 CLARK 1954		3 LOWE 1952	4 COMPROMISE AFTER LEAKEY 1953	

convincing. It seemed worth while to re-examine these correlations with the time span represented more or less to scale.

As far as the Pleistocene time scale is concerned, exact dates for the major events are lacking (except for the last thirty thousand years) and the estimated figures vary considerably. The time scale suggested by Flint (1947), modified to some extent by dating of ocean-bottom sediments (Hough, 1950), has been adopted as convenient and generally acceptable.

Table I shows the results obtained by setting out against the glacial-interglacial time scale the European cultural sequence as interpreted by a number of eminent prehistorians; a *rigid* equivalence of European glacial and East African pluvial periods is then assumed and the East African cultural succession is set out against the pluvial sequence in accordance with the stratigraphic evidence (Leakey, 1950, 1953). The general agreement is good but in detail it is clear that the length of the Kamasian-Kanjeran interpluvial here indicated is directly contrary to the archaeological and geological evidence at Olduvai, which suggests a moderately short break; the Oldowan seems to come too late and the early Acheul of East Africa cannot be regarded as developing so long after the European equivalent. Equating the Northern Rhodesian climatic cycles to the East African ones and inserting the typological sequence in accordance with Clark's suggestions (1954), similar broad agreement and similar discrepancies occur. Equating likewise the correlation and sequence suggested by van Riet Lowe (1952) for the Vaal River Basin, major discrepancies appear which are not improved by adopting a compromise equivalence in accordance with Leakey's latest tables (1953). One cannot help concluding that *precise* equivalence of glacial and pluvial periods is highly improbable, though the measure of agreement shown in some instances suggests that a less precise equivalence probably exists for some areas. It is not claimed that this statement is novel, nor is it suggested that so precise an equivalence was ever envisaged by the compilers of the typical published type-set tables.

Table II is an attempt to reverse the procedure of Table I and to use stone tools more or less as zone fossils, equating typological equivalents on the time scale and evaluating the climatic background accordingly. The results are interesting and there do not seem to be any serious discrepancies, though the glacial-pluvial relationship appears to be a vague rather than an exact one. The South African climatic sequence shows some measure of agreement but also displays some apparent inversions which cannot be circumvented by anything but a radical rejection either of the typological or of the geological interpretation of the material and evidence. Such a denial of the geological and archaeological interpretation of the deposits in the Vaal River basin seems unreasonable; the failure of this South African succession to fit the simple frame of glacial-pluvial equivalence provides suggestive evidence that the supposed simple equivalence is not, in fact, simple at all. The solution seems to lie in finding a reasonable theory of Pleistocene climates which will fit the *total* evidence and not just part of it. This is largely a meteorological problem and it is probable that an adequate theory will eventually come to light. In the meantime, it is felt that correlations based on an *assumed* universal equivalence of glacial and pluvial episodes must be made with caution.

While it is not proposed in this brief summary to present any discussion of the meteorological problems of Pleistocene atmospheric circulation and precipitation patterns, it is worth while pointing out that most theories so far advanced involve poleward and equatorward movements of the climatic belts as well as general changes in circulation patterns and pressure gradients. The equatorial region is likely to have changes of precipitation fairly closely related to polar glaciation but the regions of semi-arid climate related to the subtropical anticyclonic belt are likely to be particularly sensitive to latitudinal shifting of pressure systems. It is not at all difficult to visualize conditions which will, in some circumstances, involve precipitation changes in some of these areas which are in the opposite sense to those taking place in the periglacial areas and in the equatorial rainfall belt. Such an explanation might serve to resolve the apparent anomalies in the Vaal River sequence.

TABLE II

CULTURE RELATIONSHIPS ASSUMING TYPOLOGICAL EQUIVALENCE

ALPS	EUROPEAN CULTURES	EAST AFRICA		NORTHERN RHODESIA		SOUTH AFRICA	

UPPER

- ALPS: W, Last Inter-Glacial
- EUROPEAN CULTURES: Mesolithic Neolithic Magdalenian Solutrean Aurignacian; Micoquian; Levalloisian; Mousterian; Tayacian
- EAST AFRICA: Kenya Wilton etc. Magosian; Kenya Capsian; Kenya Stillbay; Fauresmith; "Levalloisian"; Sangoan; Fluctuating Dry — GAMBLIAN PLUVIAL; Inter-pluvial
- NORTHERN RHODESIA: Wilton etc. Magosian; Rhodesian Stillbay; Rhodesian Proto-Stillbay; Rhodesian Sangoan; Fluctuating Dry — PLUVIAL; Semi-arid
- SOUTH AFRICA: Wilton Smithfield Magosian; "Middle Stone Age Complex"; Fauresmith; S.A. Sangoan; Fluctuating Dry — SEASONALLY WET; Semi-arid; WET; Semi-arid

MIDDLE

- ALPS: R, Great Inter-Glacial
- EUROPEAN CULTURES: Acheulian; "Clactonian"
- EAST AFRICA: Acheulian stages; KANJERAN PLUVIAL; Inter-pluvial
- NORTHERN RHODESIA: Hope Fountain; Acheulian stages; PLUVIAL; Semi-arid
- SOUTH AFRICA: Acheulian stages; FLUCTUATING WET; Semi-arid

LOWER

- ALPS: M; First Inter-Glacial; VILLAFRACHIAN — G, PG
- EUROPEAN CULTURES: Chellean; Pre-Chellean
- EAST AFRICA: Chellean stages; Oldowan; Kafuan; KAMASIAN PLUVIAL; Inter-pluvial; KAGERAN PLUVIAL
- NORTHERN RHODESIA: Chellean stages; Oldowan; Kafuan; PLUVIAL; Arid; PLUVIAL
- SOUTH AFRICA: Chellean stages; Oldowan; Kafuan; WET; Semi-arid; Arid; PLUVIAL

PLIOCENE

Quaternary Glacio-Pluvial Correlation in East and Southern Africa

Notable from Table II is the apparently early onset of pluvial conditions as compared with glacial extension. It is suggested here that this may be capable of explanation through the effects of sea-ice on atmospheric circulation, at least in the southern hemisphere, before the establishment of large continental ice areas in the northern hemisphere. This theory will be elaborated elsewhere but, like other meteorological theories, is handicapped by lack of data. The geological and archaeological evidence from Africa may well provide the meteorologist with the ultimate key to the formulation of an acceptable theory of Pleistocene climatology. It is felt that presentation of this evidence should at the existing stage of our knowledge remain objective and uninfluenced by oversimplified theories which are not yet adequately substantiated.

REFERENCES

Clark, J. D. (1954), 'A provisional correlation of prehistoric cultures north and south of the Sahara', *S. Afr. Archaeol. Bull.*, IX (33), pp. 3–17.

Flint, R. F. (1947), *Glacial geology and the Pleistocene period*, New York : John Wiley & Sons.

Hough, J. L. (1950), 'Pleistocene lithology of Antarctic Ocean-bottom sediments', *Jour. of Geol.*, 58 (3), pp. 254–60.

Leakey, L. S. B. (1950), 'The lower limit of the Pleistocene in Africa', *Proc. Int. Geol. Cong.* 1948, IX (H), pp. 62–5.

Leakey, L. S. B. (1953), *Adam's Ancestors*, 4th Ed., London, Methuen & Co.

Lowe, C. van Riet (1952), 'The Vaal River chronology: an up to date summary', *S. Afr. Archaeol. Bull.*, VII (28), pp. 1–15.

Oakley, K. P. (1949), *Man the Toolmaker*, Brit. Mus. (Nat. Hist.).

6

A Pollen Analytical Investigation of the Florisbad Deposits (South Africa)

by E. M. VAN ZINDEREN BAKKER

THE Florisbad site, 48 km. N.W.–N. of Bloemfontein in the Orange Free State, has for some considerable time attracted attention from scientists in various fields, as its deposits have given much valuable information about prehistory.

Anthropologists throughout the world have shown interest in the discovery of the Florisbad skull of *Homo helmei* by the late Prof. T. F. Dreyer. Palaeontology still benefits from the wealth of fossil material collected at Florisbad by Miss A. Lyle and Drs R. Broom, T. F. Dreyer, A. C. Hoffman and A. J. D. Meiring. Many archaeologists have studied the stone implements brought to light and the dispute about their affinities and age still continues. Geologists have now shown their interest in the site and are preparing their contribution to our knowledge of the milieu of the Florisbad Man.

Up till now botany has played no part in the unravelling of Florisbad prehistory. The present report tries to depict the prehistoric vegetational background of the Florisbad events and may add to our understanding of the climatic changes which took place during the deposition of the alternating layers of clay, loam and sand of Florisbad.

General Information

The soil samples necessary for the pollen statistical investigation were easily obtained by cutting them out of the wall of the profile exposed by former excavations. The first samples were collected with Prof. T. F. Dreyer on May 7, 1947. A core of the lower layers was obtained during the digging of a deep trench in 1949 and also during the excavation in 1952.

The analysis was intermittently carried on from 1947 onward. For pollen analysis, samples taken at intervals of ±4 inches were treated with the acetolysis method and chlorinated with care.[1] Sometimes the material was also treated with 10% KOH to compare the results obtained with acetolysis. The pollen content of the layers was usually very low. It was therefore impossible to count large numbers of pollen grains. Most of the counts did not exceed 150 pollen grains; in a number of analyses only 100 and sometimes even only 50 pollen grains could be counted.

It is unfortunate that only about half the profile contained enough pollen grains to be analysed. In the uppermost 86 inches only very few grains were found and it can be assumed that the pollen grains were not preserved in these alkaline layers rich in oxygen.

The blue-green loam and clay (layer number 7) was also very poor in pollen.

THE INFLUENCE OF THE SPRING ON THE PROFILE AND THE POLLEN SPECTRA

The Profile

The deposits studied are found on the southern slope of the enormous Hagenstad saltpan around a saline, medical spring. This spring, which desposited the pollen bearing strata, is associated with volcanic action. It can be classified as a dyke spring as its outlets occur on both sides of a dolerite dyke which penetrates the Ecca beds.[2]

The percolation of the water through the Ecca-shales, mudstones and sandstones has caused these rocks to weather and the spring has in the course of time accumulated the decayed rock material in the form of a little hill. This hill, of which a profile of 21 feet 4 inches depth has been investigated, consists of layers of clay, loam and sand of different colours (Fig. 1). The colour of these anorganic strata may be due to the nature of the parent rock and to pedological processes which took place after their deposition. Chemical and mineralogical investigations of the layers can give information on these points and also on the question whether part of the material is of aeolic origin.

Between these strata four brown to black horizons occur. Another black layer is found at the bottom of the profile covering the underlying rock. These 'peaty' seams must have been formed in times when the spring was less active. These layers have always been referred to in literature as peat layers. The author did not recognize them as such and therefore had samples of them ignited. The loss in weight, determined in duplicate by Miss A. E. van Kerken is as follows:

the fourth layer ('peat IV'), 5·37%,
the third layer ('peat III'), 4·16%,
the second layer ('peat II'), 4·30%,
the first layer ('peat I'), 5·64%,
the basal layer ('basal peat'), 10·77%.

The above figures show that these layers contain only very little organic matter and can therefore not consist of peat. They are mainly composed of clay and sand which are coloured dark.

The profile studied has the following composition:

1. top layer of light grey sand - - - - - - - - - - 19 inches
2. fourth dark layer, loam and clay ('peat IV') - - - - - - - 23 inches
3. cemented yellowish sand, in places greenish and white; containing parallel vertical
   stems or roots - - - - - - - - - - - - - 40 inches
4. third dark layer, sandy ('peat III') - - - - - - - - - 4 inches
5. sand layer, coarse in the top half and fine in the bottom half; containing the same
   plant remains as No. 3; dark grey, white and mottled; containing some thin dark
   layers - - - - - - - - - - - - - - - - 54 inches
6. second dark layer, sand with many plant remains ('peat II') - - - - - 24 inches
7. blue-green clay and loam with plant remains as in No. 3; at the bottom containing
   more sand - - - - - - - - - - - - - - - 42 inches
8. first dark layer, black waxy clay ('peat I') - - - - - - - - 30 inches
9. brown sand, mottled - - - - - - - - - - - - - 20 inches
10. basal dark layer - - - - - - - - - - - - - thin layer
11. dolerite rock.

Samples of the dark layers have been submitted for radio-carbon dating. A set of samples was first sent to the Geochronometric Laboratory of Yale University and later by other workers to the Institute for Nuclear Studies at Chicago. In 1954 Libby[3] published the ages determined for the dark layers I, II and III as follows*:

layer III: 6,700 ± 500 years,
layer II : 9,104 ± 420 years,
layer I : older than 41,000 years.

* The last figures published have been determined by Columbia University as follows: peat III 19,600±700, II 29,000±2,000, I 37,000. This places the whole sequence at least in the Upper Pleistocene (Meiring, A. J. D., *Res. Nat. Mus.* 1 (9), 1956). For 'old carbon' see p. 64.

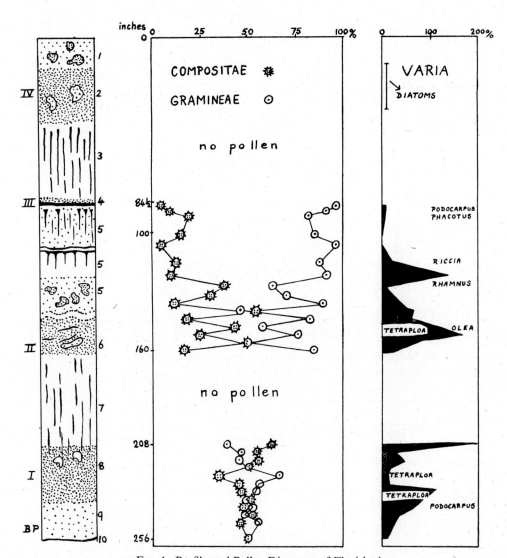

FIG. 1. Profile and Pollen Diagrams of Florisbad

As the profile is mainly the product of the spring with its many outlets or 'eyes', which worked during different periods, the disturbing influence of the spring on the stratigraphy should be well understood. The outlets of the spring, which have made holes of about 18 inches in diameter in the rock, are in the case of inactive eyes filled with gravel. 'In the case of extinct eyes it could be seen that the patches of gravel had apices of different height and were continued upwards as pipes (cone-like in shape) of pure white sand passing right through the strata enumerated above' (Dreyer and Lyle,[4] p. 7). The debris at the base of these cones consists of artefacts, bones, teeth, gravel, etc. 'The columns of white sand do not continue to the surface but are terminated at different levels of the stratified deposits, thus allowing us to correlate, in time, the contents of these eyes with the layers' (Dreyer,[2] p. 71).

New eyes have been formed in former times with much force as is described by Hoffman[5] for

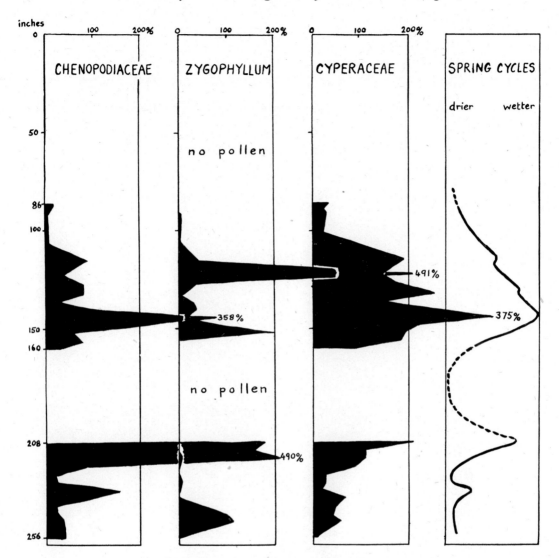

FIG. 2. Pollen Diagrams of Florisbad

the geyser-like activity of the fountain in September 1912, when enormous quantities of water, sand, gas and fossils were brought up. Explosive actions like these will have disturbed the original stratification by bringing older material on to the surface, where it was later on embedded in the spring deposits. The utmost care has therefore to be taken in using the stratification to date implements, fossils, etc. The tooth of *Orangiatherium*[12] found under peat layer III most probably is an example of such disturbances of the profile (Dreyer,[2] p. 71).

In macroscopic and microscopic structure the profile shows the influence of running water. The wavy demarcations between the layers give the impression that the 'peat' was sometimes eroded superficially and replaced by sand. Often in the dark layers, intrusions of white and grey sand were found. These parts had to be avoided for pollen analysis.

Section One

The Water of the Spring

The water in the bath, which has been excavated above the thermal spring, has a temperature of 28–30° C., so that it must come from appreciable depth. This water contains about 70% methane and therefore must have contact with old organic deposits in the Ecca.

The composition of the water was investigated by Rindl.[6, 7] He classified Florisbad as a salt spring. The characteristic ions in the water are: Na˙ 0·74405, Cl′ 1·30458, Ca¨ 0·09342 gms. per litre of water. The taste of this oligohaline water is slightly brackish. The pH of it determined on June 10, 1955 was 7·8.

This saline water may in former times have had much influence on the formation of the Hagenstad saltpan. Pans of this type are very abundant in the Western part of the Orange Free State, especially in the Boshof district. During periods when the spring was very active its saline water may have accelerated the weathering of the shales. The usual conception about the formation of these pans is that the disintegrated rock material was blown away by the wind in an arid climate. There are indications that at some stage the Hagenstad pan contained much water. Horizontal deposits of lime on the slope of the pan near the Florisbad spring may indicate the edge of a former inland lake.

The Vegetation (Fig. 3)[8, 9]

The present-day vegetation of the Northern and Eastern half of the Orange Free State consists chiefly of sweet and mixed grassveld, which occupies the flat to undulated grassveld. This plateau,

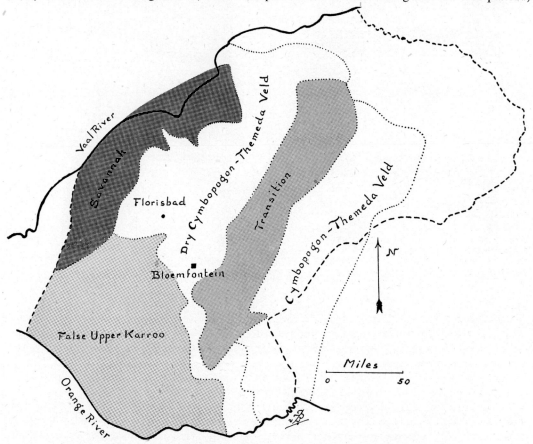

FIG. 3. The Vegetation of the Orange Free State (cf. Acocks[8])

which has an altitude of about 4,000 feet in the West, gradually rises to 6,000 feet above sea level in the foothills of Basutoland in the East. The higher rainfall of up to 35 inches per year in the Eastern part favours the mixed grassveld, the *Cymbopogon-Themeda* veld. A transitional area, which runs right down the middle of the province, leads to the sweet grassveld, the Dry *Cymbopogon-Themeda* Veld, in the N.W. sector in which Florisbad is situated. The rainfall here is only 15–20 inches per year. Few herbs, bulbs and undershrubs are found in this veld, which is very rich in *Themeda triandra* Forsk., *Aristida congesta* R. & S., *Eragrostis lehmanniana* Nees, *E. superba* Peyr. and many other grasses. In this dry and frosty region treegrowth is only limited to the few stony hills (koppies) which occur.

The Hagenstad pan is at present exploited as a saltpan by pumping up underground saline water. The vegetation near the saltpan consists mainly of widely scattered halophytes, viz.: *Salsola geminiflora* C.H.Wr., *S. glabrescens* Burtt Davy, *Suaeda fruticosa* Forsk., *Atriplex vestita* (Thunb.) Allen, *Sporobolus tenellus* Kunth., *Diplachne fusca* (L.) Beauv., *Heliotropium curassavicum* Linn., *Malephora smithii* H.E.Br. and *Zygophyllum simplex* Linn.

Further away from the saltpan the less saline water occurring in large shallow depressions is overgrown by communities of Cyperaceae, mainly *Scirpus muricinux* C.B.Cl.

About 80 km. west of Florisbad another type of vegetation is found, the savannah of *Acacia giraffae*. The grasscover in this savannah is of about the same composition as that of the Dry *Cymbopogon-Themeda* Veld around Florisbad. In the south the so-called False Upper Karroo, an invasion of a Karroo vegetation of undershrubs, is rapidly advancing towards the North and already covers the S.W. part of the Orange Free State.

The Pollen Sum

The pollen sum, which is used in pollen analytical investigations as basis for calculations, should comprise the pollen of all the species from the topmost layer of the vegetation. In order to establish this sum the pollen spectrum of the recent sweet grassveld surrounding Bloemfontein has been studied in a previous publication.[17] This vegetation round Bloemfontein closely resembles the veld near Florisbad. It was found that atmospheric pollen gives a more general picture of the spectrum produced by the grassveld community than can be obtained in analysing surface soil samples. These samples are apparently much more influenced by local conditions. Consequently it could be expected that the saline spring must have had a profound influence on the local fossil pollen spectra.

To investigate this point pollen spectra of surface soil samples of the saltpan were compared with the result of the above-mentioned survey of atmospheric pollen. Spectra of the following samples were compared:

(a) the atmospheric pollen of the grassveld near Bloemfontein, where no saltpans occur, was collected over a period of a year from September 6, 1947, to September 6, 1948.

(b) surface sample No. 692 of mud which contains much salt, collected in the Hagenstad salt-pan in a vegetation of halophytes.

(c) surface sample No. 694 of mud from the Hagenstad pan collected in a community of Cyperaceae.

In order to compare the figures obtained they are tabulated in Table I in two different ways. The first three columns give the percentages calculated for all the pollen types included in the pollen sum. In the last three columns only the Compositae, Gramineae and the tree pollen is included in this sum. The result shows that it is necessary to exclude the pollen of Chenopodiaceae, Cyperaceae and varia from the pollen sum. This pollen is only produced in the immediate surroundings of the sample. The three pollen spectra with the restricted sum provide a clear and identical picture of the monotonous vegetation of the grassveld in the wide surroundings. It must however be admitted that this sum gives a narrow basis for calculations.

TABLE I

THE INFLUENCE OF THE IMMEDIATE SURROUNDINGS ON THE POLLEN SPECTRUM

Number of sample	All pollen types included in the pollen sum			Chenopodiaceae, Cyperaceae and varia not included in the pollen sum		
	Atmosph. pollen	Hagenstad		Atmosph. pollen	Hagenstad	
		692	694		692	694
Number of pollen grains counted	12941	750	150	12941	750	150
	%	%	%	%	%	%
Gramineae	90·32	4·8	63·0	95·2	96·0	95·4
Compositae	4·06	0·2	3·0	4·3	4·0	4·6
Trees	0·47	—	—	0·5	—	—
Chenopodiaceae	1·14	91·0	6·0	1·2	1820·0	9·1
Cyperaceae	0·34	3·2	27·0	0·4	64·0	40·9
Varia (partly unknown)	3·67	0·8	1·0	3·9	16·0	1·5

This result is of importance for the explanation of the fossil pollen spectra as the spring has been intermittently active in the past. These cycles in the production of saline water must have had great influence on the fossil pollen spectra and should not obscure the general picture of the vegetation of the wider surroundings.

The Spring Cycle

Figure 2 gives a representation of the graphs of the pollen of CHENOPODIACEAE, CYPERACEAE and ZYGOPHYLLUM. The diagrams of the former two roughly show two maxima. After a low maximum in the bottom part of dark layer I, the rise in both curves starts near the top part of this layer. This rise coincides with the deposition of sand in dark layer I and above it. Unfortunately pollen grains were too rare in the blue-green layer number 7 to be counted, but the few grains which were found were mainly CHENOPODIACEAE pollen. This might show that many CHENO-PODIACEAE were growing near the spring during the deposition of this layer, but that this pollen was not well preserved or that the clay was laid down in a short period of time.

A second maximum is found in both curves in the bottom part of dark layer II and this rise coincides with the deposition of all the sand layers between the bottom part of dark layer II and the horizon of − 100 inches. The maximum in the CHENOPODIACEAE curve diminishes before that of the CYPERACEAE and both show some secondary low tops.

The general trend of these curves might well indicate that these two pollen types show two maxima in spring activity. Prof. Dreyer described an eye (the third one in the Western group, in which the Florisbad skull was found), which was sealed by the green clay. He also mentions eyes (from the Eastern group), the sand columns of which ended just below dark layer III. These facts suggest that the eyes during their maximum activity ejected much sand and clay particles and that the saline water formed swamps which fed a community of halophytes, mainly consisting of CHENOPODIACEAE and a number of CYPERACEAE in the less brackish parts.

A Pollen Analytical Investigation of the Florisbad Deposits

The ZYGOPHYLLUM curve shows a maximum at the onset of the first spring cycle and one at the beginning and at the end of the second cycle. This might indicate that the species concerned flourished in a milieu of a special salinity. These species and their ecology are however not known, but most of the species of ZYGOPHYLLUM prefer a certain percentage of salt.

The following finds indicate wet to flooded conditions: many *Tetraploa* spores in layer I, *Tetraploa* spores in layer II, *Phacotus* (*Volvocales*) in layer III and many Diatoms in layer IV.

THE POLLEN DIAGRAM OF THE CENTRAL ORANGE FREE STATE

The graphs of the pollen included in the pollen sum and of the varia are given in Fig. 1. The picture is very simple as can be expected with a pollen sum which shows so little variety. The representation however gives a clear picture of the changes which took place.

The pollen spectra indicate that the country has been practically treeless, as it is today. Only rarely was a pollen grain of *Podocarpus*, *Rhamnus* or *Olea* encountered.

The percentages of GRAMINEAE and COMPOSITAE pollen are about equal in the bottom parts of the diagram. COMPOSITAE pollen is not easily distributed by wind and judging by the great number of COMPOSITAE pollen grains found, the veld must have been very rich in plants of this family. This suggests a vegetation as described by Acocks[8] for the Great Karroo and the Central Upper Karroo. The pollen spectra of these vegetation types with their many undershrubs is unfortunately not known, but should come near the fossil spectra in the bottom part of the diagram. The rainfall in these parts of the Karroo varies between 5–10 inches, while Florisbad today receives 18–20 inches per annum.

In the top part of dark layer I, conditions seem to change more or less and if we may accept a continuity in the blue-green clay the second part of the diagram shows these changes more clearly. A more detailed analysis at smaller intervals might show more of these changes, but it is clear from the diagram that the GRAMINEAE pollen gradually becomes predominant. In terms of vegetation this means that the climate became more wet. This stage is almost reached at the level of − 122 inches. RICCIA spores were found in the − 115 inch sample and these indicate that the water was no longer brackish but fresh.

The top part of the diagram shows much resemblance to the recent pollen spectra of the area. This resemblance is indicated in Table II.

TABLE II

RECENT POLLEN SPECTRA IN THE REGION WEST OF BLOEMFONTEIN COMPARED WITH THE SPECTRA OBTAINED BETWEEN THE − 86 AND − 122 INCH LEVEL

Number of sample	300	144	143	142	692	694	Top part of diagram
Number of pollen grains counted	250	150	250	300	750	150	50–150
POLLEN SUM							
Gramineae	78·1	79·3	90·8	85·1	96·0	95·4	81–96
Compositae	11·8	9·9	8·7	14·1	4·0	4·6	4–19
Trees	10·1	10·8	0·5	0·8	0	0	1–0
POLLEN NOT INCLUDED IN THE SUM							
Chenopodiaceae	9·3	10·7	7·8	14·1	1820·0	9·9	4–88
Cyperaceae	0	4·3	0	0	64·0	40·9	23–193
Varia	0·8	6·6	7·8	24·3	16·0	1·5	4–137
Zygophyllum	0	0	0	0	0	0	1–491

The part of the profile above dark layer III does not contain enough pollen to be counted, but in all the samples analysed in the uppermost dark layer DIATOMS were found. Their presence proves that this layer originated under relatively wet conditions.

The pollen diagram in general shows a change from a dry to a slightly wetter climate with a transitional stage in which climatic conditions changed appreciably. The general physiognomy of the vegetation will however not have changed so much.

DISCUSSION

It would be of interest to find whether these results agree with the conclusions obtained by other workers. We can therefore consider the research done along other lines on the Florisbad deposits and also the climatic sequence built up on the evidence obtained from the study of the Vaal River terraces.[10] The results of the geological and archaeological survey of the Caledon River Valley will in future give another valuable sequence of events which can be used to calibrate the Florisbad sequence.

The pollen analytical results fit in remarkably well with the chronology of the Vaal (Table III). The arid conditions which prevailed when the bottom parts of the deposits up to the middle part of dark layer I were formed, seem to coincide with the early HOLOCENE or the early UPPER PLEISTOCENE. The entire profile then covers the HOLOCENE and perhaps part of the UPPER PLEISTOCENE. If the beginning of the HOLOCENE is placed at the onset of the final amelioration of the climate, as is done in Europe, the border between HOLOCENE and PLEISTOCENE must in our chronology be shifted to a higher level where a period equivalent to the Makalian wet phase started.

The oscillating climatic conditions, coeval with the Makalian wet phase, are represented in the pollen spectra of the middle part of the diagram. The diagram does not suggest that these climatic oscillations are of a seasonal nature, but indicate variations of a longer cycle.

The top part of the diagram is proof of a semi-arid climate which eventually led to the recent conditions.

The radiocarbon age determinations of the dark layers published by Libby[3] have been mentioned already in the description of the profile. For the appreciation of these results the following possibility should be considered. The production of much methane by the spring shows that the water in percolating through the rock must have contact with Ecca coal deposits or with carbonaceous shales or their distillation products formed under the influence of the intruding dolerite. This contact may have had an important influence on the result of the age determination, as indicated by Oakley.[12] The dark layers may be dated too old as they may contain 'old carbon' from the above-mentioned Ecca strata. A careful comparison of Ecca spores and of the spore content of the dark layers might perhaps give a clue to solve this problem. Besides this it will be necessary to await radio-carbon dates obtained with the acetylene method developed by Suess without the risk of contamination caused by the testing of atomic bombs.

If the determinations published by the Chicago Laboratory give the correct age, dark layer III is of the same age as the Atlanticum, the climatic optimum in N.W. Europe. Dark layer I would in that case be of at least lower UPPER PLEISTOCEINE age.

In setting up a chronology of the Florisbad deposits, the possibility must be considered, that the profile studied is not complete. The uncertainty about the blue-green layer No. 7 should not be overlooked. The absence of sufficient pollen makes it impossible to establish the continuity of the pollen graphs and the great difference in age between the underlying and the covering dark layers also shows that either the building up of the profile at this stage came to a standstill or that erosion took place after dark layer I was formed. Erosion would indicate a wet climate and would suggest the influence of the 'wet' Gamblian Pluvial. In this event the bottom part of the profile would be of early UPPER PLEISTOCENE age and the time between the formation of the bottom part of dark layer

TABLE III

Chronology of the Vaal River Terraces

(Based on Van Riet Lowe[10] and Clark[11])

Geological Period	Climate	Culture	Suggested E. African Parallels
Holocene	Wetter Dry Oscillating probably seasonally wet and dry conditions Dry	Later Stone Age Middle Stone Age Complex	Nakuran Wet Phase Makalian Wet Phase
Upper Pleistocene	Wet with at least two sub-phases becoming drier Dry	 ↑ Fauresmith/Sangoan	Gamblian Pluvial Interpluvial
Middle Pleistocene	Wet Drier Wet	↑ Acheulian ⎰Chelles- ↑ ⎱Acheul Chellian ↑ Olduvan	Kanjeran Pluvial Kamasian Pluvial
Lower Pleistocene	Dry Wet	Pre- ↑ ⎰Chelles- Developed ⎱Acheul Kafuan	 Kageran Pluvial

I and of dark layer II would represent a very long period of time, beginning at the end of the MIDDLE PLEISTOCENE and ending in a time coeval with the East African Makalian.

The archaeological evidence cannot give a definite answer about the chronology of the site, as it still is the subject of much controversy. The artefacts which may or may not belong to the same association show widely different skill of the makers and are placed in the MIDDLE STONE AGE (Van Riet Lowe,[13] Oakley,[12] Cooke,[14] Broom,[15] Dreyer[2]), but also partly in a much older time as the S.A. CHELLES ACHEUL (Dreyer,[16] Hoffman[5]). The estimates of their age range from the middle MIDDLE PLEISTOCENE to the middle HOLOCENE (Makalian). It should be remembered that the artefacts, which were found in dark layer I are stratigraphically the most important, as they are not likely to have been displaced by spring action. This gives them the same age as this dark layer.

The most important find to date is without doubt the skull of *Homo helmei*. The discovery, which is described by Prof. Dreyer[2] (p. 71), was made in the debris at the bottom of one of the smaller eyes at a level underneath dark layer I and not as sometimes quoted in or on this layer. This position of the skull makes it difficult to correlate it with the stratigraphy of the site. As the sand-cap of this outlet of the spring was sealed by the 'green sand' layer the skull might be of the same age as dark layer I, but might also be much older. The same uncertainty as was discussed for the age of dark layer I therefore applies to the age of the skull.

The many fossils of mostly extinct species found, on, in and below dark layer I, also indicate that this layer may belong to the UPPER PLEISTOCENE.

Surveying all the evidence it is difficult to come to a definite conclusion at this stage, but it seems most likely that the oldest parts of the profile were formed at the beginning of the UPPER PLEISTOCENE, during the dry Interpluvial.

More research will have to be done before a chronology can be set up which gives a clear picture of the climatic, botanical, palaeontological and geological evidence. A more detailed pollen statistic investigation might help to build up this accurate chronology. The present results give the general botanical background of the most interesting Florisbad site. Further work on more borings could reveal the finer details of the changes of vegetation during the entire HOLOCENE and part of the PLEISTOCENE in the centre of the Orange Free State. The macroscopic plant remains, including the crudely shaped wooden implements, will also have to be studied for that purpose.

ACKNOWLEDGEMENTS

I feel most grateful to the late Professor Dreyer, who with his great enthusiasm encouraged me to take up this pollen study.

I wish to thank Mr Venter, the owner of Florisbad, for his friendly hospitality and help whenever I needed to collect more material.

The discussions I had with Prof. C. H. Edelman (Wageningen, Holland), Dr K. P. Oakley (London) and Prof. P. W. Thomson (Bonn), who visited the Florisbad site, were very valuable to me.

The South African Council for Scientific and Industrial Research, who so generously enabled my pollen studies since 1948, is gratefully acknowledged here.

Prof. W. J. Lütjeharms enabled the writer to carry out this investigation in the Department of Botany of the University of the Orange Free State.

REFERENCES

1. Erdtman, G. (1943), *An Introduction to Pollen Analysis*, Waltham, U.S.A., pp. 27–8, 34–5.
2. Dreyer, T. F. (1938), 'The Archaeology of the Florisbad Deposits', *Arg. Navorsing Nas. Mus. Bloemfontein*, I (8), pp. 65–77, 7 pl.
3. Libby, W. F. (1954), 'Chicago Radiocarbon Dates V', *Science*, 120 (3123), pp. 733–42.
4. Dreyer, T. F. and A. Lyle (1931), *New fossil Mammals and Man*, Bloemfontein, p. 60.
5. Hoffman, A. C. (1955), 'Important contributions of the Orange Free State to our knowledge of primitive Man', *S. Afr. J. Sci.*, 51, (6), pp. 163–9.
6. Rindl, M. (1915), 'The mineral spring on the farm Rietfontein, District Brandfort, O.F.S.', *S. Afr. J. Sci.*, 12 (12), pp. 561–88.
7. Rindl, M. (1916), 'The medical Springs of South Africa', *S. Afr. J. Sci.*, 13 (10), pp. 528–52, map, 8 tables.
8. Acocks, J. P. H. (1953), *Veld Types of South Africa*, Bot. Survey S. Afr. 28, Pretoria, pp. 87–8, 92–4, map.
9. Whitmore, J. S. (1950), 'The marginal Areas of the Orange Free State, A climatic study', *Farming in S. Afr.*
10. Van Riet Lowe, C. (1952), 'The Vaal River Chronology', *S. Afr. Arch. Bull.*, 7 (28), pp. 135–49.
11. Clark, J. D. (1954), 'A provisional correlation of Prehistoric Cultures North and South of the Sahara', *S. Afr. Arch. Bull.*, 9 (33), pp. 3–17.

12. Oakley, K. P. (1954), 'Study tour of early hominid sites in Southern Africa, 1953', *S.Afr. Arch. Bull.*, 9 (35), pp. 75–87.
13. Söhnge, P. G., D. J. Visser and C. Van Riet Lowe (1937), *The Geology and Archaeology of the Vaal River Basin*, Geol. Survey. Mem. 35, p. 119.
14. Cooke, H. B. S. (1940), *A preliminary survey of the Quaternary Period in Southern Africa*, Arch. Ser. 4, 60 pp.
15. Broom, R. (1943), 'South Africa's part in the solution of the problem of the origin of man', *S. Afr. J. Sci.*, 40, pp. 68–80.
16. Dreyer, T. F. (1953), 'The Origin and Chronology of the Fauresmith Culture', *Res. Nat. Mus. Bloemfontein*, I (3), pp. 56–76.
17. Coetzee, J. A. and E. M. van Zinderen Bakker (1952), 'Pollenspectrum of the southern Middleveld of the Orange Free State', *S. Afr. J. Sci.*, 48 (9), pp. 275–82.

7

The Physical Background to the Hopefield Discoveries

by J. A. MABBUTT

[ABSTRACT]

THE Hopefield site, at 300 feet (90 m.) above sea-level and 10 miles (16 km.) inland from the Saldanha estuary, marks the inner margin of a coastal belt of limestone ridges, product of a dune invasion lasting from Middle into Upper Pleistocene times. The characteristic fossil horizon is a nodular calcrete which descends westwards to the limestone ridges and which apparently represents the dried pan floors in which the bones accumulated. The site is traversed by ferricrete ridges, interpreted as ferruginized dune cores marking a preceding moister period; such ferricretes are regionally developed and post-date the Minor Emergence at the coast. The fossil layer is capped by surface limestones produced at the height of drought conditions, and elsewhere by ferruginous sands which represent a second moister period. Geologically, the fossils and associated final phase of the hand-axe culture mark a single episode. Shortly after cementation of the fossils and shortly before its burial, the site underwent a phase of Still Bay occupation. The geological context favours an Upper Pleistocene age for the fossil layer; the relationships of the associated climatic changes are discussed.

I THE SITE AND ITS REGIONAL SETTING

THE Hopefield fossil site lies on the farm Elandsfontein in the southwestern Cape Province, 10 miles (16 km.) inland from the head of the Sandanha estuary, 300 feet (91 m.) above sea-level and at the outer margin of an extensive sandy plateau (Fig. 1). This feature, which from its regional setting one may term the 'Sandveld Plateau', is a marine terrace, partly erosional and partly depositional, for its outer edge bears an unknown thickness of quartz sands which underlie the surface dunes. It is dissected by the river cycles of the Middle Pleistocene and later and the glacio-eustatic raised beach phenomena of the Middle and Upper Pleistocene are staged below its outer edge; thus it cannot be younger than the Lower Pleistocene, but since it undoubtedly represents a considerable period of planation, in all probability it extends back into the Upper Tertiary.

In Fig. 1 the outer margin of the Sandveld Plateau is given by the 250-feet (75 m.) contour. Four other physical features are relevant to the geological history of the site.

1. Lower marine terraces inland from Saldanha Bay at 150–200 feet (45–60 m.) and 50 feet (15 m.).

2. Three granite upland areas, former island groups, rising above the Sandveld Plateau and the lower coastal platforms.

3. Broad valleys, relicts of an earlier drainage leading down from the Sandveld Plateau between the granite uplands into the Saldanha estuary.

4. Limestone dune ridges which parallel the Atlantic coast between Yzerfontein and Langebaan, product of a littoral dune invasion during the Middle and Upper Pleistocene, and which have blocked the former plateau drainage. It is significant that the Elandsfontein site lies at the

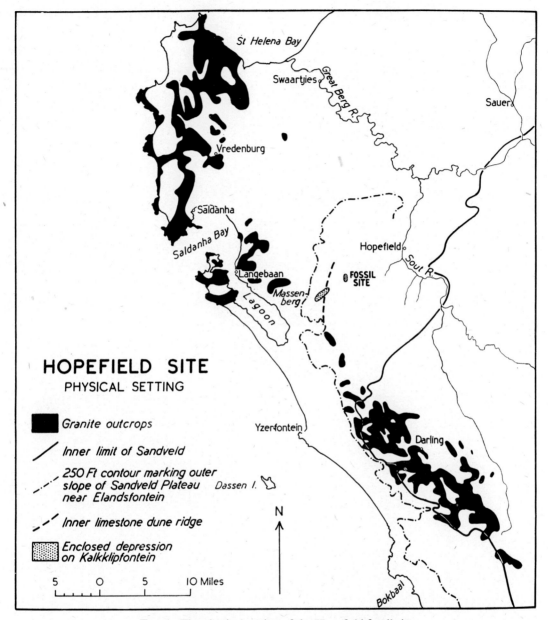

St Helena Bay

Swaartjies

Great Berg R.

Sauer

Vredenburg

Saldanha

Saldanha Bay

Langebaan

Hopefield

Sout R.

FOSSIL SITE

Massen-berg

Lagoon

HOPEFIELD SITE
PHYSICAL SETTING

- Granite outcrops
- Inner limit of Sandveld
- 250 Ft contour marking outer slope of Sandveld Plateau near Elandsfontein
- Inner limestone dune ridge
- Enclosed depression on Kalkklipfontein

Dassen I.

N

Yzerfontein

Darling

5   O   5   10 Miles

Bokbaal

FIG. 1. The physical setting of the Hopefield fossil site

inland margin of this coastal dune belt, at a point marking its maximum landward encroachment through the gap at the head of Langebaan Lagoon.

The fossil site is marked by some 2 square miles (5·2 ha.) of mobile sand dunes which represent sand stripped off by the wind in exposing the fossil layer. The area of moving sand is quite local-ized, probably man-induced, and has existed for 50 years at least.

For descriptive purposes the site may be sub-divided into 3 areas:

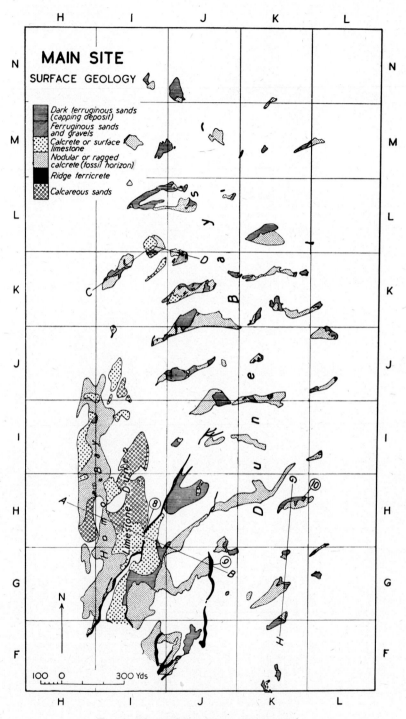

FIG. 2. The surface geology of Main Site

The Physical Background to the Hopefield Discoveries

(a) *Main Site* (Fig. 2). This is the largest and richest portion of the site, lying adjacent to and among the dunes. It is traversed by a N.–S. limestone ridge, an outlier of the coastal dunes, rising 20 feet (6 m.) above the ground to east and west, and two sub-parallel ridges of ferruginous sandstone or *ferricrete* which trend N.N.E.; the western ridge is at one point overlapped by the limestone dune. West of this dune is Homo Bay, a long depression floored by calcareous sand nodules which everywhere characterize the fossiliferous horizon; the Saldanha skull was found in its northern half. The limestone dune and this northern part of Homo Bay are partly capped by massive *calcrete*. East of the ridge are the Dune Bays, a series of N.E.- or E.-trending corridors between parallel dune ridges moving slowly northwards under the influence of the prevalent winds. Here the nodular calcrete is extensively capped by dark ferruginous sands which are fairly rapidly dissected by sand-blast into a series of low platforms, each spell of 'south-easter' weather bringing its crop of fossils.

(b) *Farmhouse Site*. Although smaller, this shows the same features as Main Site, but with the fossiliferous layer less exposed. It lies between and east of the apparent continuations of the ferricrete ridges described on Main Site, and lies half a mile (0·8 km.) to the south. Between the ferricrete ridges and the fossiliferous horizon is a layer of nodular calcrete, rather more massive than on Main Site, slightly lower (285 feet or 87 m.) and capped locally by surface-limestone. The fossil horizon is less developed east of the ferricretes and is covered by 9 feet (3 m.) of the dark sands described on Main Site.

(c) *West Site*. This consists of 4 wind-scoured hollows aligned N.–S. at the foot of a limestone ridge marking the inner boundary of the coastal limestones. The fossil 'floor' is locally exposed as a thin surface-limestone at 240 feet (73 m.) capping white calcareous sands which have been excavated by the wind to a depth of 20 feet (6 m.).

II SURFACE DEPOSITS

1. *Basal Silver-Grey Sands*. In the eastern portion of Main Site the fossiliferous horizon is underlain by quartz sands with low lime content (2%). Apart from a small number of large, well rounded and frosted sand grains of aeolian origin, the bulk consists of equidimensional but sub-angular quartz grains of medium grade, a physique which identifies them with the older sands extensively underlying the surface dunes of the Sandveld Plateau. They probably date from the emergence of this feature, and will be referred to as 'Sandveld sands'.

2. *Calcareous Sands*. West of the limestone dune on Main Site the 'Sandveld sands' pass beneath a thickening cover of calcareous sands, which may be subdivided into

(a) soft grey-white calcareous sandstones of moderate lime content (6–11%) which underlie the fossil layer on Farmhouse and West Sites, and

(b) white calcareous sands possessing a higher lime content (30%) and building the limestone ridge on Main Site.

Both types are terrestrial and aeolian, more clearly so the latter, as shown by their grading, the occurrence of dune bedding and by their content of mammalian fossils and of the shells of land gasteropods.

The calcareous sands on the site clearly relate to the coastal limestones mentioned above, named Dorcasia Limestones by Du Toit (1917); they are similar to the latter chemically and physically and contain shells of the Dorcasianae from which the formation derives its name. Du Toit's interpretation of the limestones as aeolian sands 'accumulated on a beach or in close proximity to the sea' has been borne out by more recent survey, although an estuarine facies may be present locally at 105 feet (32 m.) above sea-level at Langebaan Road (Haughton, 1932). They overlie the 20–25 feet (6–8 m.) raised beach at the coast and formerly extended as terrestrial sands below present sea-level. Dune invasion thus accompanied and may have been motivated by the regressional shore changes of the Middle and Upper Pleistocene. The occurrence of Upper Pleistocene mammalian fossils in the limestones of the immediate coastal tract (Cooke, 1955) sets an upper age limit for the Formation at the coast.

3. *Ridge Ferricretes*. The ferricrete ridges on Main Site resemble others traceable beneath sand ridges beyond the confines of the site, but here the sand has been stripped off, laying bare the ferruginous sand cores, which have hardened on exposure. Ferruginization has occured along narrow zones and to considerable depth, for although the ferricretes become less compact downwards the base has not been revealed, despite sectioning to a depth of 15 feet (5 m.). Sinuous in detail, they exhibit an obvious linearity and a general north-easterly trend. They are asymmetrical in section, with prominent west-facing escarpments and imperceptible eastern slopes; thus the two ridges on Main Site form steps descending westwards and the western crest lies 10 feet (3 m.) below the eastern, both descending south-westwards with the regional slope.

The grading of these ferruginous sandstones identifies them with the 'Sandveld' sands; they are cemented by iron oxides and lime (average 12% and 8% respectively), the grading indicating that calcification has occurred through upward enrichment in the parent material rather than by admixture of the calcareous sands. At one point on Main Site the ferricrete ridge is overlapped by the limestone dune, and a section here revealed the zone of ferruginization to pass into the latter proving that the emplacement of the limestone preceded the period of ferruginization.

The sections in Fig. 3 illustrate that the ferricrete ridges were barriers against or between which the fossils and the capping deposit accumulated; they appear to have controlled the extent and, locally, the altitude of the former and the thickness of the latter. With the exception of a few fossils and artefacts found embedded in their upper surfaces, the ridges are sterile, and are judged to antedate the fossils.

Ferricretes are surprisingly widespread in this now semi-arid Sandveld. In the Great Berg River valley to the north, they both cap and underlie low gravel terraces containing Middle Stone Age débitage, and at one point, only 5 miles (8 km.) inland, the basal ferricretes extend out below the present channel. At Bok Baai (Mabbutt *et al.*, 1955), ferricrete platforms bearing artefacts characteristic of the Hopefield assemblage descend between headlands planed by the 20–25 feet to within 16 feet (5 m.) of the present sea-level, and provide evidence of ferricrete formation on a regional scale *following* the Minor Emergence beach.

4. *The Fossiliferous Horizon*. Apart from their occurrence on the calcareous dune, the fossils form a single layer at the upper level of a zone of lime-enrichment marked by a band of calcareous sand nodules or, in the lime-rich environments closer to the calcareous dune ridge, by cellular white calcretes. This band probably originated as the dried floors of seasonal lime pans which had been the cause of the faunal concentration. The fossil bones frequently show slight evidence of transport since their initial emplacement; many have undergone no movement, neither can there have been contemporary deposition, as evidenced by their occurrence at a single horizon. This implies a state of balance unusual in a dune environment, suggesting that the fossil accumulation must be regarded as a single episode of relatively short duration in the geological history of the site, a fact already indicated by the uniform fluorine content of the bones (Oakley, 1954).

The condition of the fossils and the unrolled state of the associated artefacts argue against the existence of strongly flowing water. If we reconstruct the contours of the fossil layer we find that it forms a fairly even surface descending westwards from 310 feet (94 m.) to 240 feet (73 m.) above sea-level, the continuity and the height range of this slope being incompatible with a single body of standing water. The environment suggested is a series of shallow, sand-trapped pools and connecting channels of a seasonal character; the fossils becoming cemented in their limestone floors and so preserved from subsequent erosion.

5. *Calcrete and Surface-Limestone*. The limestone ridge on Main Site retains a partial capping of sandy limestone or calcrete 1–2 feet (30–60 cm.) thick, remnants of which also cap the fossiliferous horizon at the north end of Homo Bay. This weathering crust was developed on the limestone dune when the nodular calcretes were forming in adjacent pan floors. It has subsequently

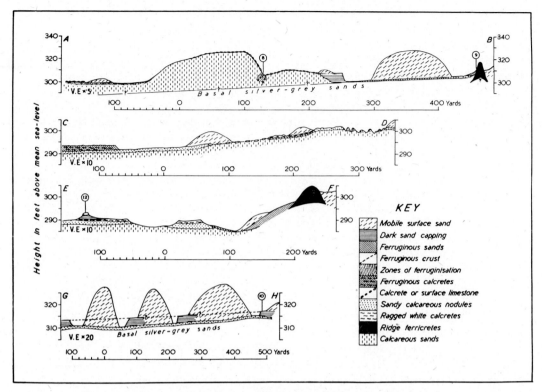

FIG. 3. Geological cross sections. Sections A-B, C-D and G-H are on the Main Site as indicated in Fig. 2; section E-F is a west-east section on Farmhouse site

undergone solution weathering as shown by surface channelling and numerous breccia-filled pipes, features common to the whole belt of coastal limestones. The equivalent deposit on the lower ground is a white tufaceous limestone of great purity, typically developed on West Site, where it both contains and caps the fossil layer.

6. *Capping Deposit*. In the eastern part of Main Site the fossils are capped by 2–9 feet (0·6–3 m.) of dark sands physically similar to the Sandveld sands and now reduced to low platforms extending beneath the mobile dunes. They bear a slightly indurated crust of ferruginous gravel which grades into a red-brown cellular ferricrete near the limestone dune, where the capping overlaps and is therefore seen to post-date the calcretes. The sands have accumulated by blowing and surface wash upslope from the barriers formed by the ferricrete ridges and limestone dunes, and the capping thickens south-westwards.

The deposit everywhere shows subsequent ferruginization which has extended into the fossiliferous horizon and caused the mineralization of the bones, for analysis has shown this to have involved little more than the replacement of organic matter by ferric hydrate. Sands resembling the capping deposit are today typical of moist depressions in the area, and we may reasonably postulate a period of higher water table to account for this second phase of ferruginization. West of the limestone dune, ferruginization has occurred by downward leaching beneath a dune cover, for a ferruginous sand horizon may be seen below the dunes on West Site, and a relic of such a cover forms a light brown calcareous sandstone locally capping the calcrete at the north end of Homo Bay.

Section One

III THE ARTEFACTS AND THEIR GEOLOGICAL SETTING

The artefacts* comprise a rich collection of the final stage of the hand-axe sequence in the western Cape Province and a smaller, classic series of the Still Bay culture. Geologically and physically, there is some evidence for the disassociation of the two groups, despite their technological continuity. The hand-axes undoubtedly occur in the calcareous fossil horizon with which they are invariably exposed. They often reveal severe sand-blasting, leaching or heavy patination and frequently retain a crust of the containing calcrete. In contrast, implements and débitage of the Still Bay culture were found *on* the fossiliferous calcrete in test trenches, they are generally fresher and less sand-blasted and often exhibit a deep iron-staining from the capping deposit which is absent from the hand-axes. Some Still Bay material has come from a higher stratigraphic level, i.e. on the ferricrete ridges and above the capping deposit. Whether or not this separation of the two groups of artefacts be accepted it is a geological fact that the fossils and Saldanha Man must be associated with what is typologically oldest among the stone implements.

The implements, particularly the hand-axe group, consist of a variety of rocks, including granite, quartzite and, commonly, fine-grained silcrete. As a probable source we may mention the association with the artefacts of numerous water-worn boulders, including undoubted beach material, of a similar lithological range, which it is suggested have been carried to the site from beach or river gravels in the vicinity, now hidden by sand, or even from the present coast. No solid rock outcrop occurs within 5 miles (8 km.) of the site and none of the surface deposits has been utilized. The silcretes, which notably predominate among the Still Bay implements, may have come from a deposit above the Malmesbury Series, now presumably sand-covered.

IV GEOLOGICAL HISTORY OF THE SITE

Stage 1. The history of the site begins with spasmodic emergence during the Lower and Middle Pleistocene, as expressed in the relative uplift of the Sandveld Plateau, the cutting of lower marine terraces, the incision of the Great Berg River system and the linking to the mainland of the granite island groups. Open valleys were cut into the plateau margin.

Stage 2. Emergence continued to below present sea-level and was accompanied by coastal dune invasion forming the Dorcasia Limestones and blocking the plateau drainage west of the fossil site. Dune invasion was long-continued and embraced the subsequent transgression marked by the 20–25 feet raised beach.

Stage 3. Shallow pans formed along the inner margin of the coastal dune belt, and a higher water table on the site led to ferruginization of N.E.–S.W. Sandveld dunes in the area, giving rise to the ferricrete ridges. Shallow pans must have existed in the intervening depressions.

Stage 4. The fossil remains and the associated hand-axe culture fall into a subsequent period of desiccation, during which they were cemented into surface and sub-surface limestones forming on the drying pan floors and into the calcrete crust on the limestone dunes.

Stage 5. A period of human occupation marked by the Still Bay culture ensued, at the close of which the fossil horizon was buried beneath surface sand and underwent ferruginization in a second moister period, during which the bones were fossilized.

V CLIMATIC CHANGE

Deductions concerning former climates in a dune area such as Hopefield need to be based on the regional occurrence of superficial deposits, whereby localized drainage effects are eliminated. The present climate is semi-arid, with an annual rainfall of 11 inches (28·5 cm.), tending to surface calcification.

---

* The typological data given reflect in the main the conclusions of Mr K. Jolly, who has been entrusted with the archaeology of the site.

The Physical Background to the Hopefield Discoveries

The integrated former drainage of the Sandveld Plateau, as in the arid coastal region further north at the same period, indicates a heavier rainfall than at present during parts of the Lower and Middle Pleistocene, and it is significant that the contemporaneous raised beach fauna indicates warm coastal waters in contrast to the cold oceanic currents associated with the present aridity. The dune invasions of the late Middle and Upper Pleistocene, however, point to a drier climate, as shown by the depth of penetration and lack of leaching of these coastal limestones and by their content of desert-inhabiting species of land snail. In accordance, the fauna of the associated Minor Emergence raised beach is that of a cold water coast. The climatic oscillations referred to above were, however, of long duration, and more than one change may have occurred.

The formation of ferricretes on a regional scale during the regression from the 20–25 feet raised beach definitely indicates pluvial conditions. These were in turn giving place to an arid phase when the fossils accumulated, as shown by the formation of associated surface-limestones and calcretes. The fauna is that of a bush-steppe environment, and increasing aridity may have been the reason for its localized concentration.

The ferruginization of the capping deposit and of the underlying bones points to a reversion to wetter conditions closely following on the Still Bay occupation. Since such surface ferruginization is no longer typical, we must postulate subsequent desiccation to the prevailing semi-aridity.

The correlation of this climatic sequence with that of East Africa is difficult, not only because of inadequate knowledge of the Quaternary geology of the region, but also because the site occurs in a winter rainfall area, which might conceivably not exhibit the changes of the tropical and summer rainfall regions. The association of the main period of ferruginization with regression from the 20–25 feet raised beach (probably the Late Monastirian of the Mediterranean) and hence with the oncoming Gamblian I of East Africa would seem to contradict this possibility. The subsequent drier phase of fossil accumulation would be set shortly *after* the first peak of the Gamblian were the climatic pattern of this region equivalent to that of East Africa, and shortly *before* this peak if in reverse. In the same way, the second period of ferruginization would relate either to the Gamblian II pluvial peak or to the preceding intra-pluvial dry phase, and its association with the Still Bay is compatible with either interpretation.

VI DATING

The ridge ferricretes, which antedate the fossils, seem to have coincided with an early stage in the withdrawal from the 20–25 foot sea-level, which latter almost certainly equates with the Late Monastirian beach of the Mediterranean. The ferricretes cannot therefore be placed earlier than the onset of the Upper Pleistocene, and the somewhat younger fossils and associated implements must on geological grounds be regarded as early Upper Pleistocene. It is furthermore difficult to reconcile the palaeoclimatic sequence with anything other than the Gamblian (i.e. Upper Pleistocene) pluvial. The geological evidence for the age of the site is thus consistent with its dating on archaeological and palaeontological grounds, despite minor differences of interpretation.

REFERENCES

Cooke, H. B. S. (1955), 'Some Fossil Mammals in the South African Museum Collections', *Ann. S. Afr. Mus.*, XLII, pp. 161–8.

Du Toit, A. L. (1917), *Report on the Phosphates of Saldanha Bay*, Geol. Surv. Mem. No. 10, Govt. Printer, Pretoria.

Haughton, S. H. (1932), 'On the Phosphate Deposits near Langebaan Road, Cape Province', *Trans. Geol. Soc. S. Afr.*, XXXV, pp. 119–24.

Mabbutt, J. A., J. Rudner and R. Singer (1955), 'Geomorphology, Archaeology and Anthropology from Bok Baai, Darling District, C.P.', *S. Afr. Archaeol. Bull.*, X, pp. 85–93.

Oakley, K. P. (1954), 'Study Tour of Early Hominid Sites in Southern Africa, 1953', *S. Afr. Archaeol. Bull.*, IX, pp. 75–87.

The Dating of the Broken Hill, Florisbad and Saldanha Skulls

by KENNETH P. OAKLEY

THE Broken Hill skull was recovered in 1921 from a steeply dipping cave, in dolomitic limestone, which had been filled with broken bones and other debris of human occupation. So little was known about the age of the skull that until a few years ago it could not 'even be placed in one of the three major divisions of the Pleistocene' (Zeuner, 1946, p. 296). During the First Pan-African Congress, Dr L. S. B. Leakey pointed out that analysis might help to establish the dating of the skull relative to other finds, because the bone-cave deposits had been heavily mineralized, and there were two levels of mineralization with lead below and zinc above.

The skull had been recorded as from the lead level, and if the implements were considerably later they should have zinc matrices. Dr Desmond Clark and I took up this matter in 1949 and with the aid of spectroscopic analysis carried out in the Government Chemists' Department in London we obtained mineral evidence suggesting that all the human remains and implements were broadly contemporaneous (Clark *et al.*, 1950). Dr Clark reconstructed the stratigraphy of the cave and showed that it had been remarkably similar to that of the Mumbwa caves. He concluded that the industry was of the Middle Stone Age, ranging from Proto-Still Bay to Still Bay, and that the skull probably belonged to the earliest phase rather than the latest.

The whole of the kopjie (No. 1) containing the cave has now been quarried away. Around the sides of the opencast Dr Clark and I found in 1953 a series of loams with ferricrete zones and implement horizons: Upper Acheulian, Sangoan and a Middle Stone Age industry comparable with that in the Bone Cave (Oakley, 1954, p. 77). Dr Clark has since excavated the Acheulian level and obtained a most interesting assemblage of hand-axes, cleavers, missile stones and flake tools; he found it was underlain by a level yielding an industry of Hope Fountain type.

Mennel (1929, p. 663) has set it on record that when the bone-cave material was being mined, the dumps were carefully searched for hand-axes and that none was found. The evidence from Montagu Cave (Cape) and the Cave of Hearths (Transvaal) leaves no doubt that Upper Acheulian man frequented caves. If the 'bone-cave' had existed and was accessible prior to the time of the Proto-Still Bay culture, Acheulian hand-axes would surely have been found in this cave in view of their being left in abundance on the surrounding ground. Thus the new discoveries re-inforce the conclusion that the Broken Hill skull came from a post-Acheulian cave deposit.

Recently at the British Museum (Natural History) we have begun to study systematically the fossilization of bone from the point of view of obtaining evidence of the relative ages of bones at particular sites. We find that the rate of disappearance of the protein (collagen) in bone is much slower than has generally been supposed. The amino-acids of bone protein have recently been identified in fossil marine fish remains some 300 million years old. Under the conditions in terrestrial deposits, particularly in hot climates, the protein disappears much more rapidly, but nevertheless under certain conditions the nitrogen content of bones even in African Pleistocene deposits can be most revealing, and its determination sometimes helps to solve problems of relative age

(Table I). In case it were ever to be suggested that the Broken Hill skull was a pathological or atavistic specimen of comparatively modern date, it is useful to have on record the fact that its nitrogen content is negligible. The second Broken Hill skull judged by nitrogen content is equally ancient. The nitrogen content of at least some of the bone implements is appreciably higher, and when our investigations are complete it may be necessary to reconsider the question of whether they may be slightly younger.

Nitrogen analysis has also given confirmation that the Fish Hoek skull is contemporary with the Magosian deposit in which it lay and a clear indication that it is vastly older than the shell-mound skeleton above, which contains almost the same quantity of protein as fresh bone.

The rate at which bone protein disappears is dependent on a great variety of factors which we are now investigating. It is interesting to note that in the sand flats of Cape Province the rate of disappearance is apparently slower than under the near-Kalahari conditions at Taung. The high nitrogen content of the Australoid skull from Cape Flats is more consistent with its being of the Late Stone Age than of the Middle Stone Age.

TABLE I
N-Analysis of Bones, Southern Africa

	%N
1. *Cape Province Sand Flats*	
Recent bone, Hopefield - - - - - - - - -	2·4
Cape Flats Skull - - - - - - - - - -	1·7
Fossil hyenid, Hopefield - - - - - - - -	0·5
Saldanha Skull, Hopefield - - - - - - - -	0·2
2. *Skildergat Cave, Fish Hoek, C.P.*	
Shell-midden skeleton - - - - - - - - -	4·6
Animal bone, Howieson's Poort (Magosian) layer - - - -	0·6
Fish Hoek Skull - - - - - - - - - -	0·6
3. *Florisbad spring deposits, O.F.S.*	
Bone from uppermost sand - - - - - - - -	0·3
Bone from sand between Peats II and III - - - - - -	0·2
Florisbad Skull (Peat I), maxilla - - - - - - -	1·7
Bone from sand below Peat I - - - - - - - -	0·1
4. *Buxton Limeworks, Taung, Bechuanaland*	
Bone from Late Stone Age cave-earth - - - - - -	0·2
Bone from M.S.A. breccia - - - - - - - -	0·1
Bone from *Parapapio* breccia - - - - - - - -	0·1
5. *Broken Hill Bone Cave, N. Rhodesia*	
Bone implement E.701a - - - - - - - - -	0·4
Broken Hill I Skull - - - - - - - - -	0·1
Broken Hill II maxilla - - - - - - - - -	0·1
Crocidura bones - - - - - - - - - -	0·0

Analysis of samples of bone from Florisbad has given some interesting results (Table I). At first sight they might suggest that the Florisbad skull was a recent interment. However, if one considers the situation in which it was found the result may be consistent with high antiquity. According to Professor T. F. Dreyer it was found in a pocket at the margin of the main 'spring eye', which is not a good circumstance from the point of view of being certain of the stratigraphic age of a specimen. But Mr Venter, who was present when the skull was dug out, has stated that it was embedded in the so-called Peat I, which is really a peaty clay. In the course of the Piltdown research we found that bones preserved in clay have often retained their protein after bones of the same age in sand have lost it. Fluorine analysis is a useful cross-check in such cases, although its reliability as a dating method in warm spring deposits, such as those of Florisbad, is problematical. All these questions are now under investigation.

Doubts have been felt about the radio-carbon dating of Florisbad Peat I as 'more than 41,000 years' old (Libby, 1954, p. 741). This result was based on the fact that Dr Libby found the material had no measurable radio-activity. It is worth bearing in mind, however, that the Florisbad deposits were accumulated by spring waters possibly arising from an underlying Palaeozoic formation which includes Ecca coal measures. Although there is no question that the 'peat' does contain Pleistocene plant material, the possibility should be borne in mind that it also contains derived Palaeozoic carbon. If the percentage of this 'dead' carbon were high, the point of 'no measurable radio-activity' would be reached in *less* than 41,000 years.*

The new methods of relative dating have also been applied to material from the Saldanha Man site at Hopefield (Cape).

The fluorine content of the Saldanha skull is well within the range of the *Palaeoloxodon-Mesochoerus* fauna found scattered on the same site (Table II, A). The only material showing an appreciably lower fluorine content comes from the calcreted dune sand overlying the main fossil horizon. The question of whether there are two Pleistocene faunas or only one at Hopefield may be settled by analysing a larger series. We are now in a position to do this, by estimating the uranium

TABLE II
URANIUM AND FLUORINE FIXATION IN BONES, S. AFRICA

	eU_3O_8 p.p.m.	$\dfrac{F\%}{P_2O_5} \times 100$
A. *Sands, Hopefield, C.P.*		
Modern Bone - - - - - - -	0	0·1
Horn-core, shelly calcreted dune - - - -	6	5·2
Bone from below 'later ferricrete' - - - -	18	5·4
- - - -	13	5·9†
	13	
	15	5·9‡
	15	
Bones from Main Fossil Bed	17	7·3
	17	
† *Palaeoloxodon*	18	7·6
‡ *Saldanha Skull*	20‡	
- - - -	25	7·8
B. *Calcreted Breccias, Transvaal and Bechuanaland*		
Bone from Kromdraai - - - - - -	6	—
Bone from Swartkrans - - - - - -	6	av. 2·3
Bone from Sterkfontein - - - - - -	7	1·1
Bone from Makapan Limeworks - - - -	7	2·2
Bone from Taung (oldest breccia) - - - -	21	3·8
Bone from Taung (MSA breccia) - - - -	6	3·8

* By the same token, the revised C 14 date of Peat I (37,000 years, according to van Zinderen Bakker—see p. 57) is also judged to be excessive.

content in place of fluorine. Whereas fluorine analysis is laborious and time-consuming, uranium content can be assessed by radiometric equipment which is largely automatic. Uranium like fluorine is absorbed from ground water and accumulates in fossil bones with the passage of time. The radiometric results so far obtained with Hopefield material (see Table) re-inforce the conclusions based on the fluorine analysis, indicating that there is only one faunal assemblage below the later ferricrete. It is possible that the few bones found in the calcreted dune sand above are appreciably later, but their lower uranium and fluorine contents could be accounted for by the fact that a calcitic matrix is a barrier to the passage of these elements.

The ways in which fluorine and uranium accumulate in bones preserved in calcreted breccias are at present being investigated (Table II, B). The results so far obtained indicate that while fluorine is useless as a means of relative dating in such deposits, the distribution of uranium is sometimes more revealing.

These researches were aided by a grant from the Wenner-Gren Foundation.

REFERENCES

Clark, J. D., *et al.* (1950), 'New Studies on Rhodesian Man', *J. Roy, Anthrop. Inst.*, 77, pt. I (1947), pp.7–32.

Libby, W. F. (1954), 'Radiocarbon Dates, V', *Science*, 120, pp. 733–42.

Mennel, F. C. (1929), 'The Evidence for the Age of *Homo rhodesiensis*', *S. Afr. J. Sci.*, 26, pp. 659–64.

Oakley, K. P. (1954), 'Study Tour of Fossil Hominid Sites in Southern Africa', *S. Afr. Arch. Bull.* 9, No. 35, pp. 75–87.

Zeuner, F. E. (1946), *Dating the Past*, London.

9

Chronologie préhistorique du Sahara

par MARIE-HENRIETTE ALIMEN

[ABSTRACT]

LA première partie de la note présente un recensement des industries préhistoriques sahariennes, qui met en lumière l'existence de hiatus successifs. Ces hiatus sont vraisemblablement synchroniques des Arides sahariens (un Aride probable au cours des temps de la Pebble-Culture, un second en parallèle avec le Chelléen, un troisième entre Acheuléen et Atérien, l'avant-dernier entre Atérien et Méso-Néolithique, le dernier étant l'Aride actuel). Cette chronologie locale ne pouvait jusqu'ici être accrochée à une chronologie générale africaine que grâce au gisement de l'erg Tihodaïne (à Acheuléen et *Elephas recki*), contemporain de la fin du Kamasien.

Les grands cadres de la géologie quaternaire ont pu être récemment précisés dans la vallée de l'oued Saoura (existence de trois Pluviaux suivis de trois phases humides), et des études sont en cours pour établir l'âge des civilisations préhistoriques, par le moyen de récoltes systématiques, sur les surfaces topographiques fossiles, d'âge géologiquement connu. Les premiers résultats en sont indiqués. Enfin, il est fait mention de la découverte récente (1955) d'industries acheuléennes (Acheuléen moyen évolué) dans des couches qui s'insèrent nettement dans la chronologie géologique de la Saoura. La fin du Deuxième Pluvial saharien se met ainsi en corrélation avec le Kamasien II.

JUSQU'À ces dernières années, la chronologie préhistorique du Sahara est demeurée fort peu élaborée, malgré l'extraordinaire richesse du grand désert en pierres taillées. Cet état de choses tient d'une part à la nature même des stations sahariennes, qui sont essentiellement des stations de surface, et d'autre part à l'absence, ou du moins à l'imprécision de la chronologie géologique des formations quaternaires sahariennes. De nombreuses récoltes ont été faites, à partir de 1905, et un important outillage a été décrit, mais les déterminations chronologiques reposaient à peu près uniquement sur les affinités typologiques des pièces et sur le degré relatif de patine. Des observations nouvelles relatives aux successions géologiques quaternaires et la découverte toute récente d'industries anciennes en place dans les séries géologiques du Sahara Nord-Occidental, nous incitent à tenter une mise au point de la chronologie préhistorique saharienne.

I LES SÉRIES ARCHÉOLOGIQUES SAHARIENNES

Après les premières récoltes (missions Flatters et Foureau) sont venues les collections recueillies par divers officiers (Minette de St.-Martin, César, Fretay, Roulet, etc.), puis celles de missions scientifiques (Th. Monod, M. Reygasse, J. Bourcart, M. Dalloni, P. Graziosi et, avec des documents non encore publiés, B. Champault, H. Alimen, J. M. Freulon, J. et N. Chavaillon etc.).

(1) La *Pebble-Culture*, récemment identifiée, est présente dans le sud marocain (d'après G. Mortelmans, G. Choubert, H. Hollard, 1952), au Fezzan et au Tibesti (M. Dalloni, 1948), dans la région Saoura-Ougarta (H. Alimen, 1952), aux Tassilis des Ajjers (J. M. Freulon, 1955). Autant qu'on en puisse juger, cette Pebble-Culture ne possède ni la même richesse, ni la même continuité qu'en Afrique Orientale.

(2) Le *Chelléen* est peu ou pas représenté au Sahara. L'*Acheuléen* est très abondant et très beau, avec des formes très variées, et il doit couvrir une longue durée, bien qu'il soit impossible

actuellement d'y tenter une discrimination évolutive (formes en amande, formes ovalaires, formes allongées et lancéolées, types cordiformes; certaines pièces sont réellement bifaces, d'autres sont sur éclat, avec surface d'éclatement à peine retouchée). Les hachereaux sont nombreux et souvent de très belle facture. Il paraît évident que certaines pièces sont peu évoluées et typologiquement apparentées à l'Acheuléen inférieur, d'autres à un Acheuléen moyen; d'autres enfin évoquent un Acheuléen supérieur. La présence du *Micoquien* est moins clairement affirmée.

(3) On n'a pas, jusqu'ici du moins, identifié un ensemble typologique pur qu'on puisse rapporter au *Levalloiso-Moustérien*; les techniques levalloisienne et moustérienne sont présentes cependant, mais plus ou moins incorporées à l'Acheuléen (technique levalloisienne), à l'Atérien, voire même à des civilisations plus récentes (technique moustérienne). L'*Atérien* paraît succéder, après un hiatus vraisemblablement, à l'Acheuléen.

(4) Un Paléolithique supérieur de type *capsien* ou *ibéro-maurusien* n'existe pas nettement caractérisé au Sahara. Du moins aucune étude systématique n'est encore parvenue à séparer, sans contestation possible, ces civilisations des outillages *méso-néolithiques* avec lesquels, si elles existent, elles se mélangent dans les stations de surface.

Telle apparaît la succession des grands ensembles sahariens, définie d'après les récoltes de surface et par comparaison avec l'évolution maugrébine, égyptienne ou africaine orientale. Cette vision globale met en lumière l'existence de hiatus, ou du moins de périodes de raréfaction manifeste du peuplement humain, de précarités interrompant, à plusieurs reprises, les épanouissements. Il est naturel de mettre ces pulsations en corrélation avec les alternances de phases pluviales et arides, dont l'existence domine l'histoire quaternaire de l'Afrique entière, et dont les témoignages sont d'ailleurs inscrits dans les sédiments sahariens. Une phase aride paraît intervenir au cours des temps de la Pebble-Culture; une seconde expliquerait l'absence du Chelléen, une troisième sépare l'Acheuléen final de l'Atérien, une quatrième se place entre l'Atérien et le Méso-Néo-lithique, tandis que l'époque actuelle correspond à l'Aride post-néolithique.

Ainsi s'ébauche une première esquisse de chronologie préhistorique saharienne, dans un cadre strictement local. Cependant un accrochage de cette séquence avec celles d'autres parties de l'Afrique a pu déjà être tenté, grâce aux recherches de C. Arambourg, dans le gisement de l'erg Tihodaïne (1948), l'une des cuvettes lacustres du pourtour du Hoggar qui ont livré des pierres taillées associées à des restes de Mammifères. Une étude générale du Quaternaire de ces régions n'étant pas faite, il n'est possible de fixer l'âge géologique de ces formations que par des considérations paléontologiques. A Tihodaïne, C. Arambourg a déterminé, associée à *Rhinoceros*, *Bos primigenius*, *Bubalus* (sp. *antiquus?*), à des gazelles, antilopes, zèbres, hippopotames, la présence caractéristique de *Elephas* (*Archidiskodon*) *recki*. Or, une industrie acheuléenne de technique évoluée a été recueillie dans ces mêmes dépôts. Il paraît normal de paralléliser les argiles de la cuvette de Tihodaïne avec les couches supérieures d'Oldoway à *Elephas recki* (fin du Kamasien) d'une part, et avec les derniers dépôts du Maghreb contenant la faune à *Machairodus*, *Elephas recki* et *Bubalus antiquus**, ainsi que l'outillage acheuléen, d'autre part. Dans ces perspectives, la lacune anté-atérienne daterait de l'Aride post-kamasien, tandis que l'Acheuléen du Sahara couvrirait une plus ou moins grande partie du Pluvial kamasien.

En dehors des gisements du pourtour du Hoggar, une seule station dans le Sahara a été signalée comme contenant une industrie en place, c'est la célèbre station de Tachenghit, dont B. Champault vient de reprendre l'étude, mais les conditions d'âge géologique n'en ont pas encore été élucidées.

II La chronologie geologique du quaternaire de la Saoura
(Sahara nord-occidental)

Depuis le piedmont sud-atlasique jusqu'au Touat, l'oued Saoura inscrit une entaille N.-S. (la Saoura), où s'enregistrèrent, dans des cycles répétés de creusement et de remblaiement, les

* Décrit comme *Homoioceras singae* (Bate, 1951).

alternances pluviales et arides du Quaternaire. Après les travaux de mes devanciers (J. Letourneur, 1943, et H. Schoeller, 1945), j'ai pu établir, au cours de missions échelonnées de 1950 à 1955, les grands traits de la géologie quaternaire de la Saoura, dont je résumerai ainsi l'essentiel :

Premier Pluvial. Je rapporte à un premier pluvial quaternaire les plus anciens stades de creusement dans les formations hamadiennes, correspondant à un réseau fluvial très élevé au dessus du thalweg actuel (45–50 m.). Les dépôts qui ont suivi ce creusement sont des conglomérats à ciment siliceux dur et des grès qui ne subsistent qu'en placages très érodés (*sables et grès de Mazer*).

Second Pluvial. Une très importante phase de creusement marque le début de ce pluvial, sciant toute l'épaisseur des dépôts pliocènes jusqu'au substratum primaire et descendant à un niveau voisin de celui de l'oued actuel. Le remblaiement se présente également sous forme de conglomérats à ciment siliceux, épais de 10 à 15 m. Le type peut en être pris dans les *conglomérats et grès de la garu Taourirt*, près de Béni-Abbès. Une interruption, au cours de la formation de ces conglomérats, définit l'existence de deux phases dans ce pluvial.

Troisième Pluvial. Une importante érosion a démantelé ces conglomérats de fond d'oued, recreusant le lit jusqu'au substratum primaire, sauf aux quelques points où sont conservées les formations de type Taourirt. Le remblaiement qui a suivi, accumulé dans des conditions de semi-aridité manifeste, est formé de sables assez cohérents, gris-vert en général, qui ont noyé les conglomérats précédents. Ces sables, qui constituent la terrasse principale de la Saoura (30–20 m.), forment un repère très constant et très précieux dans la géologie quaternaire de notre région[*] (*sables gris-vert de la Saoura*).

Dernières phases humides. Trois phases humides, d'importance inégale, succèdent au Troisième Pluvial. La première n'a donné qu'une terrasse d'érosion (alt. relative 15–10 m.), où prédominent les écoulements latéraux ; il en est sensiblement de même de la deuxième (alt. relative 10–5 m.), avec cependant parfois des remblaiements où interviennent davantage les apports longitudinaux. La troisième est plus importante. Son creusement atteint le socle primaire, et le remblaiement longitudinal qui a suivi, de type semi-aride, est formé de sables gypseux jaune-brun. Le lit majeur actuel est creusé 5–2 m. en contrebas de ce dernier remblaiement.

III PLACE DES INDUSTRIES PRÉHISTORIQUES DANS LA CHRONOLOGIE QUATERNAIRE DU SAHARA NORD-OCCIDENTAL

1. *Première phase des recherches*

En 1945, H. Schoeller signala la présence probable, en place dans les alluvions de la dernière terrasse (5–2 m.) de la Saoura, de haches en pierre polie. Mes recherches, jusqu'en 1955, n'ont amené aucune nouvelle récolte en couche, du moins en couche géologiquement datable. J'ai donc entrepris, le long de la Saoura, la récolte des industries de façon systématique, par surfaces topographiques géologiquement datées. L'inventaire de ces récoltes poursuivies de 1950 à 1955 est loin d'être achevé. Il permettra d'établir, par éliminations successives, les correspondances chronologiques des civilisations et des époques d'achèvement des terrasses. Actuellement je ne peux indiquer que les grandes lignes de ces correspondances.

La Pebble-Culture, les industries à bifaces (Chelléen? et Acheuléen) et l'Atérien ne se rencontrent pas sur la surface de la terrasse de 30–20 m., mais seulement sur les surfaces plus anciennes (Hamada et surfaces du Quaternaire ancien du type 'sables et grès de Mazer' et leurs équivalents). Ces industries sont donc, dans leur ensemble, antérieures à la phase ultime du remblaiement du Troisième Pluvial saharien. Cependant, tandis que l'Acheuléen possède une très

---

[*] Une tournée récente dans le sud marocain, sous l'aimable conduite de J. Margat qui étudie le Quaternaire de cette région, nous a permis de constater la similitude des sables jaunes des oueds sud-marocains, dits 'limon des palmeraies' dans cette région, et des sables gris-vert de la Saoura. Le raccord des chronologies saharienne et marocaine trouvera là une de ses articulations.

vaste répartition sur les surfaces du Quaternaire ancien et du Pliocène, en des régions aujourd'hui totalement arides, et correspond indiscutablement à un Pluvial de forte pluviosité, l'Atérien se localise davantage et se rencontre plutôt au niveau de 'daïas' mortes, vestiges d'un réseau hydrographique fossile. L'Atérien correspond donc à une pluviosité beaucoup moins accentuée que l'Acheuléen.

Le complexe industriel de la fin du Paléolithique supérieur (?) et du Méso-Néolithique abonde sur les terrasses de 20–30 m. (Troisième Pluvial) et sur les terrasses postérieures d'érosion, mais ne se rencontre pas sur la terrasse de 2–5 m. Notons en passant qu'il y aura évidemment plusieurs faciès successifs à distinguer sur l'ensemble de ces terrasses. Le Néolithique (H. Schoeller) s'achèverait avec le dépôt des sables de la dernière terrasse. L'ensemble de ces industries a une répartition générale qui contraste fortement avec celle des industries antérieures : elles sont désormais concentrées autour de points d'eau (rives d'oueds, daïas, sources), dont certains peuvent d'ailleurs n'être plus fonctionnels aujourd'hui. Elles datent de périodes humides et non plus pluviales.

2. *Découverte d'industries acheuléennes en place dans des alluvions chronologiquement définies*

Les considérations précédentes, prenant appui sur les hiatus dans le déroulement des civilisations et sur les rapports des industries de surface avec les terrasses de la Saoura, conduisent à attribuer le Méso-Néolithique (et le possible Paléolithique final) aux dernières phases humides ; l'Atérien doit se situer vers les débuts du Troisième Pluvial, tandis que l'Acheuléen doit couvrir les temps du Deuxième Pluvial. La lacune chelléenne et la Pebble-Culture se placent quelque part au cours de l'Aride entre le Deuxième et le Premier Pluvial et au cours du Premier Pluvial. La

FIG. 1. Biface acheuléen, trouvé *in situ*, dans les alluvions de la Saoura, à Kerzaz. Sommet des conglomerats du Kamasién II. Face supérieure, à gauche ; face inférieure, à droite ; profil droit, au milieu. Échelle en cm.

83

FIG. 2. Hachereau acheuléen, trouvé *in situ*, dans les alluvions de la Saoura, à Kerzaz. Conglomérats, du Kamasien II. Face supérieure et profil droit, en haut ; face inférieure et profil gauche, en bas. Échelle en cm.

question en était à ce point, lorsque, au premiers mois de 1955, j'ai eu la bonne fortune de recueillir, dans la Saoura, à Kerzaz, des quartzites taillés, dans les 'conglomérats de type Taourirt', plus précisément dans leur moitié supérieure (deuxième phase du Deuxième Pluvial). Grâce à deux pièces typiques, un biface et un hachereau (Figs. 1 et 2), on peut dire qu'il s'agit d'un Acheuléen assez évolué, comparable aux stades 7 à 9 d'Oldoway. La partie inférieure des conglomérats (première phase du Deuxième Pluvial) contient de l'industrie, mais je n'y ai encore recueilli aucune pièce typique. La comparaison de ces formations avec celles de l'Afrique Orientale, notamment avec la série d'Oldoway, suggère donc de paralléliser les conglomérats de type Taourirt dans leur partie supérieure avec le Kamasien II.

Ces notions sont confirmées par d'autres récoltes *in situ* d'un outillage acheuléen, dans un oued, aujourd'hui pratiquement non fonctionnel, des Monts d'Ougarta, l'oued Farès, qui aboutit au piedmont par le Foum Tlaïa. L'oued Farès est au voisinage du massif ryolithique du Bou Khbaïssat (feuille d'Ougarta, latitude 30° 50′). Dès 1951, j'avais discerné la présence de quartzites taillés dans les alluvions de l'oued Farès, mais il m'était impossible à ce moment de dater ces couches. En février 1955, avec la collaboration de Jean Chavaillon, je viens de faire de nouvelles récoltes en ce point. Je peux affirmer maintenant que les conglomérats de l'oued Farès, qui sont sous-jacents aux 'sables gris-vert', sont l'homologue de la moitié supérieure des conglomérats de Kerzaz, celle d'où proviennent le biface et le hachereau. L'ensemble industriel de l'oued Farès (11 pièces au total, dont 4 recueillies en place dans le conglomérat, sous les sables gris-vert, et les autres dans ce même conglomérat mis à nu au cours des phases humides postérieures aux sables gris-vert), forme un tout assez homogène, qui se rattache aux stades 7 à 9 d'Oldoway et au Stellenbosch IV–V d'Afrique australe. Notons particulièrement, parmi les pièces en couche, un grand et beau nucleus de technique comparable à celle de Victoria-West II. Tout ceci nous place dans le Kamasien II.*

CONCLUSIONS

Nous avons voulu, en ces quelques pages, dégager à la fois les méthodes mises en œuvre pour résoudre les problèmes de la chronologie préhistorique saharienne et faire le point des résultats. Quant aux méthodes, on en sait la difficulté dans ce grand désert, où jusqu'ici aucune industrie n'avait été trouvée en couche datable, sauf aux pourtours du Hoggar. Nous avons essayé de dégager les diverses voies de la recherche : mise en parallèle des hiatus dans le déroulement des civilisations et des phases arides, d'une part ; récoltes systématiques par surfaces géologiquement datées, d'autre part. La découverte récente d'Acheuléen dans les alluvions de la Saoura, dont la chronologie géologique s'élabore peu à peu, confirme pleinement les conclusions obtenues par les autres méthodes, et celles paléontologiquement établies, grâce à C. Arambourg, à Tihodaïne. Elle nous permet d'entrevoir l'accrochage de la chronologie préhistorique saharienne avec celle d'autres régions africaines. Ces observations nous autorisent aussi à espérer, pour l'avenir, des précisions nouvelles par la prospection systématique des stations que nous venons de reconnaître, et sans doute par la découverte de nouvelles stations stratigraphiquement datables.

* Les fouilles systématiques que j'ai réalisées en 1956 donnent maintenant des séries importantes de Paléolithique inférieur en place (*note en cours d'impression*).

10

Note on Raised Shore-Lines of the Gold Coast

by M. M. ANDERSON and W. D. BRÜCKNER

[SUMMARY]

Evidence for three distinct raised shore-lines along the coastal belt of the Gold Coast has been found by the authors. The uppermost of variable height has been preserved at only a few places, whereas the two lower shore-lines, with cliff bases at approximately 6–12 feet and 2–4 feet respectively above sea level, occur at many points along the coast. The upper shore-line is older than the lateritic crusts and the last structural movements in the country and is therefore believed to be of young Tertiary or old Quaternary age. The two lower shore-lines are of pre- and post-Gamblian age respectively (or possibly older and younger post-Gamblian) and probably the result of world-wide changes in sea level. Other planated surfaces of the Gold Coast previously described as marine levels are considered to be of continental origin.

INTRODUCTION

THE Gold Coast lies on the Gulf of Guinea and has a coast line of some 360 miles in length. Except in the eastern and western sections where it is formed of Cretaceous and Tertiary to Recent sediments without rocky exposures, the coast shows plentiful exposures of rocks ranging in age from Pre-Cambrian to Devonian or Carboniferous (Fig. 1).

Along the coastal belt there occur at various levels relics of old marine platforms indicating that there have been changes in the relative positions of land and sea. Members of the Geological Survey of the Gold Coast have recorded their presence in several publications since the Survey was established in 1913. Its first Director, A. E. Kitson (1916), mentioned '. . . the occurrence of several well marked marine terraces or platforms, one of which is from 70 to 100 feet above present sea level, and at least two others of more recent age, at 20 feet and 8–10 feet above it'. N. R. Junner (1940) gave the following brief account of their observations up to 1940: 'Well preserved marine terraces and wave cut benches occur at 3–5 feet, 10–20 feet, 30–40 feet, 70–80 feet, and 100–120 feet above mean sea level, indicating that the land has risen since they were formed, or more likely that the sea level has fallen. In addition there are several flat-topped, laterite-capped residuals along the coast at 180–220 feet above sea level. These are regarded as peneplain residuals as the laterite cap must have been formed under subaerial conditions; it is possible, however, that they were formed by marine erosion and were later lateritised.' Finally A. T. Crow (1952) dealing with the Takoradi-Cape Coast area confirmed some of Junner's levels, namely those at 30–40 feet, 70–80 feet, and in particular 100–120 feet.

This note gives a brief outline of the results of a recent investigation into the raised shore-lines of the coastal belt of the Gold Coast, excluding however the western section beyond the Butre river near Dixcove, and the eastern section beyond Prampram. The coastal region has experienced continental and marine planation at different levels in past times and, therefore, the chief problem has been that of distinguishing the flat erosion surfaces of marine origin from those of continental origin. Morphological criteria taken in conjunction with the nature of the deposits on these surfaces have been used to make the distinction clear. On this basis only three of the planated levels were found to be of undoubted marine origin, the remainder being the result of continental planation. Two of the three marine levels belong to shore-lines whose cliff bases have been established at about 2–4 feet and 6–12 feet above sea level respectively, while the third, since it is only preserved as remnants of variable height, cannot be referred to a definite height above sea level and is, therefore, called for convenience the 'uppermost shoreline'.

THE UPPERMOST SHORE-LINE

The westernmost relics of a high marine platform that have so far been found by the authors occur west of Komenda where a line of hills, whose crest varies from 40 feet to over 150 feet above sea level, runs parallel with the shore. The hills that reach 150 feet are relatively flat-topped, and well-rounded quartz pebbles, indicative of wear in the surf zone, abound on the tops as well as along the flanks of the whole range. The number of pebbles decreases rapidly inland, and no cliff line representing the landward boundary of the platform has as yet been found here.

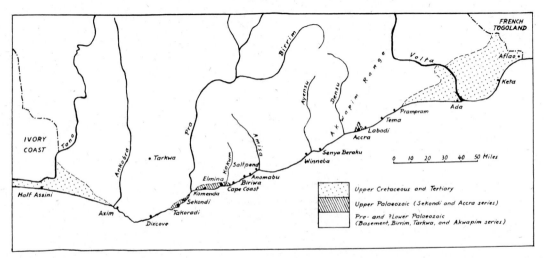

FIG. 1. The Coast Line of the Gold Coast

In the Elmina area, about 11 miles east of Komenda, a well-defined raised cliff line runs nearly E.–W. about 1 mile north of the town. Its base is approximately 75–80 feet above sea level, and running up to it at several points are remnants of a clearly defined platform. In the town of Elmina itself there are several hills about 100 feet high on the upper surfaces of which can be found numerous small well-rounded pebbles. These hill tops can again be interpreted as relics of a marine platform whose level here appears, however, to be higher than at the cliff base to the north of Elmina. Small marine pebbles, dominantly of quartz, also occur along a low ridge about 40 feet high bordering the coast east of the town almost as far as the river Kakum where it dies out. This ridge probably does not represent the actual level of the old platform, but the pebbles indicate its former extension before lowering by subsequent continental erosion.

A study of the pebbles in this area is complicated by the presence of 'pebbly horizons' in the sandstones of the 'Sekondi Series' which outcrop north of Elmina. These Sekondian pebbles are, however, poorly sorted, and only the larger ones show a fair degree of rounding, the smaller being predominantly angular. They are thus in contrast to those found on the raised marine platform of this region which have been well sorted and are very well rounded in all grades. The 'pebbly horizons' have, of course, been the source of many of the pebbles found on the platform, as the sea was able to rework them easily when it stood at this higher level.

Several quite extensive remnants of a high platform are preserved further to the east between Cape Coast and Saltpond, and the town of Anomabu and the village of Biriwa have largely been built on this erosion surface. The main road between Cape Coast and Saltpond, where it runs close to the coast from Biriwa eastwards, passes over a succession of low, steep sided hills whose crests reach the level of the platform and on which can be found well-rounded pebbles and small boulders. The cliff line of these remnants of the platform is best preserved about a mile and a quarter east of Anomabu just north of the main road where its base is between 60 and 70 feet above sea level.

East of Saltpond the next place at which relics of a high marine platform are known to the authors is Senya Beraku where it is 60 to 75 feet above sea level. It is sometimes covered there by large pebbles and boulders mainly of quartzite. No associated cliff line has been found in this area.

Finally in the Accra area a fairly flat level extends, at about 20–30 feet above sea level, from the town eastwards towards Labadi. A number of well-rounded pebbles occur on this surface and it may, therefore, at least in part, represent a raised marine platform. The country east of the Akwapim range has, however, suffered continental planation at a low level which in the coastal region merges with the pebble-covered stretch as no cliff line that would separate them can be traced. Therefore, the coastal region may have been more or less lowered throughout by continental erosion from a height more in accord with those recorded for the high platform relics of the Saltpond and Senya Beraku areas. The position in the Accra area is also complicated by the fact that occasional scattered pebbles have been found further inland up to a height of about 300 feet. The latter have probably been derived from the destruction of marine Cretaceous or Eocene beds, remnants of which are still *in situ* east of the Volta river.

It will have been noted that the relics of high-lying marine platforms and cliff lines along the coastal belt of the Gold Coast are in general lower in the east and higher in the west. They can be interpreted as remnants of several different shore-lines, but as the authors have found no indications of more than a single high platform or cliff line at any one place, they prefer to assume that all the remnants belong to the same raised shore-line which has become deformed by subsequent structural movements, i.e. mainly by a slight tilting, and probably also by faulting, particularly in the Elmina area. Such comparatively recent structural movements are also supported by the far greater 'young' fluviatile dissection of the coastal belt in the west as compared with the east.

On none of the relics of the high marine platform have the pebbles actually been observed resting strictly *in situ* on the old wave-cut surface. They occur now embedded in horizons of the quaternary continental mantle rock (W. Brückner, 1955).* They are found either loose in the 'Upper stone layer'—as is most frequently the case—or included in the 'Upper limonitic crust' where conserved, or even in fragments of the 'Lower limonitic crust'. The uppermost shore-line must, therefore, have already been cut by the sea before the development of the 'Lower limonitic crust' which was formed during the 'Older interpluvial'—a period probably corresponding to the great European interglacial (Mindel-Riss). The age of the uppermost shore-line of the Gold Coast is therefore at least older Pleistocene and may even be pre-Pleistocene.

Wherever the uppermost platform has existed and subsequently been lost by continental erosion, its pebbles have been carried down to lower levels where their presence has unfortunately

---

* The succession and probable ages of the more important of these horizons are as follows:

Upper loamy sand	Gamblian pluvial to Recent
Upper stone layer ⎫	
Upper limonitic crust ⎬	Younger interpluvial
Lower stone layer ⎭	
Lower loamy sand	Kamasian pluvial
Breccia ⎫	
Lower limonitic crust ⎬	Older interpluvial

resulted in the past in these levels being recorded as evidence of other marine benches. It may seem surprising that these pebbles were not entirely removed, but the erosion must have been active over areas that were only gently inclined so that it consisted predominantly of a washing out of fine grained material resulting from both chemical decomposition and physical disintegration, the more resistant coarser bodies thus reaching lower levels with little or no lateral transport.

THE 6–12 FEET SHORE-LINE

Numerous relics of the platform and cliff line of the 6–12 feet shore-line are preserved along the whole of the coastal stretch under consideration. They lie either at, or only a short distance beyond the present beach. The height of the cliff base is approximately the same at all points observed so that the shore-line has suffered no deformation by crustal movements since it was cut. The remnants of the platform vary in width from a few feet to 100 yards or more. Where the width is small the relics form isolated flat areas standing step-like above the present level of the sea (or the lowermost raised platform) with the old cliff line at their inner edge and frequently a clear wave-cut notch at its base. At their outer edge they are generally being actively eroded by the sea, and spray from breaking waves falls on them, washes them free of debris, and modifies the form of the old wave-cut surface. At those rather rare places where the old platform is wider, it has become hidden beneath sand when close to the beach, and beneath soil and other debris further inland.

The fossil cliff line of the 6–12 feet shore-line is finely displayed east of Komenda where it forms the seaward face of the line of hills mentioned in the preceding section. These cliffs rise steeply up to between 45 and 150 feet, and although some parts are still rocky, most of the old cliff face has become overgrown with vegetation clearly indicating that it has been out of reach of the sea for a considerable time. Only at the western end of this line of hills has the sea now reached a position practically coincident with that of the old shore, and its platform has, therefore, nearly all been destroyed. Along the remainder of the old cliff the platform is hidden beneath a sand bar. Very similar features to those west of Komenda may be seen along the coastal stretch about six miles north-east of Senya Beraku.

Notable examples of the 6–12 feet platform occur at Sekondi and at Saltpond. In Sekondi around the headland on which the lighthouse stands, there is an extensive wave-cut platform as much as 30 yards across in places, free of deposits, and backed by a low cliff. East and west of Saltpond the platform may be up to 100 yards wide but it is covered and obscured by a thick layer of soil.

The only contemporaneous deposit belonging to the 6–12 feet shore-line that has so far been found* rests on the platform for about one mile of its length along the coast at Labadi (Fig. 2). The deposit consists of angular to subrounded boulders and stones derived from the bed rock, embedded in, and overlain by, well rounded and well sorted quartz pebbles that are predominantly of medium to small size. This marine pebble bed is penetrated and covered by the continental 'Upper loamy sand' (see footnote on p. 88) which is as much as 10 feet thick in places. In a drainage channel opening on to the beach at Labadi the pebble bed can be traced inland for about 30 yards, and beyond it, after a short distance without exposure, there is a low rocky cliff. On the upper surface of the cliff instead of the pebble bed there is a layer of predominantly angular† stones accompanied by ferruginous and calcareous nodules of continental origin forming the 'Upper stone layer'. The low cliff observed in the channel must therefore be that of the 6–12 feet shore-line. The pebble bed of this raised beach was probably formed at the same time as the 'Upper stone layer' inland as both these formations have been covered by the same blanket of 'Upper loamy sand' which now hides most of the old cliff line. Since the 'upper stone layer' has been interpreted as a product of the dry period preceding the Gamblian pluvial (Brückner, 1955), it can

---

* See Note 1 on p. 92.
† There are also a few well-rounded pebbles in this layer which have been derived from the deposits on the uppermost platform, or possibly from Cretaceous or Eocene beds (see the preceding section).

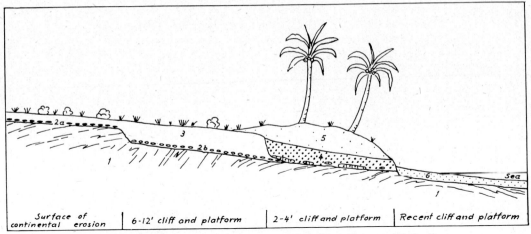

| Surface of continental erosion | 6-12' cliff and platform | 2-4' cliff and platform | Recent cliff and platform |

FIG. 2. Idealized section through the coastal stretch west of Labadi

6.	Young beach sand	Recent
5.	Dune sand	Subrecent
4.	Old beach sand with remnants of 'beach rock'	Post-Gamblian
3.	'Upper loamy sand' (terrestrial)	Gamblian pluvial to recent
2a.	'Upper stone layer' (terrestrial)	Pre-Gamblian interpluvial
2b.	Labadi pebble bed (marine)	
1.	Bedrock	Pre-Cambrian

be assumed that the 6–12 feet shore-line with its pebble bed also belongs to the pre-Gamblian interpluvial. As this period probably corresponds with the last interglacial in the northern hemisphere it seems reasonable to relate the 6–12 feet shore-line to a eustatic rise of sea level resulting from world-wide deglaciation.*

THE 2–4 FEET SHORE-LINE

Relics of the platform and cliff line of the 2–4 feet shore-line are still more frequent along the coast than those of the 6–12 feet shore-line. The cliff line generally lies only a very short distance inland—often only a matter of feet—although there are exceptions where the platform measures 100 yards or more across. Where remnants of the 6–12 feet shore-line are preserved, the two platforms are separated by a low cliff, only a few feet high, that has frequently been so modified by recent wave erosion that the lower level merges with the upper along an inclined surface. Everywhere the outer edge of the 2–4 feet platform is being actively eroded by the sea, and at many places it is under water at high tide.

A contemporaneous deposit is found resting directly on the platform at several places along the coast. It consists of an old beach sand, which is generally dark reddish-brown in colour, is compact, fine to medium grained in character, poorer in calcareous matter than the recent beach sands but with a far higher content of clay and iron oxides, and which contains shell fragments as well as occasional lines of small pebbles. It is evident that the brown colour and the clay present are secondary features that arose from the introduction of fine particles of clay and iron oxides by water that seeped in laterally from neighbouring continental soils. At the same time the water has gradually decalcified the old beach sand. Occasionally the basal portion may be found strongly ferruginized and consequently very compact—a rare condition that may be observed near the western end of the Golf Club beach at Takoradi. The upper part of this deposit is often lighter in colour and less compact, and even becomes a loose yellow sand due to the removal of the clay and

* See Note 2 on p. 92.

iron oxides under the changed conditions of weathering of today. A coarse facies of the old beach sand also occurs, as e.g. at the back of a small bay about $1\frac{1}{2}$ miles north-east of Sekondi, where the —roughly stratified—deposit is predominantly pebbly. The diameter of these pebbles rarely exceeds 1 centimetre, and they are beautifully rounded. Beneath both the sandy and the pebbly facies there may occur a boulder bed which is generally only 1–2 feet in thickness as the boulders are rarely more than one or two deep. The boulders, which have mainly—if not throughout—been derived from local rocks, are rounded to subangular, up to 2 feet in diameter, and set in a matrix of the old beach sand. Some of the boulders and many of the pebbles probably represent material reworked from the deposits of the 6–12 feet shore-line. This is particularly clear in the coastal stretch west of Labadi which exhibits the best exposures of the old beach sand so far seen (Fig. 2).

There are still places where the old beach sand has retained its original character practically unaltered, i.e. without significant introduced clay and iron oxides, apart from a strengthening due to calcification. Thus at the extreme western end of the Golf Club beach at Takoradi local quarrying for sand has revealed beyond the present limit of the sea the 2–4 feet platform overlain by its old well-bedded beach sand, relatively hard due to some secondary calcification but otherwise resembling a modern beach both in its colour and in its abundance of shells and shell fragments. A number of these 'fossil' shells have been extracted and identified, and in all cases they were found to belong to species still living along the West African coast today. Further calcification of the old beach sand has resulted along other stretches of the platform in the development of sandy limestone or 'beach rock'. This beach rock can now rarely be observed as a continuous layer apart from at Prampram where it occurs on one of the widest relics of the 2–4 feet platform to be preserved. Elsewhere solution subsequent to its formation has left only tiny residuals sticking on the bed rock and a series of disconnected blocks and smaller pieces with irregularly rounded contours now embedded in the decalcified brown beach sand. These remnants indicate the former existence of a continuous beach rock horizon.

The changes undergone by the old beach sand since it was deposited on the 2–4 feet platform as a normal loose deposit may be summarized as follows:

1. Calcification, probably under warm and fairly dry climatic conditions, contemporaneously with the regression of the sea to its present, or a still lower level.
2. Decalcification accompanied by introduction of clay and ferruginous matter by seeping water entering from neighbouring continental soils. Humid period.
3. Removal of clay and iron oxides in the upper part of the deposit under present-day conditions of decreased humidity and/or deforestation.
4. Gradual destruction by current marine erosion and re-working of the pebbles and boulders on the recent beach.

The 2–4 feet shore-line is obviously younger than the 6–12 feet shore-line since the sea when it was cutting the platform of the lower level destroyed the upper one in its advance. A unique section at the town of Labadi shows the beach rock overlying not only the bed rock as in other sections but also the pebble layer on the 6–12 feet platform and the lower part of the 'Upper loamy sand' (Fig. 2). The latter at this point contains a horizon of sharp-edged quartz and quartzite flakes some of which have been identified by Dr O. Davies, of the Archaeology Department of the University College of the Gold Coast, as stone implements of Quasi-Magosian age. Since the 2–4 feet shoreline has cut off this horizon it must be younger than it, i.e. later post-Gamblian in age. It seems possible that this shore-line resulted from a eustatic rise in sea level during the post-glacial climatic optimum.

CORRELATION

The correlation of the three raised shore-lines described in this note with the marine terraces mentioned by members of the Gold Coast Geological Survey can only be tentative because they have not stated whether the height given for a particular terrace was measured at its inner edge, i.e. at its cliff base, or merely at some point on its surface. In the latter case there is always the possibility that some of the Survey levels are really the same terrace measured at different distances from its cliff line. This is improbable, however, in the case of the two lower shore-lines with generally narrow terraces, and there is little doubt that Kitson's 8–10 feet terrace corresponds to the platform of the 6–12 feet shore-line, and that Junner's 3–5 feet terrace represents perhaps slightly lower portions of the same platform rather than the platform of the 2–4 feet shore-line. The terraces of Kitson and Junner between 70 and 150 feet may in some cases be the different parts of the platform of the uppermost shore-line with its variation in height discussed above, or in other cases may be planated surfaces of continental origin as in the Takoradi area where the authors could find no evidence of a marine origin for the 100–150 feet plain described by Crow (1952).

Space does not permit correlation of the raised shore-lines of the Gold Coast with those found in other parts of the world, and in particular around Africa. Brief mention may be made, however, of the fact that observations by workers in many parts of the world indicate recent relative changes in sea level which appear to be of world-wide significance (see P. E. Cloud Jr, 1954), which would confirm that the 6–12 feet and 2–4 feet shore-lines are the result of eustatic changes in sea level. These conclusions are also in accord with those put forward by Junner (1940).

ACKNOWLEDGEMENTS

The writers wish to express their gratitude to Dr O. Davies for identifying the stone implements of Quasi-Magosian age and for presenting their note at the Congress in Livingstone. They also wish to thank the University College of the Gold Coast for the financial aid which has made this investigation possible.

REFERENCES

Brückner, W. (1955), 'The Mantle Rock ('Laterite') of the Gold Coast and its origin', *Geologische Rundschau*, 43, No. 2, pp. 307–327.

Cloud, P. E. Jr, (1954), 'Superficial Aspects of Modern Organic Reefs', *The Scientific Monthly*, 79 (4), pp. 195–208.

Crow, A. T. (1952), 'The Rocks of the Sekondi Series of the Gold Coast', *Gold Coast Geological Survey Bulletin*, 18, pp. 30–1.

Junner, N. R. (1940), 'Geology of the Gold Coast and Western Togoland', *Gold Coast Geological Survey Bulletin*, 11, pp. 33–6.

Kitson, A. E. (1916), 'The Gold Coast: Some Considerations of its Structure, People, and Natural History', *The Geographical Journal*, XLVIII, pp. 370–1.

NOTE 1. Contemporaneous deposits have been found at two other localities since this paper was presented at Livingstone, i.e., along the beach west of Accra and at the new harbour site of Tema about 16 miles east of Accra. The latter occurrence, uncovered by excavations for a railway, was shown to the authors by Dr O. Davies of the Archaeology Department of the University College of the Gold Coast.

NOTE 2. Studies made since the Congress at Livingstone have shown that the 'Upper loamy sand' and the 'Upper stone layer' may, in some areas, have been partly eroded and reformed because of a dry phase after the main Gamblian pluvial. If this applies to the Labadi section, then the 6–12 feet shore-line might be of early Post-Gamblian age.

11

The History of Groenvlei, a South African Coastal Lake

by A. R. H. MARTIN

GROENVLEI is one of a group of six lakes lying in a narrow belt between Wilderness and the Goukamma River. This belt consists of roughly parallel ridges of Quaternary and Recent sand dunes, rising to 200 m. in places, with the lakes—from the west: Eilandvlei, Langevlei, Rondevlei, Swartvlei, Karatara and Groenvlei—in long valleys between them. Ruigtevlei, a former lake, is now a large fen draining into the Karatara River (Fig. 1).

The area is backed by the edge of the Tertiary peneplane which forms a wide shallow cliffed bay in which the sands have accumulated.

Wishing to study the history of the Knysna forests by pollen-analysis, the author chose Groenvlei owing to the formation (mainly from the Sedge, *Cladium Mariscus*) of deep peat there. Subsequent discoveries appear to be of more than local interest owing to the implication of an eustatic ocean-level change.

Groenvlei is a shallow lake 2·2 m. above sea level. Its length is about 3·7 km., maximum width 0·9 km., maximum depth 5·6 m., and surface area 248 hectares (Fig. 2). The lake is without exit, the floor of the valley being blocked between Groenvlei and Swartvlei. The salinity is 0·37%.

Underlying the fen at the eastern end of the lake are calcareous lake muds formed in a small basin cut off from the main part of the lake by a sand bar. Below these, and continuous with the main lake under the sand bar, are brackish and marine muds, then older peat and lake muds, again of fen type.

Analysis of a core 6·3 m. long, from the deepest part of these sediments indicates, from the bottom upwards, 45 cm. freshwater mud with *Cymbella cymbiformis* and other non-halophytic diatom species, 65 cm. of terrestrial peat, 130 cm. of marine mud with *Biddulphia* and *Triceratium* spp., Foraminifera, and bands of mollusc shells, 90 cm. of brackish mud with mesohalobic species such as *Amphora Proteus*, gradually merging into freshwater conditions, 140 cm. of freshwater mud with *C. cymbiformis* and *Anomoeoneis sphaerophora*, a few persisting brackish elements and *Burnupia capensis*, and 160 cm. of coarse detritus mud and fen peat, devoid of diatoms. The surface of the peat at this point is 3 m. above mean sea level. While it is impossible to draw an exact line of demarcation across the gradient of decreasing salinity, the point at which foraminifera cease to be recorded or the point at which marine diatoms fall permanently below 50% might be arbitrarily chosen, to represent the end of marine contact, these giving levels of 300 cm. and 330 cm. respectively, i.e. very close to modern sea level. A transgression with a nett rise in sea level of c. 3·3 m. (10·8 feet) is indicated.

Sediments equivalent to the marine mud and separating an upper and lower terrestrial peat bed have also been found at Ruigtevlei. Since these two lakes are the most easterly and landward of the series, it appears that the formation of all the lakes is largely a result of post-glacial drowning of the coastal belt with its pre-existing ridge-valley system. The first result of this would be increased marshiness in the valleys, and peat formation; then the sea would enter. All the dune

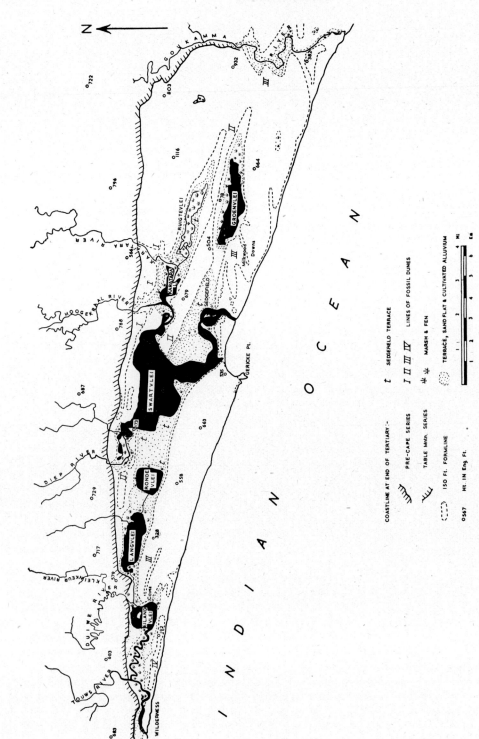

Fig. 1. Map of the coastal strip from Wilderness to the Goukamma river, showing the former coastline (after Potgieter, 1950), the ridges of Pleistocene and Recent dunes lying in front of it, and the coastal lakes in parallel low-lying valleys between the ridges. The symbols I, II, III, IV indicate only approximate homology of the parts of the broken dune ridges, most of which are multiple

From *S. Afr. Journ. Sci.*

The History of Groenvlei, a South African Coastal Lake

ridges, except perhaps about a mile at the Wilderness end, are underlain by old consolidated dune rock which in many places outcrops on the present shore as cliffs and even below tide marks, showing that at least in part these dunes were formed with a lower sea level than at present. The explanation of the origin of the lakes put forward here differs somewhat from those of Schwartz (1905) and Potgieter (1950).

Pollen analysis suggests a climate similar to that of today; over 100 pollen forms have been identified and none appear to represent genera absent from the modern local flora. The pollen spectrum is dominated by heath with *Erica, Cliffortia, Anthospermum*, and other coastal sclerophyllous and ericoid genera. During and before the transgression trees were scarce, but increased slowly, and above 300 cm. more rapidly, this coinciding with the end of the transgression. The

FIG. 2. Groenvlei from the south shore, showing the north shore dune ridge beyond which lies Ruigtevlei. The distant, higher ridge is sand piled against the Tertiary peneplane and rising to over 300 m.

tree pollen spectrum by this time had a composition resembling that of modern coastal woodland.

Ruigtevlei is still open to occasional flooding by Swartvlei water. Groenvlei is isolated from Swartvlei by a 7 m. terrace at Sedgefield, containing a marine shell bed, cemented in places, and separated by a compact red terrestrial sand from the recent loose sandy surface soil (Fig. 3). This sand is continuous with a red band in the local dunes (Fig. 4) which appears to correspond in every way with the red sands which separate the upper Stellenbosch and Fauresmith in this region (Dreyer, 1934, Haughton *et al.*, 1937). This terrace is therefore most probably of late Pleistocene age. At Gericke Point on the far side of the Swartvlei estuary there is a wave-cut bench which also indicates a higher Pleistocene level. A post-Pleistocene sea level, 2 m. or more higher than today has also been suggested (e.g. Mabbut, 1954); the evidence at Groenvlei itself as yet does not indicate such a level.

There must have been a channel below the level of the 7 m. terrace joining the lake to the sea.

95

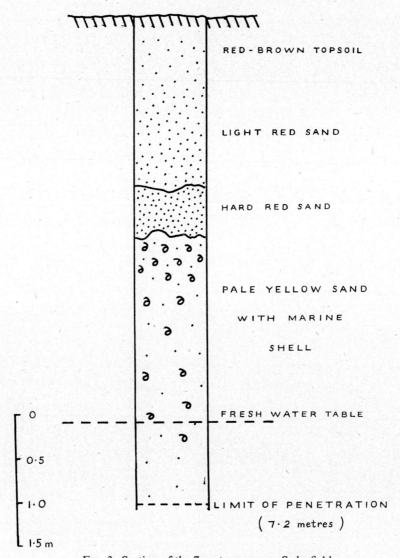

RED-BROWN TOPSOIL

LIGHT RED SAND

HARD RED SAND

PALE YELLOW SAND

WITH MARINE

SHELL

FRESH WATER TABLE

0

0·5

1·0

LIMIT OF PENETRATION

(7·2 metres)

1·5 m

FIG. 3. Section of the 7 m. terrace near Sedgefield

Sediments which may represent this former channel have been traced eastwards for about 150 m. at the Sedgefield end, and westwards for 900 m. at the Groenvlei end. The middle section is lost below a comparatively recent and unconsolidated dune to the south of the valley. No precise dating can be offered as yet. Eustatic rises in sea level mark the whole of the Recent period and may be still continuing. The spread of woodland does not necessarily represent recent pluvial conditions, though a small climatic amelioration is perhaps the most likely explanation. One may not, however, draw this conclusion from a single pollen diagram unbacked by other evidence. Linking up these data with other diagrams, with phases of human occupation, and radio carbon dating seem to be the likeliest means of further advance. The author is much indebted to the C.S.I.R. for financial assistance in this research.

Fɪɢ. 4. Sedgefield Quarry. Dune profile above the consolidated dune rock. From below: 1·2 m. cemented (but not wind-bedded) calcareous sand; 5 m. red, weakly cemented, sand; 2·2 m. yellow-buff unconsolidated sand; 1 m. grey sandy surface soil. The true wind-bedded dune rock is not exposed, but probably lies not far below the floor of the excavation

REFERENCES

Dreyer, T. F. (1934), 'The stratification of the superficial deposits at Mossel Bay', *Trans. Roy. Soc. S. Afr.*, 22, (3), pp. 165–9.

Haughton, S. H. and Visser, D. J. L. (1937), 'The geology of the country round Mossel Bay'. Explanation of sheet 201, *Geol. Surv. S. Afr.*, Pretoria.

Mabbut, J. A. (1954), 'Cape Hangklip, a study in coastal geomorphology', *Trans. Roy. Soc. S. Afr.*, 34, (1), pp. 17–24.

Potgieter, C. T. (1950), 'The George granite plutons and invaded Pre-Cape sedimentary rocks', *Ann. Univ. Stellenbosch*, 26a, pp. 323–412.

Schwartz, E. H. L. (1905), 'Geological survey of the coastal plateau in the Divisions of George, Knysna, Uniondale and Humansdorp', *10th Ann. Rept. Geol. Comm., Cape Dept. Agric.*, pp. 49–93.

12

Les Brèches ossifères de Kakontwe

par DOM ADALBERT ANCIAUX DE FAVEAUX, O.S.B.

Ces brèches furent découvertes il y a des années déjà. Le front de l'exploitation des bancs calcaires se trouvait à cet endroit et entamait la colline au niveau inférieur, éventrant une vieille grotte comblée où, au plafond et sur les parois, s'étaient ressoudés des blocs de calcaire et autres éléments d'éboulis.

Le sens de l'éventrement est Nord-Sud.

Vers 1938, des éléments osseux, spécialement des dents de grands mammifères et des débris de chauve-souris, furent recueillis par le Dr F. Cabu.

Ces récoltes se trouvent au Musée Léopold II à Elisabethville. Des déterminations furent faites par le Dr H. B. S. Cooke.

En 1953, l'extraction a été reprise par nous de façon plus systématique, aidé en cela par M. Hédo, exploitant des carrières.

Le front de la carrière B, actuellement beaucoup plus au Sud, a laissé la petite colline contenant les brèches hors de l'exploitation.

Cette colline composée d'éléments hétéroclites ressoudés par un ciment calcaire n'offre aucun intérêt industriel.

LES BRÈCHES

A part quelques éléments dans une brèche très dure sur le front Nord, les brèches ossifères se trouvent, de façon générale, sur le front Est (Fig. 1).

Nous pouvons y reconnaître trois groupes distincts, ou peut-être quatre.

1. Une brèche d'une dureté faible, rouge-foncé, la plus importante, formée dans des cheminées descendant à travers le massif jusqu'à sa base.

Une poche à droite à l'angle Nord-Est, vers le bas, a livré de nombreux éléments.

2. Ce second groupe comprend des brèches plus dures, de teinte plus claire, souvent encadrées de travertin. Dans la Fig. 2 de l'angle Nord-Est, cette brèche se rencontre au-dessus à droite de la petite excavation inférieure.

Les éléments recueillis dans ces deux groupes ne paraissent offrir que peu de différences, si ce n'est, dans le groupe 2, des traces abondantes de coquilles non déterminées encore.

La variation de teinte provient probablement de variations climatiques mineures.

3. Ce groupe comprend de petits niveaux, souvent alternés, de brèches dures et de niveaux de calcite, plafonds et planchers de petites excavations comblées. Les éléments sub-fossiles y sont, en règle générale, ceux de chauve-souris et de petits rongeurs.

L'EXPLOITATION

Celle-ci a débuté par l'excavation de la petite poche de l'angle Nord-Est.

De très gros blocaux de brèche libres en face de cette excavation, probablement descendus de la partie supérieure, a donné de très nombreuses dents de mammifères : equidés, bovidés et une molaire humaine.

Le surplomb central, miné par le haut, a libéré une brèche actuellement en exploitation.

FIG. 1. Front Est

FIG. 2. Angle Nord-Est

(*a*) (*b*)

FIG. 3. Pointe de javeline 'Still Bay'

Section One

ÉLÉMENTS PRÉHISTORIQUES

Dans la brèche du premier groupe a été trouvée une très belle pointe de javeline 'Still Bay' en quartz, parfaitement typique. Fig. 3 (a) et (b) en donne les deux faces ainsi que des éléments osseux l'accompagnant.

Quelques rares éléments de technique levallois sur quartz ont été également trouvés dans la brèche ainsi qu'un gros galet de quartzite ayant servi de percuteur.

L'un ou l'autre os, entre autres une dent d'équidé, paraissent bien avoir été appointés. Le travail y est sans finesse.

De très nombreux fragments d'os ont été refendus intentionellement.

ÉLÉMENTS SUB-FOSSILES

Un premier lot de plus de 250 dents a été confié au Dr H. B. S. Cooke de l'Université de Witwatersrand qui a bien voulu en assumer la détermination. Je lui dois de très vifs remerciements ainsi qu'à Mr James Kitching de l'Institut Bernard Price pour la Recherche Paléontologique qui a bien voulu terminer le dégagement du matériel de sa gangue et en assurer la conservation par un vernis. Qu'ils soient assurés de toute ma reconnaissance. Un lot plus important encore, si toutefois ce n'est pas abuser de leur complaisance, sera envoyé dans un très proche avenir.

SHORT REPORT ON A COLLECTION OF FOSSIL MAMMALS FROM KAKONTWE, BELGIAN CONGO
by Dr H. B S. Cooke, University of the Witwatersrand, Johannesburg

MATERIAL

The collection comprises more than two hundred and fifty teeth or fragments of teeth discovered in a calcareous breccia at Kakontwe in the Belgian Congo by Dom Adalbert Anciaux de Faveaux, O.S.B., and sent to the writer for identification. The teeth are heavily mineralized and resemble very closely in state of preservation those from the Australopithecine-bearing cave breccias of Taung and the Transvaal. The specimens were cleaned free of adhering matrix mainly by dissolving the adhering matter in weak acetic acid solution while organic matter is protected from attack by means of a coating of varnish. Thanks are due to Mr James Kitching of the Bernard Price Institute for Palaeontological Research for undertaking much of this delicate task.

FAUNAL CONTENT

A few milk teeth of antelopes have not been certainly identified and the rodent material requires further study. The faunal list given below comprises eighteen species, none of which is extinct, and it is unlikely that the few unidentified specimens will add more than two or three species to this list.

Primates
Homo sapiens is represented by a single lower molar of a young adult individual, the crown of the tooth being unworn.
Papio ursinus. There is one unworn lower molar of a baboon.

Insectivora
Myosorex and *Elephantulus* appear to be present.

Rodentia
Hystrix africae-australis is present and *Cryptomys* may also be represented.

Carnivora
Crocuta crocuta is represented by six teeth.
Felis pardus—four teeth.
Thos mesomelas is shown by two partial lower jaws, one of which has lost its teeth.

Perissodactyla

Equus burchelli is plentifully represented by thirty upper cheek teeth or milk teeth and by twenty-three lowers. Some of the upper and lower teeth can be grouped into partial dentitions and from the states of wear it is possible to state that there are at least fifteen different individuals present in the collection.

Suidae

Potamochoerus choeropotamus is present and the eleven specimens belong to at least six individuals.

Phacochoerus aethiopicus is plentiful. There are seventeen teeth or fragments, including nine third molars.

Bovidae

Connochaetes cf. *taurinus* is abundant, there being eleven upper and fifteen lower teeth.

Onotragus leche. There are three upper and nine lower cheek teeth.

Also represented by from five to one specimen each are: *Damaliscus* cf. *pygargus*, *Cephalophus* cf. *natalensis*, *Sylvicapra* cf. *grimmia*, *Strepsiceros strepsiceros* and *Taurotragus oryx*.

CONCLUSIONS

The assemblage represents a typical African savannah and bushveld fauna and includes only living species. It is most probably of late Pleistocene age.

Du matériel envoyé, 138 éléments ont été déterminés. La répartition en pourcentage se faisant comme suit:

Primates	Homo	1	0·72%
	Babouin	1	0·72%
Carnivores	(6 + 4 + 2)	12	8·9%
Equidés	(30 + 23)	53	38%
Bovidés	(11 + 15 + 3 + 9 + 5)	43	32%
Suidés	(11 + 17)	28	20%

CONCLUSIONS

Nature du gisement

Étant donné les éléments rencontrés dans ces brèches du 1 et 2—proportion extraordinairement prédominante de dents, grand nombre des os refendus, rareté, pour ne pas dire absence de grands éléments osseux tels crânes, bassins, etc.—il nous semble que le gisement doit être interprété comme représentant les résidus d'un habitat humain.

Celui-ci devait se trouver en plein-air sur le plateau dominant le site.

Les restes du cuisine, éléments de petites dimensions, entrainés par les eaux dans les fissures du massif, ont été repris par le ciment calciteux.

Age du gisement

Aussi bien les éléments préhistoriques que les conclusions des déterminations faites par le Dr Cooke paraissent nous reporter à la finale du Pleistocène supérieur: industrie 'Still Bay' et faune actuelle.

Il nous paraît toutefois prématuré de donner en ce domaine une affirmation définitive; ces brèches sont toujours en exploitation et il est difficile de prévoir ce qu'elles nous réservent.

Nous ne voudrions pas terminer ces quelques mots sans remercier M. Hédo pour l'amabilité avec laquelle il nous a aidé dans notre travail, en mettant à notre disposition de la main d'œuvre et en faisant exécuter les minages nécessaires.

13

Répartition de la grande 'faune éthiopienne' du Nord-Ouest Africain du Paléolithique à nos jours

par R. A. MAUNY

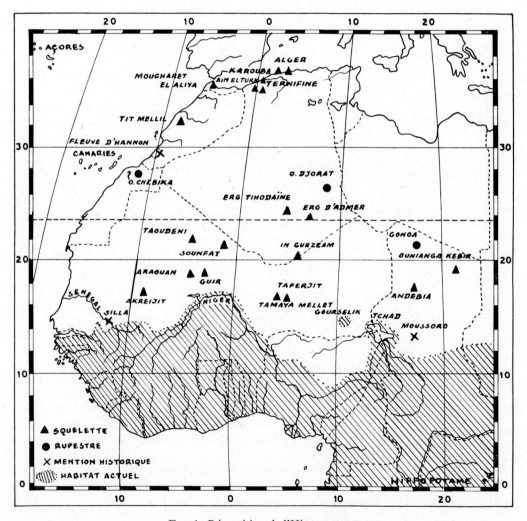

FIG. 1. Répartition de l'Hippopotame

La grande 'faune éthiopienne' du Nord-Ouest Africain du Paléolithique à nos jours

QUATRE Vertébrés de grande taille ont été choisis parmi d'autres afin d'illustrer le recul de la grande 'faune éthiopienne' du paléolithique à nos jours dans le Nord-Ouest Africain: l'Hippopotame, le Rhinocéros, l'Eléphant et la Girafe.

Une carte a été établie par espèce, chacune portant:

(*a*) les points où des restes ostéologiques ont été découverts;

(*b*) les sites rupestres où l'espèce considérée est représentée;

(*c*) les points où une mention historique de la présence de ces animaux a été faite hors de l'habitat actuel;

(*d*) en grisé, l'habitat actuel de l'espèce considérée.

A l'époque paléolithique, les quatre espèces étudiées sont présentes dans pratiquement toute l'aire du Nord-Ouest. Les restes sont particulièrement abondants dans le Maghreb, mais au Soudan, l'Erg Tihodaïne a fourni Hippopotame, Rhinocéros et Eléphant.

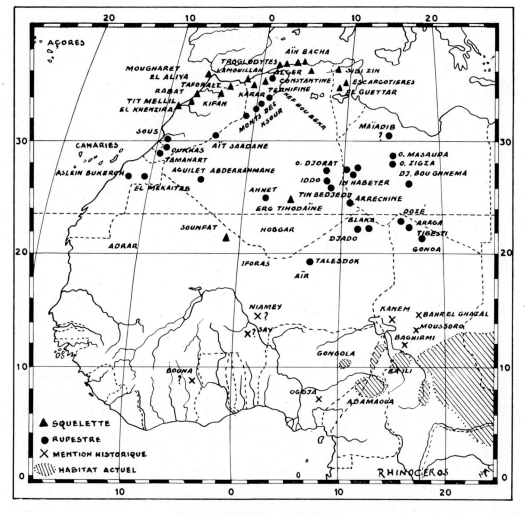

FIG. 2. Répartition du Rhinocéros

103

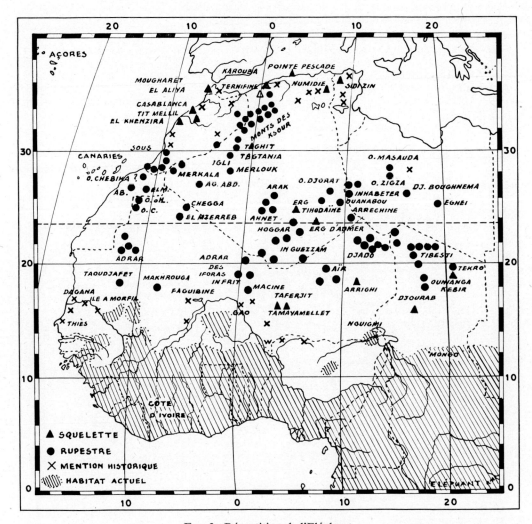

Fɪɢ. 3. Répartition de l'Eléphant

Au néolithique, l'habitat se fragmente en îlots reliques, dont les plus importants sont le Maghreb et les massifs montagneux sahariens. Mais la limite de l'aire de la grande faune éthiopienne est nettement plus septentrionale et arrive au 2° N. avec des saillants englobant les massifs situés plus au Nord. Les représentations rupestres nous fournissent entre autres d'excellentes indications à cet égard.

Seul des quatre espèces considérées, l'Eléphant s'est maintenu au Maghreb pendant l'Antiquité classique; à la même époque, l'on ne peut signaler que deux seules mentions douteuses d'Hippopotame vers le Sud Marocain et de Girafe au Fezzan.

Les mentions historiques de la présence des animaux considérés ne sont abondantes qu'à une époque très récente, à partir du dix-huitième siècle. Elles soulignent le recul effarant enregistré depuis lors, surtout par la faute des soi-disant 'chasseurs' européens, qui ont fait des hécatombes de gibier. La situation se stabilise depuis quelques années par la constitution de réserves de faune.

La grande 'faune éthiopienne' du Nord-Ouest Africain du Paléolithique à nos jours

Tous les points portés sur la carte et la répartition actuelle de la faune ont été établis par le dépouillement de la littérature adéquate du Nord-Ouest africain.

Un article plus détaillé sur la question, avec le renvoi aux sources pour les sites rupestres, est destiné au *Bulletin de l'I.F.A.N.* (Série Sciences Naturelles).

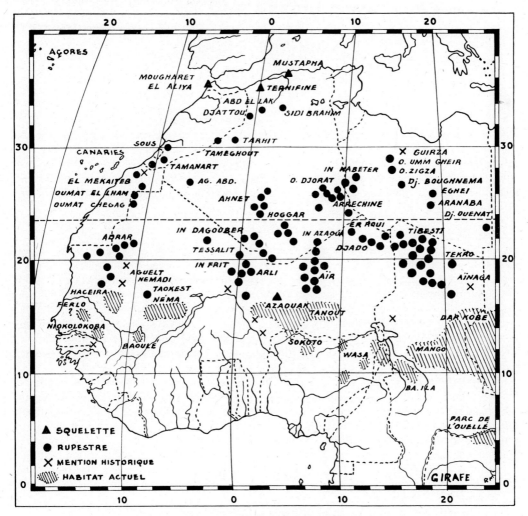

FIG. 4. Répartition de la Girafe

105

14

Kalahari Sands

by ARIE POLDERVAART*

[ABSTRACT]

PETROGRAPHIC work on Kalahari sands in the Bechuanaland Protectorate indicates that the older sands were transported by wind in a general easterly and southeasterly direction. Many of the sands fringing the central Kalahari appear to be redeposited and younger in age. Those in the southeastern Protectorate were probably blown back in a westerly direction from the Bushveld region. Those in the northeastern Protectorate may have been blown in a general southerly direction.

INTRODUCTION

VAN RIET LOWE recently called for a definition of the term 'Kalahari sands', and indeed it would appear that such a definition is long overdue. Wayland† has responded to this appeal and has defined the Kalahari sands as 'the desert sand that was blown over much of southern Africa approximately during the post-Acheulean/pre-Levallois times of that sub-continent. Neither its beginnings or its endings are likely to have been everywhere completely synchronous, but differences in this respect were probably not great. Its general contemporaneity with the great Gamblian Interpluvial of eastern Africa can hardly be doubted, and the period of its desert régime should be called the Kalaharian'. Many authorities will agree with Wayland's definition of the Kalahari sands, others will not.

Throughout the Bechuanaland Protectorate and in various parts of countries surrounding this territory, there occur deposits of sands of various hues which have been described as Kalahari sands. No doubt these essentially aeolian sands have been wind-transported again and again since their original deposition, and even today the sands are being redistributed in spectacular sandstorms. Are these redeposited sands to be regarded also as Kalahari sands? If not, how can redeposited Kalahari sands be distinguished from original sands—the 'true' Kalahari sands? Finally, what proof is there of the age of the earliest sands? Bond (1950) has remarked, 'There is no difficulty in dating the various redeposited Kalahari sands. The difficulty is with the dating of the earliest phase.'

Unfortunately nearly all research on Kalahari sands has been geological-archaeological, without parallel petrographic work, and nearly all the work has been conducted in outlying areas of Kalahari sands. It remains to be proved whether the earliest sands of these outlying areas are also the earliest sands of the Kalahari proper. Lacking detailed petrographic data it is impossible to compare the sands with one another. In several instances it has been proved through the writer's work that sands from the eastern Protectorate from which Wayland derives most of his evidence

---

* Published with permission of the Director, Geological Survey, Bechuanaland Protectorate.

The substance of the present paper was originally written as a contribution to a joint account of the sands of the Kalahari. The first part of this account was written by E. J. Wayland, then Director of the Geological Survey of the Bechuanaland Protectorate. Wayland's contribution has already been incorporated in a more comprehensive paper (1954).

† Unpublished manuscript.

for a post-Acheulean/pre-Levallois age of 'the Kalahari sand' are redeposited sands. In other cases the same appears likely, though final proof is still lacking.

A most promising new line of investigation has been opened through King's (1951) studies of cave deposits in the Transvaal. Unfortunately this work is so far unaccompanied by detailed petrographic studies, a serious handicap when it comes to comparing these sands with surface sands in other areas. In various caves King has found 'older red sands', below implementiferous sands, which contain Australopithecines and are therefore regarded as Villafranchian. The extension of this work to the caves of the Aha Mountains in the remote region of the northwestern Protectorate, and the inclusion of detailed petrographic studies, may eventually lead to the solution of the problem of the Kalahari sands.

Scope of Present Investigation

Over a hundred surface samples of sands have been collected from various parts of the Protectorate, in addition to many borehole samples, and preliminary work has been carried out on these samples. The work done by the writer at Lobatsi includes: (1) sieving of the sands to 5 fractions, (2) determination of the total heavy residue in the two finest fractions, (3) counts of non-opaque heavy minerals in these two fractions, and (4) measurements of the size of certain non-opaque heavy minerals.

Distribution and Characters of the Sands

About 85 per cent of the area of the Protectorate is covered by wind-blown sands, through which protrude only very occasional monadnocks of older rocks. The Kalahari cover is absent from most of the eastern Protectorate, but even here tongues of the sands may extend into the Union, as between Artesia and Palla Road and in the south along the Molopo River.

The colour of the sands is red, pink, brown, buff, white, or grey when mixed with soil. The white sands consist almost entirely of rounded to sub-rounded quartz grains, the degree of rounding varying with the grain-size. The smallest grains are usually the most angular, while the largest grains are well-rounded and frequently show etched and pitted surfaces. Reddish or brownish sands derive their colour from thin coatings of hydrous iron oxides on the grains, easily removed by boiling with dilute acid. The total heavy residue generally amounts to less than 0·5 per cent and is most often 0·1–0·3 per cent by weight of the total sand, but a few sands (e.g. those from the Victoria Falls) may contain heavy residues aggregating to more than 0·5 per cent. Most prominent among the heavy residue minerals of typical Kalahari sands from the central parts of the Protectorate are zircon, tourmaline, staurolite, kyanite, and rutile, including brookite which together aggregate to more than 95 per cent of the non-opaque heavy minerals. Other minerals such as garnet, sillimanite, epidote, and andalusite may become conspicuous and exceed 5 per cent in the redeposited sands. Augite, amphibole, green spinel, lawsonite, monazite, and corundum have been found in some sand samples, but always in small quantities.

The sands of the northeastern Protectorate, between the Rhodesian border, Makarikari, and the Okavango swamps, vary in colour on the surface, but in depth usually below one or more horizons of silcretes and calcretes, there are thick deposits of remarkably pure white sands which in several places also come to the surface. The general surface rises gently towards the Rhodesian border which follows a natural water-shed, and the sand cover also becomes thinner in that direction. Along the border itself there is a large area of black turf with occasional outcrops of Karroo basalts. In Southern Rhodesia on either side of the Gwaai River, there are extensive deposits of red sands, apparently without equivalents of the white sands found in the northeastern Protectorate. In the writer's opinion both the Gwaai River and the Victoria Falls sands represent various redeposited Kalahari sands. The heavy residues of sands of the northeastern Protectorate contain much kyanite which increases in amounts westwards, but the Gwaai River and Victoria Falls sands contain only minor amounts of this mineral.

Section One

Near Makarikari, Lake Dow, and Lake Ngami several sands were collected which rest on former lake deposits. In every case, petrographic data for these sands differ from those of neighbouring sands, and the evidence indicates that they are also redeposited sands. Near Toteng a dune was found which consists of an even younger sand and shows none of the heavy residue minerals which characterize the various Kalahari sands.

South of the Okwa River the sands are generally reddish in colour, though even here white sands may occasionally be found. Staurolite is the characteristic heavy residue mineral of these sands and increases in amounts in westerly direction. The extreme southwestern Protectorate and the adjoining portions of South-West Africa and the Union of South Africa are characterized by long parallel dunes of vivid orange-red, fine-grained sands trending roughly north–south. Between Upington and Kakamas several such dunes extend up to the Orange River, but south of the river the dunes are small, irregular in shape, and trend roughly east–west. No petrographic work has yet been done on these sands.

Between Artesia and Palla Road a tongue of reddish, fine-grained sands extends into the Union. The sands here are thrown up into large dunes trending roughly east–west, and are without doubt redeposited sands. Later redistribution of the sands is evident from examination of various dunes, and is schematically represented in Fig. 1. The sands in the extreme southeastern Protectorate are likewise redeposited sands. It is noteworthy that these sands contain andalusite which increases in amount eastwards. Since andalusite is absent from both the Kalahari sands of the central Protectorate and from the older rocks of the southeastern Protectorate, the presence of this mineral indicates that the sands were derived in part from the Bushveld area. However, other heavy residue minerals characteristic of the typical Kalahari sands, are also present in the redeposited sands. Hence it is thought that these redeposited sands were in first instance blown eastwards or southeastwards, but at a later period were blown back into the Kalahari.

Borehole records and field observations indicate that silcretes and calcretes may occur at any level in the sands and do not form part of a continuous horizon, but are probably present as intercalated lenses of varying size. Often calcretes occur immediately below silcretes and examination of thin sections indicates that practically all silcretes are calcretes replaced by silica, there being a continuous series between typical silcretes with little or no calcite, and typical calcretes with little or no silica. Ferricretes occur below the sands in several places in the southeastern Protectorate, but in nearly all cases the sands in question have been shown to be redeposited. It is doubtful whether ferricretes underlie the typical Kalahari sands in the central parts of the Protectorate.

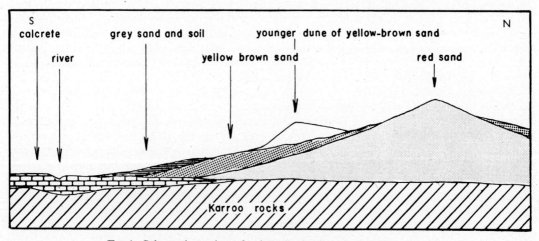

FIG.1. Schematic section of a dune in the Artesia-Palla Road area

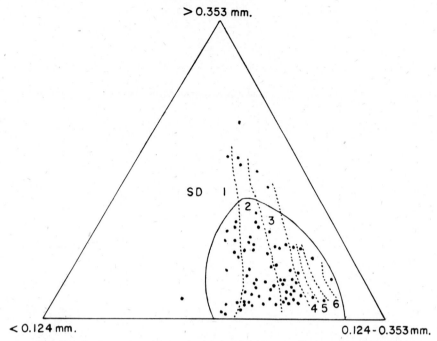

FIG. 2. Size distribution of quartz grains in Kalahari sands, Bechuanaland Protectorate

Wayland* considers the Botletle quartzite (silcrete?) to underlie the true Kalahari sands near Samedupe Drift, but the alternative explanation of the Botletle rocks (and the dark clay which apparently underlies them) occurring below redeposited sands, with older Kalahari sands below the dark clays, has not been ruled out entirely. A borehole north of Makarikari encountered successively sand, silcrete and calcrete, diatomaceous earth, dark clay, silcrete and calcrete, and was finally stopped at 124 feet, in sand. Evidently there are Kalahari sands and Kalahari sands and caution should be exercised in declaring any sand to be 'the Kalahari sand'.

GRADING OF KALAHARI SANDS

Seventy-seven samples of surface sands have been sieved using B.S.I. sieves Nos. 22, 30, 44, and 120. In Fig. 2 weight percentages of the three fractions >0.353 mm., 0.124–0.353 mm., and <0.124 mm. diameter are plotted on a triangular diagram. The various fields are drawn to include samples for which the ratio $SD = \dfrac{\text{weight percentage } 0.124\text{–}0.353 \text{ mm.}}{\text{weight percentage} < 0.124 \text{ mm.}}$ equals 1, 2, 3, 4, etc. As shown in Fig. 3, this ratio diminishes in easterly and southeasterly directions, indicating that more fine-grained material is present in the sands of the eastern and southeastern Protectorate. This in turn may be interpreted as an indication of a northwesterly derivation of the sands.

Various sands of mixed origin show anomalous grading results and fall outside the field of typical Kalahari sands (including wind-blown redeposited sands) delineated in Fig. 2. Their heavy residues show angular fragments of minerals of local derivation (e.g. epidote, amphibole and garnet), in addition to the rounded heavy minerals which characterize the typical Kalahari sands. However, it should be noted that sands may fall within the field of typical Kalahari sands even though they are of mixed origin, or of younger age. This is the case for the dune sand of Toteng, for example.

* Unpublished manuscript.

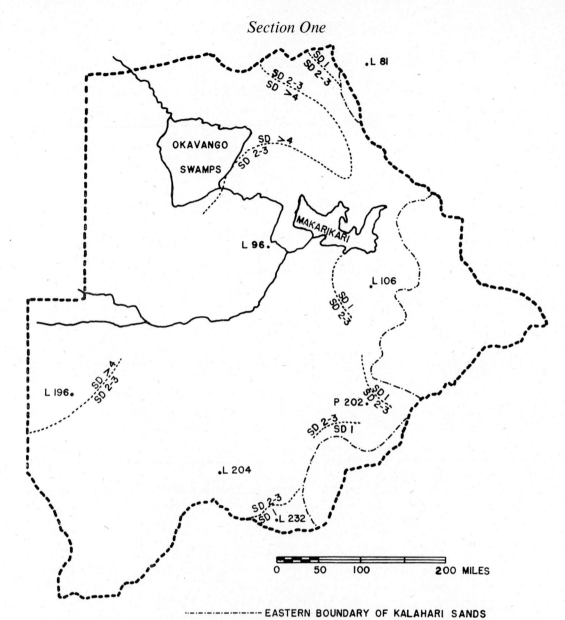

FIG. 3. Geographic distribution of SD (sand-dust) ratios in Kalahari sands, Bechuanaland Protectorate

NON-OPAQUE HEAVY RESIDUE MINERALS OF KALAHARI SANDS

Data for total heavy residues of sand samples show no zonal regularities in the distribution of the sands. As noted, most of the sands contain 0·1–0·3% of heavy residue, but in a few samples this exceeds 0·5%. Sands of mixed origin, or of younger age generally contain greater amounts of heavy residue than the so-called 'typical Kalahari sands'. The Victoria Falls sands contain more than 0·5% of heavy residue.

Characteristic heavy residue minerals of typical Kalahari sands are zircon, tourmaline, staurolite, kyanite, and rutile. It might be expected that zircon, tourmaline, and rutile increase or remain constant in heavy residues of series of samples away from their source while kyanite and staurolite decrease in amount and size (Smithson, 1950). Table I lists data (in percentages) for 19 Kalahari surface sands between Ukwe Pan and Kanye. It may be seen that in a general manner staurolite and kyanite decrease while zircon increases from west to east. These tendencies are by no means regular, nor can great regularity be expected in the variation of heavy mineral constituents of the sands. Tourmaline and rutile vary in irregular fashion and no conclusions can be drawn from variations in the amounts of these two minerals. Fig. 4 shows histograms of the diameters of 100

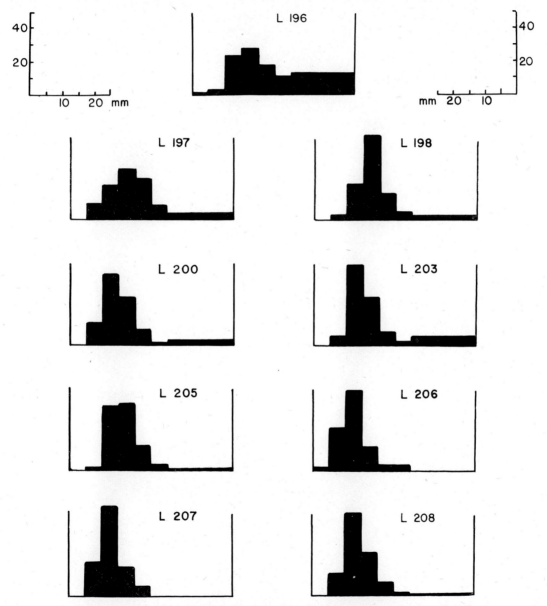

FIG. 4. Histograms of maximum diameters of 100 staurolite grains in series of Kalahari surface sands from Ukwe Pan to Kanye

111

staurolite grains in 9 of the samples. Again variations are not regular, but the general tendency is for the majority of staurolite grains to become smaller eastwards.

Bond (1948) measured diameters of the largest staurolite grains in heavy residues of Southern Rhodesian sands and found that these diminished in regular fashion from north to south, which fact was regarded by him as evidence that the sands were derived from the north (Miami area) and transported southwards. Statistically, the method of measuring only the largest grain of any mineral is of doubtful value and it is surprising that Bond found a regular variation in his results. Table II

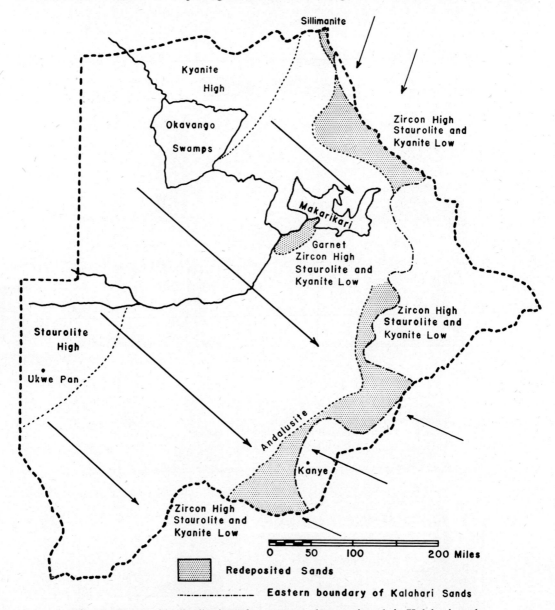

FIG. 5. Geographic distribution of non-opaque heavy minerals in Kalahari sands, Bechuanaland Protectorate

TABLE I

CHARACTERISTIC NON-OPAQUE HEAVY MINERALS IN KALAHARI SAND SURFACE SAMPLES FROM UKWE PAN TO KANYE

Index	L 196	L 197	L 198	P 292	P 285	P 291	L 200	P 286	P 283	L 203	P 287	P 284	P 290	L 205	P 282	L 206	L 207	L 208	P 289
Distance from Ukwe Pan (miles)	32	36	46	113	130	133	137	147	176	194	195	201	208	218	231	246	276	288	303
Zircon	23	25	36	40	41	35	36	43	42	41	52	50	39	43	47	44	46	48	48
Tourmaline	22	26	27	29	29	33	30	25	28	30	23	21	32	32	26	33	33	30	29
Staurolite	41	36	22	20	22	19	20	18	20	18	15	16	19	15	17	16	14	15	15
Kyanite	6	6	8	5	3	4	4	4	3	4	3	5	4	4	3	3	2	2	2
Rutile	8	7	7	6	5	9	10	10	7	7	7	8	6	6	7	4	5	5	6

TABLE II

DIAMETERS OF LARGEST STAUROLITE, ZIRCON, AND ANDALUSITE GRAINS IN KALAHARI SAND SERIES UKWE PAN TO KANYE

Index	L 196	L 197	L 198	P 292	P 285	P 291	L 200	P 286	P 283	L 203	P 287	P 284	P 290	L 205	P 282	L 206	L 207	L 208	P 289
Distance from Ukwe Pan (miles)	32	36	46	113	130	133	137	147	176	194	195	201	208	218	231	246	276	288	303
Diam. largest staurolite (mm.)	0·66	0·48	0·60	0·41	0·52	0·42	0·38	0·64	0·50	0·51	0·46	0·32	0·36	0·42	0·48	0·45	0·51	0·36	0·68
Diam. largest zircon (mm.)	0·33	0·37	0·31	0·30	0·34	0·30	0·33	0·28	0·36	0·40	0·46	0·26	0·30	0·39	0·30	0·39	0·39	0·48	0·32
Diam. largest andalusite (mm.)	—	—	—	—	—	—	—	—	—	—	—	—	—	—	—	—	0·29	0·52	0·56 0·44

TABLE III

ELONGATION OF ZIRCONS IN KALAHARI SANDS, BECHUANALAND PROTECTORATE

Sample Index	No. zircons	Elongation					
		1·0–1·4	1·5–1·9	2·0–2·4	2·5–2·9	3·0–3·9	4·0
L 196	200	99	68	28	2	3	—
L 81	200	82	81	23	6	7	1
L 96	200	112	62	18	4	4	—
L 106	200	109	74	14	2	1	—
L 204	200	105	60	26	5	3	1
P 202	200	107	64	16	6	7	—
L 232	200	83	69	36	9	3	—
Total Zircons	1400	697	478	161	34	28	2
Per cent		49·8	34·2	11·5	2·4	2·0	0·1

shows the largest diameters of grains of staurolite, zircon, and andalusite encountered in the heavy residues of sands between Ukwe Pan and Kanye. Angular grains of andalusite are present in the eastern sands, but rarely exceed 2% of the non-opaque heavy minerals. There is little regularity in the values for the diameters of the largest grains. Table III shows elongations of zircons measured in 7 samples of Kalahari sands (for locations see Fig. 3). Most striking is the lack of consistent variations in these data.

Fig. 5 shows in a generalized manner the variations of zircon, staurolite, and kyanite in surface sands throughout the Protectorate. Arrows show the directions in which kyanite and staurolite decrease (also andalusite and sillimanite when indicated) and zircon increases. They are believed to represent directions of transport, small arrows representing directions of transport of the redeposited sands. Shaded areas represent redeposited sands characterized mainly by the minerals shown. Borehole samples from the northeastern Protectorate indicate that in vertical sections the sands may show great variations in grain-size and heavy residue minerals. Unfortunately, borehole samples are only available from the northeastern Protectorate and not from other parts of the Kalahari.

CONCLUSIONS

Wayland's definition of the 'true' Kalahari sands being of post-Acheulean/pre-Levallois age admits the possibility of there being older, pre-Kalahari desert sands, while the upper age limit of the Kalahari sands remains undefined. The present writer's petrographic work on Kalahari surface sands indicates that many of the sands in outlying areas are redeposited and of younger age than the surface sands which occur in the western and central parts of the Protectorate. It is not known whether these sands cover yet older desert formations. The solution to the problem of the Kalahari sands is evidently to be found in these remote parts of the Protectorate, rather than in the regions marginal to the Kalahari where geological-archaeological work has so far been concentrated. Detailed work on cave deposits, as carried out by King in the Transvaal, appears a most promising line of investigation.

Petrographical data obtained so far indicate that the older surface sands were derived from the northwest and blown in easterly to southeasterly directions. These sands are characterized by zircon, tourmaline, kyanite, staurolite, and rutile, other non-opaque heavy residue minerals being scarce, rare, or absent. In the northwest kyanite predominates, while further south its place is taken by staurolite. Redeposited sands are characterized by these same minerals, while in addition other minerals may become prominent (e.g. epidote, garnet, sillimanite, or andalusite). The southeastern sands all contain andalusite, which is regarded as evidence that these sands were in later times blown back into the desert from the Bushveld region, banking up against and spreading out over the older sands. Evidently there are Kalahari sands and Kalahari sands, their ages extending into most recent times. The age of the earliest sands is as yet not established; meanwhile it is largely a matter of choice which sand is to be called the 'true' Kalahari sand, while it is as yet unknown what distribution in depth and in area the various sands have in the Protectorate.

REFERENCES

Bond, G. (1948), 'The direction of origin of the Kalahari sand of Southern Rhodesia', *Geol. Mag.*, 85, pp. 305–13.

Bond, G. (1950), in J. D. Clark, *The Stone Age cultures of Northern Rhodesia*, South African Archaeol. Soc., Cape Town.

King, L. C. (1951), 'The geology of the Makapan and other caves', *Roy. Soc. South Africa, Trans.*, 33, pp. 121–51.

Smithson, F. (1950), 'The mineralogy of arenaceous deposits', *Sci. Progress*, 149, pp. 10–21.

Wayland, E. J. (1954), 'Outlines of Prehistory and Stone Age climatology in the Bechuanaland Protectorate', *Mem. Acad. roy. Sci. Colon.*, Sect. Sci. Nat. et med., XXV, fasc. 4.

15

Quaternary Sands at the Victoria Falls

by GEOFFREY BOND

[ABSTRACT]

GRADING curves and surface texture analysis of Kalahari Sand and sands derived from it in the recent river deposits of the Zambezi show significant differences. These results have been applied to various Quaternary sands from the Victoria Falls area in an attempt to show whether they have been redeposited by wind, water or hill-wash. The bearing of these results on the climatic interpretation of the deposits is briefly discussed.

    I. Introduction
   II. The Parent Kalahari Sand
  III. Recent Zambezi river sands
  IV. Quaternary sands
       (1) Stratigraphy
       (2) The sub-Rubble sands
       (3) The supra-Rubble sands
       (4) Sands associated with terraces
   V. Discussion
  VI. References

I INTRODUCTION

THE Quaternary sequence around the Victoria Falls includes sandy deposits generally stained some shade of red by iron oxides, and containing a high proportion of well-rounded grains. This combination of colour and grain shape is reminiscent of sands of aeolian origin, and there has been a tendency to interpret them as wind-blown sands. The parent material from which they were all derived was, however, the Kalahari Sand, which overlies the Karroo Basalts throughout this part of the Zambezi valley. There is no doubt that this was originally an aeolian sand; no other origin could account for its distribution and characters.

Because this aeolian sand was the only one available for redistribution within the area during the Quaternary, the climatic significance of sands derived from it must be carefully assessed, since they are bound to have inherited some of its features. Once the Zambezi had cut a valley through the Kalahari Sand, scarps were formed from which, by short journeys, redeposited sands could be derived. Such short journeys enhance the chances of inherited features in the resulting deposits.

Under such conditions of topography and supply of raw material, there are three main ways in which redeposited sand could be formed. These are hill-wash, river transport and wind transport, each of which might imply a different climatic setting. The topographic setting of the resulting sediment may not be sufficient criterion for distinguishing between such redeposited sands. This applies particularly to sands overlying gravels on terraces.

The presence of a high proportion of well-rounded grains in these sands must be expected as an

115

inherited feature. Roundness is merely a measure of the maturity of a sand grain; once acquired it is stable and hard to modify. Iron oxide staining is a secondary character not diagnostic in itself. Neither of these features can be used in this sedimentary context as criteria of aeolian action. Features more sensitive to change under limited transport must be found in such a case.

The two most easily modified features of such deposits are the surface textures of the grains of various size fractions, and the grain size distribution itself. The first is a feature of individual sedimentary particles, and the second of the sediment in bulk.

Owing to the unusual simplicity of the regional geology, the grain sizes, shapes and surface textures of the parent material are already determined and uniform over the area. The first stage in this investigation was, therefore, to determine them in the parent sand and see how they are changed during transport in the waters of the Zambezi, in the placid reaches above the Falls, and in the turbulent gorges below. One aspect of this work has already been published (Bond, 1954), but only dealt with surface textures of well rounded grains of quartz in a restricted size range. Briefly, it was found that grains of about 0·5 mm. diameter in the aeolian sand were dull and frosted all over, due to minute bruises and scratches, but after transport in the Zambezi the frosting was removed and replaced by a brilliant glassy polish.

During the present work surface textures of grains between 0·75–0·125 mm. have been examined in conjunction with grading analysis over the same size range. It was thought that this combination of characters might decide whether a redeposited sand was blown or transported by the Zambezi itself.

The grading analyses are shown on non-logarithmic paper and need little explanation. As it proved of little value to examine the surface textures of the very fine particles the size range shown on the curves only goes down to 0·125 mm.

On each figure there is an upper set of curves which is an attempt to show surface textures of the various size fractions on at least a semi-quantitative basis, and needs some explanation. For grading analysis the sands were divided into eight fractions and a large number of grains from each fraction dry mounted and examined for surface texture.

It is easy to see if all grains are frosted or polished, but in the narrow range of sizes where these textures overlap results were recorded as 'majority frosted, a few polished'; 'some polished, some frosted'; 'majority polished, a few frosted'. With the two end points 'all frosted' and 'all polished' this gives 5 points, and taking 'some polished, some frosted' as 50% they can be plotted as rough percentages of polished and frosted grains. The size at which the two textures exchange dominance can be found within narrow limits from these diagrams.

Actual counting of grains would perhaps have been more satisfactory, but at this stage it was not felt that the extra labour involved was justified. Repeating the observations after a lapse of several days showed that results were reproduceable within very narrow limits by observation alone, without the need for grain counts.

II The Parent Kalahari Sand

The older Kalahari sand has a wide distribution in the western part of Southern Rhodesia, and wherever it has been sampled its grading curves and surface texture characters are remarkably uniform.

Fig. 1 (ABC) shows the grading curves for size fractions down to 0·125 mm. for three typical samples from widely spaced localities. The maximum distance between samples is over 200 miles yet the two features in question are almost identical. The grading curve is rather straight, the percentage of fines below 0·125 mm. is about 20% and the upper size limit is about 0·75 mm. The critical size where frosted grains give way to polished ones is about 0·25 mm.

These are the characteristics of the raw material for all the Quaternary sands in the Victoria Falls area.

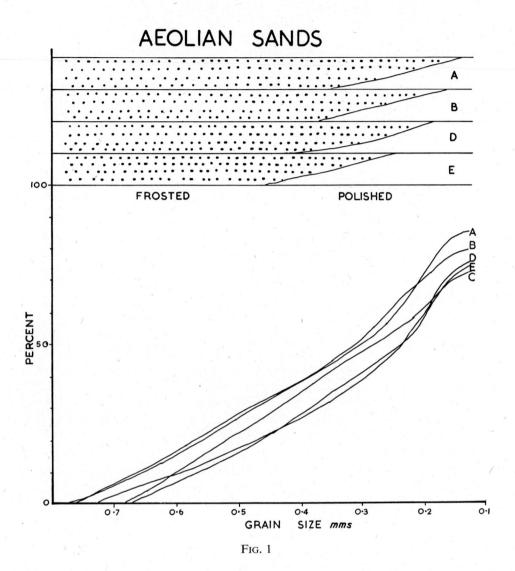

FIG. 1

III RECENT ZAMBEZI SANDS

Figure 2 shows grading curves for 3 samples of sands from the present Zambezi sand islands and flood platforms. They differ considerably between themselves, reflecting differing fluviatile environments, but none of them has a shape like the typical Kalahari Sand curve. They are strongly concave upwards.

The frosting curves are just as distinct. Within the size ranges present all grains are highly polished. Both features differ so much from the aeolian pattern that, in combination, they offer some hope of distinguishing between aeolian and fluviatile sands in the Quaternary deposits.

RIVER SANDS

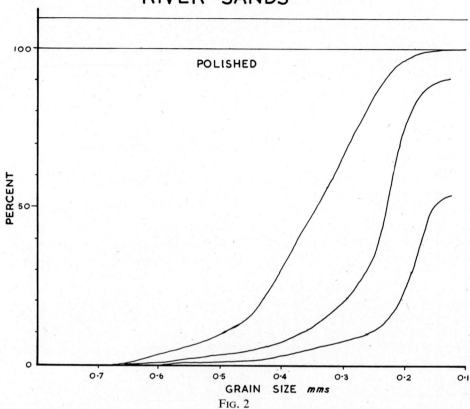

FIG. 2

IV THE QUATERNARY SANDS

(1) *Stratigraphy*

The Quaternary succession at the Victoria Falls is rather complex. It has been described in detail by Clark (1950) and may be summarized as follows:

	Recent Sands	(3)
Erosion		
	Low level degradation terrace Sand	(3)
	Calcareous Alluvium	(1)
Erosion		
	Sand of Kalahari type Gravels and sands	(5)
Erosion		
	Redeposited Kalahari Sand (supra-Rubble sand)	(1)
	Younger Gravels group	
Erosion		
	Land Rubble Older gravels group	(1)
	Sand of Kalahari type (sub-Rubble sand)	(1)
Erosion		

Quaternary Sands at the Victoria Falls

The numbers in brackets indicate the horizons and numbers of samples studied.

(2) *The sub-Rubble sands* (= No. 3 *Sable rouge* of Cahen and Lepersonne)

These sands are well-exposed in the railway cutting near the hotel, in the section originally described by Maufe (1939). They have been referred to in various publications since, and were shown to be redeposited sand by Cahen and Lepersonne (1952). They are red, unbedded and closely similar to Kalahari Sand. The grading and surface texture curves are included in Fig. 1 (D), and there is no feature in either curve by which they can be distinguished from the parent material. There seems little doubt that they were redistributed by wind action.

(3) *The supra-Rubble sand* (= No. 6 *Sable rouge à industrie sangoenne* of Cahen and Lepersonne)

This is exposed in the same section as the sub-Rubble sand, but there is a much greater thickness of it. It was called by Maufe (op. cit.) 'Red Kalahari Sand', and has a thickness of 40 feet in the exposures in the northern cutting.

This sand overlies the Carstone Rubble Bed with a Sangoan Industry and is known to be a redistributed sand, in spite of its close similarity with Kalahari Sand, to which its relationship is clearly shown in Fig. 4 of Cahen and Lepersonne (1952). Its grading and surface texture curves are shown in Fig. 1 (E) and are indistinguishable from Kalahari Sand. There can be little doubt that this sand was blown, and its thickness indicates that the process continued for some time.

(4) *Sands associated with terraces* (Fig. 3)

A rather varied assemblage is included in this section and the question of sampling raises some problems. The work was done on sand samples already in the collection of the National Museum, which were not specifically taken for the purpose. Consequently conclusions based upon them should be regarded as tentative, but they may indicate a useful approach to the problem. Grading and surface texture curves are given in Fig. 3.

All the samples overlie terraces and consequently could have been deposited either by the river itself or by wind action. In some cases they could even have reached their present resting places by hill-wash either from the original Kalahari Sand, or more probably from scarps exposing the supra-Rubble sands, which themselves were redistributed Kalahari Sand.

Most of the sands are reddened appreciably by iron oxides, but this is regarded as probably a post-depositional change, unless it is inherited. However, very short journeys in water seem to remove iron oxide films.

Only one sample (F) overlying Older Gravels was available. Its grading curve is unlike Kalahari Sand but similar to some from the recent river sands. The critical size for polishing is 0·5 mm. which is much larger than in the aeolian samples. It is concluded that this sand was laid down by the river itself.

Three samples (E, G, H) overlie Younger Gravels. One of these (E) has a grading curve unlike Kalahari Sand and nearly all the grains are polished. This cannot be regarded as aeolian, since it cannot be distinguished from the recent river sands in these two characters.

The second (G) has a grading curve unlike Kalahari Sand and critical size for polishing of 0·65 mm. These characters make it unlikely that the sand was blown, and it was probably deposited by the river itself.

The third sample (H) from sand overlying a Magosian Industry on the 4th Gorge Spur has a grading curve not unlike Kalahari Sand and the critical grain size for polishing is 0·45 mm., which is rather large for aeolian action. Close examination of the grains of this critical size suggests that they were all polished and have been partially refrosted. This may indicate that the sand was first deposited by the river, but that a minor re-arrangement has been made by blowing later. Since, however, polishing is easily damaged by any mechanical disturbance of the sand, it would be unsafe to base conclusions on one sample.

Two samples (C, D) come from 'Terrace III'. Both show grading and surface textures more consistent with deposition by the river than by wind action.

119

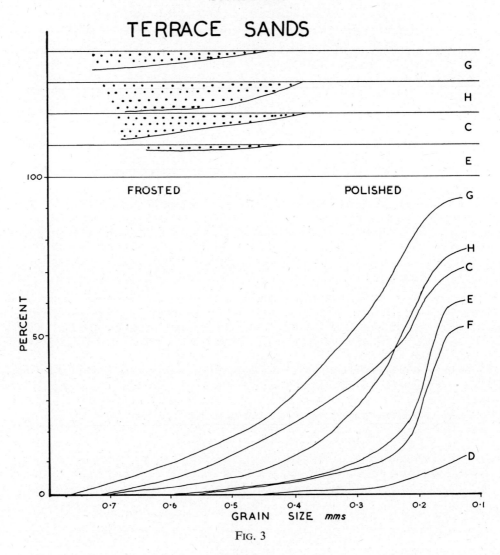

FIG. 3

V DISCUSSION

The number of samples so far examined from the terrace deposits is rather too small on which to base any firm conclusions, but from what has been done so far it seems likely that they were mainly deposited by the waters of the Zambezi itself.

There seems no doubt, however, that the red sand overlying the Sangoan Industry in the railway cuttings was redistributed by wind. A similar red sand overlies a Sangoan-like Industry near Serowe in Bechuanaland, 300 miles to the south. A dry phase of climate is, therefore, indicated at this horizon. Magosian implements are found in the top part of this sand, without any break being apparently noticeable in the field. It would be interesting to apply these techniques to the sand overlying these implements, because from the topography it seems impossible for fluviatile action to have had anything to do with its redistribution. A dry phase is postulated and supported by the evidence of the sand overlying the same industry on the 4th Gorge Spur.

So far no examples of redistribution by hill-wash have been discussed in this paper, but three samples of such deposits have been analysed. They were taken from a single section at Lusu from depths of 2 feet, 2 feet 8 inches and 3 feet 6 inches. The middle horizon contains charcoal and has been dated by radio-carbon as an average of 2139 ± 150 years B.P. In appearance this sand cannot be distinguished from the parent Kalahari Sand, but its grading and surface texture curves show some interesting features.

All three grading curves are very similar and lie in stratigraphical order one above the other. In shape they more closely resemble fluviatile sands than the parent aeolian material. The critical grain size for polishing is however 0·35 mm. which is much closer to the aeolian than fluviatile figure. Such a combination of characters might be expected in a hill-wash. Transport is more or less similar to the bottom load in a stream and there is the same cushioning effect of water between the grains. The distance travelled is short, but may well be sufficient to change the distribution of size fractions. It is probably too short materially to affect the surface textures of the grains, but the change will almost certainly be towards polishing rather than frosting because of the presence of water. The curves for these samples are shown in Fig. 4.

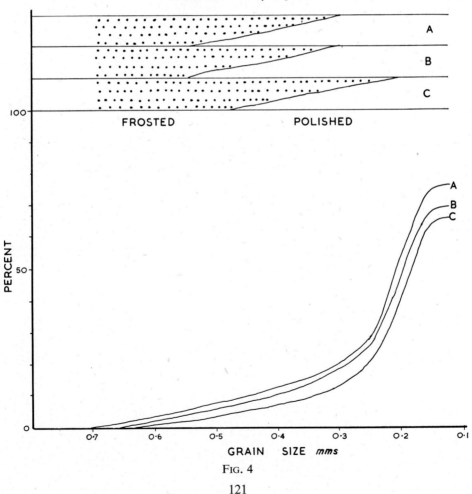

Fig. 4

121

Section One

Although the work done so far has not produced many concrete results, it is felt that since new techniques are involved, an account of it at this stage is worth while.

REFERENCES

Bond, G. (1954), 'Surface textures of sand grains from the Victoria Falls area', *Journ. Sed. Pet.*, 24, No. 3, pp. 191–5.

Cahen, L. and J. Lepersonne (1952), *Equivalence entre le Système du Kalahari du Congo Belge et les Kalahari Beds d'Afrique Australe*, Géol. Soc. Belg. Mem. No. 4.

Clark, J. Desmond (1950), *The Stone Age Cultures of Northern Rhodesia*, S. Afr. Arch. Soc. Memoir.

Maufe, H. B. (1939), 'New sections in the Kalahari Beds at the Victoria Falls', *Trans. Geol. Soc. S. Afr.*, XLI, pp. 211–24.

16

Physiographic Evidence for the Age of the Kalahari Sands of the Southwestern Kalahari

by J. A. MABBUTT

[ABSTRACT]

The red sands of the Southwestern Kalahari overlie unconformably the Kalahari Limestone plain, regarded as an interior expression of an early to mid-Tertiary ('African') erosion cycle. They pre-date the Lower Pleistocene entrenchment of the Kalahari rivers into the Limestone and do not characteristically extend into the end-Tertiary valley plains along the southern Kalahari border. An Upper Tertiary age is accordingly attributed to the original sand emplacement. The direction of movement appears to have been southeasterly, with the physical grain of the underlying surface. Redistribution has formed the seif ridges of the southwestern Kalahari and has led to the invasion by tongues of red sand of the valley plains of end-Tertiary and later date. In this later movement there has been a notable southwesterly component.

WITH increasing knowledge of the ages of the erosion cycles which have fashioned the African landscape, the geomorphological setting has become progressively more important as a dating factor. This is particularly true in dealing with the widespread unfossiliferous terrestrial deposits which characterize much of the interior of this continent, and notably the surface deposits of the Kalahari. The isostatic emergence of the African continent since the close of Karroo deposition has involved upwarping of marginal zones and relative basining of the interior. Repeated uplift has led to the formation of a stepped series of cyclic erosional levels in the 'rim' areas, the age of these surfaces decreasing with altitude. These erosional chapters are recorded in the downwarped areas as depositional phases, and the planed surfaces of the marginal zones may be traced laterally with descending altitude into the unconformities separating these phases. Here, however, they occur in reverse order, with the oldest at the base (Fig. 1). The dating of an erosional level may therefore set a lower limit to the age of any deposit which rests on the corresponding unconformity.

Cahen and Lepersonne (1952) have applied this principle to the dating of their 'Kalahari System' in the Congo Basin and its surrounds. The Plateau Sands (Upper Kalahari) were found to overlie the down-warped early to mid-Tertiary ('African') land surface, and in turn to be bounded by the valley plains of an end-Tertiary erosion cycle. An Upper Tertiary age could therefore be ascribed to the *original* Kalahari Sands of this area, although later redistributions were shown to have occurred on younger river terraces. Corroborative results were obtained by Janmart (1953) in North-east Angola.

Recent work on the geomorphology of Namaqualand has allowed a similar approach to the dating of the sands of the Southwestern Kalahari (Mabbutt, 1955). Red sands of Kalahari type overlie with marked unconformity the Kalahari Limestone, the upper surface of which forms a plain regarded as the interior or 'Kalahari' expression of the African erosion cycle. Surface-limestone on a corresponding erosional level on the Bushmanland Plateau, south of the Orange River,

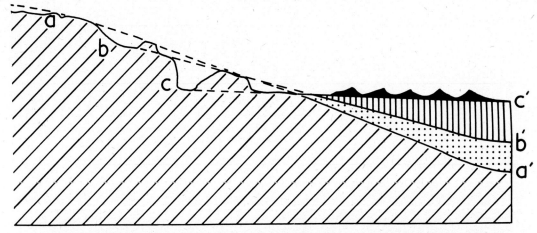

FIG. 1. The relationship of successive erosion surfaces in an upwarped 'rim' area to the corresponding depositional sequence in an adjoining basin. Erosion levels *a*, *b*, and *c*, are downwarped and appear within the basin in reverse order as the unconformities *a'*, *b'*, *c'*

has yielded fossil fragments of an early Pliocene horse, *Notohipparion namaquense* (Haughton, 1932). The physical setting therefore sets a mid-Tertiary date as an *ante quam non* for the red sand cover of the Southwestern Kalahari.

In this region the Kalahari Limestone plain is traversed by a simple N.W.–S.E. drainage, consequent on the regional slope, and which, on geological grounds, must already have existed in the later stages of formation of the Limestone, prior to the emplacement of the Kalahari Sands. Since it is improbable that such effective sand movement could have occurred discordantly to the regional gradient and the lines of the pre-existing drainage, and in view of the signs that river transport may have been partly responsible (Rogers, 1934), there is, on physiographic grounds, strong *prima facie* evidence that the direction of original sand advance was southeastward. The postulated movement is in accord with the northwesterly wind direction which prevails during the summer months in these latitudes.

Although the physical setting of the sands differs in detail from that in the Congo and Zambezi basins, where red sand scarps bound the end-Tertiary valley plains, the surface sands of the South-western Kalahari likewise occupy the interfluves, and the entrenched valleys of the Auob, Nossob and Molopo Rivers remain effective barriers to sand movement, despite post-Tertiary desiccation and decline in flow. As the incision of these rivers below the Kalahari Limestone surface occurred in the Lower Pleistocene, the emplacement of the original sand cover across the area must have been completed by the close of the Tertiary Era. Along the southern border of the Kalahari, also, unbroken sandveld does not extend significantly beyond the limits of the African erosion surface (Fig. 2); except as restricted dune belts the sands are lacking from the broad valleys and Lower or Middle Pleistocene terrace gravels of the Bak and Hygap (Lower Molopo) Rivers (Brain and Mason, 1955). This distribution is entirely in accord with the evidence from the interior of the Kalahari given above, namely that the original sand cover is of Upper Tertiary age.

That redistribution has occurred more than once, notably before and after the period of the African Chelles-Acheul culture (Middle Pleistocene), is known from geological and archaeological evidence in the Bechuanaland Protectorate (Wayland, 1954) and in the Vaal River valley (van Riet Lowe, 1952), and the effects of such redistributions have naturally been most marked along the southern fringe of the Kalahari sandveld, where the sand cover was thinnest and most mobile. South of Rietfontein, in the only area in which the Kalahari Sands significantly transgress beyond the lower limit of the African surface, the sands are restricted to sub-parallel dune belts separated

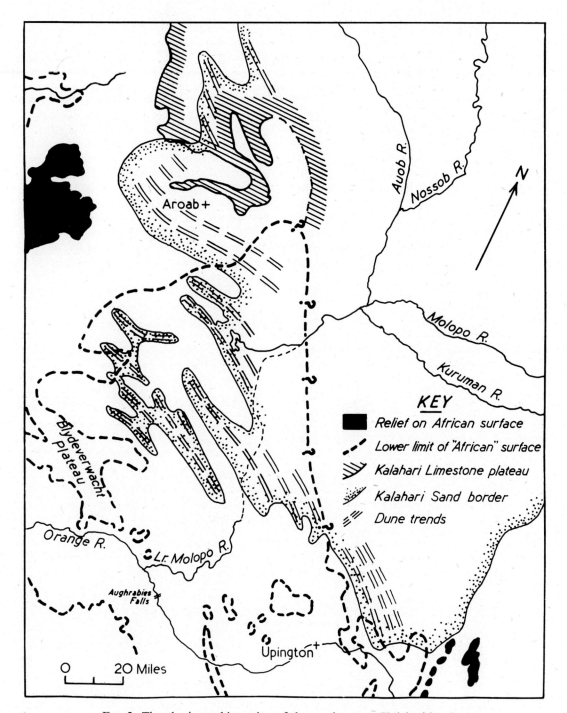

FIG. 2. The physiographic setting of the southwestern Kalahari border

by corridors of hard ground. These sand tracts may reasonably be attributed to one such Pleistocene phase of renewed movement, also possibly fluvial in part, since red sands underlie Lower or Middle Pleistocene gravels in the Bak River valley (Brain and Mason, op. cit.). The map evidence indicates a movement essentially westwards, into the eastern portion of the end-Tertiary embayment about the Lower Molopo River (Fig. 2).

As a result of subsequent redistribution, the level sandveld of the inner Kalahari gives place, along its southwestern fringe, to a zone of parallel seif dunes which exhibit a fairly regular trend. In the south, particularly, these dune lines run obliquely to the river valleys, and yet maintain a regional continuity, which must indicate that the rearrangement of the sand cover was unaffected by, and therefore occurred later than the Lower Pleistocene pluvial period of valley entrenchment.

The dune trend swings from N.N.W. north of Upington to W.N.W. across the Mier Country, and thence back to N.W. and N.N.W. in South-West Africa. These trends are in keeping with the current direction of the prevalent summer winds, which is chiefly northwesterly, but seif dune formation is essentially characteristic of areas with a notable sub-prevalent wind component (Bagnold, 1941). This would seem to have been easterly and northeasterly at the time of seif formation, as shown by the former slip faces on minor dune crests (Lewis, 1936), by the encroachment of dunes on northeast valley margins, as at Askham in the Kuruman River valley, and by the sand-barred eastern margins of the larger pans in the Mier Country, such as Haakschein Vlei (Du Toit, 1926). Winds from these quarters are now more characteristic of the winter half of the year, and it is interesting to speculate whether the greater frequency of easterly winds during the period of sand movement might not have been associated with a longer duration of 'winter season' conditions within the climatic year, and hence with the drier climate then prevailing. These dunes are now fixed and vegetated, and, like the still older river valleys, are fossil features of the landscape, but they would appear to record a Pleistocene period of Kalahari Sand redistribution in which the earlier southeastward movement was replaced or modified by a southwesterly or westerly component.

REFERENCES

Bagnold, R. A. (1941), *The Physics of Blown Sand and Desert Dunes*, Methuen, London.
Brain, C. K. and R. J. Mason (1955), 'A Later African Chelles-Acheul Site near Nakop, South Kalahari', *S. Afr. Archaeol. Bull.*, X, pp. 22–5.
Cahen, L. and J. Lepersonne (1952), 'Équivalence entre le Système du Kalahari du Congo Belge et les Kalahari Beds d'Afrique Australe', *Mem. Soc. Belge de Géol.*, Sec. 8, No. 4, pp. 1–64.
Du Toit, A. L. (1926), 'The Mier Country', *S. Afr. Geog. Journ.*, IX, pp. 21–6.
Janmart, J. (1953), *The Kalahari Sands of the Lunda (N.E. Angola), their Earlier Redistributions and the Sangoan Culture*, Diamang Museu do Dundo, Publiçaçoés Culturais, No. 20, pp. 1–64, Lisbon.
Lewis, A. D. (1936), 'Sand Dunes of the Kalahari', *S. Afr. Geog. Journ.*, XIX, pp. 22–32.
Mabbutt, J. A. (1955), 'Erosion Surfaces in Namaqualand and the Ages of Surface Deposits in the South-western Kalahari', *Trans. Geol. Soc. S. Afr.*, LVIII, pp. 13–30.
Rogers, A. W. (1934), 'The Build of the Kalahari', *S. Afr. Geog. Journ.*, XVII, pp. 3–12.
Van Riet Lowe, C. R. (1952), 'The Vaal River Chronology', *S. Afr. Archaeol. Bull.*, VII, pp. 135–49.
Wayland, E. J. (1954), 'Outlines of Prehistory and Stone Age Climatology in the Bechuanaland Protectorate', *Mém. Acad. roy. des Sciences coloniales*, XXV, 4, pp. 1–46.

The Kalahari System in Southern Africa and its Importance in Relationship to the Evolution of Man

by V. L. BOSAZZA

THE southern part of the Continent of Africa is covered by a mantle of consolidated and unconsolidated materials in which skeletal remains, stone implements and other evidences of human occupation occur. The greater part of these materials are more typical of desert to semi-arid environment, although some of the gravels and sands have been considered to be evidence of 'pluvial' periods. In this work I shall attempt to synthesize (1) the grouping of these rocks stratigraphically so that they fit into the general geological picture, particularly in relationship to the Karroo System in the interior and the Tertiary and Cretaceous Systems in the coastal zones, and (2) to give some petrographic data showing the nature of these rocks and the probable environmental conditions.

1. *The Kalahari System*

The late Dr A. L. du Toit described the Kalahari Beds in some detail down to the base, but it is not clear from his work (1939) whether this data is from one geological section or from data collected over many geological sections and boreholes. Starting in the middle of 1953 and continuing into 1954, the Portuguese Government drilled a number of boreholes (core drills) at the 14th Mark on the Mozambique-Southern Rhodesia border about 60 kms. to the northeast of the village of Pafuri. These boreholes, one over 700 feet deep (210 metres), gave very valuable information on the Kalahari Beds in a new area, but more than that, showed how correct du Toit's early geological work on these continental rocks was.

I must stress here that the cores have been very thoroughly examined, chemical and physical analyses have been done, a great deal of microscopy and many photographs have been taken showing the various features of these cores. This data is to be published as a bulletin by the Portuguese Government. Summing up the data of these boreholes, the following is obtained:

1. Carbonated reddish-brown clays, at the base, sometimes laminated. These are very similar to the Red Marls of du Toit, and are sterile in these cores, of fossils. Similar red clays occur in the Mafeking-Setlagoli-Muse Hill area and in the Bray area further down the Molopo River.

2. Calcareous sandstones often very white in colour but showing very distinct leaching. These appear to be correlatable with the Pan Sandstones of Passarge.

3. Opaline Silcretes representing an old desert surface.

4. The Pipe sandstones containing very much less calcareous matter than the Pan Sandstones.

5. Gravels lying on the Pipe Sandstones, ranging from small pebbles to very large pebbles and boulders of rhyolites, banded ironstones but mainly quartzites and vein quartzes. Sands, very fine grained and whitish to dirty brown in colour.

6. The Plateau Sandstone containing the mineral montmorillonite and yellow-brown pebbles of agate.

The upper portion of this section is quite easily related to Maufe's section at the Victoria Falls. The Red clays can be seen lying on the basalts near Pafuri Village, but the basalts were not reached in these boreholes. Further east I have identified the basal Kalahari Limestones and gravels, and it is possible that these are a different facies of the red marls. Some stone implements have been recovered from the gravel bed but no macro nor micro fossils were found in the borehole cores. It appears that this whole plateau, considered very tentatively by Rhodesian workers to be Cretaceous, is in fact formed by rocks of the Kalahari System.

At this stage it is well to bear in mind that (du Toit 1939, op. cit., p. 374) in one of the Inyaminga boreholes desert conditions were noted. Furthermore du Toit indicated in 1937 that the Isalo Sandstone in Madagascar can be paralleled precisely with the red sandstones of the Zambezi-Shire area.

I have traced the Kalahari Rocks on the surface and in boreholes further eastwards to Chigubo and still further eastwards escarpments of the Pipe Sandstone can be found about 40 km. west of Mabote, and silcrete small scarps about 60 km. north of Mabote. All these rocks have been carefully analysed and examined microscopically. There remains the gap between these continental rocks and those of the Zambezi Valley near Vila Sena.

The Vila Sena rocks are very coarse-grained with many large fragments of feldspar and very typical of river erosion in a desert area. On the north bank of the Zambezi, just near Dona Ana Station, a small basalt-glassy rhyolite pipe has penetrated these sandstones. How to relate these to the materials found in the Inhaminga boreholes and those further south has not been solved but there is very little doubt that they are the same phenomena.

On the other side of the continent and further northwards in Angola and the Belgian Congo, a great deal more work has been done but comparitively little petrographic work. Cahen and Lepersonne (1952), Jean de Heinzelin (1952) and Janmart (1953) have all given data showing the very great extent of this continental desert cover. As a bridge there is the recent work by Desmond Clark in which Dixey has written a valuable geological description.

In 1947 with my colleagues Adie and Brenner, I wrote a short description of the work we had done on the materials found at Makapan, Sterkfontein and Taungs. Since that date I have carried out a large number of chemical analyses as well as size determinations and mineralogical determinations on these materials, far too voluminous to quote here. This early work has been substantially supported by King (1951) and some of it by Tobias (1954).

Before relating these findings to the sections in the Makapan caves I must point out that the red coastal sands shown by du Toit on his 1939 map are still there and as they are often as much as 100 to 150 m. thick and stretch from the Vilancoulos area to near the Ponte da Ouro, their significance is very great. These red sands lie on a limestone of marine type, with highly developed karst structure.* The red sands penetrate into the caverns of the limestone in a remarkable manner and have at their base a boulder gravel very well cemented by red clay. According to Borges (1939) the limestones are post-Pliocene in age. They can be traced into the Polana Cliff which appears to be of the same nature as the Bluff at Durban (Kent, 1937). Whether these red sands are of desert origin or in fact the red colour may be due to humid hot conditions as described by Dunham (1953) is difficult to say at this stage. While Brain *et al.* (1955) have criticized my early findings no details have been given, but here I may add that in regard to the Makapan, Kromdraai, Sterkfontein and Taungs materials, all of which I have examined in detail, they are all reddish-brown in colour and that the iron oxide coating is very strongly fixed to the quartz grains, that there are foreign materials such as chromite, ilmenite and quartz with tourmaline, which could not have come from the areas by water transport but must have reached their present position by wind.

Below the fossiliferous layers in Makapan are some very well laminated clays, which have been thoroughly impregnated by calcium carbonate and are now hard rocks. The clay from these rocks has been removed and analysed and this compared with the data of the red marls. The rocks are very similar in nature and could quite easily be of the same environment. I suggest therefore that these laminated carbonated clays are in fact the *Kalahari Red Marls*.

* Bosazza (1956).

The Kalahari System in Southern Africa

The reddish-brown carbonated red windblown soils containing the faunal remains and which I previously divided into two (Bosazza *et al.*, 1947) are equivalent to the *Pan Sandstones*. In a cave environment and under alkaline dolomite waters leaching of the iron oxide was not possible and hence the distinction from the Pan Sandstones which were deposited in river and pan systems.

The opaline and montmorillonite silcretes (Bosazza, 1947) could not have formed in a cave and are therefore absent. At this stage the cave section ends and the rest of the formation can only be found outside of the limeworks cave at Makapan and the other caves at Kromdraai, Sterkfontein and Taungs.

TABLE I

	1	2	3	4	5
SiO_2	76·70	62·30	86·20	88·60	91·7
Al_2O_3	9·37	13·70	5·55	5·02	—
FeO_3	3·56	8·70	1·76	1·30	—
TiO_2	0·29	0·60	0·15	0·50	—
Mn_3O_4	1·58	1·12	0·15	0·55	—
CaO	2·30	2·23	0·94	1·02	—
MgO	0·40	1·32	0·28	0·32	—
Ignition Loss	4·15	4·86	2·64	0·70	1·30
$- H_2O$	3·86	5·25	1·23	0·54	—
	102·21	100·08	99·40	98·55	

1. Brick-red windblown soil (Phase 1) Makapan Limeworks Cave. Analyst V.L.B.
2. Brick-red windblown soil (Phase 1) Makapan Limeworks Cave. Analyst V.L.B.
3. White windblown sand, just outside the village of Rooiberg. Analyst V.L.B.
4. Red windblown sandy soil, west of Mafeking. Analyst V.L.B.
5. Partial analysis of white windblown sand, Great Brak River, near Mossel Bay. Analyst V.L.B.

2. *The Petrographic Nature of the Cave Materials at Makapan and Sterkfontein*

Cooke (1938) gave a brief description of the Sterkfontein Bone Breccia and later Haughton gave a qualitative description of the Australopithecene rocks of the Union of South Africa. An unpublished paper on the materials enclosing the human fossils was read by the late Dr A. L. du Toit and he felt that the word 'loess' used in the original paper I wrote was not applicable. I feel now that the description of these materials as 'windblown soil' is far more suitable and in this description I have used it exclusively.

The chemical analyses are given in Table I after the removal of 20 to 30% calcium carbonate by dilute hydrochloric acid treatment. No or very little iron oxide staining went into solution. For the sake of comparison some windblown sands from near Rooiberg and Brak River are given. Note how low the silica content is for the white windblown sands, but that one windblown red sand from the area west of Mafeking has about the same composition as the white sands.

The physical analyses are given in Table II, and it will be noted that there is very little coarse material. The greater part of the grains are less than 200 microns in diameter. Although Bagnold (1941) has shown that the conditions of movement by wind are difficult to generalize, nevertheless none of these materials are so coarse that they could only have been moved by water (cf. Brain *et al.*, 1955). The microscopic examinations showed that for Specimen No. 1 the coarse fraction down to 589 microns consists of chert from the dolomite with occasional rounded quartzite grains. In the range down to 88 microns, there is a great deal of chert, with iron-manganese oxide staining. Note that the grains are irregular in shape.

In the case of Specimen No. 2 the coarse fraction again consists of angular chert with some grains of weathered quartzite. There are some acicular grains which may be tourmaline. In the 1,200 to 1,400 range the degree of rounding increases markedly. Some red jasper grains appear with feldspar. From 210 microns the degree of rounding reaches a maximum and the quartz is relatively free from iron oxide staining. Below 100 microns there are practically no rounded grains. In the 88 and 74 micron fractions there are some highly altered minerals equidimensional but not well rounded. Some chromite was also noted. It is important to bear in mind that in this 'dolomite' soil there are potash and plagioclase feldspars, some metamorphic rock fragments probably from the Swaziland System and chromite and ferro-magnesian minerals possibly from the Bushveld Complex. The freshness of the feldspars is noteworthy (a feature of the Mark 14 Pafuri Rocks and the Polana Sandstones) right down to the fine mineral sizes. In the finer fractions clay minerals with iron oxide are dominant. Note that feldspars do not occur in the normal dolomitic limestones of the Transvaal System.

TABLE II

Nominal size in microns	Percentage by weight				
	1	2	3	4	5
1651	1·7	0·7	—	0·9	—
1190	0·6	1·8	3·8	0·9	—
840	1·1	4·0	4·6	2·6	—
589	1·7	6·9	5·5	3·9	—
417	1·1	9·4	6·0	7·4	—
297	4·7	11·0	8·7	14·9	—
210	5·3	7·7	10·2	27·0	3·4
177	2·8	2·8	5·4	8·3	—
149	1·1	3·8	5·5	9·9	3·9
88	8·5	9·1	25·5	10·9	25·3
74	3·4	4·1	5·3	2·9	15·4
54	5·8	5·4	2·5	2·7	7·2
Silt	} 62·2	} 28·3	—	2·6	—
Clay			—	5·1	—
43	—	—	—	—	26·4
31	—	—	2·8	—	3·6
22	—	—	1·5	—	1·0
11	—	—	1·5	—	1·7
5·5	—	—	} 11·2	—	1·3
2·0	—	—		—	3·2
	100·0	100·0			92·4

1. Brick-red windblown soil (Phase 1) Makapan Limeworks Cave.
2. Windblown reddish-brown soil (Phase 1) Makapan Limeworks Cave.
3. Red windblown sandy soil just outside Mafeking.
4. White windblown sand just outside the Village of Rooiberg.
5. White windblown sand from Great Brak River, Mossel Bay.

Specimen No. 3. The grains in the coarse fractions are all fairly well rounded and coated with iron oxide (desert varnish?). Down to 200 microns when the grains are not well rounded as a whole, the edges have been worn. In the 177 micron fraction there are a number of heavy minerals chiefly black opaque in colour. Below the 177 micron size the quartz is very angular and flakelike in appearance, with few or no rounded grains. In the 31 and 22 micron fractions the kaolinite and illite are obscured by iron hydroxide staining, which is easily removed in this case by hydrochloric acid.

Specimen No. 4. The quartz is all clean and in the fractions coarser than 417 microns rather angular. From 417 to 210 microns the degree of rounding increases and some feldspar appears. In the 149 and 88 micron fractions potash and plagioclase feldspars are quite abundant and fresh. In the 74 micron fraction the feldspar is decomposed and some green tourmaline noted. In the 'silt' fraction, that is 20 microns, some sponge spicules and diatoms were seen. This sand corresponds to what du Toit has designated fluvio-aeolian sand. In the field the sand occurs in a shallow depression, so that lacustrine-aeolian conditions occur as the rains and dry seasons alternate.

Specimen No. 5. This is a dirty white fine-grained material with a low degree of rounding. It consists of quartz with kaolinite and some calcite.

Dr S. Brenner collected a number of samples from the Sterkfontein and Kromdraai Caves and after removal of the carbonates, the residues were examined microscopically. In the Kromdraai material *Paranthropus* was found and this material is very fine grained. It is a chocolate-brown in colour after the removal of the carbonate. It consists of angular quartz grains about 40 microns in diameter, but the bulk appears to be less than 14 microns, and consists of clay minerals. The Sterkfontein windblown soil on the other hand contains some chert grains of about 140 microns diameter, with another size fraction of 28 to 42 microns. As noted for the Makapan materials, there are plenty of feldspar grains and other minerals which could not have been derived from the dolomitic limestones.

Some of the clays occurring in caves were examined and these are little different from the clays found in present lakes in the dolomite and the older deposits. Desmond Clark has described a red aeolian clay from the Mumbwa Cave in Southern Rhodesia (Goodwin, 1946).

Only a small amount of the total petrographic work can be quoted here and as work is still in progress in the case of the Mozambique red sands, silcretes, Pipe Sandstones, ferricretes and calcretes, it would be imprudent at this stage to reach fixed conclusions. Suffice it to say that from studies of the red, white and yellow sands in Mozambique that it is easy to say when a sand can only have been moved by water but in fact fine-grained sands are very difficult to determine exactly as regards transport. The nature of the red sands has been far from satisfactorily solved, and particularly the nature of the red iron oxide coating. If the origin of the red coating can be solved for those sands, then the same conclusions can be applied to the reddish-brown windblown soils of Makapan, Taungs, Sterkfontein, Kromdraai and other deposits of the same nature.

I have shown how during the past ten years in the Union of South Africa soil storms have occurred, many raging over many days. Thus at Makapan I saw in September 1946 and again in September 1947 soil storms after a drought carry up to the 6,000 feet beacon on the farms Portugal and Spanje; during October 1949 soil storms in the Marquard-Ladybrand area covered the hills 500 to 700 feet above the plains and lasted for over *two weeks during heavy rains*. Part of the transportation was by saltation along the ground and partly by actually being airborne. The airborne particles obscured the foothills of Basutoland near Maseru (see Bosazza, 1953).

In December 1951 soil storms in the Eastern Transvaal ranged from Springs to Piet Retief and samples caught on vaselined slides gave a wide range in grain size. The soil storms again occurred in December 1952 and January 1953 from Klerksdorp to Fourteen Streams and from Brandfort to Vredefort. Often the deposits of windblown soil on the roads reached depths of 3–4 inches. Flying at heights of 3,000 feet above the ground, fine particles of dust entered the aircraft. The soil storms appear to follow drought and are not settled by rain until a grass cover protects the surface of the soil.

Section One

ACKNOWLEDGEMENTS

I am greatly indebted to Prof. R. A. Dart who has given me a great deal of material at various times, and also to him I am indebted for interest in the problem. To His Excellency the Governor-General of Mozambique Flag-Captain Gabriel Teixeira I am indebted for permission to publish an abstract of the Mark 14, Pafuri Borehole Results.

REFERENCES

Bagnold, R. A. (1941), *The Physics of Blown Sand and Desert Sand Dunes*, Methuen, London, 265 pp.

Borges, A. (1939), 'Depositos terciaros e post-pliocenicos do distrito de Inhambane', *Serv. Industr. Geol. Moc. Bol.*, No. 3, pp. 5–24.

Borges, A. (1945), 'Geologia e pre-historia de Magude', *Serv. Industr. Geol. Moc. Bol.*, No. 7, p. 7.

Bosazza, V. L. (1947), *The Petrography and Petrology of South African clays*, Johannesburg, 313 pp., p. 176 in particular.

Bosazza, V. L. (1953), 'On the Erodibility of Soils and its bearing on soil erosion in South Africa', *Sols Africain* (Paris), 2, pp. 336–50.

Bosazza, V. L. (1955), 'The Geology of the Country Around Mark 14, Pafuri' (unpublished).

Bosazza, V. L. (1956), 'The Geology and Development of the Bays and Coastline of the Sol do Save of Moçambique', *Bol. Soc. Est. Moc.* No. 98, pp. 19–28.

Bosazza, V. L., R. Adie and S. Brenner (1946), 'Man and the Great Kalahari Desert', *Natal Univ. Col. Sci. J.*, 9 pp.

Brain, C. K., C. van Riet Lowe and R. A. Dart (1955), 'Kafuan Stone artefacts in the Post-Australopithecine breccia at Makapansgat', *Nature*, 175, pp. 16–17.

Cahen, L. and J. Lepersonne (1952), 'Équivalence entre le Système du Kalahari du Congo Belge et les Kalahari d' Afrique Australe', *Mém. Soc. Belge. Geol.*, Serie No. 8 (4), pp. 1–64.

Clark, J. D. (1950), *The Stone Age Cultures of Northern Rhodesia*, S. Afr. Archaeol. Soc., 157 pp.

Cooke, H. B. S. (1938), 'The Sterkfontein Bone Breccia', *S. Afr. J. Sci.*, 35, pp. 204–8.

Dixey, F. (1932), *An Outline of the Physiography, Geology and Mineral Resources of Nyasaland.* 34 pp., p. 8 and 19 onwards.

Dunham, K. C. (1953), 'Red Coloration in desert formations of the Permian and Triassic Age in Britain', *XIX Congr. Intern. Geol. C.R.*, Section VII, pp. 25–9.

Du Toit, A. L. (1937), *Our Wandering Continents*, Oliver & Boyd. 366 pp., p. 123 onwards.

Du Toit, A. L. (1939), *The Geology of South Africa*, Oliver & Boyd, London. 539 pp., p. 374 in particular.

Goodwin, A. G. H. (1946), 'The Loom of Pre-History', *S. Afr. Archaeol. Soc. Bul.*, Series No. 11, p. 51.

Haughton, S. H. (1947), 'Notes on the Australopithecine-bearing rocks of the Union of South Africa', *Trans. Geol. Soc. S. Afr.*, 48, pp. 55–9.

Heinzelin, J. de (1952), *Sols, palaeosols, et desertifications anciennes dans le secteur Nord-Oriental du Bassin du Congo*, Publ. Inst. National. Étude. Agron. Congo Belge, 168 pp.

Janmart, J. (1953), *The Kalahari Sands of the Lunda (N.E. Angola), their earlier redistributions and the Sangoan Culture*, Diamang. Museu do Dundo, Publicacoes Culturais, No. 20, 65 pp. Lisbon.

Kent, L. E. (1938), 'The Geology of a portion of Victoria County Natal, with special reference to the Pleistocene and Recent Sands and the evolution of the coastline', *Trans. Geol. Soc. S. Afr.*, 41, pp. 1–36.

King, L. C. (1951), 'The Geology of the Makapan and other caves', *Trans. Roy. Soc. S. Afr.*, 33 (1), pp. 121–51.

Maufe, H. V. (1938), 'New sections in the Kalahari Beds at the Victoria Falls, Rhodesia', *Trans. Geol. Soc. S. Afr.*, 41, pp. 211–24.

Polinard, E. (1948), 'Considérations sur le système du Kalahari, et ses dérivés du Sud du Congo belge, entre Kwango et le Katanga', *Inst. Roy. Col. Belge*, 17, Fasc. 2, pp. 1–55.

Tobias, P. V. (1954), 'Climatic fluctuations in the middle Stone Age of South Africa as revealed in Mwulus Cave', *Trans. Roy. Soc. S. Afr.*, 34 (2), pp. 325–34.

Tyndale-Biscoe, R. (1949), 'Notes on a geological reconnaissance of the country east of Beit Bridge, Southern Rhodesia', *Trans. Geol. Soc. S. Afr.*, 52, pp. 405–11.

18

Sur l'âge des faunes de Rongeurs des Grottes à Australopithèques

par R. LAVOCAT

CETTE étude aurait dû, pour être aussi concluante que possible, tenir compte des Rongeurs de l'ensemble des grottes connues. J'ai tenu compte seulement de la grotte de Makapan, dont le Professeur Dart m'a confié la microfaune lors de mon passage à Johannesburg, et d'un petit lot provenant de Sterkfontein, confié par le Docteur Oakley; la Wenner-Gren Foundation m'a accordé un fonds pour cette étude.

Les conclusions tirées ne pourront être que très prudentes. Même en ayant en main la faune de toutes les grottes, c'est déjà en effet une gageure que de tenter de parler d'autre chose que d'un âge relatif des grottes entre elles. En effet nous ne connaissons ailleurs aucun équivalent des faunes de Rongeurs dont il est question. Nul gisement stratifié classique, nulle couche préhistorique à outillage n'ont fourni, que je sache, en Afrique du Sud, de faune notable de Rongeur étudiée. Le gîte le plus proche est celui d'Oldoway, dont les rares échantillons fournissent une base de comparaison des plus incertaines.

S'il y a une gradation d'âge entre les diverses grottes, on pourrait, sans doute, la faune recueillie étant très abondante, observer dans celle-ci quelques différences utilisables pour leurs interrelations, mais cela ne nous donnerait pas pour autant le moyen de nous situer dans la préhistoire générale. Cet élément lui-même faisant défaut pour le moment, seule peut intervenir l'appréciation du taux d'évolution des populations en cause, par comparaison avec d'autres populations constituées également par des Rongeurs. C'est là un élément qui s'apprécie plus qu'il ne se mesure, et qui conduit à des conclusions incertaines et sujettes à révision.

Ayant l'intention de publier par ailleurs une étude paléontologique des faunes en question, je donnerai ici seulement, en l'accompagnant de quelques remarques, la liste des formes actuellement identifiées.

MAKAPAN: *Mystromys hausleitneri* (très abondant), *Mystromys* nov. sp. de petite taille très rare, *Heterocephalus* sp. (très rares), *Palaeotomys gracilis* (abondant), *Malacothrix*, *Dendromus*, *Dasymys*, *Pelomys* (?), *Lemniscomys* (?), *Zelotomys* (?).

STERKFONTEIN: *Mystromys* (abondant), *Palaeotomys* (abondant), *Dendromus*, *Dasymys*, *Arvicanthis* (?), *Mus minutoides*, *Tatera*.

Hormis trois portions de crânes de *Palaeotomys* et une de *Mystromys*, ces formes ne sont représentées que par des mandibules ou des dents isolées, ce qui explique que l'indication de certains genres soit accompagnée de points d'interrogation. En effet, on sait que en général les dentures mandibulaires sont peu caractéristiques. D'autre part, en ce qui concerne les Murinés seuls, ceux-ci sont représentés actuellement dans les régions interessées par 18 genres vivants, comprenant 37 espèces divisées en multiples sous espèces; à quoi il faut adjoindre les autres formes pouvant exister dans des territoires voisins. Or, on sait que les caractères des dents sont extrêmement peu étudiés par les zoologistes; il est donc impossible de trouver dans la Bibliographie des descriptions vraiment précises, encore moins des figurations des diverses formes actuelles. Grâce aux collections du British Museum, j'ai pu étudier les caractères dentaires de tous les genres de

Muridés indiqués dans *Check list of the South African Mammals.* Si ces caractères sont généralement très typiques avec des dentures complètes, il faut reconnaître que il peut être difficile de décider entre certains genres voisins pour des dents isolées, d'où les points d'interrogation dans la liste ci-dessus. Il n'en va pas de même pour les Dendromurinés, extrêmement caractéristiques, et représentés d'ailleurs par un nombre de formes réduit. Il reste que, quand on se trouve en face de formes fossiles rares, inconnues actuellement on peut se demander si elles sont réellement éteintes, ou si elles ont seulement échappé aux recherches à cause de leur rareté.

L'examen des listes montre que aucune des espèces ne parait s'évader du cadre générique actuel. Certaines, comme *Mus minutoides*, ne se distinguent pas notablement de l'espèce actuelle. *Dendromus, Malacothrix* ne semblent pas au premier examen rencontrer de strict équivalent spécifique dans la nature vivante. *Mystromys hausleitneri*, que R. Broom a distingué à la fois par la tête et par les dents, reste extrêmement voisin de la forme actuelle, *Tatera* paraît au même degré évolutif que les formes vivantes.

Les Otomyinés sont plus originaux. On retrouve en effet les caractères attribués par R. Broom à *Palaeotomys gracilis*, mais en outre on constate qu'une proportion assez notable des échantillons, au moins à Makapan, présente des indices absolument probants de la présence de tubercules distincts au sommet des lamelles, à l'état frais, et deux échantillons de M_1 inférieur *à 5 lobes* montrent les deux premiers lobes constitués par des tubercules distincts, sur presque toute la hauteur pour le premier lobe, à un degré encore très important pour le deuxième. Si l'on s'en remet aux indications des travaux relatifs aux formes actuelles, cette présence de tubercules distincts ne s'y manifeste jamais. S'il en est bien ainsi, il s'agit là d'un caractère primitif notable.

Quant à *Heterocephalus* sp., il est représenté par 3 échantillons notamment une mandibule, dont les dents gardent deux plis opposés l'un à l'autre, jusqu'à un degré d'usure avancé mais guère plus semble-t-il que dans la forme actuelle, si même une différence existe. L'apophyse coronoide est basse et très réduite, presque vestigiale, mais elle est signalée comme variable dans *Heterocephalus glaber*. Les molaires sont très grandes, mais cela aussi est un caractère variable. On notera surtout que le genre n'est pas signalé actuellement en Afrique du Sud, mais en Afrique Orientale. La nouvelle espèce de *Mystromys* que je signale est représentée par M^{1-2} sup. et M_1 inf., avec les caractères essentiels du genre, mais de très petite taille (à peu près celle de *Peromyscus*).

Que pourrons nous conclure de cet ensemble?

Je crois tout d'abord que l'on peut dire que cette faune s'accorde avec les indications, tirées de la présence du genre *Equus* dans certaines grottes, pour interdire absolument de considérer les grottes interessées comme plus anciennes que le Villafranchien. Grâce au remarquable découvertes de P. Ellenberger et d'un jeune chercheur français, mon élève L. Thaler, on connait maintenant la faune de Rongeurs d'un remplissage pliocène de la région de Sète. Elle a tout autre aspect, beaucoup plus archaïque par rapport à la faune actuelle que celle qui nous occupe; on y trouve des genres qui n'ont que des affinités très lointaines avec les formes actuelles.

Ce n'est pas le cas ici, où la présence de formes identiques, même spécifiquement, aux formes actuelles, empêche en particulier de vieillir à l'excés la faune de Sterkfontein.

Par contre, il faut reconnaître, que, si les caractères que j'ai relevés dans *Palaeotomys* ont bien l'originalité que je leur attribue, en m'appuyant sur les travaux des zoologistes, ils parlent pour un âge quaternaire ancien. La différence existant entre la forme fossile et les formes actuelles paraît assez comparable à celle existant entre les *Mimomys pliocaenicus* du Villafranchien d'Europe et les *Arvicola* actuels de la même contrée.

Sans pouvoir émettre des conclusions définitives et irréformables, il ne semble donc pas déraisonnable, en se basant sur les faunes de Rongeurs telles qu'elles sont actuellement connues, d'admettre que Makapan puisse être d'âge Villafranchien, sans exclure entièrement l'éventualité d'un âge un peu plus récent. Pour Sterkfontein, le nombre assez réduit d'échantillons rend les conclusions plus incertaines, car il ne permet pas d'affirmer que *Palaeotomys* soit aussi archaïque que celui de Makapan.

19

Faunal Evidence on the Dating of the Australopithecinae

by R. F. EWER

As is well known, in Africa faunal dating presents great difficulties, owing to the absence of any abrupt change in faunal composition marking the transition from the Pliocene to the Pleistocene. Typically 'Pliocene' forms commonly survive well into the Pleistocene, and the presence of archaic types cannot therefore be taken as proving that a deposit is of great antiquity. The full consequences of this absence of abrupt change are not, however, always fully appreciated. Many early Pleistocene African species represent Pliocene relics; but similarly many of our modern species may be early Pleistocene survivors. Just as there is no point in the record at which archaic forms disappear abruptly, so too it is not to be expected that there will be any point at which modern species suddenly become common; but rather it is to be expected that they will appear first in small numbers at a very early stage, and then increase gradually until they come to dominate the fauna.

Clearly, in assessing the age of an African deposit, we can neither assume that the presence of an archaic form indicates great antiquity; nor yet that the presence of a modern species proves the deposit to be very recent. Consideration of isolated cases is of little value. What is necessary is a quantitative picture of the fauna as a whole: and the question we must ask is: 'Is this fauna predominantly ancient, with a few modern forms putting in a first appearance; or is it predominantly modern, with a number of ancient survivors lingering on?'

Only too frequently in the literature we find a view on Australopithecine dating expressed, followed by the statement that this 'is in agreement with the faunal evidence', this being supported by reference to the distribution in the deposits of one or two genera. It would be possible, by picking out individual genera as our examples, to support almost any conceivable view on the question of dating. For these reasons, in what follows, consideration will be restricted to those groups of mammals in which the whole of the available fossil material has been studied. These now comprise the Primates (Robinson, 1953, 1954; Freedman, in press), the Hyracoidea (Churcher, 1956), the shrews (Meester, 1955), the Carnivora (Toerien, 1952, 1955; Ewer, 1954, 1955, 1956), and the Suidae (Broom, 1948; Dale, 1948).

The question of the relative datings of the deposits will first be considered, beginning with those of Sterkfontein, Swartkrans and Kromdraai. The faunas of these three sites are very similar in general character, indicating that no significant ecological differences exist. Since the sites lie so close together, the considerable differences in detailed composition of the faunas can hardly be accounted for otherwise than as reflecting the fact that the deposits are not exactly contemporaneous.*

Table I gives a list of the species belonging to the groups mentioned above which have, to date, been identified in the various deposits. Swartkrans shares at least 8 species, and probably 10, with

---

* It should be remembered that the Kromdraai faunal site lies about 100 yards from the outcrop in which the Kromdraai Australopithecine was found. In what follows 'Kromdraai' refers to the faunal site. Our knowledge of the fauna of the Kromdraai Australopithecine site is not at present sufficient to permit the drawing of any conclusions about its relative age.

135

TABLE I

	Ta.	St.	Mk.	Sk.	Ka.
PRIMATES					
Telanthropus capensis				x	
Paranthropus robustus crassidens				x	
Australopithecus africanus africanus	x				
Australopithecus africanus transvaalensis		x	x		
Parapapio antiquus	x				
Parapapio jonesi	x	x	x	x	x
Parapapio broomi		x	x		
Parapapio whitei		x			
Papio izodi	x				
Papio robinsoni				x	x
Papio angusticeps					x
Simopithecus darti			x		
Simopithecus danieli				x	
Dinopithecus ingens				x	
Gorgonopithecus major					x
Cercopithecoides williamsi	x	x	x		
Cercopithecoides molletti				x	
INSECTIVORA					
Crocidura taungsensis	x				
Myosorex robinsoni		x	x	x	
Suncus sp.		x	x	x	x
HYRACOIDEA					
Procavia transvaalensis	x	x	x	x	x
Procavia antiqua	x	x	x	x	x
CARNIVORA					
Lycyaena silberbergi		x		x	
Lycyaena nitidula		x?		x	
Leecyaena forfex				x	
Hyaena makapani			x		
Hyaena bellax					x
Hyaena brunnea dispar				x	
Crocuta venustula				x	
Crocuta crocuta angella				x	
Crocuta spelaea capensis					x
Crocuta ultra					x
Crocuta cf. brevirostris			x		
Nimravidae indet.				x	
Therailurus barlowi (? = Machairodus darti)		x	x		
Therailurus piveteaui					x
Therailurus sp.				x	
Megantereon gracile		x			
Megantereon eurynodon					x
Megantereon sp.				x	
'Felis' crassidens					x
Panthera pardus incurva		x?		x	
Kromdraai 'lion' (? = Panthera shawi)					x
Swartkrans 'lion'				x	
Canis brevirostris		x			

	Ta.	St.	Mk.	Sk.	Ka.
CARNIVORA (*cont.*)					
Canis mesomelas pappos - - - - - - -		x		x	x
Canis atrox - - - - - - - - -					x
Vulpes pulcher - - - - - - - - -				x?	x
Cynictis penicillata subsp. - - - - - - -				x	
Herpestes mesotes - - - - - - - -					x
Crossarchus transvaalensis - - - - - -					x?
SUIDAE					
Pronotochoerus shawi - - - - - - - -				x	
Potamochoeroides hypsodon - - - - - - -				x	
Tapinochoerus meadowsi - - - - - - -		x		x	
Phacochoerus antiquus - - - - - - -				x	x
54	8	17	14	27	20

Sterkfontein and 8 with Kromdraai; but Kromdraai has only 5 in common with Sterkfontein (Fig. 1A). A few species occur in all three deposits, and these therefore do not help us when our aim is differentiation. If we neglect these we find that Swartkrans is left with at least 3, probably 5, species in common with Sterkfontein and 3 in common with Kromdraai; while there is none in common between Kromdraai and Sterkfontein (Fig. 1B). These facts clearly indicate that Swartkrans must lie between the other two deposits. The presence of *Lycyaena* at Sterkfontein, but not

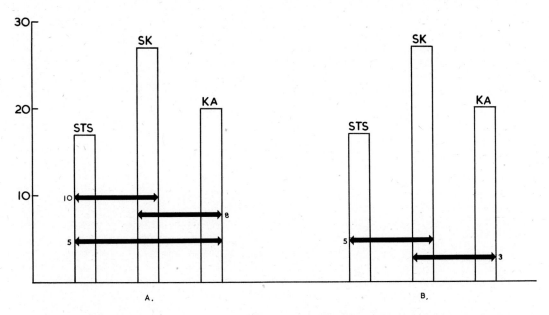

FIG. 1. Comparison of deposits at Sterkfontein (STS), Swartkrans (SK) and Kromdraai (KA). The vertical columns give the numbers of species in the deposits. A horizontal double-headed arrow shows the number of species occurring in both the deposits marked by its two ends. The horizontal axis represents time, but no attempt to provide a scale is made. In 1A all species are included; in 1B those present in all deposits have been discounted in drawing the arrows

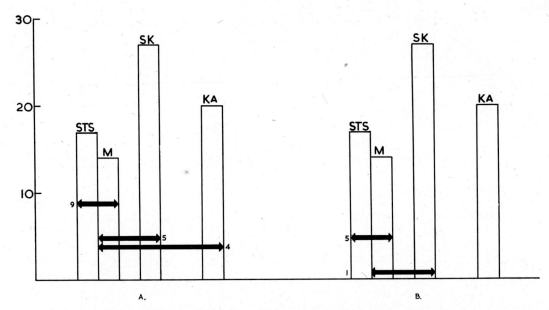

FIG. 2. Comparison of the Makapan deposit (M) with those at Sterkfontein, Swartkrans and Kromdraai. Conventions as in Fig. 1

at Kromdraai; and of *Papio* and *Equus* at Kromdraai, but not at Sterkfontein, would seem to indicate that Kromdraai is the most recent and Sterkfontein the most ancient, with Swartkrans occupying an intermediate position.

The position of Makapan is less easy to estimate. Not only is it geographically more remote, but the general composition of the fauna is rather different from those of the other three deposits, indicating somewhat different ecological conditions. Nevertheless the following figures are highly suggestive. Of 17 species listed at Sterkfontein 9 (= 53%) are also found at Makapan; of 27 Swartkrans species only 5 (= 18·5%) are present at Makapan, while of the 20 Kromdraai species 4 (= 20%) occur at Makapan. As before, we may also make a comparison discounting the species which occur in all deposits. This gives us the following: Makapan shares 5 species with Sterkfontein, 1 with Swartkrans and none with Kromdraai. These facts clearly indicate that Makapan is closest in time to Sterkfontein.

We may also attempt a comparison cutting across the ecological and geographical differences between Makapan and the other sites. Thus, with Sterkfontein we may compare both Makapan (geographically and ecologically dissimilar) and Swartkrans (geographically and ecologically similar). The numbers of species which the former site shares with the two latter are almost equal: 9 and 10 or 8 respectively. Similarly Kromdraai shares approximately equal numbers of species (4 and 5) with the dissimilar Makapan and the similar Sterkfontein. We must, however, remember that the geographical and ecological differences weight the figures against Makapan, and these near identities therefore really indicate that Makapan is closer to Sterkfontein than is Swartkrans; and that Kromdraai is closer to Makapan than to Sterkfontein.

There is only one possible time-sequence that fits all these facts: Makapan must come immediately after Sterkfontein, with Swartkrans following after a slight interval (Fig. 2).

It may be felt that the argument from the 'cross comparisons' is too circuitous to carry conviction, and that all we may legitimately do is make the direct comparison of Makapan with each of the other deposits. In this case all we may conclude is that Makapan lies closest to Sterkfontein.

Faunal Evidence on the Dating of the Australopithecinae

This could mean either (as before) that Makapan lies between Sterkfontein and Swartkrans, but closer to the former; or that Makapan is contemporaneous with or immediately precedes Sterkfontein, Swartkrans following after an interval (Fig. 3). It may be noted, however, that while *Equus* remains occur at Makapan and Swartkrans they have not been found at Sterkfontein: this favours the placing of Makapan immediately after, rather than immediately before or contemporaneous with, Sterkfontein. Although the value of such negative evidence is always open to question, it should be remembered that the Sterkfontein deposit is a large one and has been extensively studied. Thus, on the basis of the faunal evidence alone, the sequence shown in Fig. 2 is the most probable, but the alternative shown in Fig. 3 cannot be completely rejected. Possibly the geological evidence may provide a decisive ruling on this point.

The dating of the Taung deposit presents some difficulties. The fauna is rather incompletely known, and the indications are that the environment was distinctly more desert-like than at the other deposits. However, the presence of *Procavia transvaalensis*, *Procavia antiqua* and *Parapapio jonesi* is sufficient to show that, in age, Taung does not differ widely from the other deposits. The presence of *Australopithecus africanus* and *Cercopithecoides williamsi* would seem to indicate that the relationship is closest with Sterkfontein and Makapan.

The question of absolute dating must now be considered. For this purpose, although the deposits are not exactly contemporaneous, they will have to be treated as a unity. This is hardly likely to be a serious source of error, since, in any case, we can hardly hope to answer any question more precise than: 'Do the deposits belong to the Kageran, or to the middle Pleistocene?' For this purpose a comparison with the faunas of Omo, Laetolil and Olduvai may be made. The fauna list for these sites have been taken from Arambourg (1947), Dietrich (1942) and Leakey (1951) respectively. In dealing with Laetolil those species which Dietrich does not consider to belong to the older fauna have been discounted. For Olduvai Hopwood's list (Leakey, 1951, pp. 21–2) has been used, with the addition of those extra species mentioned by Leakey (p. 24).

For each deposit two calculations have been made: (i) the percentage of genera which are extinct and (ii) the percentage of species which are extinct, as compared with the percentage not

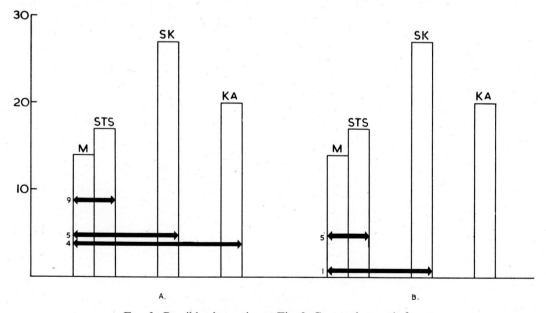

Fig. 3. Possible alternative to Fig. 2. Conventions as before

139

more than subspecifically distinct from living forms. The figures are given in Table II. It should be pointed out that in the case of the Australopithecine deposits only the groups of mammals listed above are considered, while for the other deposits the total mammalian fauna is involved. It is thus possible that further knowledge of the fauna of the former deposits may modify the picture, and the conclusions drawn from the comparison must therefore be regarded as an interim report, rather than a final statement.

TABLE II

Deposit	Genera	Species	
	% extinct	% extinct	% not more than sub-specifically distinct
Australopithecine deposits	53	88	12
Omo	40	79	21
Laetolil	30	71	29
Olduvai	40	64	36

The number of modern species shows a steady increase from Omo, through Laetolil to Olduvai, with the Transvaal deposits giving a distinctly lower value, the difference being significant. The relatively small proportion of extinct genera at Laetolil, and large proportion at Olduvai is difficult to explain. Statistical testing of the significance of the differences in the proportions of extinct genera occurring in the two deposits is of little assistance. A difference of as little as 10%, no matter how real it may be, would have to be based on over 100 genera from each deposit before its significance could be established by the χ^2 test, and the actual numbers available are, of course, much smaller. If we assume that for some reason, the Laetolil figure is deceptively low, and the Olduvai figure a trifle high, it appears that from Omo to Olduvai there was not a great deal of dying out of archaic forms. The Transvaal deposits, however, contain a distinctly larger proportion of extinct genera, although again, the numbers are so small that statistical significance cannot be attained. Comparisons of this sort, if not exactly odious, are at least full of pitfalls, and the fact that one man's genus is another man's species is a perennial palaeontological problem. Nevertheless, it is difficult to believe that the figures given for the Australopithecine deposits can be reconciled with a dating later than that at which the Omo deposits were laid down.

Consideration of a few of the faunal elements individually leads to the same conclusion. *Lycyaena* is typically a Pliocene genus, and elsewhere only one species, *L. lunensis* del Campana, is known from the Villafranchian, and none is as late as the middle Pleistocene. The curious genus *Leecyaena*, found at Swartkrans, is elsewhere known only from the Chinese Yüshê beds of upper Pliocene age. Sabre-tooths are abundant in the Transvaal deposits; but elsewhere in central and southern Africa they are known only by a small jaw fragment from Omo (Arambourg, 1947) and a humerus head from Kaiso which probably belongs to this group (Hopwood, 1926). Here, however, we encounter the difficulty of attempting to compare cave deposits with open sites, and it is difficult to decide how much importance should be attached to the absence of sabre-tooths from an open site, such as Olduvai. In Europe sabre-tooths persisted until a late date, but the South African species do not belong to the same genera as these late survivors. In all four deposits occur representatives of a genus in which machairodont specializations are relatively poorly developed. These have been referred to Piveteau's genus *Therailurus*, elsewhere known only from the upper Pliocene. *Megantereon eurynodon*, from Kromdraai, while it shows certain peculiarities in the width of the blade of the canine tooth, most closely resembles *M. nihowanensis* (Teilhard and Piveteau) of Villafranchian age.

This, however, is only one side of the picture: against it we must set the occurrence of *Tapinochoerus meadowsi* (Broom), known elsewhere as a middle Pleistocene species; and of 4, possibly 5, extant species. As mentioned before, it is to be expected that living species will begin to appear early in the fossil record. The extant species constitute only a small proportion of the total (12%). Judging from the figures for the other deposits, a proportion of this magnitude is to be expected, even in an early Pleistocene deposit. In fact, Table II gives precisely the sort of picture we should anticipate: modern forms appearing in small numbers early on, and showing a steady increase in numbers, while the archaic genera disappear very slowly. Thus the answer to the question posed at the beginning of this paper is that the fauna of the Australopithecine deposits as a whole is predominantly an ancient one, with modern species beginning to appear; and not a modern fauna with an admixture of ancient survivors.

The conclusions drawn from the faunal evidence may be summarized as follows:

1. The probable time sequence of the deposits is Sterkfontein and Makapan close together, with the former very probably the earlier; then Swartkrans and lastly Kromdraai, while the Taung deposit is most probably closest in time to Sterkfontein and Makapan.

2. Taken as a whole the 'mean age' of the deposits can hardly be less than early Pleistocene; that is to say they belong to a time corresponding to the Kageran pluvial of central Africa. Within this broad frame of reference we must leave it to the geological and climatic evidence to determine the detailed spacing of the deposits.

ACKNOWLEDGEMENTS

My thanks are due firstly to the Wenner-Gren Foundation for a travel grant enabling me to attend the Congress. I am also indebted to J. T. Robinson and C. K. Brain for many helpful discussions; and to the South African Council for Scientific and Industrial Research for research grants.

Much of the faunal evidence which has been discussed has been accumulated in the course of a programme of work being carried out under the auspices of the Transvaal Museum, with the object of describing fully the fauna associated with the Australopithecinae in the caves near Krugersdorp. The fauna of Makapan is similarly being studied in Professor Dart's Department in the University of the Witwatersrand. I should like to express my thanks to the workers concerned, Dr M. J. Toerien, C. S. Churcher and L. Freedman for their generosity in allowing me to use their results, many of them then unpublished, in the preparation of this paper.

REFERENCES

Arambourg, C. (1947), *Mission scientifique de l'Omo 1932–33. I. Géologie, Anthropologie*, Mus. nat. Hist. nat. Paris, pp. 75–562.

Broom, R. (1948), 'Some South African Pliocene and Pleistocene mammals', *Ann. Transv. Mus.*, 21, pp. 1–38.

Churcher, C. S. (1956), 'The fossil Hyracoidea of the Transvaal and Taungs deposits', *Ann. Transv. Mus.*, 22, pp. 477–501.

Dale, M. M. (1948), 'New fossil Suidae from the Limeworks Quarry, Makapansgat, Potgietersrust', *S. Afr. J. Sci.*, 11, 114–16.

Dietrich, W. O. (1942), 'Ältestquartäre Säugetiere aus der südlichen Serengeti, Deutsch-Ostafrika', *Palaeontogr.*, 94, pp. 43–133.

Ewer, R. F. (1954), 'The fossil carnivores of the Transvaal Caves. The Hyaenidae of Kromdraai', *Proc. Zool. Soc. Lond.*, 124, pp. 565–85.

Ewer, R. F. (1955), 'The Hyaenidae, other than *Lycyaena*, of Swartkrans and Sterkfontein', ibid., 124, 815–37.

Section One

Ewer, R. F. (1955), 'The Lycyaenas of Sterkfontein and Swartkrans, together with some general considerations of the Transvaal fossil hyaenids', ibid., 124, pp. 839–57.

Ewer, R. F. (1955), 'Machairodontinae', ibid., 125, pp. 587–615.

Ewer, R. F. (1956), 'Felinae', ibid., 126, pp. 83–95.

Ewer, R. F. (1956), 'Canidae', ibid., 126, pp. 97–119.

Ewer, R. F. (1956), 'Two new viverrids, together with some general considerations', ibid., 126, pp. 259–274.

Freedman, L. (in press), *The fossil Cercopithecoidea of South Africa*.

Hopwood, A. T. (1926), *The geology and palaeontology of the Kaiso bone beds*, Uganda Protectorate Geol. Survey Dept. Occas. Pap. 2, pp. 13–36.

Leakey, L. S. B. (1951), *Olduvai Gorge*, Cambridge.

Meester, J. (1955), 'Fossil shrews of South Africa', *Ann. Transv. Mus.*, 22, pp. 271–8.

Robinson, J. T. (1953), '*Telanthropus* and its phylogenetic significance', *Amer. J. Phys. Anthropol.*, 11, pp. 445–502.

Robinson, J. T. (1954), 'The genera and species of the Australopithecinae', ibid., 12, pp. 181–200.

Toerien, M. J. (1952), 'The fossil hyaenas of the Makapansgat valley', *S. Afr. J. Sci.*, 48, pp. 293–300.

Toerien, M. J. (1955), 'A sabre-tooth cat from the Makapansgat valley', *Palaeontol. Africana*, 3, pp. 43–46.

New Evidence for the Correlation of the Transvaal Ape-Man bearing Cave Deposits

by C. K. BRAIN

IN the past there has been considerable controversy over the correlation of the Transvaal ape-man sites. Opinion on this subject has passed through two distinct stages and is now entering a third. The original opinion was Broom's, namely that the fossil sites varied considerably in age from the Upper Pliocene into the Middle Pleistocene. Then followed a period in which it was suggested that all the deposits represented contemporaneous arid-period accumulations. At the moment, however, the widely accepted opinion is that the deposits form a series in time spanning a considerable part of the Lower Pleistocene period. This current opinion has been built up as a result of both faunal and geological analyses. The results of the faunal analysis have been presented by Dr R. F. Ewer, and it is the purpose of this paper to give some recently acquired evidence on the geological aspect of the site sequence.

At an early stage in the geological investigation on which I am engaged it became apparent that the most profitable approach to the problem of geological correlation would be a palaeo-climatological one. As will shortly be shown it has been possible to deduce the type of climate that prevailed during the accumulation of any particular cave deposit. Although this deduction is possible, we still have no means, apart from the palaeontological one, of arranging the sites in their correct time sequence. So it has been found necessary to arrange the deposits in the order most logical to their fossil contents. The sequence already described by Dr Ewer is briefly this: Sterkfontein the oldest, then Makapan Limeworks followed by Swartkrans and finally Kromdraai A. Kromdraai B, the ape-man site, is in the process of being excavated and will not be considered here. To this sequence can then be applied the results of the climatic analysis for each particular site.

Although climatic deductions are frequently possible from a cave deposit, it must be stated that the Transvaal dolomitic cave deposits often consist of several distinct accumulation phases not all of equal value as climatic indicators. In fact some types of deposit are of no value whatsoever. Thus it is an obvious necessity that the relationships and characteristics of the several phases of breccia formation be clearly understood.

Fig. 1 shows a series of sections through a hypothetical dolomite hill containing a cavern. In section A the cavern has not yet acquired a direct opening to the surface, and the only deposits forming in it are travertines, both roof and floor varieties, occasionally contaminated with grey breccias in thin bands. Such grey breccias consist of highly calcified material left behind as the dolomite was dissolved to form the cavern. In section B the cavern has developed a small opening to the surface and the deposit forming is referred to as a Phase 1 breccia. This represents a contaminated travertine, with the contamination consisting of material derived partly from inside the cave, as in the grey breccias, and partly from the ground surface. As Phase 1 breccias accumulate very slowly they are often exceptionally rich in bone, providing them with great palaeontological value. As climatic indicators however their significance is slight since the breccia residue cannot be

VERTICAL SECTIONS

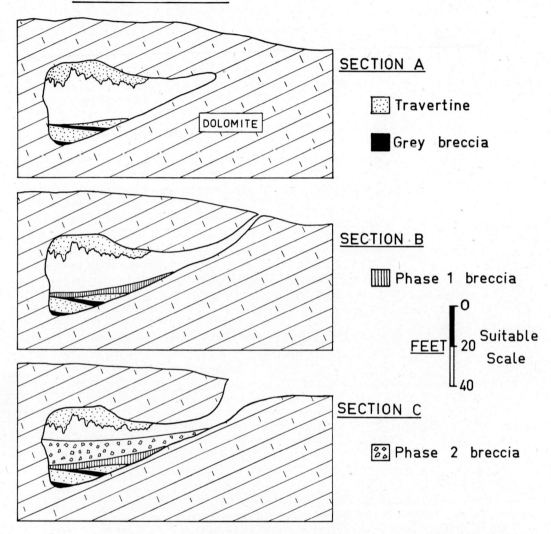

SECTION A

░ Travertine

■ Grey breccia

DOLOMITE

SECTION B

▥ Phase 1 breccia

FEET

⌐0
20 Suitable
40 Scale

SECTION C

⬚ Phase 2 breccia

THE NORMAL DEPOSITION CYCLE IN TRANSVAAL
DOLOMITE CAVES

FIG. 1.

regarded as a representative sample of the surface material, as a result of its residual cave earth content.

Section C shows the cave at a stage when the opening has enlarged considerably. Surface derived material will now be entering the cave very much faster than previously and this usually means that bones will be more sparsely scattered through the matrix than in the Phase 1 breccias. It also means however that for all practical purposes the material forming what is termed a Phase 2 breccia is in equilibrium with surface conditions. The amount of residual cave earth present in the breccia has been reduced to a negligible quantity. Thus Phase 2 breccias are of considerable value as indicators of surface conditions and the essential nature of such deposits will now be considered.

Any normal Phase 2 breccia can be resolved into two distinct constituents: the residue and the carbonate cement. The nature of the residue is most conveniently studied if the cement is dissolved in dilute acid, and the insoluble fraction is washed and dried. Grading analyses can then be done on these insoluble residues and the results show that, as far as grading is concerned, normal Phase 2 breccia residues cannot be distinguished from modern dolomite soils, but are quite distinct from typical wind-borne sands of Kalahari type. This conclusion is graphically demonstrated in Fig. 2. The composition of the various grading fractions may then be analysed and it has been found that from fine gravel to clay no significant difference is detectable between the breccia residue and the dolomite soil. This conclusion is applicable not only to the Swartkrans material but to almost every Phase 2 breccia residue so far investigated.

As far as the breccia cement is concerned, chemical analysis has shown it to consist very largely of calcium carbonate, and there is substantial evidence to believe that the original source of this carbonate was drip from the roof of the cave.

Attention may now be turned to the way in which cave deposits are used as climatic indicators. Two lines of approach have proved to be most profitable and although other methods can provide useful additional information, they will not be considered here.

The two methods in question are both based on the characteristics of the sandy fractions of the breccia deposits. As already stated, the Phase 2 breccias can be regarded as calcified or fossil dolomite soils. This being so, it is possible to make direct comparisons between the breccia residues and the modern soils of the area in which the caves occur.

The sandy fraction of the modern dolomite hillside soils in the Sterkfontein area is found to consist of grains of two distinct types: those consisting of quartz and those of chert. The chert grains are of strictly dolomitic origin as are a small proportion of the quartz grains. Many of the quartz grains, however, come from rocks other than the dolomite in the surrounding areas and when such grains are found in the dolomite hillside soils they must have been blown there. As a result of the study of a large number of modern dolomite soil samples from the Sterkfontein area it has been possible to show that, in the sandy fractions of these samples, the ratio of chert to quartz grains is constant between fairly close limits. If one then studies a Phase 2 cave deposit, representing a fossil dolomite soil from the same area, and one finds that its ratio of chert to quartz grains differs considerably from that in the modern soil, then the reason for the difference is very probably a climatic one. An increase in the proportion of foreign quartz grains, over the observed range of variation for the modern soil, tends to indicate drier conditions associated with more intense wind action. Likewise, a very low proportion of quartz grains suggests generally wetter conditions.

There are of course several precautions that have to be taken before the method can be applied. It has to be established first that one is dealing with a hillside soil in which the dynamic balance exists between new soil formation and the erosion of the existing soil. The method is certainly not applicable to alluvial deposits or to deep soils along the bottom of valleys. Secondly, before applying the method to a cave deposit, it is essential to understand the stratigraphical details and mode of accumulation of that deposit.

Briefly the method used in analysing a cave deposit is as follows. A vertical section is taken through the breccia and eight samples are collected at each five foot level throughout the profile. Approximately 100 gm. of each sample are then dissolved in dilute hydrochloric acid, and the insoluble residue is washed and dried. From the residue, the sand fraction of particle size between 0·42 and 0·15 mm. is isolated by screening and cleaned by boiling it in 50% hydrochloric acid. The individual sand grains are then mounted, preferably in Canada Balsam, and the ratio of chert to quartz grains is determined by microscopic counting. This is done most conveniently between crossed nicols using a mechanical stage and keyboard counter. Adequate accuracy is obtained if

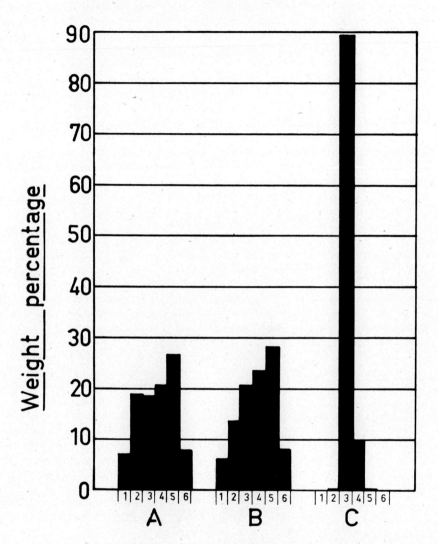

GRADING DIAGRAM

A : Average Swartkrans pink breccia.

B : Average modern dolomite soil.

C : Typical kalahari-type sand.

Grading fractions:

1 : Fine gravel   2 : Coarse sand   3 : Sand

4 : Fine sand   5 : Silt   6 : Clay

FIG. 2.

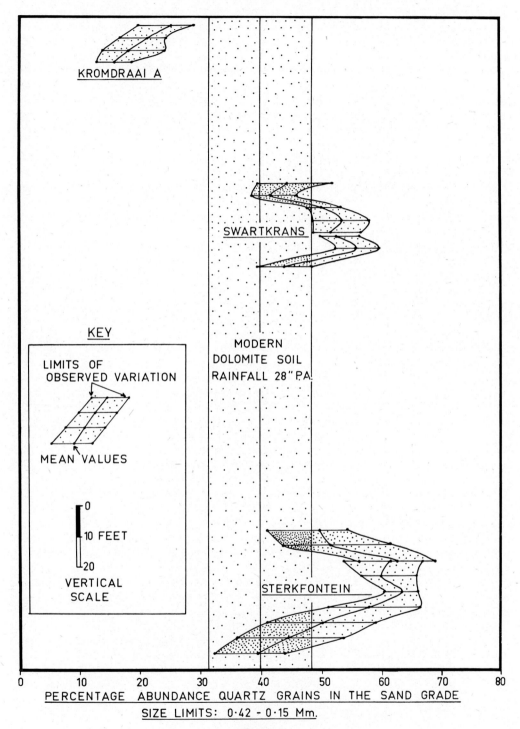

KROMDRAAI A

SWARTKRANS

KEY

LIMITS OF
OBSERVED VARIATION

MEAN VALUES

0
10 FEET
20

VERTICAL
SCALE

MODERN
DOLOMITE SOIL
RAINFALL 28"P.A.

STERKFONTEIN

0   10   20   30   40   50   60   70   80

PERCENTAGE ABUNDANCE QUARTZ GRAINS IN THE SAND GRADE

SIZE LIMITS: 0·42 - 0·15 Mm.

Fig. 3.

500 grains are counted per sample and the small indeterminate fraction is discarded. This has been done for the sites of Sterkfontein, Swartkrans and Kromdraai A. Unfortunately the method is not applicable to the Makapan Limeworks as the deposit there does not represent a pure hillside soil but has been contaminated with alluvial debris. The results for the sites with the exception of Limeworks are shown in Fig. 3. It will be seen that if one assumes an increase in quartz grains to indicate drier conditions, then the Sterkfontein deposit begins to accumulate under conditions similar to those of the present day. The climate then tends steadily to the dry side until a dry peak is reached between the 15 and 30 foot levels. Conditions then return to overlap present-day ones at the top of the deposit. The same trend is apparent at Swartkrans, the only difference being that the dry interval was very much less intense. Kromdraai A on the other hand formed under conditions much wetter than those at present prevailing. The tendency at this site however is from wetter to less wet. It should be appreciated that the time gaps shown between sites are not necessarily to scale.

Although the results of the method just described give an indication of what the climate did over the period covered by the sites, it does not tell one how dry the dry periods were or how wet the wet. Fortunately the alternative analysis method can help in this connection. The basis for this method is the readily observable fact that the modern dolomite soils from dry environments, such as the 10 to 15 inch rainfall area in the Kuruman district, contain a very much higher percentage of wind-abraded sand grains than do the soils formed in moister regions.

Again analysis of the sandy fractions of modern dolomite hillside soils from the 25–30 inch rainfall area in the Transvaal has shown that the percentage abundance of wind-abraded sand grains in these sands is constant within observable limits. In the same way as before any fossil dolomite soil from the same area showing a significant variation from these limits was in all probability formed when the climate was different. For analysis, the breccia deposits are sampled in the same way as for the chert-quartz ratio. The sand grains are isolated and cleaned with hydrochloric acid. In the analysis method that I have used up to now, the grains were then mounted on adhesive tape, following the system devised by Dr Bond. The percentage abundance of wind-abraded sand grains, or grains with frosted surface texture falling within Pettijohn's class limits 0·25–100, was then determined by counting. This was done under a high-power microscope, and between 1,000 and 1,500 grains were counted per sample, of which eight were taken at each five foot level in the deposits.

The analysis results with this method for the various sites were similar to those provided by the chert-quartz ratio. The results for Limeworks showed the deposit to represent a fluctuation superimposed upon the present day conditions of the area.

The method of estimating the percentage abundance of wind-abraded sand grains by microscopic counting is not a particularly easy one. It necessitates a personal decision being made on every grain examined and is consequently a most time-consuming and exacting pastime. Moreover the results must have a considerable personal element in them, and consequently are probably not accurately reproducible by different observers. For these reasons, an alternative method for estimating the shape of sand grains has been devised by the writer. It is a bulk method, in which the individual sand grains are not examined at all, and this is found to successfully eliminate all personal factors. This method is at present being applied to the sites and the results will be considered in detail elsewhere.

Although an attempt has been made to show how the climate changed over the period covered by the sites, it is still not possible, from the geological point of view, to distinguish one pluvial from another. For this reason, I am not in a position to say what particular climatic oscillation of the Pleistocene we are dealing with here. It is hoped however that the future analysis of a large number of deposits of differing ages will ultimately provide a Pleistocene chronology independent of both palaeontological and cultural considerations.

21

Les Fouilles 1955 au terril de Makapansgat
(N. Transvaal)

par ÉDOUARD-L. BONÉ, S.J.

AYANT eu l'occasion, grâce à la générosité du Gouvernement sud-africain et surtout à l'obligeance du Professeur Raymond A. Dart, de participer activement, pendant plus d'un mois, aux fouilles du site à Australopithèques de Makapansgat (N. Transvaal), reprises au début de cet hiver, en avril dernier, je compte exposer sommairement le bénéfice de cette récente prospection, la situation actuelle de la fouille au gisement de Limeworks, et faire part des quelques réflexions qu'un séjour prolongé à la fameuse grotte et un contact direct avec la brèche ossifère me suggère.

La grotte des Limeworks, située dans le massif dolomitique du Transvaal, à quelque 150 pieds au dessus du niveau actuel de la vallée, résultat de phénomènes de solution, de remplissage consécutif par travertin, puis par formation de brèches plus ou moins ossifères à partir du moment où le travail d'érosion ménagea une ouverture vers l'extérieur, fut signalée dès 1925 à l'attention des paléontologistes : à cette date en effet, Dart (1925) repérait un site d'occupation humaine très primitive à Makapansgat. Ce n'est qu'en 1945 pourtant que les travaux de fouille systématique sont entrepris. En 1947, Mr James Kitching exhume le premier fragment australopithèque, l'écaille occipito-pariétale d'*Australopithecus prometheus* (Dart, 1948a). Depuis lors, sans connaître le rythme de Swartkrans ou de Sterkfontein, les découvertes se sont multipliées, et la collection des fossiles de Limeworks compte aujourd'hui 21 fragments (Boné et Dart, 1955): essentiellement trois fragments craniens, trois mandibules ou parties de mandibule, trois maxillaires ou parties de maxillaire et un bassin; un certain nombre de dents isolées aussi, ou de fragments d'os longs moins spectaculaires, encore que fort intéressants. Le matériel odontologique en particulier compte 41 dents.

A une seule exception près (Dart, 1955), tous ces fragments ont été découverts à l'extérieur de la grotte, dans les *dumps*, c'est à dire les déchets de l'exploitation commerciale calcaire d'il y a quelque 30 ans. Il s'agit là d'un énorme terril à base triangulaire, s'étendant à l'heure actuelle sur une centaine de mètres de long, 2 à 30 m. de large et 5 à 10 m. de haut. En 1945, lors du début de la fouille, on estimait à 10,000 tonnes environ le poids de la brèche ossifère entassée sur le terril. Bon an, mal an, l'équipe de fouille trie 7 à 800 tonnes : elle entame le terril sur un front continu, rejetant derrière elle le matériel stérile définitivement abandonné. Il semble qu'on soit arrivé aujourd'hui à la moitié du travail : près de 5,000 tonnes de brèche ont ainsi été triées, 35 tonnes de matériel fossilifère ont été retenues. Parmi ces 35 tonnes, le vrai fossile noyé dans la matrice calcaire ou sableuse ne figure que pour 10% environ (Dart, 1954) : trois à quatre tonnes d'ossements ont donc été récupérées sur le terril de Makapansgat : nos 21 fragments australopithèques et les milliers d'os appartenant à la faune d'ongulés, de rongeurs, de carnivores et le reste.

Le triage des *dumps* fut repris en avril dernier. Outre les nombreux fossiles animaux qui doivent être progressivement dégagés de la matrice, étudiés et classés, cette récente prospection du terril a jusqu'ici apporté essentiellement deux pièces nouvelles au moins, intéressant la connaissance des Australopithécinés de Makapansgat.

Fɪɢ. 1. Le fragment mandibulaïre MLD 19 vu de haut, face mésiale à gauche, linguale en haut du dessin

Le 21 avril 1955, nous avions la bonne fortune de mettre la main sur un fragment mandibulaire, portant une troisième molaire inférieure gauche en place (cf. Fig. 1). Le fragment, brisé en avant au niveau de la racine de M2 lors du dynamitage du dépôt, porte l'indice d'une autre fracture plus ancienne à l'arrière: la branche montante fut détachée dès avant fossilisation. Il s'agit d'un tronçon assez restreint puisqu'il ne mesure que 21·6 à 30·0 mm. de long, sur 26·4 de haut et 24·7 de large. Nous publions ailleurs (Boné, 1955) une description fouillée de ce specimen (désormais catalogué sous le No. MLD 19); qu'il suffise de dire ici l'intérêt particulier de cette pièce, tant au point de vue du corps mandibulaire que de la nouvelle molaire dont on dispose pour la connaissance du groupe des Australopithèques, de l'*A. prometheus* de Makapansgat spécialement.

Il s'agit manifestement d'un individu adulte — l'usure de M3 en fait foi — et vraisemblablement femelle, si du moins la comparaison avec le matériel réuni jusqu'ici autorise des déductions que ne déroutent pas trop les phénomènes de variation à l'intérieur d'un même sexe. Le corps mandibulaire est à la fois le plus bas et le plus large de tous les specimens australopithèques retrouvés jusqu'à présent. Le module $\frac{(L + H)}{2}$ est extrêmement réduit, et correspond au module de la mandibule d'adolescent (Dart, 1948b). L'indice de robustesse est au contraire très élevé, en fonction même de l'allure trapue du corps mandibulaire: il atteint 93·5, chiffre très proche encore une fois du specimen adolescent (96·2). La mandibule femelle adulte de Makapansgat (Dart, 1954) procure des mesures très voisines d'ailleurs: une moyenne établie sur les mesures des deux corps mandibulaires précédemment connus de Limeworks montre que la hauteur, la largeur, l'indice de robustesse et le module diffèrent toujours de moins de 7% des mesures correspondantes sur le nouveau fragment; tandis qu'une moyenne établie sur 4 individus *Paranthropus crassidens* (Broom et Robinson, 1952) propose des valeurs s'écartant toutes de 14 à 31% des valeurs parallèles de Makapansgat. La ressemblance avec *Telanthropus* (ibid.) est plus impressionnante

Les Fouilles 1955 au terril de Makapansgat (N. Transvaal)

encore : les quatre valeurs considérées plus haut s'écartent toutes de moins de 5% chez le Télanthrope des chiffres calculés pour la récente découverte de Limeworks (cf. Tableau I et Fig. 2).

La dent elle-même, une troisième molaire inférieure gauche, plus usée que les deux troisièmes molaires retrouvées précédemment dans le même gisement et appartenant à la femelle adulte (Dart, 1949 et 1954), se situe très exactement dans le cadre des dernières molaires de Makapansgat. Ici encore (cf. Tableau II et Fig. 3) les diamètres ne diffèrent pas de 5% d'un specimen à l'autre, le module et l'indice de robustesse sont pratiquement identiques. Il est clair que les dimensions désignent un groupe très homogène ; un groupe très moderne aussi, car les dernières molaires de Makapan sont — parmi le matériel odontologique australopithéciné — les plus proches de l'homme récent, exception faite du Télanthrope, étonnamment semblable, à vrai dire, au *prometheus*. Si l'on exprime les valeurs dimensionnelles considérées — et leur index — en % des mesures correspondantes chez le nouveau specimen de Limeworks, on constate que les dernières molaires inférieures de la femelle adulte *prometheus* sont situées à chaque coup tout contre l'axe representatif de la dent récemment retrouvée ; le Télanthrope s'en écarte à peine ; aux extrémités du graphique, figurent d'une part l'homme récent (il s'agit d'une moyenne calculée sur les Bushmen, Bantous, Esquimaux, Australiens et Américains blancs), annoncé lui-même par le Sinanthrope, de l'autre, l'australopithéciné de Swartkrans, *Paranthropus crassidens*. Le *prometheus* de Makapansgat (les anciens et le nouveau) occupe une position véritablement intermédiaire, très voisine du Télanthrope, et constitue indubitablement une unité homogène.

Plus important et plus significatif peut-être que les chiffres — encore que leur unanimité soit particulièrement éloquente quand il s'agit d'un élément anatomique aussi variable qu'une dernière molaire — il y a le gabarit dentaire. La dent nouvellement exhumée est du type pentacuspidé classique chez *Australopithecus* et *Paranthropus* ; mais ici encore l'unité du *prometheus* s'affirme

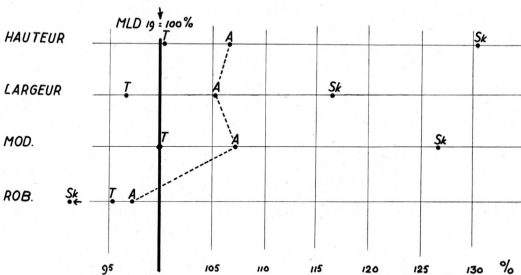

FIG. 2. Diagramme figurant les valeurs moyennes du corps mandibulaire exprimées en % des valeurs correspondantes chez MLD 19, le fragment récent de Makapansgat.
Abbrév. : A = *A. prometheus* (moyenne établie sur les mandibules adolescente et femelle adulte), T = *Telanthropus*, Sk = *Paranthropus crassidens* de Swartkrans (moyenne établie sur 4 individus, d'après Broom et Robinson, 1952), Mod = Module, Rob = indice de robustesse mandibulaire (L × 100/H)

TABLEAU I

DIMENSIONS DU CORPS MANDIBULAIRE CHEZ *A. prometheus* ET QUELQUES
AUTRES AUSTRALOPITHECINÉS

Specimen	Hauteur en arrière M2 (mm.)	Largeur en arrière M2 (mm.)	Module $\dfrac{L+H}{2}$	Indice de Robustesse $\dfrac{L \times 100}{H}$
Fragment nouveau MLD 19	26·9	24·7	25·5	93·5
Moyenne *A. prometh.* (adolesc. + femelle)	28·7	26·0	27·4	91·1
Moyenne *Par. crass.*	35·1	28·8	32·3	80·4
Telanthropus	27·0	24·0	25·5	89·0

TABLEAU II

DIMENSIONS ET INDICES DE M3 CHEZ *A. prometheus* ET QUELQUES AUTRES
HOMINIDÉS FOSSILES ET RÉCENTS

Specimens	A–P (mm.)	Bucc.–L (mm.)	Module $\dfrac{A\text{–}P + B\text{–}L}{2}$	Indice de Robustesse $A\text{–}P \times B\text{–}L$	Indice des Largeurs $\dfrac{B\text{–}L \times 100}{A\text{–}P}$
MLD 19	14·7 (100·0)*	13·4 (100·0)	14·0 (100·0)	197·0 (100·0)	91·3 (100·0)
A. prometheus Moy. MLD 8 + 18	14·2 (96·5)	14·0 (104·6)	14·1 (100·8)	199·0 (101·0)	98·5 (108·0)
Telanthropus	14·1 (95·9)	12·3 (109·0)	13·3 (95·0)	173·4 (88·0)	87·3 (95·7)
Paranthrop. crass. Moy. 4 individus	17·4 (118·6)	14·5 (92·3)	16·0 (114·4)	252·3 (129·0)	83·0 (91·0)
Sinanthropus	11·7 (79·6)	11·2 (83·6)	11·5 (82·3)	180·0 (91·3)	95·7 (104·6)
Homme récent	11·0 (74·8)	10·3 (76·9)	10·7 (76·4)	114·1 (58·0)	94·1 (103·1)

* Les chiffres entre parenthèses indiquent la valeur immédiatement supérieure exprimée en % de la mesure correspondante chez MLD 19, le nouveau fragment de Makapansgat.

Les Fouilles 1955 au terril de Makapansgat (N. Transvaal)

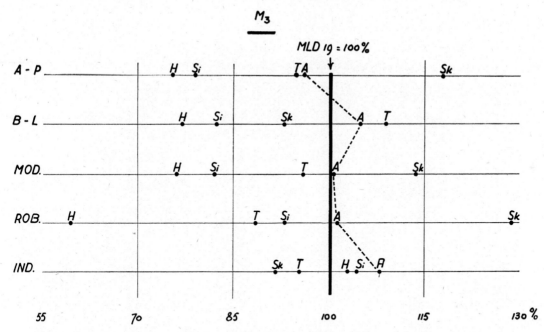

FIG. 3. Diagramme figurant les valeurs moyennes de M3 exprimées en % des valeurs correspondantes chez MLD 19, la récente molaire de Makapansgat.

Mêmes abbréviations qu'en la Fig. 2, sauf :

A = *A. prometheus* (moyenne établie sur les molaires no. MLD 4 et 18 de la femelle adulte), Si = *Sinanthropus*, H = Homme récent [moyenne établie d'après cinq populations, i.e. Bushman (Drennan), Bantou (Shaw), Esquimau (Pedersen), Australienne (Campbell) et Américains blancs (Black)] ; A–P = diamètre antéro-postérieur, B–L = diamètre bucco-lingual, Mod = Module (demi-somme des diamètres précités), Rob = indice de robustesse molaire (produit des diamètres précités), Ind. Larg. = indice des largeurs molaires, soit B–L × 100/A–P.

davantage : comme précédemment, on relève la *fovea* postérieure, à l'extrémité du sillon longitudinal, la tendance à la formation d'une sixième cuspide au bord lingual du sillon transversal — sur le territoire du métaconide pourtant — une très légère indentation carabelliforme au niveau de la cuspide antéro-externe, enfin le gabarit virtuellement cruciforme.

La seconde trouvaille digne d'intérêt est constituée par l'extrémité acromiale d'une clavicule droite (No. MLD 20, cf. Fig. 4). Il s'agit d'un fragment minime : sa longueur totale n'excède pas 55 mm. Un examen attentif n'a pas permis jusqu'à présent d'attribuer le spécimen à aucun animal reconnu dans le gisement, en particulier à aucun des grands primates. Par ailleurs, on ne possède encore à l'heure actuelle aucune clavicule de l'Australopithèque qui permette la comparaison et donc l'interprétation de la récente découverte. C'est tout ensemble la faiblesse et l'intérêt de ce nouveau fragment. Au point de vue dimensions, il est parfaitement intermédiaire entre la clavicule d'adulte bushman et celle d'un bantou, et se superpose en particulier très harmonieusement à la clavicule restaurée de *Sinanthropus pekinensis* (Boné, 1955). Il est donc sous ce respect parfaitement humanoïde. L'un ou l'autre détail de structure, en particulier le bourrelet osseux régulier limitant la surface acromiale, la dépression circulaire occupant le centre de la partie supérieure de l'extrémité directement adjacente à la facette articulaire (peut-être zone d'insertion des fibres distales du deltoïde) suggèrent pourtant une distinction d'avec la clavicule humaine moderne, encore que l'on sache la variation étonnante affectant — à l'intérieur d'un même groupe — forme et dimensions de la clavicule. Les ressemblances avec la clavicule d'un être doué de station droite,

FIG. 4. Le fragment claviculaire MLD 20, encore engagé dans la brèche calcaire, reposant sur sa face inférieure

dont le membre antérieur est marqué de son conditionnement fonctionnel anatomique, en l'occurrence la libération de la marche et de la brachiation tout ensemble, nous invite à penser que le fragment récemment exhumé des *dumps* de Makapansgat serait bien le premier fragment signalé d'une clavicule australopithèque.

BIBLIOGRAPHIE

Boné, Éd.-L. (1955), 'Une clavicule et un nouveau fragment mandibulaire d'*Australopithecus prometheus* (MLD 20 et MLD 19)', *Palaeontologia Africana*, sous presse.

Boné, Éd.-L. et R. A. Dart (1955), 'A catalogue of the fossil Australopithecinae from Limeworks, Makapansgat', *Amer. J. Phys. Anthropol.*, sous presse.

Broom, R. et J. T. Robinson (1952), *Swartkrans Ape-Man: Paranthropus crassidens*, Transv. Mus. Mem. No. 6, Pretoria.

Dart, R. A. (1925), 'A note on Makapansgat: a site of early human occupation', *S. Afr. J. Sci.*, 22, p. 454.

Dart, R. A. (1948a), 'The Makapansgat proto-human *Australopithecus prometheus*', *Amer. J. Phys. Anthropol.*, 6 (3), pp. 259–84.

Dart, R. A. (1948b), 'The adolescent mandible of *Australopithecus prometheus*', *Amer. J. Phys. Anthropol.*, 6 (4), pp. 391–411.

Dart, R. A. (1949), 'The cranio-facial fragment of *Australopithecus prometheus*', *Amer. J. Phys. Anthropol.*, 7 (2), pp. 187–214.

Dart, R. A. (1954), 'The second, or adult, female mandible of *Australopithecus prometheus*', *Amer. J. Phys. Anthropol.*, 12 (3), pp. 313–44.

Dart, R. A. (1955), *Nature*, sous presse.

22

Dating the Australopithecines

by KENNETH P. OAKLEY

AFTER a study tour in the Transvaal in 1953 I published a review of the evidence regarding the dating of the Australopithecines. My provisional conclusion was that the oldest Australopithecine deposits dated from the end of the Kageran stage and that some were early Kamasian. Since then a great deal of new work on the geology and palaeontology of the deposits has been done, mainly by Mr C. K. Brain and Dr R. F. Ewer, and this has necessitated some revision of the scheme of classification which I suggested, although in its essential outlines I believe it can still be maintained.

It may be useful to indicate briefly the nature of the evidence which led me to place the earliest known Australopithecines in the Pleistocene (and not only so, but considerably above the Plio-Pleistocene boundary). The fundamental evidence comes from Taung in S. African Bechuanaland. Here the original *Australopithecus* skull was found in 1924 in the indurated sand filling a tunnel-like cave within tufaceous limestone deposited by springs issuing from the dolomite scarp. There are four main masses of tufaceous limestone at Taung, formed at different times. They were studied in 1948 by Professor F. E. Peabody, who was able to show that the *Australopithecus* cave was in the oldest of the main masses, i.e. in the Thabaseek Travertine. The cliff against which the tufa mass is banked appears to be a pre-Karroo feature and it is clear from Dr Basil Cooke's work on the Vaal that it cannot have been exposed before the river was beginning to deposit gravels on the 200 feet terrace. We now know that these gravels contain in their upper layers advanced pebble-tools, and therefore can be most reasonably equated with the Kanam (Kageran) stage in East Africa. In other words the situation of the Taung tufas makes it extremely unlikely that even the oldest of these can be older than early Pleistocene (Villafranchian).

Moreover, it is difficult to conceive that the Taung tufas can have been laid down under conditions other than pluvial. At the present day, tufa is only forming round a few springs in that part of Africa, and then only on a very limited scale. The tufa masses at Taung are so extensive that they were evidently formed when the springs and streams issuing from the dolomite escarpment were more copious than they are today. The fact that the tufas are free from *disseminated* sand grains indicates that they were accumulated under conditions which were wetter rather than drier than today. Dust-devils are commonly seen at Taung, where constant vigilance is needed to prevent the development of dust bowls. The purity of the tufas indicates that winds blowing sand were less frequent when these deposits were being deposited than they are today.

If the tufas indicate pluvial conditions it is inconceivable that they are older than Lower Pleistocene, for the preceding Pliocene period was distinguished, in the semi-arid parts of Africa, by conditions that were *drier* rather than wetter than today.

The situation of the Taung tufas banked against a feature in the sub-Karroo surface rules out all possibility that they are older than Pliocene, and all lines of evidence converge to indicate that they were accumulated during periods of increased rainfall in Pleistocene times. That is to say, in terms of the nomenclature that has been current during the last decade, the oldest tufa masses cannot be older than Kageran. Whether the Kageran (Omo-Kanam) stage includes one or *two* pluvial phases is a detail which does not affect this main conclusion.

155

Section One

If the oldest tufa mass represents a Kageran pluvial, the *Australopithecus* cave deposit itself must be a stage later, either inter-Kageran or end-Kageran or post-Kageran. (Judging by the published evidence it was a cave deposit and not a mass of sand enveloped by growing tufa. This was also Professor Peabody's conclusion.) The cave had to be formed by solution and then filled by sand. The nature of this cave-filling is a matter of considerable importance. As the original site has been quarried away, attention has been paid to the material filling another cave, originally probably continuous with it, which is exposed at a higher level, about 100 yards to the east. This is known as Hrdlicka's site. Peabody concluded that this cave system was occupied by two deposits, a lower layer formed under dry conditions and an upper deposit accumulated when the conditions were damper. He considered that the *Australopithecus* skull came from the upper deposit.

Professor Peabody kindly sent me samples of the deposits which he had recognized at Hrdlicka's site for comparison with those which I collected. Through the kindness of Professor R. A. Dart I have also been able to make a preliminary comparison with the matrix of the *Australopithecus* skull, and as a result I am now convinced that the latter corresponds more closely with the lower dry phase, than with the upper so-called damper phase deposit.

The dry phase deposit consists of pink aeolian sand in a calcareous cement. The matrix of the *Australopithecus* skull is very similar, but the modal grain size is smaller. This is to be expected if the cave was a tunnel-like passage descending from the surface obliquely and running parallel with the tufa front as Peabody believed. Since the skull was found in the deeper part of the cave, the sand there would have been further from the mouth and one might expect it to be finer in grain. The smallest grains in the matrix of the skull are below the size at which rounding can occur in aeolian transport, that is to say they show angularity similar to the grains in loess. The grains in the so-called wetter-phase deposit seen at Hrdlicka's site are very poorly sorted but the carbonate content of the deposit is higher.

Professor Peabody based his conclusion that the *Australopithecus* skull came from the wetter-phase deposit on the observation that baboon skulls from this layer at the Hrdlicka site had their interiors lined with calcite crystals, and that calcite crystals were visible on the broken interior of the *Australopithecus* skull. Close examination, however, shows that the calcite crystals are not *lining* the latter but are coating a joint surface or bedding plane in the hard sandy limestone which must have already filled the interior of the skull before the crystals were formed.

The Taung skull, generally regarded as the oldest of the known Australopithecines, belongs it would seem to a dry period following a pluvial phase. Provisionally we may conclude that it dates from driest part of the interpluvial which terminated the Kageran or Omo-Kanam stage.

Since the publication of my first provisional classification of the Australopithecine deposits, Mr C. K. Brain has carried out his detailed petrographic and mineralogical researches on the breccias of the Sterkfontein and Makapan districts. I had the opportunity early in July 1955 to revisit these sites in his company and to hear the details of the work which he has outlined to this section of the Congress. I would like to pay tribute to the care and ingenuity with which he has tackled this difficult subject.

Mr Brain has found evidence that led him to conclude that the basal deposit in the Makapan Limeworks Cave was formed at a time when the climate was slightly drier rather than slightly wetter than now. This fact, taken into conjunction with new faunal evidence, indicates that *Australopithecus* of Makapan is slightly later than that of Sterkfontein, rather than earlier as I had suggested in 1953.

The above revision still keeps the three more generalized species of *Australopithecus* together and places them earlier than the more gerontomorphic sub-genus *Paranthropus* found at Swartkrans and Kromdraai.

Although the sequence is now more or less agreed, it may well be, as Dr Ewer's evidence suggests, that there is a greater gap in time between the Swartkrans deposit and the Kromdraai group than I have allowed. The Kromdraai phase seems to be somewhat comparable

Dating the Australopithecines

PROVISIONAL DATING OF AUSTRALOPITHECINES
(1955 Revision)

Stages		Rainfall	Associated Mammalia	Sites of Australopithecines	Cultures in Vaal
Olduvai I–II	Early Kamasian	Maximum			Chellean
		Increasing	Equus zebra & Papio*	Kromdraai Swartkrans	Oldowan
Kanam & Omo	Kageran	Minimum	Parapapio broomi	Makapan Sterkfontein	Early Oldowan & 'Kafuan'
			Parapapio africanus	Taung	
		Maximum	·		None known

*After this paper had been prepared, it was reported that *Papio* had been identified in the Taung fauna. However, it remains true that the replacement of *Parapapio* by *Papio* is characteristic of the later Australopithecine deposits.

with the damper phase following the Kaiso Bone Bed. As Professor G. Mortelmans pointed out, the mollusca in this epi-Kaiso deposit appear to be Kageran in their affinities rather than Kamasian. Yet the climatic evidence clearly indicates the initiation of a new pluvial cycle.

A great deal more palaeontological research is required before the detailed correlation of the Australopithecine deposits is on a firm basis, but there now appears to be a wide measure of agreement that those so far investigated range in time from the second half of the early Pleistocene to the beginning of the middle, and that they overlap in time the earliest pebble-tool culture of South Africa.

REFERENCES

Oakley, K. P. (1954), 'The dating of the Austropithecinae of Africa', *Am. J. Phys. Anthrop.*, n.s. 12, No. 1 (March), pp. 9–28.

Peabody, F. E. (1954), 'Travertines and Cave Deposits of the Kaap Escarpment of South Africa, and the Type Locality of *Australopithecus africanus* Dart', *Bull. Geol. Soc. Am.*, 65, no. 7 (July), pp. 671–706.

23

Meganthropus and the Australopithecinae

by G. H. R. VON KOENIGSWALD

EARLY types of the Hominidae occur at the beginning of the Pleistocene in two widely separated regions: in Java and in South Africa. While in Asia, by the presence of *Pithecanthropus* and *Sinanthropus* a direct connection with early neanderthaloid types and modern Man is evident, the South African group known as the Australopithecinae is more difficult to judge. The known forms, with large molars, shortened premolars, small canines, no diastema, reduced incisors and the tendency of a molarization of the first deciduous molar are in some respects even more specialized than modern Man.

The most primitive representative of the Asiatic Hominidae—who, together with these forms, Neanderthal Man and modern Man belongs to Heberer's group of the 'Euhomininae'—is *Meganthropus*. We do not regard the species *palaeojavanicus*, but do consider the genus as ancestral to *Pithecanthropus*. *Meganthropus* has its robustness in common with the Australopithecinae, and both most probably have a common ancestor in the Upper or Middle Pliocene.

To which group does *Meganthropus* belong? Has he also lived in Africa? A small fragment of an upper jaw from East Africa, collected by Kohl-Larsen, has been described by Weinert as *Meganthropus africanus*, but according to W. Abel, Teilhard de Chardin, Robinson and Von Koenigswald most certainly belongs to an Australopithecus. On the other hand, Robinson (1953, 1954) recently has tried to show that *Meganthropus palaeojavanicus* from the Lower Pleistocene of Sangiran (Central Java) should be included in the group of the Australopithecinae. As he uses for his comparison only the cast and Weidenreich's figures of the cast, while he has no knowledge of the additional material not yet published, it is necessary to make some corrections which will show that the similarity with the Australopithecinae has been overrated and that his conclusions cannot be confirmed. A detailed discussion of this question will be included and a definitive description of the *Meganthropus* material, and we will confine ourselves here to certain problems concerning the dentition.

First of all the lower teeth of *Meganthropus* differ from those of the Australopithecinae by the presence of an uninterrupted connection between the protoconid and the metaconid, that is to say, by a complete posterior trigonid crest. This is a primitive feature, and also visible in the last deciduous molar. This tooth shows another very primitive feature, namely the presence of a minute paraconid.

The Australopithecinae generally all show very small incisors especially in the lower jaw, this in contrast with the early Euhominids. In *Meganthropus* the incisors surely are of the latter type, as can be shown in Weidenreich's reconstruction of the mendibular arch (Weidenreich, 1945, Pl. 7).

There is a large isolated canine from Sangiran, which does not fit in any other jaw but the *Meganthropus* mandible, and surely belongs to the same species although to a different individual;

158

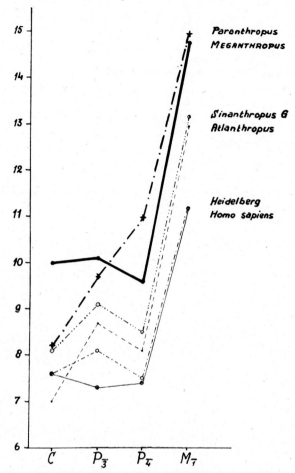

FIG. 1. Mesio-distal length of the canine, the premolars and the first molar of
Paranthropus, *Meganthropus* and other Hominidae

this tooth has a mesio-distal length of 10·0 mm. and a breadth of 11·0 mm. and is therefore larger than the same tooth in *Paranthropus*, where the mesio-distal length varies between 7·9 and 8·4; 8·1 and 8·9 mm. respectively. From the morphological point of view there is not much difference. The anterior premolar of *Meganthropus* according to Robinson should be a typically 'australopithecine tooth'. This is not entirely correct as the anterior fossa is broad as in the Euhominids and not a pit like in the Australopithecinae. In the posterior premolar the marked asymmetry of the posterior part is greater in *Paranthropus* than in *Sinanthropus*, but it should be borne in mind that this too is a feature common to many Anthropoids. While in the Australopithecinae this tooth has two roots, in *Meganthropus* this tooth has a single root, as is typical for the Euhominids. There is a certain similarity in the first lower molar which is, however, not greater than between first molars in higher primates in general. A labial cingulum as can be observed in *Meganthropus* and in *Paranthropus robustus*, also occurs among Anthropoids; it is typically developed in certain specimens of the fossil orang-utan of Java.

Of the greatest importance, however, are the relative dimensions of the two premolars, a point which is dismissed by Robinson. 'How important this feature is—its phyletic valency—is a little difficult to assess. As demonstrated, there is a considerable degree of variation among the various hominids as well as among individual specimens of a particular form.' If we look over the predominance of the first premolar we will find that it is a typical feature for all primitive Euhominids as *Sinanthropus*, Heidelberg Man, and the newly discovered *Atlanthropus*. In Neanderthal Man, both premolars might be of equal size and among modern man (white races) the first premolar might be smaller than the second, the Canadian eskimos still have a large anterior premolar. In American whites the first premolar is 0·2 mm. smaller than the second one. In the Australopithecinae these conditions, in connection with an exaggerated reduction of the incisors and canines have already influenced the first premolar, which in *Paranthropus crassidens* is 1·3 mm. smaller than the second. If we look at *Meganthropus*, we will see that it has the typical Euhominid condition, with predominant first premolar. For illustration we have made this accompanying diagram. For *Paranthropus crassidens* we have used the average values given by Robinson, as in that case the first molars of *Meganthropus* and *Paranthropus* show practically the same mesiodistal length. As is evident there is a definite similarity between the diagram for *Meganthropus* and those of the other Euhominids, while *Paranthropus* shows a marked difference.

These few remarks might be sufficient to show that *Meganthropus* is not a member of the Australopithecinae.

SUMMARY

The dentition of *Meganthropus* differs from that of the Australopithecinae in the following essential points:

1. The canine although of Euhominid character is larger than in the Australopithecinae with canines of a similar type.

2. The first premolar is larger than the second, a feature common to all primitive members of the Euhominidae.

3. The second premolar is of a more primitive type than in *Sinanthropus*, and in its asymmetrical posterior part similar to the same tooth in the Australopithecinae and the higher Anthropoids.

4. The posterior premolar has only one root as in the Euhominidae and not two as in the Australopithecinae and the Anthropoids.

REFERENCES

Broom, R., J. T. Robinson and G. W. H. Scheppers (1950), *Sterkfontein Ape-Man Plesianthropus*, Transvaal Museum, Memoir No. 4, pp. 1–117.

Broom, R. and J. T. Robinson (1952), *Swartkrans Ape-Man, Paranthropus crassidens*, Memoir No. 6, pp. 1–123.

Koenigswald, G. H. R. von (1953), 'The Australopithecinae and Pithecanthropus', *Kon. Ned. Akad.*, 56, pp. 403–13, 428–37.

Koenigswald, G. H. R. von (1954), 'The Australopithecinae and Pithecanthropus', *Kon. Ned. Akad.*, 57, pp. 85–91.

Koenigswald, G. H. R. von (1954), 'Pithecanthropus, Meganthropus and the Australopithecinae', *Nature*, 173, p. 795.

Robinson, J. T. (1953), 'Meganthropus, australopithecines and hominids', *Am. J. Phys. Anthrop.*, 11, No. 1, pp. 1–38.

Robinson, J. T. (1954), 'The genera and species of the Australopithecinae', *Am. J. Phys. Anthrop.*, 12, No. 2, pp. 181–200.

Weidenreich, F. (1937), 'The dentition of Sinanthropus pekinensis: a comparative odontography of the Hominids', *Palaeont. Sinica*, No. 101, pp. 1–180.

Weidenreich, F. (1945), 'Giant early man from Java and South China', *Anthropol. Papers Am. Mus. Nat. Hist.*, 40, pp. 1–134.

Weidenreich, F. (1946), *Apes, Giants and Man*, University of Chicago Press.

Weidenreich, F. (1948), 'About the morphological character of the Australopithecine skull', Robert Broom Commemorative Volume, *Spec. Publ. Roy. Soc. S. Afr.*, pp. 153–8.

24

The Makapansgat Australopithecine
Osteodontokeratic Culture

by RAYMOND A. DART

GENERAL

IN 1945 a party of Witwatersrand University students came back from Makapansgat valley with the news that the Limeworks fossil site was a mile away from the Cave of Hearths with its early stone age implements; they bore in their hands fossils from the Limeworks including a baboon similar to the Sterkfontein baboon *Parapapio broomi*. As a result I was able to report at the first Pan-African Congress on Prehistory at Nairobi in 1947 that the Makapansgat Limeworks deposit, which had looked so human as to be called human at the outset, would probably prove an australopithecine site and one of major importance. Shortly afterwards in September of that year the first occiput was found and a succession of bones has followed.

During the decade that has since passed the Cave of Hearths has been excavated with the help firstly of the late Dr Bernard Price and more recently of the Wenner Gren Foundation. Incidentally we have sorted about 5,000 tons of the dump outside the Limeworks. From that sorting we have retrieved some 20–25 tons of bone-bearing breccia. A quarter of this breccia has yielded 7,159 bone fragments representing parts of at least 433 creatures. The other ¾ should bring the number up to nearly 2,000 beasts.

As only about a half of the dump has been sorted we hope to get ultimately 40–50 tons of bone-breccia from that source alone without reckoning on the stratified masses of breccia still *in situ* in the Limeworks cavern system. So we may one day have materials from 4,000 beasts, and perhaps more; but the 7,159 fragments we already have seem to afford a representative cross-section of the fauna contemporaneous with *A. prometheus*.

This report is not concerned with zoological systematics: it is a study of what the creatures did with their prey. Of the 7,159 fragments only 4,560 are analysed in the table, because they have been fully identified as to body source; the remainder are 2,552 (i.e. 35·6 per cent) bone-flakes and 40 damaged teeth and 7 broken pieces of jaw so fragmentary that their position or seriation was in doubt.

As these 40 cracked teeth, 7 fractured remnants of jaw and 2,552 flakes as well as the 3,971 fully identified fragments are all from antelopes, it is obvious that *6,570 or 91·7% of the total 7,159 fragments are antelope (i.e. bovid ungulate).*

TOTAL FRAGMENT DISTRIBUTION

Ungulate		Non-Ungulate	Total
6,570 Bovid	284 Non-Bovid	305	7,159
91·7%	4·0%	4·3%	100·0%
(3,971 analysed in table)	(589 analysed in table)		(4,560)

Bovid remainder = 2,552 flakes and 47 jaw and dental fragments

Section Two

The fundamental food-supply of the carnivorous *Australopithecus prometheus* was venison. Further these australopithecines were expert hunters; they could deal with any sort of antelope, because parts of at least 293 antelopes have been found: 39 of whom were large like the roan antelope and kudu, 126 medium like the wildebeeste, 100 small like the gazelle and only 28 of them very small antelopes like the duiker. Human beings have also been characteristically hunters of Bovidae. Makapansgat shows that the ancient Levitical injunction, 'whatsoever parteth the hoof, and is cloven-footed, and cheweth the cud, that shall ye eat', was based on very much more ancient australopithecine precedents.

The second most numerous group of fragments is really quite small (284 or only 3·9 per cent of the total 7,159) and is formed by a rather select group of non-bovid ungulates. Yet those 284 fragments chiefly of heads represent parts of 4 horses (like a larger and a smaller species of extinct zebra), 6 extinct chalicotheres (or tree-bears that are supposed to have browsed on trees whose branches they pulled down with their claw-like hooves), 5 rhinoceroses, 20 examples of an extinct pig, 1 of an extinct hippopotamus, and 6 of an extinct giraffe: i.e. 42 non-bovid ungulate beasts altogether.

The third most numerous group (140 or 1·95 per cent of the total 7,159) are also chiefly skull

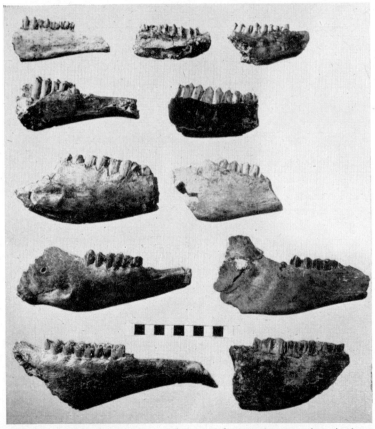

FIG. 1. Antelope lower jaw fragments are the most frequently occurring single type of fossil bone remains found in this Makapansgat Limeworks series. This assemblage of 11 antelope mandibles illustrates their appearance when found. Their frequency and condition is attributed to their employment as saws and knife-blades by *Australopithecus prometheus*

The same centimetre scale appears in each of these six plates

The Makapansgat Australopithecine Osteodontokeratic Culture

TABLE I

ANATOMICAL DISTRIBUTION OF 4,560 IDENTIFIED OSTEODONTOKERATIC BRECCIATED REMAINS FROM MAKAPANSGAT

SKELETAL COMPONENTS	BOVIDAE Large	Medium	Small	V. small	Totals	OTHER UNGULATES Totals	PRIMATES Totals	CARNIVORA Totals	RODENTIA Totals	NON-MAMMAL Totals	TOTALS (NON-BOVID)
Minimum number of individuals	39	126	100	28	293	42	50	30	10	8	140
Trunk — Vertebrae											
1st cervical	15	2	3		20		1				1
2nd cervical	21	2	2		25						
Remainder	47				47						
Thoracic	1 sp.	23 / 4 sp.			24						
Lumbar	15	5	10		30						
Sacral	3	12	1		16						
Coccygeal		1			1						
Rib or Exoskeleton	2	43	21		66					16	16
Upper Limb Bones											
Scapula	14	76	36		126	3					3
Humerus Proximal	26	7			33			4			4
Humerus Distal	45	238	53		336		1	4			5
Humerus Middle Portion	9	89	51		149		1	1			2
Radius Proximal	74	69	34		177		1				1
Radius Distal	41	60	13		114		1	3			4
Radius Middle Portion	42	45	2		89						
Ulna	49	47	6		102			2			2
Lower Limb Bones											
Innominate	13	54	40		107	1	2	1			4
Femur Proximal	17	5	6		28		1	1			2
Femur Distal	33	16	7		56						
Femur Middle Portion	6	11			17						
Tibia Proximal	38	18	8		64						
Tibia Distal	30	78	11		119			1 + 1c			2
Distal Limb Bones — Tarsal & carpal											
Talus	8	45	8		61	4					4
Calcaneus	26	39	10		75						
Other carpals and tarsals	10	19	44		73						
Metacarpal											
Proximal	20	97	12		129			1			1
Distal	19	135	7		161	3					3
Middle Portion	6	25	9		40	1c		2c			3
Metatarsal											
Proximal	18	79	10		107			1			1
Distal	13	76	21		110	14		1			15
Middle Portion	6	40	15		61			1c			1
Hand & Foot											
Phalanges	17	16	10		43	6		5			11
Hooves				4	4	3					3
Head — Bones and Horn-cores											
Skulls and skull fragments	13	35	58	2	108	7	50	19		4	80
Horn cores	10 / 1 cr	122 / 3 cr	78 / 9 cr		210						
Maxillae	47	46	66	13	172	48	25	1	6		80
Mandibles	27	98	191	53	369	50	36	21	7		114
Loose Teeth											
Maxillary	63	73	156	3	295						
Mandibular	26	86	92	3	207	144	21	48	14		227
TOTALS	869	1933	1095	74	3971	284	140	118	27	20	589

Bovid fragments
analysed here 3971
flakes and scraps 2599
i.e. 6570
or 91·8% of all fragments

Total fragments analysed 7159
Total analysed here 4560
Remainder (Bovid flakes and scraps) 2599

sp = spines
c = complete
cr = on cranium

163

parts of primates! Baboons being the more numerous are represented by 121 (1·7 per cent of the total 7,159), *Australopithecus prometheus* by 19 fragments (or 0·26 per cent of the total 7,159). In other words there are nearly 7 times as many baboon as australopithecine fragments and only 1 out of each 376 bone fragments is australopithecine. However at least 45 baboon and 5 australopithecine creatures are represented in the remains recovered: 9 times as many baboons as australopithecines.

The fourth most numerous group (118 or 1·6 per cent of the total 7,159) of fragments are also mostly skull parts but those of carnivores. Of these the 17 hyaenas represented were the Carnivora present in greatest quantity and after them 7 small carnivores, 2 of medium size, 1 leopard, 1 sabre-toothed tiger, 1 jackal and 1 wild dog: 30 carnivores altogether.

The fifth group represented only by 27 cranial fragments are rodents (2 hares and 8 porcupines, one of the latter type being a giant porcupine).

The sixth group, consisting of only 5 fragments (4 crania and a sternum), are birds including a shrike, guinea-fowl, buzzard and maribou stork.

The seventh and final group are reptilian fragments, which comprise 15 pieces of the exoskeleton of two specimens (small and large) of the water-turtle and one specimen of tortoise. Like man *A. prometheus* hunted anything; he was in the process of taking dominion over every beast of the field, every fowl in the air and every creeping thing that creepeth over the earth.

In consequence of the dietetic preference of *Australopithecus prometheus* for bovid as compared with non-bovid creatures (293 : 140), it is convenient to consider each of these categories (non-bovid and bovid) separately.

THE NON-BOVID BRECCIA

From the 284 non-bovid ungulate and 305 non-ungulate fragments, it is clear:

1. that the deposit cannot be due to the hyaena because:

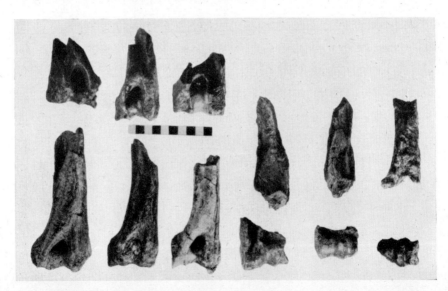

FIG. 2. The distal ends of antelope humeri are the second most frequently occurring single type of fossil bone remains found in this Makapansgat Limeworks series. This assemblage of 12 distal ends of antelope humeri illustrates their appearance when found. The damage localized upon their epicondylar ridges and the breakages of the articular ends and shafts is attributed to their systematic employment as clubs or pounding tools

FIG. 3. Antelope upper jaw and palatal fragments are numerically less than one-half as frequent as lower jaw fragments; but isolated maxillary teeth are more numerous than isolated mandibular teeth. The damage to the teeth and their dislocation from the jaws is attributed to their instrumental employment. The upper jaws were scrapers

(*a*) hyaenas are not cannibals;
(*b*) hyaenas are not the prey of any other carnivorous creature except early man;
(*c*) hyaenas do not and cannot prey upon porcupines, especially giant porcupines; and
(*d*) hyaenas do not fish in streams for water-turtles nor smash up tortoise-shells.
 An intact tortoise-shell was the only bony object that Mr Alun R. Hughes, Chief Laboratory Assistant in the Department of Anatomy, and his assistant Mr H. N. F. Harington found in the hyaena lair that they excavated completely at *Malamala* alongside the Kruger National Park in 1953.
2. that since this is the kitchen midden of australopithecines of the *A. prometheus* type they were cannibalistic, but were only occasional cannibals;
3. that wide as is their variety, the individual types of creatures they symbolize were only casual or adventitious dietary articles, not chief sources of sustenance; and
4. that the features of the non-bovid portion of the breccia (which represents at least 140 creatures) corroborating its human characteristics are:
 (*a*) *501 or 85·1 per cent of the 589 fragments are cranial fragments*, i.e. pieces of skull, upper and lower jaws or dislodged teeth. The breccia-makers were head-hunters! With man also head-hunting is characteristic; it has been, and still is in some senses, universal.
 (*b*) Except for 1 baboon atlas *there is not a single non-bovid vertebra* in the 7,159 fragments. They were professional decapitators. They must have been capable of cutting off those 140 heads with some sort of carving knife in a regular, traditional, one can say in almost a ritual fashion so flush across the throat and above the atlas, that only in one case, a baboon, was it included.
 (*c*) Of these non-bovid beasts, whose heads were so prized, *the most numerous are* in descend-

ing order the baboons (45), pigs (20), hyaenas (17), porcupines (8) and small carnivores (7): *creatures characterized by possessing either curved, slashing and ripping canines or long chiselling incisors.* In this connection it is important that at Die Petershöhle, Hörrmann found 3,000 canines of bears that he took to Nürnberg Museum, 1,000 broken ones that he threw away, and many hundreds that visitors took away as mementoes. He estimated that between 1,500 and 2,000 bears were represented in that palaeolithic alpine cavern in Europe.

(*d*) Next in numerical order come giraffes (6), chalicotheres (6), rhinoceroses (5) and horses (4); they also are represented chiefly by maxillary and mandibular fragments and isolated teeth. They and the other parts present indicate careful selection and purpose.

(*e*) Of the 80 (or 14·9 per cent) post-cranial fragments, 15 are indigestible, broken, blocks of turtle, and tortoise exoskeleton; and 42 (i.e. over 50 per cent of the remainder) are from those parts of the fore- and hind-limbs that lie distal to the wrist and ankle (or hock) in the horses, chalicotheres, pigs, hippopotamus, wild-dog, hyaena, and small carnivores.

(*f*) The horses and chalicotheres are particularly interesting because the presence of 4 horse astragali (or tali) shows that the persistent site of severance was the ankle-joint and through the tendon of Achilles above the hock or heel. The breccia-makers were professional hockers (or hamstringers) as well as decapitators. The distal phalanges of two horses and one chalicothere also show that they were interested principally in the kicking, scratching, clawing, digging and scraping abilities of these distal limb-parts; but they also carried off the shoulder-blades of the rhinoceros and hippopotamus, the hip-bone of the rhinoceros and a few carnivore limb-bones, especially their humeri.

THE BOVID BRECCIA

Of the 3,971 (or 4,018 if we include the 7 pieces of jaw and 40 fragmented teeth) fully-identified bovid fragments only 1,361 (or 34·5 per cent) are cranial and 2,610 (or 65·5 per cent) are post-cranial. This does not mean that the breccia-makers were less fascinated by the heads of antelopes than by those of other creatures; antelopes being their fundamental food, their curiosity ranged in them over the entire bovid skeleton.

The analysis of the bovid or antelope remains has been greatly facilitated by Dr H. B. S. Cooke's dividing them into Large, Medium, Small and Very Small Bovidae. By putting together the bones of the same size that occur most frequently we have assessed the minimum number of each of these four classes at the disposal of *A. prometheus* in this breccial segment: 39 L, 126 M, 100 S and 28 V S, i.e. 293 antelopes in all.

Trunk

1. An antelope has more than 40 vertebrae so the 293 antelopes exhibited by these fragments must originally have had at least 11,750 vertebrae; but only 163 vertebral fragments have been found. Of these, 92 (i.e. 56·4 per cent) are cervical; and 45 (or nearly one-half) of these cervical vertebrae are either atlases (20) or axes (25). Apparently antelope heads also were systematically cut off high up but with less care before being carried into the cavern.

2. A typical ungulate, such as the horse or ox, has on the average 18 caudal vertebrae and carnivora are also well-furnished with tails! Of all these 433 creatures bovid and non-bovid, only 1 solitary, bovid, coccygeal vertebra has remained behind in the cavern to tell the tale of the 433 lost tails. Apparently *A. prometheus* also cut off their *tails*, as well as their heads, with a carving knife.

The only animals known hitherto to hold both heads and tails in special esteem are human beings! It is at first sight disconcerting to find at Makapansgat that partiality for heads is shown by their prolific presence, while respect for tails is expressed by their virtually total absence. It seems to be the oldest known case of 'heads you win, tails you lose'. At any rate from our experience with non-bovid, post-cranial bones it is clear that absence of post-cranial

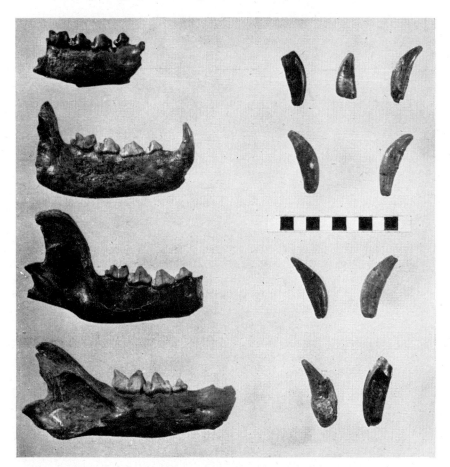

FIG. 4. The most frequently occurring single type of non-antelope fossil bone remains in this Makapansgat Limeworks series is also lower jaws. The most frequently occurring animals are baboons, pigs, hyaenas, and porcupines. Their lower jaws are characterized by possessing curved slashing canines or chiselling incisors.
This series of hyaena (and lower left: sabre-toothed tiger) lower jaws and dislodged canine teeth (some with bone attached) illustrates their employment as slashing tools

bones from the deposit can be just as informative as the presence of the skull parts or of some particular limb-bones, when we are dealing with such creatures as have bone-selecting habits.

To 'tail' anything still signifies to 'track it down'. The leaders of Bushmen hunting parties, when tracking down their prey, signal to one another silently with the brushes or tails of the Cape fox. Tails spontaneously form flexible whips or flagella for beating thickets and grass-lands after game. The flagellum was one of the badges of the Pharaoh! The brush of a fox is the trophy of the chase. The warriors of Predynastic Egypt all wore bushy tails, that look suspi-ciously like fox-tails, and Pharaohs are delineated on Egyptian monuments retreating from the presence of their gods looking back and trailing the bushy tails of an animal behind them. Horse-tails used to be emblems of rank formerly in Turkey, the rank depending on the number of tails (e.g. a pasha of three tails). Every South African witch-doctor carries an animal's brush preferably that of a wildebeeste as every European witch carried a broom. It seems likely from the significance attached to tails universally by mankind in myth and history that their disappearance from the Makapansgat breccia is significant; they were all probably in great demand as signals and whips in organized group-hunting outside the cavern. The hairs of the manes and especially the skin and hairs of the tails of animals were mankind's first string and cord: especially in South Africa are the tails of the giraffe, wildebeeste and elephant prized for those purposes.

3. The thoracic region is represented by 24 vertebral pieces (1 broken-off, thoracic spine of a large antelope and 23 fragments of thoracic vertebrae—4 of which are broken spines—of medium-sized antelopes), and by 66 rib fragments (2 L, 43 M, 21 S). So thoracic parts of even large antelopes were taken into the cavern whenever required; but usually the bovid vertebrae must have been eaten up or used up; the long flat spines probably served as levering tools. Use of the vertebral bodies as projectiles would also help to account for their disappearance.

4. Of lumbar vertebrae too there are only a few, 30 (15 L, 5 M, 10 S); and of sacra only about half that number, 16 (3 L, 12 M, 1 S). I do not know of any particular significance attaching to these low figures; but it should be noticed that of the total of 163 vertebrae the largest number (102 or 62·6 per cent) come from large antelopes; it looks as though the bodies of the biggest antelope were those brought in most frequently. Of the medium vertebrae there are only 25 or a quarter of the number of large vertebrae; of the small there are still fewer, 15; and of the Very Small Bovidae none at all. At any rate we are entitled to say that *A. prometheus* transported the bodies of the biggest antelopes into the cavern just as readily as those of any other sorts of antelope. Even if they could carry in big antelopes only after dividing them into parts, there was nothing to prevent them from carrying in small and very small antelopes whole.

Proportions

Actually there are neither vertebrae nor any limb-bones of the very small antelopes present: only 74 cranial fragments. Proportions such as the minimal numbers of beasts to the total fragments for each group and the number of cranial relative to post-cranial bones for each of the four types of antelope are therefore significant.

	Beasts Number	Fragments Total	Proportion	Fragments Cranial	Fragments Post-Cr.	Proportion
L	39	869	1:22	186	683	1:3·1
M	126	1933	1:16	460	1,473	1:3·2
S	100	1095	1:11	641	454	2:1·4
VS	28	74	1:3	74	0	74:0

From this table it is clear that the proportion of beasts to fragments diminishes as we proceed from the largest to the smallest types but the proportion of cranial to post-cranial bones, while virtually identical in the large (1:3·1), and medium (1:3·2) groups, is almost reversed (2:1·4) in the small group and is so entirely reversed as to become non-existent (74:0) in the very small antelope group.

In other words the proportion of post-cranial bones preserved increases with the size of the beast (either because they were less easily pulped and digested, or simply because the bones of the larger beasts were the most useful as tools and weapons); but the proportion of cranial bones rises so immoderately with the diminution in size of the beasts that the only part of the very small antelopes worth preserving was the skull.

Limb Bones: Proportions

1. In general fore-limb fragments far exceed hind-limb fragments and the peripheral parts of both fore- and hind-limbs tend to disappear altogether.

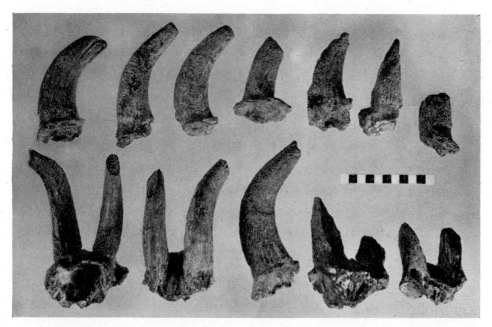

FIG. 5. Antelope core fragments are somewhat more numerous than upper jaw fragments; but they exhibit practically every stage in their separation from the skull and from one another, as well as their breakage and their wear as a result of use. This series of 12 such fragments derived from a single type of an as yet undescribed gazelle demonstrates that this animal's horns furnished a favourite type of pick or digging tool

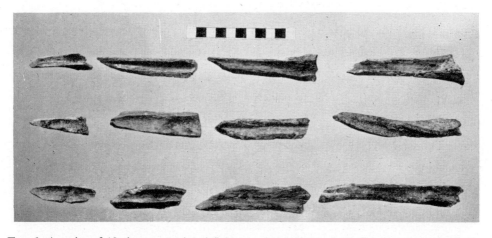

FIG. 6. A series of 12 sharp or pointed flakes to show that they are found with both freshly-broken and smoothed or worn edges and that they occur too frequently and are too uniform in appearance for their presence to be explained by chance. Their sharply broken-across bases are probably due to their having been broken off from some longer bone during use

	Fragment Totals	Proximal Ends	Distal Ends
Scapula : Innominate	126 : 107	—	—
Humerus : Femur	518 : 100	33 : 28	336 : 56
Radius : Tibia	380 : 180	177 : 64	114 : 119
Metacarpal : Metatarsal	330 : 278	129 : 107	161 : 110
Totals	1,354 : 665	339 : 199	611 : 285
Compare Ulna : Talus	(102 : 61) and Calcaneus : Phalanges		(75 : 47).

Only 7 ungual phalanges have been found : 2 out of 4 horses ; 1 out of 6 chalicotheres ; only 4 out of the 2,344 possible in 293 antelopes and none of any of the other animals, whatever their type.

The antelope limbs were apparently severed at the hocks and the other main joints and the skeletal parts subjected to violent treatments. If the distal parts of limbs, after severance at the wrist or ankle, were used as double-ended clubs this would explain the disappearance of the hoof parts (and also of the ankle bones) relative to metacarpals and metatarsals ; and the loss of all of these distal limb parts relative to upper limb parts. Calcanei are found in articulation with tali and one was rammed into a hyaena temporal fossa between the skull and its zygomatic arch. The tali too are grossly injured. They and other tarsal and carpal bones were probably used as projectiles, when detached from the clubs by use.

2. There are also *marked discrepancies* between the proximal and distal extremities of one and the same bone : e.g. humerus 33 : 336, femur 28 : 56, radius 177 : 144, tibia 64 : 119. In each case, except the femur, presumably through use as clubs, the bulkiest part has disappeared most frequently. The femora and tibiae would be the heaviest clubs to use outside the cavern ; that is probably why these bones are the least common. Humeri are the most common of the long bones ; probably because they would be the most convenient clubs for the women-folk and children to use at home. Not even the 336 humeral distal ends, however, can compare in number with the total of 586 that ought to be there, representing the minimum number of 293 antelopes.

3. The essential *blade tools* were scapulae (126) innominates (107) and halves of mandibles (369) before their angles and ascending rami were broken off. Although there should be 78 of each of these bones in the group of 39 large antelopes at their disposal there are only 14 fragments of scapulae, 13 of innominates and 27 of mandibles. Many of them therefore disappeared from the cavern after having been brought into it.

4. The *ulna* owes its relative infrequency to the fact that it forms a natural dagger when separated from the radius. It shares this penetrant function with horns, horn-cores, and all broken long-bones (more especially those that break spirally like the tibia and humerus, and longitudinally like the cannon-bones).

5. The majority of the 2,552 *flakes* (i.e. 1,432 or 56·1 per cent) were produced before fossilization. Of these 1,432, 237 (or 9·3 per cent of the total) are blunt ; and 1,195 (or 46·8 per cent of the total) are sharp. So the sharp flakes form 83·4 per cent of the 1,432 prefossilizational flakes ; the other 237 (or 16·6 per cent) have apparently been blunted by use.

The pointed flakes have been divided into three categories :

(*a*) short (790 or 75·3 per cent) less than 6 cm. (under $2\frac{6}{16}$ in.).
(*b*) medium (357 or 20·7 per cent) 6–11 cm.
(*c*) long (48 or 4·0 per cent) 11 + cm. (over $4\frac{5}{16}$ in.).

These are too numerous for chance ; they show the deliberate splitting of bones (chiefly cannon-bones) to form elongated slivers to facilitate the removal of marrow from broken long bones or diminutive objects from otherwise inaccessible recesses. Not only men but bears and baboons also rob bees' nests.

170

The Makapansgat Australopithecine Osteodontokeratic Culture

Crania

1. There are 108 antelope skulls and skull fragments, some of which may have served as receptacles; but the parts that have seen unquestionable service are:
2. Horns and horn-cores (210) forming penetrant picks and digging tools.
3. Maxillae (172) that served as scrapers.
4. Mandibles (369) whose incisors were dagger sharp, whose angles were blade weapons and whose premolar-molar dental series were saws and knives. The most illuminating statistics in respect of the deliberate use of the upper and lower jaws as tools, apart from the matters already considered, lie in:

   (*a*) the fact that the most numerous of all types of bones in the deposit are mandibular fragments
   (*b*) the comparison of the number of maxillary fragments (172) with the isolated maxillary teeth (369) and the number of mandibular fragments (172) with the isolated mandibular teeth (207); to say nothing of the 47 unseriated bovid jaw and tooth fragments and
   (*c*) the fact that the remnants of the 28 Very Small Bovidae found are 74 cranial fragments, consisting of 2 pieces of brain-box, 6 isolated teeth (3 upper, 3 lower), 15 maxillary or palatal scrapers and 53 mandibular knives.

SUMMARY

The statistics of the Makapansgat bone-breccia demonstrate the activities of carnivorous creatures, whose counterpart can be found only in the bone-deposits formed by other primitive human beings. The nearest known approaches to what we find at Makapansgat are the 'bone and antler industry' demonstrated by the Abbé Breuil for *Sinanthropus* at Choukoutien and the 'bone culture' demonstrated by Bächler at St Gallen and Hörrmann at Die Petershöhle in the Alps; but the osteodontokeratic culture of *A. prometheus* at Makapansgat was rather more crude than these.

At all the later human sites stone-flakes accompany the bones, teeth and horn-cores; the cultures are combined stone and osteodontokeratic cultures. At Makapansgat in the grey breccia hitherto no stones, not even a pebble tool, have been found. In the pebble-tool industry stratum overlying the grey breccia in one part of the cavern system an australopithecine maxillary fragment has recently been found (Dart, 1955). We must therefore keep open minds about the possibility of *A. prometheus* being shown in the future to have used stone as well as osteodontokeratic tools; but, whether *A. prometheus* used stone or not, it is patent that he relied almost entirely upon the skeletal parts of his prey for fashioning his tools; that his culture was characteristically osteodontokeratic in nature.

Thereby the prelithic state of humanity is laid bare; the most primitive culture of mankind in its crudest known form, directly associated in the same stratum with one of these most primitive known types of mankind, *A. prometheus*. Thus too has been established practically, what Menghin postulated on the basis of Bächler's and Hörrmann's discoveries in the Alps, the cultural priority of bone over stone. At the same time there is shown culturally, as has been proven anatomically, the proto-human nature of the Australopithecinae.

It is not possible to acknowledge here all those who have contributed towards the information embodied in this preliminary communication, but I am particularly beholden to Miss M. George (now Mrs Greenwood of Jinga) and Mrs H. Eriksen as well as Messrs A. R. Hughes, J. Kitching, N. H. F. Harington and C. F. Brand, and for the preparation of these tables to Mrs B. E. Wilson and my wife.

25

The Place of the Broken Hill Skull among Human Types

by L. H. WELLS

THE discovery of the Broken Hill skull in 1921 had a tremendous impact upon anthropological thought. This was the first African example of fossil man not recognizably of modern *Homo sapiens* type, and the first plausible evidence in favour of Darwin's suggestion that Africa might have been the scene of Man's first appearance. Yet as recently as 1947 it appeared impossible to discuss seriously the significance of this find, in view of the many queries which enveloped it.

That the Broken Hill fossil can now be made the central theme of a study, is due almost wholly to the work of Dr Desmond Clark in elucidating the age and associations of this find. His findings indicate that if the Broken Hill skull is less ancient than some students had hoped, it is not so recent as certain sceptics had maintained. The evidence now available (Clark *et al.*, 1950) leaves little doubt that the skull should be associated with a culture of proto-Still Bay character, which belongs within the Gamblian period (broadly Upper Pleistocene) and more probably to its later than its earlier portion. This conclusion, as we shall see, aligns the Broken Hill find with several other remarkable human fossils, both African and extra-African.

At first sight the Broken Hill skull presents a remarkable and superficially gorilla-like appearance. Nevertheless, as Pycraft (1928) emphasized, most of its distinctive features are specialized rather than truly archaic. Among these are the great size of the eyebrow ridges, whose vertical thickening exaggerates the recession of the frontal region; the vertical elongation of the face, affecting both the orbito-nasal and infra-nasal regions but especially the latter; and the very large area of attachment for the neck muscles, which clearly provided the necessary counterpoise for the face and brows. Much stress has been laid upon the almost complete absence of an infraorbital or 'canine' fossa. However, Weidenreich (1943) has shown that the modelling of this region in the Broken Hill skull cannot be considered primitive; moreover it is hardly if at all outside the range of variation in modern human skulls.

The nearest counterpart to the Broken Hill skull so far discovered in Africa is the braincase found in 1953 at Hopefield near Saldanha Bay, Cape Province (Drennan, 1953; Singer, 1954). Archaeologically, though not necessarily chronologically, the Hopefield find seems to belong to an older horizon than does that of Broken Hill. Comparison of these two specimens immediately suggests that they belong not merely to the same species but to the same race of Man; there is indeed much less difference between them than is to be found, for example, among South Australian skulls. It must, however, be remembered that the face of the Hopefield man is not yet known. Moreover, while the brows and frontal region of the Hopefield fossil are practically identical with those of the Broken Hill skull, the occiput of the Hopefield specimen is steeper and the area for the neck muscles appears to have been shorter. In addition, the external auditory meatus and temporo-mandibular joint appear to have been situated further back than in the Broken Hill skull, so that the temporal fossa was longer. This inference is supported by the fragment of the mandibular ramus. These differences suggest that the Hopefield skull carried a less elongated face than that of Broken Hill.

Two other African finds demand close comparison with the Broken Hill remains; these are the crania from Lake Eyasi in Northern Tanganyika (Weinert, 1939) and from Florisbad near Bloemfontein, Orange Free State (Dreyer, 1935). The Eyasi fragments have been assigned to an Upper Pleistocene horizon closely comparable archaeologically to, but possibly earlier chronologically than, that indicated for the Broken Hill find (Leakey, 1946). Although the reconstructed braincase (Eyasi I) is smaller and more slender in build than the Broken Hill skull, the two are strikingly similar in contour. The differences are in fact of the order of those found between the two sexes in robust types of modern man. A further argument for supposing Eyasi I to be female is provided by the occipital fragment of a second skull (Eyasi II). This piece is more massively built than Eyasi I and bears a prominent occipital torus comparable with those of the Broken Hill and Hopefield skulls; in general contour the Eyasi fragment seems to correspond more closely with the Hopefield specimen. While the evidence may not suffice to assert categorically that Eyasi I is a female of the Broken Hill-Hopefield group, I think this possibility must be seriously considered. If Eyasi and Broken Hill are distinct, then Eyasi would almost certainly be the earlier and more generalized type.

Turning to the Florisbad find, both the archaeological and the chronological position of this fossil have been much debated. There are plausible grounds for assigning it to an archaeological horizon essentially the same as that of the Broken Hill and Eyasi specimens, and I am not convinced by the arguments for carrying it back to a much earlier period. The minimal antiquity of about 40,000 years indicated by C_{14} estimation of the overlying deposit is quite acceptable; evidence obtained from the Haua Fteah site in Cyrenaica (McBurney, Trevor and Wells, 1954) shows that deposits of such antiquity fall well within the limits of the Upper Pleistocene.

Compared with the Broken Hill skull, the Florisbad fragment is distinguished by having a much wider braincase, an extraordinarily broad and transversely flattened frontal region, a much more slender supra-orbital ridge, and a very wide face with deep infra-orbital excavations. Clearly it is not possible immediately to assign these two specimens to a single type, nor can either of them be regarded as directly ancestral to the other. They could however very well be divergent specializations of the same fundamental type.

An attempt to visualize a common ancestor for the Broken Hill and Florisbad skulls leads almost inevitably to something resembling a very coarse example of the South Australian type. Galloway (1938) has made an instructive comparison between the Florisbad fossil and the 'proto-Australian' Wadjak skull from Java. The Broken Hill skull can be more readily compared, as was pointed out by Dubois (1937) with the Ngandong group of skulls from Java, which are regarded as Upper Pleistocene in age and thus broadly contemporary with the African fossils. Even if some of the resemblances between the Broken Hill and Ngandong skulls are to be ascribed to parallel specialization, these effects seem to be superimposed upon a fundamental similarity of skull structure. It thus seems quite possible that the Broken Hill and Ngandong types were derived from a not very remote common ancestor.

The Broken Hill skull has naturally been freely compared with the Neandertal type of the earlier Upper Pleistocene of Europe. It must however be conceded that the most obvious similarities are to be found in features which may well be due to convergent specialization. Sergi (1948) has emphasized the divergent trends in cranial development represented by the Broken Hill specimen and by the classic Neandertal type, which is associated with the opening phase of the last (Würm) glaciation. However, in the Ehringsdorf skull which belongs to an earlier (last interglacial) horizon, we may see a fundamental cranial morphology less remote from that of the Broken Hill man. It seems at least conceivable that the Broken Hill and Ehringsdorf fossils are derived from a common ancestor not further back than the Middle Pleistocene, and that the Ehringsdorf type could have given rise in its turn to the 'classic' Neandertal. The revised reconstruction of the Mount Carmel skull Skhūl V (Snow, 1953) seems to correspond essentially with the Ehringsdorf skull.

We thus have evidence that during the Upper Pleistocene a series of broadly comparable human types was dispersed throughout the world. The phyletic schemes which have been constructed to express the relationships of these to each other and to earlier and later types can be reduced to three main patterns. One of these postulates a fundamental dichotomy between 'palaeanthropic' (neandertaloid) and 'neanthropic' (*Homo sapiens*) stocks. The various Upper Pleistocene fossils which have been reviewed would be regarded on this view as variants or local races of the fundamental Neandertal type, comparable with but wholly distinct from the existing races of *Homo sapiens*.

A second and radically different conception postulates that in each of the large land areas of the world there has been local human evolution through a comparable sequence of stages, pithecanthropic, palaeanthropic and finally neanthropic. The Broken Hill and other African fossils would on this view be considered as representing a 'neandertaloid' stage in the ancestry of existing African types of Man.

The third and in my estimation most probable scheme envisages that the primitive human (pithecanthropic) stock gave rise directly to a basic type of *Homo sapiens*, which might be loosely described as 'proto-Australoid'. This type rapidly became widely dispersed and underwent regional differentiation. In each region, however, it tended to diverge into a spectrum of types ranging from pedomorphic (infantile) to gerontomorphic (acromegaloid). The Broken Hill, Ngandong and Neandertal types on this view represent parallel acromegaloid specializations in divergent offshoots of the primitive *Homo sapiens* stock. These extremely specialized types appear largely to have become extinct, but may through hybridization have been in part ancestral to types still surviving.

REFERENCES

Clark, J. D., K. P. Oakley, L. H. Wells and J. A. C. McClelland (1950), 'New studies on Rhodesian Man', *Journ. Roy. Anthrop. Inst.*, 77, pp. 7–32.

Drennan, M. R. (1953), 'A preliminary note on the Saldanha skull', *S. Afr. Journ. Sci.*, 50, pp. 7–11.

Drennan, M. R. (1953), 'The Saldanha skull and its associations', *Nature*, 172, pp. 791–5.

Dreyer, T. F. (1935), 'A human skull from Florisbad, Orange Free State', *Proc. Acad. Sci. Amst.*, 38, pp. 119–28.

Dubois, E. (1937), 'On the fossil remains recently discovered in Java and *Pithecanthropus erectus*', *Man*, 37, pp. 1–7.

Galloway, A. (1938), 'The nature and status of the Florisbad skull as revealed by its non-metrical features', *Amer. Journ. Phys. Anthrop.*, 23, pp. 1–16.

Keith, A. (1925), *The Antiquity of Man*, 2nd Ed., London, Williams and Norgate.

Leakey, L. S. B. (1946), 'Report on a visit to the site of the Eyassi skull found by Dr Kohl-Larsen', *Journ. E. Afr. Nat. Hist. Soc.*, 19, pp. 40–3.

McBurney, C. B. M., J. C. Trevor and L. H. Wells (1954), 'The Haua Fteah fossil jaw', *Journ. Roy. Anthrop. Inst.*, 83, pp. 71–85.

Pycraft, W. P. (1928), 'Description of the skull and other human remains from Broken Hill', in *Rhodesian Man and Associated Remains*, British Museum (Nat. Hist.).

Sergi, S. (1948), 'The Palaeanthropi in Italy: the fossil men of Sacco-Pastore and Circeo', *Man*, 48, pp. 61–4, 76–9.

Singer, R. (1954), 'The Saldanha skull from Hopefield, South Africa', *Amer. Journ. Phys. Anthrop.*, n.s., 12, pp. 345–62.

Snow, C. E. (1953), 'The ancient Palestinian: Skhūl V reconstruction', *American School of Prehistoric Research, Peabody Museum, Harvard Univeristy, Bulletin* 17, pp. 5–10.

Weidenreich, F. (1943), 'The skull of Sinanthropus pekinensis', *Palaeontologia Sinica*, Ser. D., No. 10.

Weinert, H. (1939), '*Africanthropus Njarasensis;* Beschreibung and phyletische Einordnung des ersten Affenmensch aus Ostafrika', *Zeitschr. f. Morph. u. Anthrop.*, 38, pp. 252–308.

26

Investigations at the Hopefield Site*

by RONALD SINGER

INTRODUCTION

ONE thousand morgen of fossil-bearing sands are located on the farm 'Elandsfontein', 10 miles from Hopefield (in the Saldanha Bay area) and 90 miles N.-W. of Cape Town. The history and general appearance of this site, which I located in May 1951, have been described in a fairly detailed manner by Drennan (1954) and Singer (1954). Mr J. Mabbutt, a member of the University Research Team, read a report on the geology of the site at the Congress and this is now in the press (*Transactions of the Royal Society of South Africa*). Reference to the Chelles-Acheul and Still Bay cultural material collected may be found in the above publications and also in surveys by Goodwin (1953) and Singer and Crawford. An interesting feature of the site is that where a collection of fragmented or intact bones are found in one mound, they may not represent one animal, and excavation at and around that spot may produce no further remains: associated remains may be scattered widely apart. This indicates either pre-fossilized dismemberment or movement by water or carnivores, or post-fossilization movement by the elements and shifting sand-dunes.

The site is of major importance in Africa as it constitutes one of the four where Man of the earlier phases of the Upper Pleistocene has been found in association with his handiwork and the fauna of the period. In South Africa, 800 miles from Hopefield is Florisbad where many faunal remains, especially the ungulates, bear a superficial resemblance to those of Hopefield (Singer, 1956). There the oldest 'dated' *Homo sapiens* in Africa has been found with his Hagenstad cultural variation. In Northern Rhodesia is the Broken Hill site with its well-known material. In North Africa, at Ternifine, Arambourg has discovered 2 mandibles (assigned to a new genus and species —*Atlanthropus mauritanicus*) associated with the Chelleo-Acheulian biface industries and with a fauna attributed by him to the Middle Pleistocene (1955). A fifth site may also be added: in East Africa is the beautifully stratified Olduvai Gorge, first seen by Kattwinkel in 1911, with its rich deposits of extinct and extant faunal remains as well as amazing cultural sequences ranging from pebble tools through hand-axes to the Still Bay. Not far from Olduvai is Lake Eyasi on the eastern shore of which fragments of the Eyasi Skull ('*Africanthropus*' *njarensis* Weinert) were recovered in 1936. It is probable that an Eyasi type may have been responsible for at least one of those cultural sequences in the Olduvai Gorge.

Thus Man of the lower part of the Upper Pleistocene (and the terminal phases of the Middle Pleistocene) is represented in Africa at probably 5 places each a thousand miles distant from the other. Consequently there is every likelihood that the whole story of human evolution in the Pleistocene will yet be unfolded on this Continent.

---

* The main purpose of this lecture was to illustrate, by means of 35 mm. slides, the various features of the site, the major fossilized faunal types and the Saldanha Skull and mandibular fragment. As it is difficult and uneconomical to publish prints of all the slides, it is the object of this paper to record an annotated list of the specimens illustrated, to indicate the references where detailed descriptions of some may be found and to present the major conclusions drawn.

Section Two

THE FAUNA

The following skeletal remains have already been diagnosed* and are handsomely represented in the Hopefield collection housed in this Department:

PROBOSCIDEA

ELEPHANTIDAE
Loxodonta (Palaeoloxodon) antiquus recki

PERISSODACTYLA

RHINOCEROTIDAE
Diceros sp. (cf. *bicornis*)
Ceratotherium sp. (cf. *simum*)

EQUIDAE
Equus (Hippotigris) capensis
Equus (Hippotigris) sandwithi
Equus (Hippotigris) poweri
Equus (Hippotigris) fowleri (? = *grevyi*)

ARTIODACTYLA

SUIDAE
Mesochoerus lategani sp. nov.
Mesochoerus paiceae
Tapinochoerus meadowsi

HIPPOPOTAMIDAE
Hippopotamus amphibius

GIRAFFIDAE
Sivatherium olduvaiensis

BOVIDAE
Cephalophus sp., *Sylvicapra* sp., *Raphicerus* sp., *Oreotragus* sp., *Pelea* sp., *Redunca* sp., *Kobus* sp. (cf. *leche*), *Antidorcas* sp., *Hippotragus equinus*, *Hippotragus niger*, *Damaliscus* sp., *Alcelaphus* sp., *Connochaetes* sp., *Taurotragus* sp., *Homoioceras* (?*Bubalus*) sp.

CARNIVORA

CANIDAE
Canis mesomelas
Lycaon pictus magnus subsp. nov.

MUSTELIDAE
Mellivora capensis

VIVERRIDAE
Herpestes sp. (cf. *ichneumon*)

HYAENIDAE
Hyaena brunnea
Crocuta spelaea

PHOLIDOTA

MANIDAE
Manis (Smutsia) sp.

A large number of other specimens are as yet undiagnosed.

The late Dorothy Bate held (1949) that all extinct African buffaloes should be referred to a new genus *Homoioceras*, as distinct from the Asian *Bubalus* and from the recent African *Syncerus*. The Elandsfontein specimens, although generally Homoiocerine in nature, have a number of affinities to the Asian *Bubalus*, and may represent a link between the African and Asian genera. This will be discussed in detail in a paper being prepared by the author. The Elandsfontein buffalo (Fig. 1) is represented by more than 8 skulls as well as horn cores, vertebrae and long bones. This is no isolated type because I have examined a skull and horn cores recovered from 20 feet depth, similar in all respect to ours, and mounted in the Port Elizabeth Museum. Although labelled *Bubalus* (i.e. *Homoioceras*) *bainii* it is quite unlike the type specimen. Similarly, in the S.A. Museum, Cape Town, two of the mounted '*bainii*' skulls from the farm Bloembosch, near Elandsfontein, are unlike the type specimen mounted alongside, but are akin to the Elandsfontein buffalo.

The rhinoceros material falls into the 2 genera, *Ceratotherium* and *Diceros*, but brief examination indicates a larger size and variations from the living species. Further study is required to designate the specific rank.

The collection of fossil pig material was initially assigned to a new species of *Mesochoerus*, namely, *lategani* (Singer and Keen, 1955) which is akin to *olduvaiensis* from the Middle Pleistocene beds in the Olduvai Gorge. Subsequently a medical student (Mr van Niekerk) and I recovered

* In accordance with the terminology of Ellerman, J. R., T. C. S. Morrison-Scott and R. W. Hayman, *Southern African Mammals*, London, 1953; and Hopwood and Hollyfield (1954) (see References).

FIG. 1. *Homoioceras* (? *Bubalus*) sp. in situ at Elandsfontein

further specimens among which are included an M³ and M² of a *Tapinochoerus meadowsi* and an M₃ of a *Mesochoerus paiceae*. A fossilized mandible of a young *Mesochoerus* with a deciduous third premolar and an early erupted M₁ has also been found and described (Keen and Singer, 1956). The fluorine content of a *lategani* specimen is almost equivalent to that in the human Saldanha Skull (vide infra).

The Equidae are represented by a large number of teeth (including complete dentitions), snouts, mandibles and limb bones. There appear to be 4 major variations, of which the dominating species is *capensis*. The ranges of these 4 species overlap somewhat, and it is probable that at least two of the species will be included within the range of variation of *Equus* (*Hippotigris*) *capensis*. Thus far *Hipparion* has not been identified in the collection.

The various hypsodont fossil giraffe teeth may be referred to *Sivatherium olduvaiensis*, specimens of which they closely resemble. The Olduvai material forms a wide range of variation but one no wider than that exhibited for the same characters in the living giraffe species. Similar fossil giraffe teeth found in South Africa are included in the genus *Griquatherium*, but it is considered here that *Griquatherium haughtoni* (from the Vaal River) is not dissimilar from *Sivatherium giganteum*, and that *Griquatherium cingulatum* (from the Vaal River and Makapan Valley) may be referable to *Hydaspitherium magnus*.

All the relatively scanty carnivore remains have now been described (Ewer and Singer, 1956). The *Mellivora capensis* closely resembles the living honey-badger, differing only in its rather small size and in the fact that the palate is less prolonged posteriorly. A new subspecies of *Lycaon pictus*, designated *magnus*, differs from the extant form in the greater length of the mandible, larger lower canines and incisors, and longer but relatively narrower lower premolars. The *Hyaena brunnea* shows some differences from the living species, namely, a more primitive lower carnassial and lesser development of the crushing specializations of the lower premolars. However, these differences are not considered sufficient to create a distinct subspecies. Similarly, the *Crocuta spelaea*, differing only in a slightly more primitive character of the premolars from the typical European *spelaea*, cannot be considered as a new subspecies. In this feature the Hopefield specimens show affinity to *Crocuta spelaea capensis*. Most of the specimens (teeth) of *Canis mesomelas* fall within the range of the modern black-backed jackal but a number of individual measurements lie beyond the upper size limit. In respect of the length of M² the Hopefield specimens lie intermediate between the Transvaal fossil subspecies (Ewer, in the press) and the living form. A phylogenetic series is demonstrated by Ewer and Singer in which a reduction of the molars and a shortening of the premolars is taking place; the Hopefield specimens representing a form ancestral to the living black-backed jackal, and the Transvaal form in turn ancestral to the Hopefield. The carnivore specimens indicate that the Hopefield deposit is much more recent than the Transvaal deposits. No trace has been found of the archaic hyaenids and the sabre-tooths, but most of the Hopefield specimens show variations from their living counterparts. From this evidence the deposit is likely to be at least as old as the Upper Pleistocene.

The presence of such mammals as *Hippopotamus* and *Kobus* cf. *leche* and the profusion of antelopes and other large mammals indicate that the Elandsfontein site represents the dessicated basin of a prehistoric marshy vlei (lake or pool) surrounded by grassy plains and hills in which fairly dense scrub bushes and leafy trees must have been prominent features.

THE SALDANHA SKULL

The circumstances of the discovery, the reconstruction and the comparative features of the skull have been dealt with by Drennan (1953, 1954) and Singer (1954). The major features of the skull 'cap' are the markedly protuberant supra-orbital ridges which are separated from the low sloping frontal region by an accentuated ophryonic groove. The cerebral height appears to be low and there is no parietal flattening or occipital 'bunning'. The presence of the latter has at times been considered a primitive character but it is here considered to be an individual variation of no phylogenetic significance. Because the lower half of the cranium is absent it is not possible to forecast accurately, when viewing the skull in norma frontalis, whether the true Neandertaloid ovaliform shape is present or not. It is only suggestive.

The Saldanha Skull may be compared most closely with the Broken Hill (Rhodesian) Skull, of which the majority of features are a facsimile (see Fig. 2, Singer, 1954). There are some differences —the parietal flattening in the Broken Hill Skull is not really a difference as I consider it to be due to postmortem pressure (quoted by Drennan, 1955); the more marked nuchal crest may be a sexual difference, the Broken Hill Skull representing the male; slight metrical variations (Singer 1954, Table I) are of an individual variational order rather than of 'racial' or 'primitive' significance. Drennan (1955) is of the opinion that the angulated, less horizontal nuchal plane of the Saldanha Skull confers on it a more ancestral status. However, in the absence of most of the nuchal plane, of the auditory meatus, and of the orbit, i.e. in the absence of the Frankfurt Plane orientation, this is pure conjecture. Even if one uses the glabella-inion line, the degree of difference in the angle at the nuchal crest in the two skulls, i.e. the angle between occipital and nuchal planes, is such as is found within the range of variation in the Solo series of skulls. Actually the occipital inclination in both skulls falls within the Solo range of inclination, and it is generally to the latter group that both Saldanha and Broken Hill show the greatest kinship. From the relatively little evidence available and in the absence of a facial skeleton it appears to be hazardous to assign a definite status, and especially one of a lower evolutionary position than the Broken Hill Skull.

A fragment of mandible, discovered by me about 500 yards from the site where we found the skull fragments, has been described (Singer, 1954; Drennan and Singer, 1955). It is a portion of the ramus anterior to the inferior dental canal, and it indicates the presence originally of a broad ramus. On reconstruction (Fig. 2) it presents a Mauer-like appearance, its closest likeness in South

178

Africa being the Springbok Flats mandible. The large heavy mandibular ramus suggested by this fragment differs in height and width from the more slender reconstruction of the Broken Hill Skull mandible. The precise significance of this variation is speculative. Without the face and the rest of the mandible accurate diagnosis is impossible. The degree of difference between these two rami would be of the order of variation found within a collection of skulls of a particular 'race'. We tend to plumb for differences of a racial order too easily: the range of variation in skulls and mandibles of skeletal material discovered in one spot (e.g. Njoro River Cave, Willey's Kopje, Matjes River, Oakhurst Shelter, and more recent burials) is quite considerable, even if one selects the material to include those skulls which 'look most alike'. If two skulls were taken from one of these sites and placed far apart, it is quite possible that someone oblivious of this manoeuvre would tend to ascribe differences to a racial order rather than to individual or sexual variations unless he is extremely cautious.

DATING AND CONCLUSIONS

Fluorine estimations on a few specimens have been carried out by courtesy of Dr K. Oakley, British Museum (Natural History):

Fluorine content of Hopefield ground water	0·4 p.p.million
Fluorine content of 'light' and 'dark' fossils	$c.\ 2·0\%(\pm 0·3\%)$

	$\%F$
Human skull	2·0
Mesochoerus lategani (non-ferruginous)	2·3
Ferruginous bone—main site	2·2
Antelope skull below 'later' ferricrete	1·7
Antelope skull in shelly calcrete	1·7

Consequently, in respect of this table and of the evidence based on the fauna and archaeology, the following considerations are presented:

1. The fluorine contents of the Saldanha skull, the *Mesochoerus lategani* and the carnivora (personal communication of Dr Oakley; exact figure not available to me) suggest contemporaneity.

2. The carnivora indicate at least an Upper Pleistocene date.

3. The *Mesochoerus olduvaiensis* and *Tapinochoerus meadowsi* of Olduvai Gorge were found in Beds I, II and IV (Kamasian Pluvial-Gamblian). However, one cannot merely select one or two similar genera out of two deposits and ascribe similar dating. It is the *absence* of certain extinct forms in a collection rather than the presence of a few archaic forms similar to those in a comparable deposit which tends to be more important in coming to a conclusion about dating, unless these animals are known to occur in a single geological horizon only. In order to qualify for a period equivalent to the true Kamasian pluvial of East Africa, *Hippopotamus gorgops*, *Hipparion*, *Chalicotherium*, *Bularchus*, *Deinotherium*, *Pelorovis*, *Mastodon*, etc. would have to be represented in whole or in part among the extinct group of a collection. The Kamasian contains a few of the extinct (other than these listed) and a number of the extant fauna found at Elandsfontein, but these are also found in later periods.

The Hopefield fauna contains such recognized forms of the late Middle Pleistocene and early Upper Pleistocene as *Loxodonta* (*Palaeoloxodon*) *antiquus recki*, *Sivatherium olduvaiensis*, *Mesochoerus lategani* and *paiceae*, *Tapinochoerus meadowsi*, *Homoioceras* (? *Bubalus*) sp. A similar variety are found in Beds II and IV at Olduvai. The Middle Pleistocene phase of the Vaal River gravels contains many of the extinct and extant forms found at Hopefield, but in addition such archaic forms as *Archidiskodon* (= *Mammuthus*).

4. The Broken Hill skull is said to be associated with a Proto-Still Bay industry. The late Chelles-Acheul hand-axe culture (including large and 'pygmy' hand-axes, cleavers, unconventional

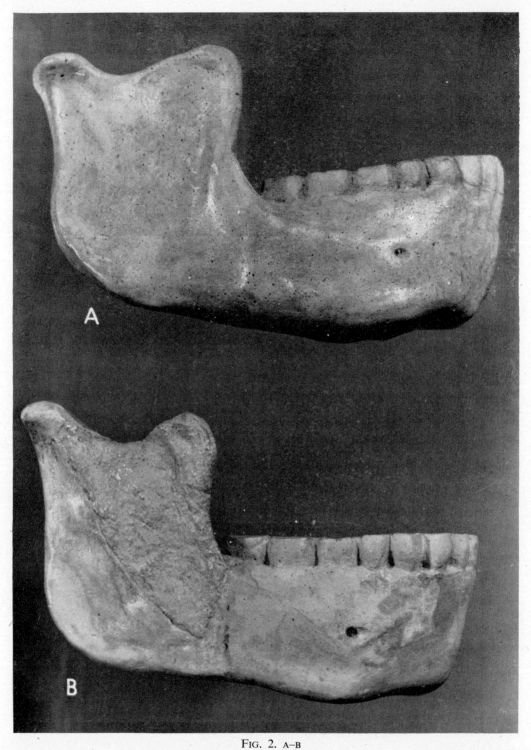

Fig. 2. A–B
Cast of Mauer (Heidelberg) mandible (A) compared with reconstruction of Saldanha Skull mandible (B) and of Broken Hill Skull mandible (C), and with cast of a mandible of Modern Man (Cape Coloured) (D). *Natural Size*

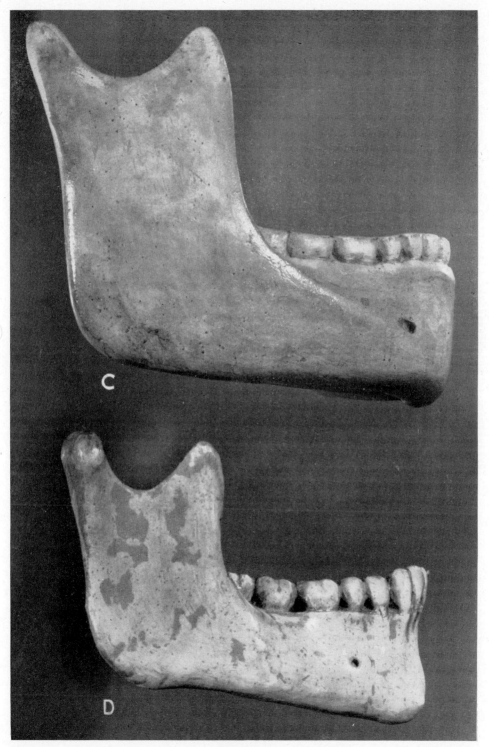

FIG. 2. C–D

181

cutting tools, choppers and bola-like stones) and the early Still Bay culture found at Elands-fontein are not in conflict with the type of Man one may have expected to find and who may have manufactured one, the other or both cultures.

Consequently, it is not unreasonable to suggest at least a very early Upper Pleistocene date (or a period overlapping the end of the Middle Pleistocene) for the most archaic of the Hopefield specimens. This period, in terms of fauna, appears to be equivalent to the Kamasian and Kanjeran Pluvials in East Africa. The correlation between the stratigraphy and climates of East, Central and South Africa is yet to be ascertained. Oakley has suggested that climatic and faunal stages in South Africa are one step behind those in East-Central Africa. Consequently, one may conserva-tively and tentatively place the bulk of the Hopefield faunal and human material into a period *equivalent to* the interpluvial between the Kanjeran Pluvial and the first Gamblian Pluvial (this interpluvial is now considered a terminal phase of the Kanjeran Pluvial). This appears reasonable in the light of the consideration that those important South African fossils—Tuinplaats (Springbok Flats) and the Border Cave (Ingwavuma) material with its Upper Pietersburg culture—are prob-ably of Upper Gamblian vintage: the intervening period seems to fit the needs of evolutionary continuity.

Acknowledgements

The Council of the University of Cape Town kindly delegated me to attend the Congress.

The Council for Scientific and Industrial Research provided a grant to enable me to study material in the Coryndon Museum, Nairobi. I am also grateful to Dr L. S. B. Leakey, Curator of the Museum for his co-operation and hospitality during my visit to his Museum. Conclusions in this paper were drawn from studies made in various other Museums—S.A. Museum, Cape Town; Nasionale Museum, Bloemfontein; Kaffaria Museum, Kingwilliamstown; Port Elizabeth Museum; and the American Museum of Natural History, New York. Grants from the Wenner-Gren Foundation, New York and the Dr C. L. Herman Research Fund of the University of Cape Town, and a Rotary Foundation Fellowship enabled me to visit some of these institutions.

REFERENCES

Arambourg, C. (1955), 'A Recent Discovery in Human Paleontology: Atlanthropus of Ternifine (Algeria)', *Amer. J. Phys. Anthrop.*, 13 (2), 191–202.

Bate, D. M. A. (1949), 'A New African Fossil Long-horned Buffalo', *Ann. Mag. Nat. Hist.*, London, 2 (12), 396–8.

Drennan, M. R. (1953), 'A Preliminary Note on the Saldanha Skull', *S. Afr. Journ. Sci.*, 50 (1), 7–11.

Drennan, M. R. (1954), 'Saldanha Man and his Associations', *Amer. Anthropologist*, 56 (5), 879–84.

Drennan, M. R. (1955), 'The Special Features and Status of the Saldanha Skull', *Amer. Journ. Phys. Anthrop.*, 13, 625–34.

Drennan, M. R. and R. Singer (1955), 'A Mandibular Fragment, probably of the Saldanha Skull', *Nature*, 175, 364.

Ewer, R. F. (in press), 'The fossil carnivores of the Transvaal caves. Canidae', *Proc. Zool. Soc.*, London.

Ewer, R. F. and R. Singer (1956), 'Fossil Carnivora from Hopefield', *Ann. S. Afr. Mus.*, 42 (4), 335–47.

Goodwin, A. J. H. (1953), 'Hopefield: The Site and the Man', *S. Afr. Archaeol. Bull.*, 30 (8), 41–6.

Hopwood, A. T. and J. P. Hollyfield (1954), *An Annotated Bibliography of the Fossil Mammals of Africa (1742–1950)*, Brit. Mus. (Nat. Hist.): Fossil Mammals of Africa, No. 8.

Keen, E. N. and R. Singer (1956), 'Further Fossil *Suidae* from Hopefield', *Ann. S. Afr. Mus.*, 42 (4), 350–60.

Singer, R. (1954), 'The Saldanha Skull from Hopefield, South Africa,' *Amer. Journ. Phys. Anthrop.*, 12, 345–62.

Singer, R. (1956), 'Man and Mammals in South Africa', *Journ. Palaeont. Soc. of India*, 1, 122–30.

Singer, R. and J. R. Crawford (in press), 'The Significance of the Archaeological Discoveries at Hopefield', *J. Roy. Anthrop. Inst.*

Singer, R. and E. N. Keen (1955), 'Fossil Suiformes from Hopefield', *Ann. S. Afr. Mus.*, 42 (3), 169–79.

27

Late Stone Age Human Types in Central Africa

by L. H. WELLS

SKELETAL remains of Man associated with Late Stone Age industries in Central Africa are regrettably scanty. For this reason an exceptional interest attaches to two skeletons recovered by Dr Desmond Clark at Hora Mountain, Nyasaland, in 1950.

The Hora site revealed a stratified sequence of deposits representing the three stages of the local Late Stone Age industry (Nachikufan I–III), capped by an Iron Age layer. The human remains were found in the second Stone Age layer (Nachikufan II), and appeared to have been buried from the top of this layer or the base of the overlying Nachikufan III. Thus the burials mark either the end of the Nachikufan II occupation, or, perhaps less probably, the beginning of Nachikufan III. They are the first human remains of determinable physical type from a Nachikufan deposit.

Of the two skeletons, the more complete (Hora II) is that of a young adult woman, slenderly built and moderate in stature with the relatively elongated forearm and leg bones which characterize both Negro and Bushman stocks. This woman's skull displays a remarkable combination of features. The braincase is exceptionally high; in a lateral view this makes it appear shorter than is really the case. It is in fact a moderately long skull. Its contours are well rounded, with none of the infantile angularity which distinguishes the Bushman skull. In contrast, the whole build of the face, including the interorbital and infra-orbital regions, the palate, and the lower jaw are essentially Bushman in character, though robust.

The other skeleton (Hora I) is that of a young adult man, short in stature but not dwarfish, and extremely robust and muscular in build. In contrast to Hora II, his forearms, though not his legs, were disproportionately short. There is however no evidence to suggest that we are dealing with a case of disordered bone growth.

In this specimen much of the braincase has survived but the face has largely disappeared except, most fortunately, for the lower jaw. The braincase is proportionately longer than that of Hora II, but is also relatively high. Its contours are rounded; the mastoid processes are strikingly large. In sum, this braincase displays no Bushman features. It could pass for Negro, but is not conclusively such, and the evidence of the lower jaw points in quite another direction. This bone is slender with a high ascending ramus and well-developed chin, and is essentially Caucasoid (Europoid) in its morphology. When the jaw is articulated with the brain-case, it is evident that the face must have been long and completely orthognathous.

It would be most simple to infer that the characters of Hora I, high rounded braincase, heavy mastoid processes, long orthognathous face, and Caucasoid lower jaw, all belong to one type, and that the same type is responsible for the high braincase and other non-Bushman features of Hora II. At the same time we have to admit the possibility that the braincase characters of either or both skulls could be ascribed to a Negro stock, although there is no direct evidence in favour of this.

I have recently been able, along with Dr J. C. Trevor, to examine the human remains from a 'Neolithic' site at Ngorongoro in Northern Tanganyika. Among these some skulls displayed a high rounded braincase essentially similar to those from Hora, also in association with a Europoid form of jaw. The same skull type seems to me to be represented in other groups of 'Neolithic' crania from East Africa. Its prototype appears to be the well-known skull Nakuru IX of Leakey (1935). This specimen and its congeners can be matched almost identically among recent Abyssinian and Somali skulls, so that the type is one which has contributed appreciably to the existing population of the Horn of Africa. The Nakuru IX type can therefore be classified as 'Ethiopian' or 'Erythriote'; it appears both legitimate and apt to include it under the term 'African Mediterranean' introduced by Briggs (1954).

It appears then that the Nachikufans of Hora included a very strong element of the East African 'Erythriote' stock, mingled with Bushman and just possibly also with Negro. In the light of this new evidence we may turn back to reconsider the fragmentary evidence for Late Stone Age human types in Northwestern Rhodesia furnished by the remains from Chipongwe, Maramba and especially Mumbwa (Wells, 1950).

Of these relics, the skull from Chipongwe has been most readily interpreted, since its principal features are unquestionably Bushman. The most complete of the older skulls from Mumbwa (IV 2), seemingly that of an individual afflicted with hydrocephalus, also reveals a preponderance of Bushman features, especially in the face. A less perfect specimen from the same horizon (IV 1) approaches the Bushman in side view, but is clearly distinguished by its ellipsoidal cranial form. In this respect it resembles the Hora skulls, more particularly Hora I. The fragments of the Maramba skull suggest a form of braincase similar to that of Mumbwa IV 1, associated with a face and lower jaw of massive but essentially Bushmanoid type, a combination of features similar to that of Hora II. It seems quite possible that in all these skulls we have the combination in differing proportions of the same fundamental types, Bushman and non-Bushman.

Another skull from Mumbwa (IV 3), which from its state of preservation must be considerably more recent, represents a distinctly different type. It combines a long and extraordinarily narrow braincase with a prominent nose which determines a frankly Caucasoid profile. This type is neither Bushman nor Negro. It can however be matched among the East African 'Neolithic' material by such an example as Willey's Kopje skull II; this in turn appears to be an offshoot of the earlier Elmenteita A type. Briggs (1954) has suggested that these East African elongated skulls can be affiliated to a stock which he has labelled 'Palaeo-Mediterranean'.

Turning towards the south, we see the long narrow braincase of Mumbwa IV 3 reappearing in combination with features of a 'Boskop' or massive Bushmanoid type in skulls from Rusape in Southern Rhodesia (Wells, 1939). This combination in varying degrees characterizes the skulls from Upington and Kakamas on the Orange River, identified as 'Hottentot' by Broom (1923) and by Dreyer and Meiring (1937), as well as historic Hottentot skulls from the eastern Cape Province. It seems plausible to see in these skulls, as Dreyer and Meiring have suggested, a southward extension of the East African 'Palaeo-Mediterranean' stock. In South Africa, however, this type seems to have arrived comparatively recently.

There is however some evidence pointing to the arrival in southern Africa of a Caucasoid physical type much further back in the Late Stone Age. The most significant of such finds are the skulls from the so-called 'Wilton' horizon of the Matjes River rock-shelter near Knysna, Cape Province (Meiring, 1937). More than one of these skulls present noteworthy similarities to Hora I in the form of both braincase and lower jaw. The direct affinity between the Matjes River 'Wilton' crania and Upper Palaeolithic types of Europe and North Africa postulated by Meiring has appeared too large an assumption to win the approval of all anthropologists. It now seems possible to see in the Hora find what may prove to be the first link in a chain connecting the Matjes River material at all events with the 'Erythriote' stock of North-east Africa. Briggs (1954) has recently made the further suggestion that the skull from a late Middle Stone Age level of the Border Cave, Ingwavuma, Zululand, may be related to his 'African Mediterranean' stock. I regret that I can find little positive evidence in favour of this interpretation.

Late Stone Age Human Types in Central Africa

The suggestion that a Caucasoid type might have been diffused along with either the 'Magosian' or the 'Wilton' culture-complex is inevitably attractive, all the more since we now see the Bushman type already firmly established in southern Africa as far back as the typical Middle Stone Age (Wells, 1952). However, the relation of physical types to cultures is rarely as clear-cut as we would like to have it. At present we cannot certainly point to any evidence for a southward spread of Caucasoid types earlier than is indicated by the Hora remains.

It is also possible that the Hora skulls might be linked with the diffusion into Southern Africa of an 'Erythriote' strain which is most clearly attested somatometrically in the Herero and related tribes. This strain is characterized by an elongated skull, vertical facial profile, and prominent nose, combined with an extremely dark skin colour. As archaeological data for reconstructing the history of the south-western Bantu tribes are entirely wanting, it is impossible to say whether the chronological position of the Hora remains is compatible with this interpretation.

REFERENCES

Briggs, L. C. (1954), 'The Stone Age Races of Northwest Africa', *American School of Prehistoric Research, Peabody Museum, Harvard University, Bulletin No.* 18, vi + 98 pp.

Broom, R. (1923), 'A contribution to the craniology of the yellow-skinned races of South Africa', *Journ. Roy. Anthrop. Inst.*, 53, pp. 132–49.

Dreyer, T. F. and A. J. D. Meiring (1937), 'A preliminary report on an expedition to collect old Hottentot skulls', *Sool. Nav. Nas. Mus. Bloemfontein*, 1, pp. 81–8.

Leakey, L. S. B. (1935), *The Stone Age Races of Kenya*, London, Oxford University Press.

Meiring, A. J. D. (1937), 'The "Wilton" skulls of the Matjes River rock-shelter', *Sool. Nav. Nas. Mus. Bloemfontein*, I, pp. 51–79.

Wells, L. H. (1939), 'A note on the human skulls from the Cornucopia site', *Trans. Rhodesia Sci. Ass.*, 37, pp. 175–80.

Wells, L. H. (1950), 'Fossil Man in Northern Rhodesia', Appendix C in *The Stone Age Cultures of Northern Rhodesia*, by J. D. Clark, Cape Town, S. African Archaeological Society, pp. 143–50.

Wells, L. H. (1952), 'Human crania of the Middle Stone Age in South Africa', *Proc. First Pan-African Congress on Prehistory*, 1947, pp. 125–33, Oxford, Blackwell.

28

Récentes découvertes de paléontologie humaine réalisées en Afrique du Nord française (L'Atlanthropus de Ternifine—L'Hominien de Casablanca)

par C. ARAMBOURG

DEPUIS la réunion à Alger du dernier Congrès panafricain de préhistoire d'importantes découvertes de paléontologie humaine ont été réalisées en Afrique du Nord française.

Ces découvertes consistent en restes humains trouvés d'une part, dans le gisement de Ternifine (Algérie) par l'auteur et par ses collaborateurs, d'autre part par Mr P. Biberson dans le Sîte de Sidi Abder Rahmane près de Casablanca, au Maroc.

I L'ATLANTHROPUS DE TERNIFINE (ALGÉRIE)

Au cours des années 1954 et 1955, l'auteur a été chargé par le Gouvernement Général de l'Algérie d'effectuer des fouilles dans le vieux gisement paléolithique de Ternifine, où, en 1931, il avait exécuté déjà des recherches. Les observations effectuées à cette époque avaient montré que le gisement préhistorique s'étendait, en profondeur, sous le niveau de l'ancienne carrière exploitée comme sablière, où il était noyé dans une nappe aquifère. C'est dans cette partie inondée que furent entreprises les nouvelles recherches avec de puissants moyens matériels (Fig. 1).

Une première campagne fut conduite en 1954 en collaboration avec Mr Hoffstetter et une seconde en 1955 avec une équipe complétée par Mlle Signeux Assistant au Muséum, Mr. Osanzoy de l'Université d'Ankara et deux techniciens du Muséum.

La sablière de Ternifine, près du village de Palikao, est le résultat du remplissage d'une ancienne cuvette lacustre alimentée par des eaux artésiennes ascendantes. Des populations humaines étaient établies autour de ce point d'eau et les déchets de leur existence se sont accumulés dans cet ancien lac sous formes d'ossements d'animaux ayant servi à leur nourriture et d'instruments et d'armes en pierres taillées. La constance de l'industrie et l'unité de la faune dans tout le gisement démontrent son homogénéité chronologique et permettent de l'attribuer au début du Pléistocène moyen.

Les fouilles

La nature particulière du gisement a nécessité la mise en œuvre de moyens matériels puissants et de techniques spéciales.

La présence d'un cimetière musulman, couronnant la butte de sable primitivement exploitée en carrière, interdisait de fouiller la partie aérienne du gisement, et, comme il a été dit, tout l'effort fut concentré sur la partie inondée, reconnue en 1931. L'abaissement progressif de la nappe d'eau par pompage permit d'atteindre des niveaux de plus en plus profonds et de suivre le fond argileux de l'ancienne cuvette, lui-même riche en industrie et en faune fossile sur une certaine épaisseur.

FIG. 1. Début des fouilles de Ternifine en 1954

Une installation de criblage et de lavage automatique des sables extraits (Fig. 2) permit la récupération d'une abondante microfaune et de nombreux ossements isolés de petite taille.

La profondeur atteinte au cours de la deuxième campagne est de plus de 5 m. au-dessous du niveau de la nappe phréatique.

L'industrie (Fig. 3)

Plusieurs centaines d'objets ont été recueillis. Ce sont des bifaces ou des trièdres de type primitif, des hacheraux et de grands racloirs discoïdes, sortes de hacheraux à tranchant courbe, enfin quelques galets éclatés de type kafuen. Tous ces objets sont en quartzite, en grès et en calcaire, quelques rares unités seulement en silex de mauvaise qualité. Tous paraissent avoir été taillés suivant une technique primitive au percuteur de pierre. Typologiquement ils correspondent, d'après Mr Balout, au Chelles-Acheul II, et, comme on le verra plus loin par comparaison avec la coupe de Sidi Abder Rahmane au Maroc, cette industrie s'inscrit chronologiquement au début de la deuxième régression marine Quaternaire contemporaine de la glaciation de Mindel.

La faune

La faune est très abondante et comprend une majorité d'espèces disparues mais de caractère africain tropical. Parmi les espèces prédominantes je citerai *Elephas atlanticus* Pom. dont un crâne avec ses défenses a été recueilli; *Equus mauritanicus* très abondant et qui est un équidé zébré apparenté aux Quagga sud africains; un Rhinocéros, voisin de *Rh. simus*; des Carnivores nombreux: Hyènes, Félins, Canidés, Viverridés, etc., et un grand nombre de Ruminants, parmi lesquels une Girafe, un Camélidé spécial: *Camelus Thomasi* Pom. et toute une série d'Antilopes variées appartenant aux genres: *Gazella, Alcelaphus, Gorgon, Taurotragus Oryx*, etc.

187

Fɪɢ. 2. Vue générale des fouilles en 1955. A gauche en haut, station de criblage automatique

Mais à ces éléments, dont l'extension est assez grande au cours du Pléistocène nord africain, il faut ajouter les suivants jusqu'ici spéciaux au gisement de Ternifine et qui permettent de le dater :

1. un *Machairodus*, genre qui généralement ne dépasse pas, en Europe et en Afrique, le Pléistocène inférieur ;
2. un Phacochère géant du genre probable *Afrochoerus* qui s'apparente aux formes de grande taille spéciales jusqu'ici aux niveaux villafranchiens de l'Afrique tropicale (Grottes à Australopithécinés, gisements de l'Omo) et aux niveaux inférieurs d'Oldoway ;
3. un Cynocéphale géant s'apparentant lui aussi aux grandes formes fossiles des Grottes à Australopithécinés, tels que *Dinopithecus* ou *Gorgopithecus*.

Ces trois éléments suffisent à eux seuls à caractériser l'archaïsme du gisement de Ternifine et conjointement aux indications fournies par l'industrie, permettent de fixer l'âge de ce gisement aux débuts du Pléistocène moyen.

Les restes humains

Des restes humains ont été découverts au cours des deux campagnes de fouilles. En 1954, une première mandibule était découverte dans le niveau sableux à une faible distance au dessus du fond argileux. Quelques jours après une demi mandibule était trouvée encastrée dans le fond argileux lui-même, à une quinzaine de mètres de la première.

En 1955, une troisième mandibule, complète, ainsi qu'un pariétal droit étaient découverts, tous deux dans le fond argileux de l'ancien lac. Enfin un certain nombre de dents isolées étaient obtenues par criblage du sable.

Tous ces documents se rapportent à un même type humain, malgré quelques différences individuelles ou sexuelles. C'est ainsi que les deux mandibules I et III, extrêmement robustes, appartiennent probablement à des mâles, tandis que la mandibule II est probablement celle d'une femelle. Le pariétal est celui d'un jeune individu aux sutures non encore ossifiées.

Les mandibules sont remarquables par leur puissance, leur massivité et leurs dimensions qui dépassent celle de tous les autres Hominiens connus sauf les Australopithécinés (Fig. 4, No. 1).

Le corps mandibulaire présente un épaississement, ou *torus marginalis*, de son bord ventral qui est comparable à celui du *Sinanthropus* G1 de Chine et évoque dans une certaine mesure celui de *Meganthropus* de Java. La symphyse est fuyante; son bord ventral présente une échancrure sous-mentale divisée par une saillie interdigastrique; un léger *tuberculum mentale*, comparable à celui du Sinanthrope, est visible sur sa face frontale. Du côté labial, le plan alvéolaire est très oblique et étroit; le *foramen supra-mentale* s'ouvre au fond d'une fossette génioglosse (Fig. 4, No. 2) peu marquée et à un niveau légèrement supérieur à celui du Sinanthrope. Ventralement, les empreintes digastriques intéressent surtout la face ventrale, mais, chez le sujet No. II, débordent légèrement sur la face linguale, ce qui diffère un peu du Sinanthrope, du Pithécanthrope ou de la mandibule de Mauer chez lesquels ces empreintes sont limitées à la face ventrale (Fig. 4, No. 3).

La série dentaire est continue, et humaine; l'arc dentaire est parabolique. Les dents sont macrodontes et brachyodontes avec une large cavité pulpaire. Les prémolaires sont volumineuses et présentent à leur bord labial des plis cingulaires bien marqués. La morphologie de P_4 rappelle celle du Sinanthrope, du *Meganthropus* et du Chimpanzé. Les molaires sont volumineuses mais la dernière un peu réduite (Fig. 4, No. 4). Toutes sont six-tuberculées et présentent dans la disposition alterne de leurs cuspides, le galbe en Y dryopithécien caractéristique. L'émail de la face

Fig. 3. Série de bifaces et hacheraux en quartzite et calcaire (1954)

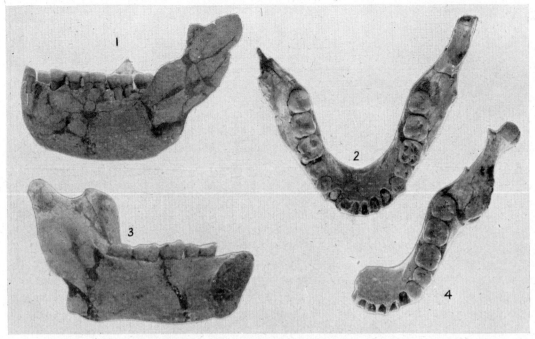

FIG. 4

(1) Mandibule d'Atlanthropus I. Face labiale $\times \frac{1}{2}$
(2) Mandibule d'Atlanthropus I. Face occlusale $\times \frac{1}{2}$
(3) Mandibule d'Atlanthropus II. Face linguale $\times \frac{1}{2}$
(4) Mandibule d'Atlanthropus II. Face occlusale $\times \frac{1}{2}$

orale de celles dont l'usure n'est pas trop avancée présente des ridules secondaires qui évoquent celles du Sinanthrope et des Anthropomorphes.

Il n'est pas douteux que, par leurs caractères anatomiques, les mandibules découvertes à Ternifine, ne se rapportent à un être voisin des Pithécanthropiens asiatiques dont on peut dire qu'il est le représentant africain. On ne peut cependant l'identifier rigoureusement à aucun des représentants connus de ce groupe et c'est la raison pour laquelle j'ai cru devoir le désigner provisoirement sous le nom de : *Atlanthropus mauritanicus*.

II L'Hominien de Sidi Abder Rahmane (Casablanca)

Depuis plusieurs années P. Biberson s'est attaché à l'étude du site fameux de Sidi Abder Rahmane où ses observations ont complété et, sur certains points, corrigé celles de Neuville et Ruhlmann.

C'est donc à lui que j'emprunte les précisions stratigraphiques ci-dessous.

On sait que, au S. de Casablanca, la côte, dont le substratum est formé par des schistes et quartzites primaires, s'élève rapidement vers l'intérieur et que, grâce à cette structure, plusieurs anciennes lignes de rivage avec plages marines y sont emboîtées.

Ces lignes de rivage et ces plages sont, en partant de la mer, les suivantes (Fig. 5) :

1. Niveau marin (L3) à *Purpura haemastoma* recouvert de sables et argiles rouges et d'une dune consolidée (D3) affleurant presque au niveau de la mer sous lequel elles plongent (D3).*

* C'est sur un lambeau de cette dune qu'est édifié le Marabout de Sidi Abder Rahmane.

Récentes découvertes de paléontologie humaine en Afrique du Nord française

Ce niveau, qui peut se suivre tout le long des côtes marocaines et sur celles de la Méditerranée jusqu'à la Syrie, correspond à la dernière oscillation du niveau marin quaternaire : c'est le tyrrhénien II des auteurs, le 'niveau à Strombes' de la Méditerranée, l''Oulgien' de Gigout. Le facies de régression qui en fait partie, argiles rouges et dune consolidée, est le gisement de l'industrie Moustéro-atérienne. Sa faune comprend, avec divers éléments tropicaux survivants comme l'Hippopotame, quelques éléments européens émigrés, comme le *Rhinoceros Mercki*, des Cervidés et des Ours.

2. Un deuxième niveau marin (Tyrrhénien II) est marqué vers l'altitude de 25 m. par une falaise morte, parfois enfouie sous des atterrissements plus récents. Le long de cette falaise morte, qui entaille généralement une dune consolidée dont il sera question plus loin, sont creusées des grottes déjà signalées par Neuville et Ruhlmann (Fig. 6) dans lesquelles la mer a pénétré en y laissant des poudingues coquilliers (L2) abondants (niveaux E à G de Neuville et Ruhlmann). Ces poudingues sont recouverts par des sables, des argiles sableuses rouges et des grès continentaux (D et C de Neuville et Ruhlmann) qui ont colmaté les grottes au cours de la régression marine consécutive au dépôt des poudingues. L'ensemble est scellé vers l'extrémité Nord de la carrière par une dune consolidée peu épaisse D_2 (C de Neuville et Ruhlmann), formée à la fin de la même régression. Une industrie abondante de bifaces d'un très bel Acheuléen évolué et une faune de Mammifères ont été recueillis par Mr Biberson dans les poudingues marins et dans les atterrissements continentaux régressifs qui les recouvrent.

3. Un troisième niveau marin (Sicilien) est celui désigné, sous la rubrique J (Fig. 6 et 7), par Neuville et Ruhlmann ; sa ligne de rivage n'apparaît point et devrait être recherchée à flanc de coteau à une altitude jusqu'ici indéterminée, car elle est vraisemblablement masquée sous la puissante dune régressive consolidée (D_1) dont la formation lui a fait suite.

Ce niveau n'a été atteint que par l'exploitation en carrière des grès dunaires en question vers l'altitude 20 m. Il est constitué d'un puissant dépôt de lumachelle à *Trochatella trochiformis* qui apparaît à la base de l'ancienne exploitation. Dans la partie ouest il repose sur les niveaux continentaux (O, N, M) de Neuville et Ruhlmann dans lesquels les auteurs ont recueilli l'industrie clacto-abbevillienne.

Ce même niveau marin apparaît aussi dans la carrière de la STIC, où il repose directement sur les Quartzites primaires et y renferme surtout *Littorina littorea*. Dans cette carrière, au-dessus de cette lumachelle, des niveaux continentaux avec calcaires lacustres ont livré, à Mr Biberson, une abondante industrie acheuléenne primitive, avec faune.

Cette industrie paraît techniquement équivalente à celle de Ternifine. Le tout est colmaté par une puissante dune consolidée (D_1) exploitée comme pierre d'appareil, et qui correspond au facies de régression consécutif à l'épisode marin qui a déposé les lumachelles. C'est dans cette dune que sont creusées la falaise morte et les grottes du niveau D_2.

L'interprétation de ces faits peut donc être la suivante : le premier complexe (L_3–D_3) : plage marine (Tyrrhénien II), dune régressive, correspond à l'avant-dernière oscillation du niveau marin, corrélative de la dernière ou quatrième glaciation dont ses facies régressifs sont contemporains. On peut donc considérer ces derniers comme *Würmiens*.

Le deuxième complexe (L_2–D_2) : grottes marines (Tyrrhénien I), atterrissements continentaux, correspond à l'oscillation marine contemporaine de l'avant-dernière, ou troisième glaciation ; ses formations continentales peuvent être considérées comme *Rissiennes*.

Le troisième complexe (L_1–D_1) : lumachelles siciliennes, calcaires lacustres, grande dune, équivaut à la deuxième oscillation marine et à la deuxième glaciation ; ses formations continentales sont donc *Mindéliennes*.

Enfin, un quatrième cycle plus ancien correspond aux hautes terrasses marines, dont les lambeaux s'échelonnent loin de la côte à des altitudes passant de 60 à 90 m. ; ce cycle paraît être assimilable au *Calabrien*.

191

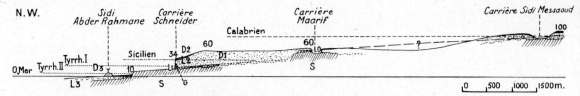

FIG. 5. Coupe schématique de la côte marocaine passant par le Marabout de Sidi Abder Rahmane

D1 Dune consolidée post sicilienne
D2 Dune consolidée post tyrrhénienne I
D3 Dune consolidée post tyrrhénienne II (un lambeau de cette dune supporte le Marabout de Sidi Abder Rahmane)
G   Grotte ayant fournie les restes humains
L0 Lumachelle des hauts niveaux (Calabrien ?)
L1 Lumachelle sicilienne
L2 Lumachelle tyrrhénienne I (au niveau des grottes) creusées dans D_1
L3 Plage à *Purpura haemastoma* (Tyrrhénien II)
S   Substratum primaire

Les chiffres indiquent les cotes d'altitude. L'échelle des hauteurs est multipliée par 10

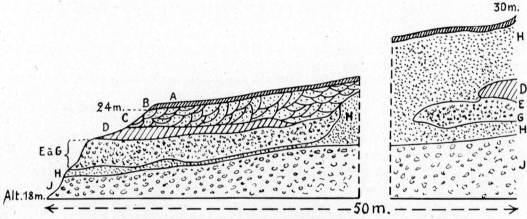

FIG. 6. Coupe d'après Neuville et Ruhlmann du sîte de Sidi Abder Rahmane

A Limons rouges
B Croûte calcaire
C Grès dunaire dégradé
D Calcaire argileux bréchoïde rose ossifère
E à G Poudingue marin avec 'traces' d'Acheuléen
H Grès dunaire
J Lumachelle avec galets par places

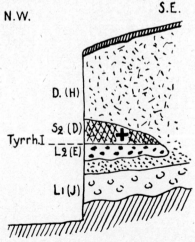

FIG. 7. Coupe du gisement de la mandibule découverte par Mr Biberson
Mêmes lettres que Figs. 5 et 6. Les lettres entre parenthèses correspondent à celles de Neuville-Ruhlmann. S2 (D) sables continentaux fossilifères, ayant livré la mandibule (+)

192

Récentes découvertes de paléontologie humaine en Afrique du Nord française

Les restes humains

C'est dans les atterrissements continentaux rissiens, exactement dans les sables recouvrant le poudingue marin du deuxième complexe, que Mr Biberson a découvert un certain nombre de fragments osseux parmi lesquels j'ai trouvé les éléments d'un fragment de mandibule humaine.

Il s'agit de la partie postérieure d'une branche horizontale droite avec les trois arrière-molaires en place et d'un fragment symphysaire gauche avec P_3.

Les caractères de cette pièce rappellent beaucoup ceux de la Mandibule II de l'*Atlanthropus* : la hauteur du corps mandibulaire, son épaisseur, son *torus marginalis* sont tout à fait comparables. Le fragment symphysaire montre que la symphyse était épaisse et fuyante (Fig. 8).

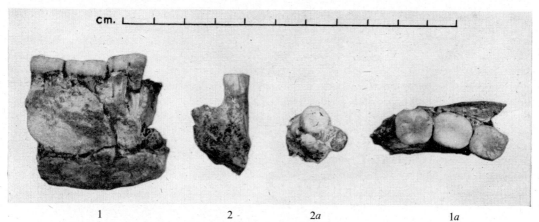

FIG. 8. L'Hominien de Sidi Abder Rahmane
1, 1*a*, Fragment de branche horizontale avec M_1, M_3
2, 2*a*, Fragment symphysaire avec P_4
Faces labiale et occlusale $\times \frac{4}{5}$

Les caractères dentaires rappellent ceux de l'*Atlanthropus*. P_3 notamment présente des plis cingulaires bien nets et sa morphologie est comparable à celle des P_3 de Ternifine.

Les molaires sont macrodontes et brachyodontes comme celles d'*Atlanthropus* ; leurs dimensions sont comparables, sauf M_2 qui est un peu plus courte. Leurs faces occlusales sont très usées, mais on y distingue cependant la présence certaine de cinq cuspides sur M_1 et M_2 et la trace probable d'une sixième ; M_3 possède six cuspides. L'émail de ces dents présente des ridules secondaires.

Ce fragment appartient donc à un Pithécanthropien probable, certainement très voisin d'*Atlanthropus*. Il est à noter toutefois que certains de ses caractères dentaires rappellent dans une certaine mesure ceux de l'Homme de Rabat ; mais ses caractères mandibulaires sont différents. L'état trop fragmentaire de ces fossiles ne permet malheureusement pas de rapprochements plus précis. Nous en retiendrons seulement l'association d'un être voisin de l'*Atlanthropus* à une industrie acheuléenne évoluée.

Conclusions

Les récentes découvertes effectuées en Afrique du Nord française conduisent aux conclusions suivantes :

1. Le problème de la nature des artisans des industries à bifaces Chelléo-acheuléennes, demeuré pendant depuis Boucher de Perthes, se trouve résolu par la découverte de l'*Atlanthropus* : ces artisans étaient des Pithécanthropiens, et la découverte de Casablanca montre que ce groupe humanoïde a persisté aussi longtemps que les industries à bifaces auxquelles il paraît lié.

2. La nature — parfois encore contestée — des Pithécanthropiens est maintenant élucidée : ce sont bien des Hommes, des '*Homo faber*' dans l'acception la plus générale du mot.

3. Les deux découvertes de Ternifine et de Casablanca se complètent mutuellement car elles nous fournissent deux jalons d'âge distinct dans l'histoire des Hominiens du Paléolithique inférieur. Ternifine, en effet, correspond paléontologiquement et archéologiquement au début du Pléistocène moyen et est, par là même, contemporain des Pithécanthropiens asiatiques. Dans la coupe de Sidi Abder Rahmane, il se situe au niveau du gisement de la STIC, immédiatement au début de la deuxième régression marine corrélative de la deuxième glaciation (Mindel).

Les restes humains découverts par Mr Biberson sont comme on l'a vu plus récents, et contemporains de la troisième régression marine qui correspond à la glaciation de Riss.

Ces deux jalons nous montrent donc la persistance du stade pithécanthropien pendant la plus grande partie du Pléistocène moyen et sa constante association aux industries à bifaces.

4. A la suite de ces découvertes, l'Afrique est la seule contrée du monde où se rencontrent en succession chronologique régulière et sans discontinuité tous les stades de l'évolution humaine, Australopithécinés, Pithécanthropiens, Néandertaliens, *Homo sapiens*, et ils s'y trouvent réunis avec tous ceux de l'évolution industrielle, depuis la Pebble Culture jusqu'au Néolithique.

Cette constatation corrobore singulièrement l'idée que l'Afrique, centre d'évolution et de dispersion des divers groupes de Mammifères, notamment des Singes catarrhiniens, a du être aussi celui des Hominiens : à diverses reprises les stades successifs de l'évolution humaine y auraient pris naissance, et supplantant chaque fois leurs prédécesseurs auraient essaimé jusqu'aux confins du Vieux Monde. C'est, en tout cas, dans l'état actuel de nos connaissances, la seule conclusion logique à laquelle puisse conduire l'analyse des faits qui viennent d'être exposés.

29

Living Tribes of the Sahara and the Problem of their Prehistoric Origins

by L. CABOT BRIGGS

THE prehistoric peoples of the Sahara Desert have doubtless left us numerous skeletal remains complete with archaeological contexts, but almost none of these have as yet been discovered for reasons that are too obvious to justify their discussion here. Thus the immediate question before us is: what living groups can be expected to throw light on the prehistory of the Sahara? What living traces, if any, remain of the peoples who made the tools that litter the surface of the Desert and the many undeniably ancient pictures among the countless numbers that so often ornament its rocks?

Clearly there can be no question of survivors, still recognizable as such, of *Atlanthropus* or of the men of Rabat and Tangier, nor probably of Haua Fteah; biologically the Palaeolithic peoples of North-West Africa can hardly have left us much more than their bare bones. We know that in Mesolithic times the northern and western marginal areas were inhabited by peoples who seem to have been fairly recent immigrants belonging to at least two and probably three major physical types, suggesting, as do their archaeological contexts, a continuing series of migrational waves from the East.* We have seen too that these groups showed some slight traces of Negro mixture, possibly picked by their ancestors along the road, and that this negroid component was very materially though sporadically strengthened during Neolithic times, presumably by trans-Saharan contacts. And finally we know that it was probably immigrants who were heavily negroid, if not out and out Negroes, that carried the civilizing torch of Neolithic culture into the southwestern Sahara at least as early as 5,000 years ago.

THE TEDA

Among the living peoples of the eastern Sahara, the Teda form a loosely knit group of essentially nomadic and semi-nomadic pastoral bandit tribes who, it has been supposed, may preserve in their veins the oldest human blood strain that survives in the area. It is therefore of more than passing interest to us that their blood shows in its *ABO* distributions a typical Berber pattern, high in *O* and very low in *B* (Ricci, cited in Boyd, 1939, p. 157). In this respect the Teda seem clearly set apart from the Nilotic and Sudanese half-Hamites as well as from Negroes in general, all of whom show more or less high percentages of *B*. But as far as outward appearance goes, both as such and as expressed in anthropometric and morphological terms, the Teda are nearly indistinguishable from such Nilotic half-Hamites as the Shilluk and the Dinka (Briggs, 1956); and in addition they speak Sudanese dialects.

Are the Teda then descendants of a Berber or proto-Berber population that has become progressively negrified, by race mixture plus the rigorous selective forces of the environment of the Tibesti massif, to the point where almost nothing remains of their original basic type except its

* On prehistoric remains from North-West Africa in general, see Briggs (1955a).

non-selective blood group characters? Or are they perhaps, as Dixon suggested (1923, p. 186), survivors of an ancient 'Proto-Negroid' stock mixed with later invaders, belonging to his 'Caspian' (our proto-Berber) type, who came into the area from the North-East in early Neolithic times? And, in either case, how is it that the percentage of blood group *B* remains so low among them? Here is a most interesting field for speculation, but one upon which it is idle to enter until we have much fuller information as to the serological characteristics in general of the Teda, of their putative cousins, the sedentary Fezzanese, and of the various Negro and negroid peoples of the eastern Sudan.

THE HARATIN

Turning to the western Sahara, we find a complex situation further complicated by the extent of our ignorance concerning the prehistoric and even proto-historic migrations in that area. We know that the western Desert was far more fertile at various times in the geologically recent past than it is now, and that it supported very considerable populations as is shown by the number and importance of its prehistoric sites. It seems then not unreasonable to suppose that the modern oases are remnants of what were once much more extensive fertile tracts, and that among the modern sedentary inhabitants there may be preserved identifiable traces of their local stone age predecessors.

The Haratin are a basically Negro population whose members are scattered throughout these residual oases where they lead the life of sedentary gardeners,* despised by and thus largely cut off from intermarriage with their nomadic neighbours; and so one wonders if they may not be residual too. Nearly 300 have been examined anthropometrically (Draper, in Augiéras *et al.*, 1931, pp. 262–4, Plates 33–5; Kossovitch, 1934, p. 760; Pales, 1952, pp. 18–19, Plates 6–10) although by no means in detail, and these seem to have been a good deal like the rather mixed bag of variable Negro types that one is apt to find in the western Sudan, though rather less negroid. It is interesting to note that blood group studies of the Haratin (Horrenberger, 1933; Kossovitch, 1934), one made as far north as Beni Ounif,† show *ABO* patterns, very different from Berber distributions, which are close to those of most Sudanese groups in their high percentages of *B* but also come very close to certain Egyptian and Congo Pygmy populations in their exceptionally high *A* percentages (Mourant, 1954, pp. 87 and 93).

This appears to suggest that the Haratin may represent an ancient cross between some early negroid element from the South or South-east and another early element that came from or through Egypt on its way westward, the whole overlaid by a veneer of later arrivals brought up from the Sudan in the slave trade, from 'time immemorial' until well within the memories of living men. Once more, however, we must exercise great caution; for *ABO* distributions appear to be sometimes quite erratic, and are never fully conclusive in themselves. Here again we must await much more extensive serological evidence than is now available before attempting to draw any definite conclusions.

THE BERBER-SPEAKING TRIBES

Whether or not we should rule out of consideration the Berber-speaking Tuareg remains doubtful. It has often been taken more or less for granted that Berber-speakers did not enter the Sahara until after the dawn of the Christian era, but this supposition is based on negative evidence alone. The fact that the Tuareg have no recollection of a prehistoric past in the Sahara (or anywhere else) has no value as evidence when we remember that the Lacondones, for example, have

---

* Kossovitch (1934, p. 760), for some unknown and apparently inexplicable reason, referred to the Haratin as 'a nomadic or semi-nomadic people, made up of Arabized Berbers with some Nigerian elements': he was followed in this by Boyd (1939, p. 158) and Mourant (1954, p. 77).

† A typographical error in Boyd (1939, p. 158) produced the blundered form *Beni Qunif* which was unfortunately rejuvenated fifteen years later in Mourant (1954, pp. 87 and 430).

no recollection—no folk memory if you prefer—of the Maya culture of less than 2,000 years ago that produced the temples and monumental inscriptions among which they still live. The Tuareg appear to be a population of Berber origin that has been profoundly modified by many centuries of warlike pastoral nomad life in an extremely harsh desert environment, and, chiefly in its southern extensions, by Negro admixture (Briggs, 1955b; Barnicot *et al.*, 1954). But we are in no position to say, even in broad general terms, when the first Tuareg ancestors did settle in the Sahara, or whether or not they were ever connected in any way with any of the prehistoric industries that we find there. We can be sure only that their mode of life must have been very different before they developed their strikingly characteristic camel culture, even if we suppose that they passed through an earlier horse or cattle riding stage.

We are equally in the dark as to the earliest immigrations of the Zenata (Briggs, 1955c) who now live mainly in the chain of oases that runs along the north-western edge of the central Sahara, and who, although still Berber-speaking, have absorbed much Negro and some Arab blood.

CULTURAL CONSIDERATIONS

Our doubts concerning the antiquity of Berber-speakers in the Sahara lead us back to take another look at the Teda; for this curious population seems to be intermediate between the Tuareg and the Sudanese culturally even more than it is physically.

Teda social organization includes a caste system that corresponds closely to that of the Tuareg. Among both peoples we find nobles and vassals, Negro serfs and slaves, and an endogamous blacksmith caste whose members are feared and at the same time despised. Although the Teda family seems to be strictly patriarchal in function, women sometimes wear swords and arm daggers, and exercise a freedom and a degree of authority which suggest that they may have enjoyed a higher status in the past.

The personal clothing of the Teda is a mixture of Sudanese and early Tuareg elements, such as the leather shirt and the mode of sandal attachment, just as is that of the modern Tuareg. Their arms include the standard Tuareg weapons, but not the rawhide shield. In addition they have not only a wooden-shafted javelin as well as the iron-shafted Tuareg form, but also an S-shaped double-edged knife, and, until only some thirty odd years ago, they used the multi-bladed throwing knife that appears in the petroglyphs of the Tibesti. There is a strong suggestion too, both in petroglyphs and in archaeological deposits, that the dromedary may have been known in the Tibesti, and so perhaps in the western Sahara as well, in Neolithic times, but whether he had already become a beast of burden or was only game, we cannot yet be sure.

The Teda have two main house types, a tent-shaped wooden framework covered with hides or mats, and a more permanent house, often round, made of stone laid up dry or with mud, that has jambed and lintelled doors and is roofed with hides, palm leaves or thatch. The first type strongly suggests the leather tent of the Tuareg, while the second is curiously reminiscent of the oldest known building in the whole Sahara, the so-called 'Tomb of Tin Hinan' at Abelessa in the Tuareg country, just west of the Ahaggar massif. And in this ruined building Reygasse (1950, pp. 100 and 105, Fig. 154) discovered a curved knife blade, among all sorts of other things, and two javelin (?) points exactly like those shown in some of the Tibesti rock engravings.

It is certain that the Teda have intermarried occasionally in recent times with their Tuareg neighbours to the westward, but only on a very limited scale. Although most of them trace their ancestry back to the South, they also show pride in traditional early ancestors whom they describe as 'red', an established technical term which they apply indiscriminately to all peoples, such as the Tuareg, who are noticeably lighter skinned than themselves. Cline (1950, p. 12) pointed out that, while the Teda speak Sudanic dialects, the linguistic evidence seems to indicate that they have tended to drift progressively in a south-easterly direction; and he went on (op. cit., p. 19) to suggest that the seventh-century inhabitants of Kawar may perhaps have been Berbers. Teda tradition divides the ancestors of their forty or so clans into two main groups, those who 'always' lived in and around the Tibesti, and those who came there from outside. The latter group includes the ancestors of the noble Teda clans that form the governing class today, and it is said to have come from the Sudan south of the Aïr, perhaps as late as the Middle Ages. But Teda tradition also preserves the memory of a time when the Tibesti enjoyed relatively abundant rainfall and rich pastures, and of a subsequent period of aridity even greater than that of today (op. cit., p. 20).

The foregoing evidence seems to suggest that, among the Teda and the Tuareg alike, we may be dealing with stratified cultures in which an ancient non-Negro complex has been progressively overlaid by Negro influence, both cultural and physical, and that this process has progressed much farther in the eastern Sahara than it has in the West.

CONCLUSIONS

The above discussion seems to indicate that there may be remnants of four main post-Pleistocene prehistoric migrational movements preserved among the living tribes of the Sahara Desert. The earliest of these may have involved people characterized by an *ABO* blood group pattern resembling that of the Teda, who, in this case, might be considered negrified descendants of stragglers from the earliest westward migrations of African-Mediterranean proto-Berbers that took place probably at least as long ago as Middle Mesolithic times. The Haratin can perhaps be regarded tentatively as having roots in the extreme westward and north-westward extensions of a racially half-Hamitic negroid migrational flow, coming possibly from somewhere around the headwaters of the Nile, that probably introduced Neolithic cultures into North-West Africa. The proto-Berber peoples of the North, once settled in the high plateaux that separate the East-West ridges of the Atlas mountain system, began to make contact during the Neolithic with Negro or heavily negroid peoples to the South, and it may be supposed that in the process they established southern outposts of Berber-speaking mixed African-Mediterraneans scattered progressively southward across the western Desert. The fourth main migrational phenomenon may then have been a series of general northward tidal movements of Negroes from south of the Sahara, which we may suppose gradually submerged both the earlier negroid proto-Haratin and the ancestors of the modern Teda, but left the ancestral Tuareg almost untouched.

This theoretical hypothesis is attractive in that it fits all of the few facts we have at our disposal, but it is highly speculative and, in truth, little more than thoughtfully reasoned guesswork. It is really constructive only in throwing into sharp relief the many serious gaps in our knowledge of the peoples of the Sahara, both of today and of the past, and so in helping to point the way for the extensive and systematic research which alone can put an end to our present far from blissful ignorance.

REFERENCES

Augiéras, E. M., W. P. Draper, E. Gierzynski, V. Besnard and T. Monod (1931), *D'Algérie au Sénégal*, Paris, Société d'Editions Géographiques, Maritimes et Coloniales, 1931.

Barnicot, N. A., E. W. Ikin and A. E. Mourant (1954), 'Les groupes sanguins ABO, MNS et Rh chez les Touareg de l'Aïr', *L'Anthropologie*, 59, pp. 231–40.

Boyd, W. C. (1939), 'Blood Groups', *Tabulae Biologicae*, 17, pp. 113–240.

Briggs, L. C. (1955a), 'The Stone Age Races of Northwest Africa', *American School of Prehistoric Research, Bulletin No. 18*.

Briggs, L. C. (1955b), 'L'Anthropologie des Touareg du Sahara', *Bulletin de la Société d'Anthropologie de Paris*, 10th ser., 6, pp. 93–116.

Briggs, L. C. (1955c), 'Contribution à l'Anthropologie des Zenata du Sahara', *Bulletin de la Société d'Anthropologie de Paris*, 10th ser., 6, pp. 214–222.

Briggs, L. C. (1956), 'Aperçu sur l'Anthropologie des Tedâ', *Bulletin de l'Institut Français de l'Afrique Noire*, ser. B., 17, pp. 280–284.

Living Tribes of the Sahara and the Problem of their Prehistoric Origins

Dixon, R. B. (1923), *The Racial History of Man*, New York and London, Charles Scribner's Sons, 1923.

Kossovitch, N. (1934), 'Recherches séro-anthropologiques chez quelques peuples du Sahara français, *C.R. de la Société de Biologie*, 116.

Mourant, A. E. (1954), *The Distribution of the Human Blood Groups*, Oxford, Blackwell Scientific Publications, 1954.

Pales, L. (1952), 'Anatomie sommaire des Maures de l'A. O. F. et notamment des Maures de Trarza', *Raciologie Comparative des Populations de l'A. O. F.*, 3, reprinted from *Bulletin de la Société d'Anthropologie de Paris*, 10th ser., 3, pp. 3–57.

Reygasse, M. (1950), *Monuments Funéraires Préislamiques de l'Afrique du Nord*, Paris, Arts et Métiers Graphiques, 1950.

30

The Origin and Distribution of the Living Korana collected for a Somatological Study

by C. S. GROBBELAAR

[ABSTRACT]

THE author, in broad outline, reviews the history of the Korana, and records their distribution past and present. The remnants of this once numerous tribe (20,000) were contacted for a somatological study. In an extensive search, the number found was not quite 400, including both sexes and all ages.

IN recent years physical anthropologists have frequently discussed the racial status of the Hottentot tribe known as the Korana, in their studies concerning the Old Yellow Peoples in Southern Africa. I wish here to refer to a few of these contributions. It is well known that Broom (1923 and 1941) believed that the Korana represented a race separate from the Bushman and traceable at least to the fossil man of the Springbok Flats (Tuinplaats), whereas Galloway (1933 and 1937), c.s., maintains that 'the term Bushman, Hottentot, Strandlooper and Korana are terms applied to various branches of the same race and do not connote separate races'. This is also the view underlying the recent publications on the Korana by Tobias (1953 and 1955). In the light of Broom's later contribution (1941), the work on the physical characters of the L'auni-Khomani Bushmen by Dart (1937) and his own investigations, Wells (1951) makes the following fruitful suggestion: 'Nevertheless', he says, 'Broom's later conclusion that the Hottentot group embraces all grades of hybridization between the Bushman and a large-headed dolichocephalic type (inaptly labelled "Korana" by Broom) is probably truer to facts. This is precisely the situation which Dart (1937) found to exist among the living Bushmen of the Southern Kalahari. But in the case of the Hottentot I consider that we must recognize the presence of not two but three hybridizing types; the small Bushman, a large-headed "Bushmanoid" ("Boskopoid") type, and a long, narrow-headed non-Bushmanoid type (the Kakamas type of Dreyer and Meiring). It has been pointed out that Broom in 1923 inferred the presence of both the latter types in his "Hottentot" (later "Korana") group, so that my suggestion in effect combines the main features of Broom's earlier and later interpretations.'

In the hope that further knowledge of the physical character of the Korana may contribute to a determination of his proper status among the Old Yellow Peoples of South Africa, I undertook the blood grouping (Grobbelaar, 1955) and a study of the somatology of that small number of Korana to be found living on the farms owned by Europeans and in the towns in the area described below. The information on their numerical strength given by Maignard and referred to by Tobias (1955, op. cit.) is taken from a report by the early German missionary Wuras. The latter estimated that they numbered about 20,000 during the middle of the nineteenth century. Writing in 1932 Maignard doubted whether there were more than 1,000 living Korana. The number I could find in an intensive search was not quite 400; and I doubt whether there are more than about twenty-five or thirty that I have not been able to contact—excepting a small number that may be found in South-West Africa. The latter, however, have in the course of time intermarried so

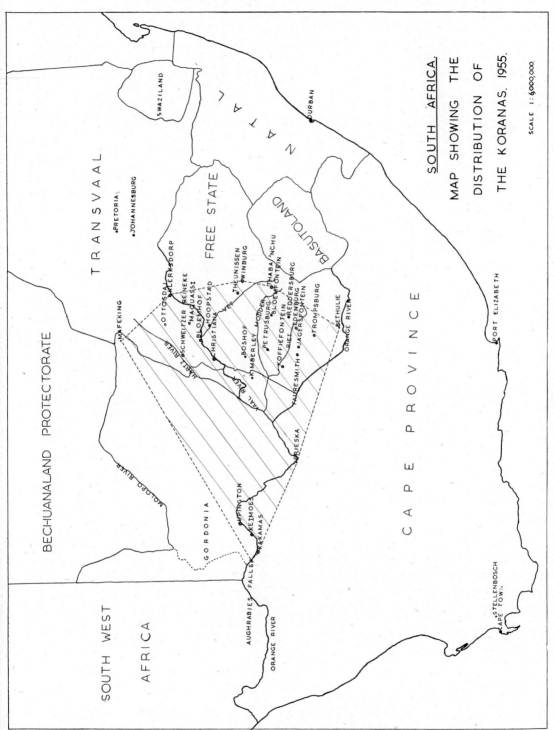

Fig. 1. Map of South Africa—the shaded area indicates the present distribution of the living Koranas

extensively with the tribes with whom they came in contact, that, for the purpose of my investigation, they would not have been taken into consideration.

Their later history, from the last quarter of the eighteenth to the middle of the nineteenth century, is interwoven with the struggles for supremacy between the rival tribes in the territory bounded by the Malopo River in the north, the Kalahari and South-West Africa on the west, and a line running roughly from Mafeking to Winburg in the Orange Free State and from there through Thabanchu to Philippolis on the east, and by the Orange River on the south. To collect my material, scattered on the farms and the towns in the area defined, I travelled over 6,000 miles.

ORIGIN AND EARLY HISTORY

In an interview with Dr H. Vedder, Okahandje, S.W.A., he explained the origin of the word 'Koran(n)a'* as follows: the Nama word *! Koran* is the plural of the masculine singular *! Korab* and the feminine singular *! Koras. ! Korana* is the accusative plural, and signifies 'the people that attacks and robs other people'. Their character as recorded by the early missionaries Wuras (1854), Wangemann (1868), Schröder (1872) and others, curiously enough corresponds very vividly with the meaning implied in the name of the tribe. It is conceivable that because of their aggressive nature and love of plunder, their leader was called Korab as reported by Wuras (1848) and that the tribe became known as Korana after the name of their leader. It is also conceivable that their hostile nature constituted a fundamental component of their genetic make-up inherited from remote ancestors and not found to the same degree in the other Hottentot tribes.

The explanation of the origin of the name Korana according to Maingard (1932) and Engelbrecht (1936) is that they were so called after their chief Kora (*Goro* or *Choro* in the *Dagverhaal van Jan van Riebeeck*) and that the Chorachoqua, a tribe that lived within easy reach of the Cape Peninsula in van Riebeeck's time, were ancestors of the Korana, and at that time generally known as the 'tobacco thieves'. For greater detail the reader is referred to Maingard and Engelbrecht cited above. The Chorachoqua were owners of cattle and sheep, and one of the tribes from whom the Dutch East India Company obtained their supply of fresh meat by barter. In the course of time, owing to the advance of the Europeans further inland, the Hottentot tribes gradually lost their coherence and became disintegrated. The Korana, however, probably on account of their aggressive character and racial pride, trekked northwards, and towards the end of the eighteenth century had established themselves first south of the Orange River (Theal), and afterwards on a broad base along the Middle Orange River. It is here that Wikar found them in his two years of wandering (1778–9) along the Orange River. Pressed by the advancing Europeans and ever desirous of establishing themselves in a country where they were not subject to European law and order, they decided to migrate further northward. At this time they were already broken up into numerous clans, each with its own leader (Maingard, op. cit.).

The Korana were a nomadic people, and the country beyond the Orange River has a very unstable rainfall—the heaviest fall being during the months November to March. The vegetation is sparse and a reliable water supply was a very important factor in the choice of a permanent settlement. It is therefore evident that further migrations took place along the bed of a river, or to places where was a permanent water supply in the form of springs. From the Orange River then there were two main streams of migration.

I THE MIGRATION EASTWARDS

Those who wandered eastwards first along the Orange River (Maingard, op. cit.) and then along the Vaal River, subsequently reached the neighbourhood of the present Taung. Here they were checked by the Bechuanas, and after severe fighting, they turned eastwards, crossed the Vaal River, and settled at Pniël near the present Barkly West, and further south along the Modder and Riet River. The first wave of migration was shortly afterwards followed by a numerically stronger party who reached Klaarwater (now Griquatown). In their attempt to trek further northwards

* Some authors write *Korana*, others *Koranna*.

they were driven back after severe fighting with the Barolongs and Batlaping, and settled for some time between the Harts and Vaal Rivers. Subsequently they trekked further eastward along the Vaal River to the neighbourhood of the confluence of the Vet and Vaal Rivers. It is here that this section split into two smaller groups. The reason for this separation is recorded by Wuras (1847). It was also told me by an old Korana at Tempe, Bloemfontein, who in turn had heard it from his father. The old leader of the clan had died, and his two twin sons were the claimants to leadership. After protracted deliberations it was decided that those who preferred the one twin brother as leader had to occupy the country along the left bank of the Vaal River when one looks upstream, and those who were in favour of the other, should cross the Vaal River and occupy the country along the right bank. The former came to be known as the Links or Left-Handed People, the latter the Right-Handed People. The latter subsequently migrated further south; some settled along the Riet River, others moved eastward under Gert Taaibosch. He was checked by the Basutos and afterwards settled not far from the present Thabanchu.

It was at this time that the Berlin Missionary Society started mission work among the Korana living between the Vaal and Orange Rivers. The first mission station Bethany ('Bethanien') on the Riet River was founded in 1834, and in 1836 it was placed under the charge of Rev. C. W. Wuras. The Korana he had gathered here were some of the Right-Handed People under Goliath Yzerbek ('Iron Mouth').

At this time (1848) the entire Korana population numbered about 20,000 according to Wuras (1848, op. cit.). They were divided into 17 clans the names and distribution of which are given by Wuras and further commented on by Stow (1906) and Engelbrecht (op. cit.). A clan consisted of at least 200 individuals. The numerically strongest were the Springbokke ('Springbucks') that numbered about 2,000. They lived at and roundabout Pniël near the present Barkley West and further southwards along the banks of the Orange River.

Towards the middle of the nineteenth century and subsequently the Orange River Sovereignty under Sir George Clark was the seat of great political activities in which the rival parties were the British Government represented by Sir George Clark, the Voortrekkers under Pretorius, the Grikwas under Adam Kok and to the east Moshesh, paramount chief of the Basutos. The history of the Koranas between the Vaal and Orange Rivers is in substance an account of the part they played in the struggles of the British Resident against, and in his negotiations with the Bechuanas under Molitzane (1852), and the Basutos under Moshesh. In the war between the Bechuanas under Marokko and the Basutos some had allied themselves with the former, others with the latter. In 1850 Gert Taaibosch and his followers left the Orange Free State and returned to the country along the Hartz River which he had formerly occupied. On his way thither, near the present Bloemhof he was attacked by the Links People who wanted to recover their stolen cattle from him. The latter were defeated, and Gert Taaibosch established himself with a considerable following not far from Bloemhof. He was succeeded by Massouw Ryt Taaibosch at whose death David Massouw became the leader of the Taaibosch People. He had his headquarters at Mamusa (now Schweizer-Reneke).

In 1885 certain irregularities on the part of David Massouw and his followers brought them in conflict with the authorities of the former South African Republic. The latter was compelled to send an armed force or commando to restore order. A skirmish between the two armed forces took place while negotiations were in progress. In the encounter David Massouw was killed and his followers put to flight. Two of the casualties on the side of the commando were the two field-cornets, Schweizer and Reneke. Mamusa has since become Schweizer-Reneke, so named after the two men who lost their lives there in the conflict with the Koranas. David Mossouw also lies buried there. The importance attached to this incident is that it was the last occasion where the Korana of the Vaal River Basin and those living further south showed some degree of co-operation and tribal coherence, for already in 1854, the German missionaries Joh. Schmidt and C. J. G. Krause reported to the Director of the Berlin Missionary Society in Berlin as follows: 'So weit wir mit unseren Augen schauen, ist eine völlige Auflösung dieses Volkes (*the Korana,*—author) als solchem nicht mehr Ferne.' In his Report from Bethany, August 5, 1854, Wuras writes: 'Ja, dieser Hochmuth ist die Wurzel des Unfriedens und der Zerrissenheit. Am meisten zeigt sich der Hochmuth bei den Korannas, der viel dazu beiträgt, dass sie sich kein Gesetz unterwerfen, und auch nicht arbeiten wollen. Um ihres Hochmuths willen werden die Korannas zugrunde gehen. Als Volk sind die Koranna schon seit langer Zeit in Auflösung begriffen, und bald wird man sie nur noch in einzelnen Kraalen finden. Aber auch da werden sie sich nicht lange halten können, denn wovon sollen sie leben? Ihre Viehherden haben sie für Branntwein, Gewehre und Pferde weggegeben, und arbeiten wollen sie nicht. O, des armen elenden Volkes.'

It is the descendants of the Korana clans that had settled in the basin of the Vaal, along the Modder River, the Vet River and the Riet River that I somatotyped. For many of them the Korana language was their mother-tongue. Many of the names of the old clans are being used as family names, such as Links, Taaibosch, Kriebos, Skerpioen, Yzerbek, Kraal, Buffelbout, Bontes, Van Neck, Kats and Springbok.

II The Migration Westwards

The second stream of migration from the Middle Orange River was to the west in the direction of the Augrabies Falls. When Wikar met them many had evidently already settled on the islands formed by the bifurcations of the main stream. These Wikar called the River People ('Riviervolk'), and records the names of several of the clans. With the river as base, their hunting expeditions and raids on the neighbouring tribes stretched northward and southward. To the north lies the large area (now Gordonia) between Great Namaqualand on the west, and British Bechuanaland and Griqualand West on the east—it also includes the southern part of the Kalahari. This vast district (18,499 square miles) consists of endless undulating plains with mountain regions at the south-west and south-east corners. The only feature of any distinction is the Valley of the Malopo River.

Towards the end of the eighteenth century, Koranas had also settled in the south of this vast area which to the north was inhabited by Bushmen. To the east were the Griquas in the present Griqualand West, and the Bechuanas, and to the west Nama tribes from Great Namaqualand. The principal Korana headquarters was at Olyvenhoutdrift (Olievenhoutdrift), the present Upington. The country now known as Gordonia was then called Korannaland.

During the sixties of the nineteenth century, the frequent raids of the Korana to carry off the cattle of the frontier European farmers brought them in conflict with authorities and jurisdiction of the Cape Government, and culminated in the first Korana War (1869). The war ended by an agreement between the Cape Government and the Korana captains, the chief of whom were Klaas Lukas and Pofadder. In effect it was that the Korana captains promised that henceforth Koranas would not occupy the 'islands' in the Orange River Basin.

In 1872 the Dutch Reformed Church of the former Cape Colony had decided to christianize the Korana. A mission station was founded at Olyvenhoutdrift and placed under the charge of the Rev. C. H. W. Schröder (1872). In the archives of the Dutch Reformed Missionary Church at Upington the marriage certificate of Klaas Lukas to Sannie Kobus has been preserved. The ceremony itself was conducted by Rev. Schröder. It is extremly doubtful whether this action of Klaas Lukas was the outcome of an honest conversion to Christianity.

Klaas Lukas and Pofadder before long violated the terms of agreement, and the Second Korana War broke out in 1878 and ended in 1879. The Koranas were driven from the 'islands', and Klaas Lukas and Pofadder were ultimately captured. Most of their followers fled to the Southern Kalahari and the present South-West Africa. Afterwards many of them, probably the majority, returned to Olyvenhoutdrift, and came under the jurisdiction of a Special Commissioner at Kenhardt, the representative of the Cape Government. For a more detailed account of the First and Second Korana War, I wish to refer the reader to Laubscher (1947).

Today the descendants of Klaas Lukas and Pofadder's people find employment in the agri-

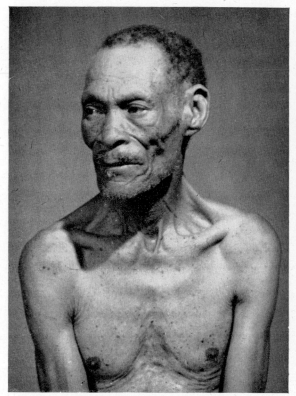

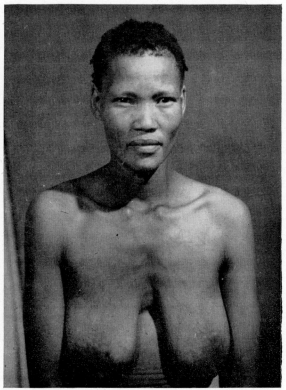

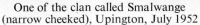

One of the clan called Smalwange (narrow cheeked), Upington, July 1952

Ellen Springbok, Upington, July 1951

cultural activities that have reached such a high degree of development on the banks of, and on the 'islands' formed in, the basin of the Orange River. As in the case of the Korana found in the Vaal River Basin and in the towns, many of them speak the Korana language, a dialect of the Nama language, fluently. Many of the old tribal names such as Kats, Links, Springbok, that were found among the Korana of the Vaal River Basin and in the towns, were also represented here. Old tribal names found here and not elsewhere, were the Smalwange (narrow-cheeked) 'Karoshebbers', Pampier (paper folk) and names of more recent origin but in use for several generations, viz. Slinger, Pofadder, Blaauw, and Jonker.

The comparatively rapid development of these parts took place during the past fifty years, and can be attributed to two factors: the settlement in increasing numbers of European farmers north of the Orange River, and the discovery and exploitation of useful metals such as asbestos, manganese and iron. Diamonds were of course discovered in 1870, and fifty years ago the Kimberley diamonds had brought a far-reaching change in the economical outlook.

The intensive cultivation of the arable lands resulting from the increase in the farming population, has become possible by subverting the waters of the Orange River at Kakamas to Upington, and of the Vaal River in the neighbourhood of Warrenton and Andalusia. The same applies to the Riet River and the Modder River. On the other hand, the wide stretches of country north of the Orange River including the districts of Vryburg and Kuruman, have become important cattle raising areas that supply the Union with beef and dairy products. Without doubt, however, the importance of this region is centred in the production of manganese and the iron that lies buried

Section Two

under the surface of the savannah country from Postmasburg to Kuruman where the nomadic Korana roamed over a century ago.

SUMMARY OF OBSERVATIONS AS RECORDED IN GROBBELAAR, 1956

The author somatotyped 57 male Korana and 40 adult females taken from the 377 individuals referred to in Table I, that were blood grouped. The average values of a considerable number of body and head measurements and indices are recorded and compared with the corresponding averages for the Hottentots of S.W. Africa investigated by Schultze (1928). At the same time he attempted to ascertain the physical type of the Korana by determining the 4-characters combination with highest frequency; comparing this with Schultze's results he comes to the following conclusion: 'From an analysis of the 4-characters combination tables it can be concluded that the Korana are longer faced (total facial index: Korana 84·9, Hottentots 80·6) and have a relatively narrower nose than the Hottentots (nasal index: Korana 93·1, Hottentots 100·1). Head measurements and indices of the two groups are compared in Table IX, Grobbelaar, 1956.

The author finds himself in agreement with Wells that in the case of the Hottentot we must recognise the presence of three hybridizing types: the small Bushmen, a large-headed Bushmanoid ('Boskopoid'), and a long narrow-headed non-Bushmanoid type (the Kakamas type of Dreyer and Meiring). The Kakamas type has been preserved to a greater degree in the Korana than in Schultze's Hottentots.

I herewith wish to thank the Council for Scientific and Industrial Research of the Union of South Africa for their financial assistance to carry out this rather arduous undertaking.

REFERENCES

Broom, R. (1923), 'A contribution to the craniology of the yellow-skinned races of South Africa', *J. R. Anthrop. Inst.*, 53, 132.

Broom, R. (1941), 'Bushman, Koranas and Hottentots', *Ann. Transv. Mus.*, 20, 217.

Dart, R. A. (1937), 'The physical characters of the L'auni-khomani Bushmen', *Bantu Studies*, 11, 176.

Engelbrecht, J. A. (1936), *The Korana*, Maskew Millar Ltd., Cape Town.

Galloway, A. (1933), 'The Nebarara Skull', *S. Afr. J. Sci.*, 30, 585.

Galloway, A. (1937), 'Man in Africa in the light of recent discoveries', *S. Afr. J. Sci.*, 34, 89.

Grobbelaar, C. S. (1955), 'The Distribution of the Blood Groups of the Koranas', *S. Afr. J. Sci.*, 51, 323.

Grobbelaar, C. S. (1956), 'The Physical Characteristics of the Korana', *S. Afr. J. Sci.*, 53, 4, Supplement.

Laubscher, J. M. (1947), 'Die Korana-Sending en die Ontwikkeling van die onderwys in Gordonia (1871–1900)'. Dissertation for the M.Ed. Degree, University of Stellenbosch. Typewritten copy in the University Library.

Maingard, J. F. (1932), *Bantu Studies*, 6, 103.

Schmidt, Joh. and C. J. G. Krause (1854), *Berliner Missionberichte*, 6, 101.

Schröder, C. W. H. (1872), *Die Kerkbode*, Official Organ of the Dutch Reformed Church in South Africa, Kaapstad, p. 173.

Theal, G. M., *History of South Africa from 1795–1872*, Vol. III, London.

Tobias, P. V. (1953), 'Report on the Springfield Skeleton: A human hybrid from Kimberley district', *S. Afr. J. Sci.*, 49, 261.

Tobias, P. V. (1955), 'Taaibosch Koranas of Ottosdal', *S. Afr. J. Sci.*, 51, p. 263.

Wangemann (1868), *Ein Reise-Jahr in Süd-Afrika; ausführliches Tagebuch über eine Inspektionsreise, ausgeführt in den Jahren 1866 und 1867, durch die Mission-Station der Berliner Missiongesellschaft*, Berlin.

Wells, L. H. (1951), 'The Broom collection of Nama Hottentot skulls in the Edinburgh University Anatomical Museum', *S. Afr. J. Sci.*, 48, p. 97.

Wikar, H. J. (1935), *The Journal of Hendrik Jacob Wikar* (1779), ed. E. E. Mossop, Cape Town, The van Riebeeck Society.

Wuras, C. F. (1847), *Berliner Missionberichte*, 12, p. 181.

Wuras, C. F. (1848), *Berliner Missionberichte*, 3, p. 33.

Wuras, C. F. (1854), *Berliner Missionberichte*, 12, p. 209.

TABLE I

LOCALITIES VISITED AND NUMBER OF KORANAS OF ALL AGES
AND BOTH SEXES FOUND THERE

	F. under 19	M. under 19	F. 20–70	M. 20–70	F. 70 +	M. 70 +	Total
Cape Province:							
Kimberley	—	—	4	2	1	2	9
Barkly West	—	—	3	2	—	—	5
Groot Drink (+)	6	1	5	4	1	—	17
Upington	—	2	20	33	2	—	57
Keimoes	14	12	39	34	—	1	100
Kakamas	7	2	11	9	—	—	29
Orange Free State:							
Austen's Post (+)	—	—	1	—	—	—	1
Bloemfontein	—	—	14	10	—	—	24
Boshof	—	—	6	8	—	1	15
Brandfort	2	3	2	4	2	1	14
Edenburg	—	—	5	7	1	—	13
Fauresmith	—	—	2	—	—	—	2
Glen (+)	2	3	1	5	—	—	11
Hoopstad	2	2	4	8	—	—	16
Koffiefontein	—	—	—	1	—	—	1
Petrusburg	—	—	3	4	—	—	7
Port Allen (+)	2	1	2	2	—	—	7
Reddersburg	—	—	5	6	—	—	11
Taba 'Nchu	—	—	—	—	1	—	1
Theunissen	—	—	—	1	—	—	1
Trompsburg	—	—	1	—	—	—	1
Winburg	—	—	2	1	—	—	3
Transvaal:							
Bloemhof	—	1	7	9	1	1	19
Christiana	—	—	4	4	2	1	11
Maquassi	—	—	—	—	—	1	1
Schweizer-Reneke	—	—	—	—	—	1	1

Total: 377

31

The Kafuan Culture

by C. VAN RIET LOWE

ALL typologists will agree that the various artefacts that are associated with the Hand-axe Culture are well up the scale of man's developing genius and skills. Whether these artefacts are on pebbles or on flakes, as so many are, the earliest and therefore the crudest Chellean or Abbevillian hand-axes and the wide-angled, Clacton-like flakes that occur integrally associated with them in Africa, clearly indicate an earlier period during which man made simpler and less diversified tools. Recognizing this, one feels great sympathy for Benjamin Harrison when, during his quest for pre-handaxe forms in England, he wrote to Sir John Evans saying that: 'If these palaeoliths represent the copper-plate hand-writing, where may I expect to find the pot-hooks and hangers of the initial stage.'[1]

Although Wayland claimed to have found pre-handaxe pebble tools in various terraces of the Kafu river valley in Uganda in 1919, the first convincing and widely accepted pre-handaxe artefacts from Africa were those discovered by Leakey in the lowermost deposits of the Olduvai Gorge eight years later.

The Oldowan pebble artefacts were trimmed in two directions and left no room for doubt. They were certainly of human origin. Nevertheless while similar artefacts occasionally turned up in many of the Kafuan assemblages that Wayland had collected, the great majority of specimens that he claimed to represent the Kafuan Culture were either trimmed in one direction only or were simply split pebbles. In addition, practically all his specimens were very rolled or abraded; so much so, that all evidence of artificiality had, more often than not, been entirely obliterated. The specimens were simply not recognizable as artefacts and were therefore rejected. In spite of this, however, Wayland persisted in his quest as well as in his views, because he could not account for these simply split and trimmed pebbles without introducing an artificial factor. He therefore continued to press his claim—but without success.

The fact that he met with no success is not surprising. No one who was not familiar with the field evidence could possibly accept as human any simply split pebble when it was divorced from its geological as well as from its geographical and archaeological context. Nearly all the specimens Wayland sent to his colleagues in various parts of the world in an attempt to convince them that there was such a pre-hand-axe culture as the Kafuan, were completely unconvincing. Yet here and there an undoubted artefact turned up. As late as 1936, Burkitt wrote to Wayland saying: 'As to the Kafuan I do believe man made some of the "tools", and that is all that matters. I am not sure that all you have classed as "tools" are really artifacts.' And as I myself have confessed, I felt the same a year later.[2]

However, with the passage of time and discoveries of Kafuan-type artefacts from the basin of the Nile in the north to the basin of the Vaal in the south, there can be no doubt that a pre-palaeolithic or pre-hand-axe pebble culture was extensively practised in Africa throughout most of the first Pleistocene or Kageran pluvial period.[3]

In my first detailed description of the Kafuan Culture, which I wrote sixteen years ago, but which was published just before the Algiers Congress, I accepted Wayland's four-fold division of the Culture. The four divisions: the Earliest, the Early, the Later and the Developed Kafuan were founded on observed geological data as much as on archaeological or typological evidence, and they still hold good. The stratification in both the Kafu and Kagera river valleys is clear. What is unfortunately not clear, however, is where the Kafuan Culture ends and the Oldowan begins. This is a problem that cannot be solved until the Oldowan has been more fully explored and more accurately described. We need more material from Bed I at Olduvai and until we get it, we must leave the question open. What I want to stress at this stage of our enquiries is the fact that since our last Congress was held, tools and artefacts that characterize the Developed Kafuan have been found in the 200 feet terrace of the Vaal and in a fossil-rich, breccia-filled limestone cave in the Makapan Valley in the Limpopo river basin.[4] With the very generous support of the Wenner-Gren Foundation for Anthropological Research, this spectacular discovery has recently been followed up by further discoveries which tell us that the Australopithecines lived on into human times during the Lower Pleistocene. My colleagues, Professor Raymond Dart, Mr C. K. Brain and Mr Revil Mason, who has devoted three uncommonly successful years to the systematic excavation of two most important sites, the 'Cave of Hearths' and 'Limeworks', in this valley, are with me here today to describe and discuss with you various aspects of our most important discoveries. My immediate task is first to describe the stone artefacts recovered during excavations at 'Limeworks' and then to correlate these discoveries with others made in the rest of Africa.

I have brought the specimens with me (Fig. 1) and for comparison, I have also brought three other small assemblages. One cannot very well carry more by air! I shall describe each assemblage separately and briefly. The first is from Uganda. It includes fifteen specimens that were collected by Mr Wayland (who is happily with us today) nearly a third of a century ago. In it we see the three commonest forms of untrimmed and simply split pebbles: the hemilith, the ortholith and the plagiolith with a variety of pebble and flake artefacts trimmed in either one or two directions.

The second assemblage includes seven specimens extracted by Drs Kenneth Oakley, Desmond Clark and myself from the highly calcified Basal Older Gravels of the 200 feet terrace of the Vaal at Klipdam. Five of these specimens were illustrated in my original description of this site.[3]

The third assemblage includes seventeen specimens found derived in the Older Gravels of the 60 feet terrace of the Vaal at Christiana. This is a particularly rich site from which many hundreds of most typical Kafuan-type artefacts have been recovered. The variety and abundance of split pebbles is worthy of note.

All these assemblages represent the most developed stage of the Kafuan. They include the first definite use of flakes as scrapers, a flake tool with a double notch and tooth, segmental points and a variety of split pebbles and typical Oldowan pebble tools.

The 'Limeworks' collection includes fourteen specimens, nine of which were illustrated in the first announcement of the discovery[4] and two further specimens which are illustrated in the accompanying text figure.

CONCLUSIONS

The evidence submitted clearly indicates that :

(1) Man arrived in South Africa in Pre-Kamasian times—possibly during the decline of the Kageran—and that even at that remote stage he was making a variety of important pebble and flake tools.

(2) As the tools I have described represent the most developed stage of the Kafuan Culture, as that culture is at present understood, we must be in contact with a skilled human being already well up the ladder of human progress.

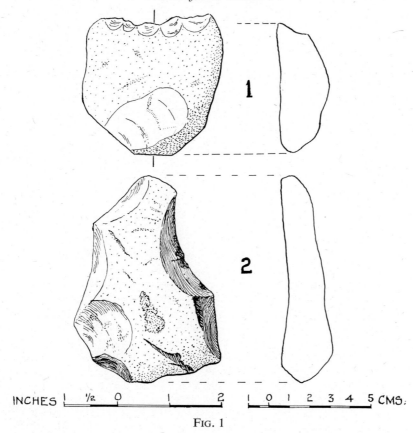

INCHES ½ 0 1 2 0 1 2 3 4 5 CMS.

FIG. 1

(3) As it is in Uganda and in Uganda only, that more ancient artefacts have been found, no region outside Equatorial Africa can at this stage of our enquiries be seriously suggested as a cradle of the human race. The facts before us not only indicate that it was in Africa that man first emerged as a tool-maker, but that it was in the equatorial region of this continent that he emerged; and finally

(4) Either the earliest tool-making men in South Africa lived side by side with an extensive colony of man-like apes of Australopithecine type, or the Australopithecines themselves manufactured the tools under discussion. The fact that no artificially shaped stones have been found in any other Australopithecine deposit, such as that at Taung or at Sterkfontein, Kromdraai or Swartkrans, suggests that it was not the Australopithecines that made the artefacts, but men who lived contemporaneously with them.

REFERENCES

1. Casson, Stanley, *The Discovery of Man*, Hamilton, London, 1939, pp. 289.
2. Van Riet Lowe, C., *The Pleistocene Geology and Prehistory of Uganda*, Part II: Prehistory, Memoir No. VI, Geol. Survey of Uganda, 1952.
3. Van Riet Lowe, C., 'The Kafuan Culture in South Africa', *S. Afr. Archaeol. Bull.*, 1953, VIII, 30, pp. 27–31.
4. Brain, C. K., Van Riet Lowe, C., and Dart, R. A., 'Kafuan Stone Artifacts in Post-Australopithecine Breccia at Makapansgat', *Nature*, 1955, 175, p. 16.

32

Une industrie sur galets spéciale aux plateaux des Biano (Katanga — Congo Belge)

par DOM ADALBERT ANCIAUX DE FAVEAUX, O.S.B.

SOUS le titre : 'Les sites préhistoriques de la Haute-Mulonga' dans les premières notes d'ensemble de la Mission des Recherches Préhistoriques au Katanga et paru dans le *Bull. Soc. Préhist. Franç.* (T. XXXV, No. 4, avril 1938, pp. 172–85), le Dr F. Cabu donne une description d'un gisement à 'Pebble' que je me dois de citer :

'Parmi les cailloux abondants qui jonchent les replats de cette haute terrasse, se rencontre sur les deux rives une industrie grossière sur galets. Les pièces les plus typiques montrent l'ablation de quelques aspérités pouvant gêner la préhension, puis la taille par coups alternes d'un des bords, généralement le gauche, déterminant une arête sinueuse, autre fois coupante. Les pièces relevant de cette technique sont très roulées. Au milieu de ces champs de cailloux on a trouvé une industrie sur simples galets fendus par la tranche, présentant généralement une pointe grossièrement aménagée par percussion au départ de la face plane, des deux côtés de la pointe.' Et plus loin : 'Nous avons relevé les niveaux des replats, suivants comme moyenne de chacune des quatre terrasses : Haute terrasse, 1580 m. . . . quatrième, 1500 m., c'est-à-dire que le replat de la haute terrasse s'étale à 30 m. sous le niveau moyen du rebord du plateau tertiaire.'

Je tiens à souligner ici la date de cette découverte : 1938, époque où les cultures sur galets étaient encore à peine connues.

De ce gisement, ont été déposées au Musée Léopold II à Elisabethville 7 pièces portant les Nos. 7090 à 7096 (1940), et que nous avons eu l'occasion d'étudier. Elles rentrent absolument dans le cadre des découvertes faites par nous de 1952 à 1954 sur les Hauts-plateaux des Biano, de gisements de 'Pebble'.

Un de ceux-ci, le XXXII, se trouve en tête même de la Mulonga.

Les nouveaux gisements se situent sur la ligne de crête des Hauts-plateaux des Biano, à une côte de niveau oscillant entre 1625 m. et 1650 m., pouvant descendre à 1600 m. et monter jusqu'à 1675 m.

Topographiquement, ils forment une vaste courbe débutant par 10° 15′ Sud–25° 50′ Est, puis s'étendant vers l'Ouest-Nord-Ouest jusqu'à 10° 10′–25° 42′, où la courbe s'incurve vers le Nord et atteint 10° 7′. Elle reprend la direction de l'Est, le dernier gisement actuellement connu se situant par 10° 2′ Sud et 25° 50′ Est.

Le nombre de sites reconnus à ce jour est d'environ une dizaine, couvrant plusieurs km². Il est plus que probable qu'à l'intérieur de la courbe indiquée, aussi bien qu'à l'extérieur, il doit s'en trouver d'autres (le gisement mélangé XXVI, par exemple). La prospection est bien loin d'être achevée.

Le matériau employé: Galets de quartzite des Kibaras de provenance encore indéterminée. Ces galets présentent parfois un feuilletage qui a servi de plan de clivage et donne à certaines pièces une forme à deux faces parallèles.

La texture du quartzite est très variable et ceci a, comme corollaire, de présenter des états

210

physiques très différents de pièce à pièce. Les terrains extrêmement acides ont fréquemment et très profondément altéré certaines pièces.

La question de l'*étage stratigraphique* de cette industrie n'est pas encore résolue. D'après le situs trouvé à la Pupa (XXVIII et XXIX), nous avons une forte épaisseur de sables soufflés, remaniés des plateaux reposant sur un niveau de sources ; un banc de latérite et des blocaux de 'grès polymorphe' l'accompagnent. Sur et dans la latérite reposent, en place, des éléments très caractéristiques d'Acheuléen et d'Acheuléo-levallois, à arêtes vives malgré la décomposition chimique subie par les éléments en 'G.P.'.

Sous ce niveau, dans des sables argileux blancs et ocres, se trouve la 'Pebble' en quartzite.

Ce même banc de latérite se retrouve en XXIV, mais nous ne l'avons pas percé, nos fouilles s'étant cantonnées au point d'affleurement du gisement.

Au sondages 3 et 4 du XXIII, nous retrouvons des éléments latéritiques cellulaires et des fragments de blocaux surmontant les sables argileux blancs ou légèrement rubéfiés contenan les galets.

En 3 la coupe se présente comme suit :

1 m. 35
- 32 cm. stérile (sable)
- 30 cm. latérite cellulaire et fragments de blocaux
- 18 cm. stérile
- 55 cm. d'argile blanche très sableuse, contenant les galets abondants (leur densité va en diminuant en profondeur. La base non atteinte)

En 4 :

1 m. 15
- 50 cm. stérile
- 35 cm. 'G.P.' et latérite :
  - 1 galet de quartzite à taille fraiche
  - 1 lame et quelques éléments Ach. ('G.P.')
- 30 cm. sable argileux un peu rubéfié. Éléments de 'Pebble' moins abondants (fond non atteint)

Dans les autres sondages du XXIII et XXIV, nous n'avons pas rencontré le banc latéritique, celui-ci ayant été enlévé par l'érosion.

Normalement, dans tous les gisements relevés, cette couche latéritique paraît bien avoir recouvert, et parfois avec un hiatus sérieux, le niveau à galets. C'est ainsi qu'à la Pupa (XXIX) l'hiatus stérile entre le banc latéritique et le niveau à galets est de 2 m. à 2 m. 50.

Il y a là une réelle différence stratigraphique entre les éléments préhistoriques. La rive gauche de la Pupa nous montre clairement la ligne horizontale du niveau des sources. La Pupa actuelle creuse son lit dans une basse terrasse (2 m. environ) peu ancienne, largement évasée. Une deuxième terrasse se trouve à 4 m. environ. Le niveau à 'Pebble' se présente horizontalement vers 10 m., en face du camp Corneille. Un hiatus stérile, cité plus haut, d'une puissance de 2 à 2 m. 50, le sur-monte ; puis vient le niveau des sources avec blocaux de 'G.P.' et latérite d'une puissance de 60 cm. environ. L'épaisseur des sables remaniés est très variable.

Sur pente, on rencontre un mélange des plus hétéroclite de tous les éléments préhistoriques du niveau à 'Pebble' et de toutes les industries situées dans ou au-dessus du niveau des sources.

Le creusement par la Pupa d'une part, et l'épanchement des terrains de couverture glissant sur le niveau des sources d'autre part, sont à l'origine de ce mélange. Ce glissement cache en fait le véritable niveau des sources qui doit se trouver plus haut. L'affouillement des eaux en bordure doit provoquer un biseau d'épanchement. Il y aurait lieu de faire là une coupe perpendiculaire pour retrouver la vraie stratigraphie.

L'ensemble des gisements XXIV bis, XXIV, XXIII–XXIV, XXIII, qui paraissent bien ne former qu'un tout, a tout à fait l'allure d'un 'oued' : densité des éléments, absence d'orientation

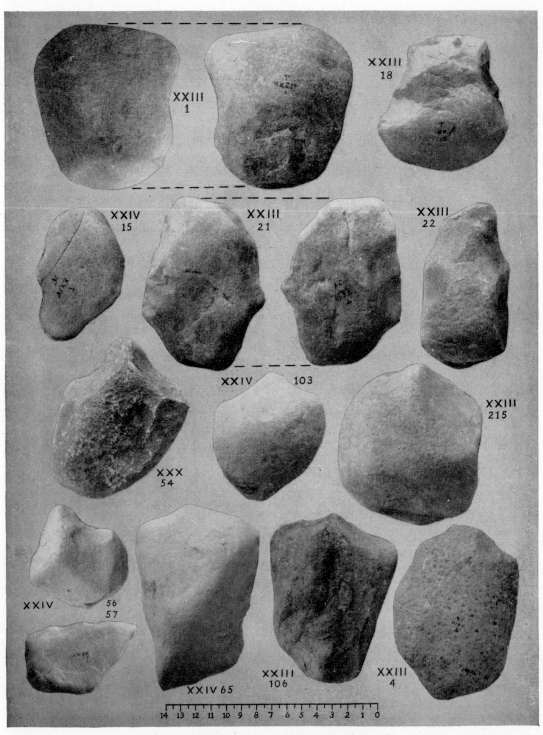

Fɪɢ. 1. Quelques éléments typiques de l'industrie

212

de ceux-ci. Tout au plus pourrions-nous trouver en bordure du XXIII une moindre densité de gros éléments et une plus forte densité de pièces réduites. Cet ensemble forme une courbe descendante. C'est ainsi que le niveau à galets se trouve à plus de 4 m. au-dessus du niveau de la Miganza dans les sondages 4, 7, 5, entre 3 et 4 m. pour les 3 et 6, entre 2 et 3 m. pour le 2, et entre 1 et 2 m. pour le sondage 1 ; le sondage 1 bis, rive droite, rencontre le niveau sous les eaux de la Miganza et plonge sous la couverture des sables remaniés. La rivière viendrait ainsi recouper un ancien torrent dans le lit duquel se trouvent les galets.

La section de la courbe correspondant à XXIII–XXIV a été reprise dans une latérite plus jeune englobant des éléments acheuléo-levallois.

Cette allure d'oued' paraît bien se retrouver à tous les gisements : XXX, XXXI, XXXII. Nulle part nous ne trouvons de terrasse.

Un fait commun à tous ces gisements, et que nous avons déjà relevé plus haut, est la côte de niveau. Celle-ci n'offre que très peu de variations :

XXIII	:	1625–50 (côtes de niveau de
XXIV	:	1650–75 la carte C.S.K.
XXIX	:	1625–50 au 1/100·000)
XXX	:	1625–50
XXXI	:	1625–75
XXXII	:	1625

Dénudés par l'érosion, ces gisements se prolongent sous les couvertures des sables de crêtes peu saillantes et en pente douce. A l'opposé de cette crête, en pente plus abrupte ou très abrupte des têtes de source, l'érosion a entrainé de nombreux éléments. Ils se retrouveront sur les replats de ces têtes de source.

Ce sont de véritables terrasses, mais où les galets ne se retrouvent que remaniés. C'est ainsi que je ne puis partager l'opinion du Dr Cabu et de Mr van den Brande relativement à la haute terrasse de la Mulonga (v. + h.).

A la Mulonga recoupée par la route conduisant à la grotte de Kiantapo, les éléments trouvés (XXXIII) ont été apportés par la rivière torrentielle après avoir été arrachés à leur situs de crête.

Cette industrie des plateaux présente de très grandes différences avec le 'Kafuen' classique, aussi attendons-nous d'avoir réuni quelques 5000 pièces pour en dresser les séries qui seules nous autoriseront à définir l'industrie et à en donner une description susceptible d'entrainer la conviction générale.

33

The Early Pebble Cultures of Katanga

by G. MORTELMANS

INTRODUCTION

SINCE my first publications on Belgian Congo prehistory, it has become well known to workers in the African field that southern Katanga, at the south-eastern tip of the Congo basin, is one of the most important and promising parts of Africa as regards the distribution and evolution of early pebble cultures [3, 8, 9]. Except for Mulundwa I site, [7] no detailed study has appeared as yet of the series collected by myself before 1946. Such a long delay in publication of this important material is mostly due first to my desire of collecting better field evidence on the geological and climatic setting, secondly to the necessity of collecting reasonably complete assemblages on which statistical methods of analysis could be tested.

This year, a very generous grant from CEMUBAC (Centre Scientifique et Médical de l'Université de Bruxelles en Afrique Centrale) gives me an excellent opportunity of doing detailed field research in central and southern Katanga. One of the aims is a thorough study both of the known pebble culture sites and of any new ones I may discover during this survey. Although this field work is to be continued after the present congress, the data already collected allows me to bring to this Symposium on the Early Pebble Cultures some new facts and provisional conclusions.

RECENT WORK ON THE EARLY PEBBLE CULTURES OF KATANGA

My present researches prove that some parts of Katanga, of which the most outstanding is the Kafila river basin north of the Elisabethville-Kasenga road, can definitely compare with western Uganda, Transvaal, Morocco and Algeria for the quantity and richness of pre-Chelles-Acheul sites. Nearly every road-metal pit cutting into limonite *cuirasses* (lateritic ironstones), or their dismantled products, yields pre-Abbevillian pebble tools, sometimes dozens or even hundreds of specimens. At Mulundwa II site, for instance, thousands of implements—chipped pebbles and secondarily worked flakes—can be collected.

The oldest and more primitive pebble tools are found on the Kundelungu plateau, west of lake Moero, in small quartzitic gravel patches, which I believe were brought from the north by rivers flowing from the Kibarian belt in early Pleistocene times, when this belt was the watershed between the Upper Lualaba system of drainage and that of an early Upper Zambezi or, perhaps, Lake Bangweolo. The chipped pebbles collected so far, all of which are not undoubtedly artificially flaked, consist only of those very simple split pebbles called 'hemiliths' and 'plagioliths' by van Riet Lowe. [10] This Kundelungu plateau stage seems identical with the Earliest or Early Kafuan Culture of Uganda, as defined by this author.

The next stage—in the present state of knowledge—still consists of small quartzitic pebbles, but with a greater variety of tool types, identical with, or strongly recalling, those of the Early Kafuan of Uganda. The complete lack of pointed or bifaced implements should be stressed. Both rolled and slightly abraded series were collected together in limonitized soils, now connected with the early Kafila drainage pattern. This fact seems to prove *inter alia* that it was during early Kafuan times that the most important physiographic changes occurred in south-eastern Katanga—for instance, reversal of river courses and formation of the present day Congo-Zambezi watershed.

214

The Early Pebble Cultures of Katanga

Following this still early Katanga Kafuan, the next stage is that found at Mulundwa I site, already published, and tentatively correlated with the end-Kageran dry phase. Here several successive series can be distinguished according to their physical state: deeply rolled, slightly rolled and unrolled. The main characteristics of the industry are the greater size of the tools (still less than 3 inches); the appearance of pointed and bifaced implements; and that of secondarily trimmed flakes. On the whole the Mulundwa I site industries are of rather early (the deeply rolled series) to rather advanced Kafuan types when compared with van Riet Lowe's stages in Uganda.

The next and, up to now, latest stage is that from Mulundwa II site, a stage which I formerly called Kafilian. Thousands of implements occur in an old river gravel bed, deeply buried under *in situ* or dismantled limonite *cuirasses*. From the appearance of this bed, and also from the characteristics of the implements contained in it, I believe it to represent an early Kamasian deposit, approximately contemporaneous with Olduvai Bed I[2] and the Basal Gravels of the 30 feet terrace of the Kagera river.[10] The implements are now of various sizes, ranging from 1 or 2 inches up to pebbles of 8 to 10 inches. A good number of flake tools also occur, up to 8 inches in length. Five successive stages, not necessarily very different in age, can be distinguished, from deeply rolled to fresh specimens; double or complex patinas control this sorting. A great number of implements conform to van Riet Lowe's types, but more refined or even different types occur, showing that in early Kamasian times there was already a good deal of local or regional variation in the early Stone Age cultures. For instance, Mulundwa II industries lack nearly completely the rostro-carinate and pebble-wedge tools so characteristic of the Kagera assemblages. The same is true of the bifaced chopping tools present in a proportion of 80% at Olduvai. On the other hand, some 'biflakes' (a type of implement described by Wayland from Bechuanaland) do occur here. Types of implements which do not seem to exist in Uganda nor at Olduvai seem quite characteristic of this latest Katanga Kafuan: one is a kind of thick hemilith which has been worked at right angles to the hemilithic splitting plane, perhaps in order to obtain flakes or blades, but perhaps also in order to produce a sharp edge duplicating more or less that of the Oldowan chopping tool. Another very frequent type consists of a rather flattish pebble from which a large flake has been chipped away in the flattening plane and from one end of the pebble; the cutting edge obtained was then submitted to a secondary trimming at right angles to this first flaking. This type of implement could be used either as a chopper-chopping tool,[1] as a scraper or a push-plane.

CONCLUSIONS

Although preliminary, the above data from recent field work seem precise enough to draw some conclusions:

1. In southern Katanga a certain number of pre-Chelles-Acheul pebble industries exist which show a definite evolution from very simple assemblages to more refined and complex ones. With some local variations, this evolution duplicates that established in Uganda by E. J. Wayland and Professor C. van Riet Lowe.

2. The different stages of this cultural complex are, as in Uganda, related to geological and climatic events; the most primitive industry is related to the oldest geological deposits, the more advanced to the later ones.

3. These two lines of field evidence prove beyond doubt that pre-Abbevillian pebble cultures do actually exist and also that these successive stages, when thoroughly worked out and defined precisely, will provide an excellent means of dividing and classifying lower Pleistocene deposits and events. It should nevertheless be borne in mind that, parallel to the pebble cultures, other primitive cultures exist: for instance the flake industry recently discovered by J. de Heinzelin in the middle Kaiso series from Lake Edward.[1]

4. In my opinion, the best way to make this thorough study of the pebble industries is to submit the material collected, where numerous enough, to a statistical treatment analagous to the one to which F. Bordes, Mme de Sonneville-Bordes and other workers in the European field are submitting their Middle and Upper Palaeolithic finds. This can easily be done by using, for defini-

tion of tool types, the list established for Uganda by van Riet Lowe, completed of course for other tool types existing in other regional assemblages. During my recent field work I have already started such a statistical approach to the problems of comparing and classifying Katanga pebble industries. The histograms and cumulative curves already drawn show significant changes from site to site, or from one series to another in the same site. This summing up of statistical data can be completed by the establishment of a series of indices giving for instance the ratio between the number of primitive tools, like hemiliths, etc., and more advanced types, or between pebble and flake implements.

5. Although still on a preliminary basis, this method seems very promising and I feel that one of the aims of the next congress should be the preparation of a list of types and the diffusion of simple statistical methods which could be used, together, everywhere in Africa. The congress should also take steps to recommend the use of such methods in the study, description and publication of material dealing with pre-Chelles-Acheul cultures.

6. Another aim of the next congress should be (in order to reassure a number of prehistorians who are not geologists) to collect, define, describe and publish more accurately natural agencies producing pseudo-pebble tools. Those participating in the Katanga excursion after the present congress will have good opportunities to study, in their natural setting, both humanly made pebble tools and natural glacial- and fluvial-chipped pebbles.

7. Another important conclusion is that, if the pebble culture complex shows simplicity and unity in its first stages, local and regional variations do appear in the later and latest stages. This can easily be seen when comparing approximately contemporaneous assemblages from Uganda, Katanga, South Africa, Olduvai and N.W. Africa. This fact makes me feel uncertain, and I should say rather uncomfortable, about the precise status of the Oldowan: truly a separate culture or a simple regional variation of one great cultural complex, the Kafuan? Personally I should prefer to classify the Oldowan as a regional variation of the latest Kafuan, which is what I do now with my former Kafilian. The main characteristic of this Olduvai variation of the latest Kafuan would be its quantity of bifaced tools, greater than in any other contemporaneous pebble assemblage; I know Dr L. S. B. Leakey has already assumed this possibility.[2]

8. Summing up the above facts and opinions, I should completely agree with a resolution replacing the expression 'pre-Chelles-Acheul pebble cultures' by the simpler one 'Kafuan' or 'Kafuan culture'.

REFERENCES

1. De Heinzelin de Braucourt, J., *Le Fossé Tectonique sous le parallèle d'Ishango*, Publ. Inst. Nat. Parcs Nat., Bruxelles, 1955.
2. Leakey, L. S. B., *Olduvai Gorge*, Cambridge, 1951.
3. Mortelmans, G., Préhistoire et Quaternaire du Sud du Bassin du Congo, *Session extraord. Soc. belges Géol.*, Bruxelles, 1946, pp. 215–47.
4. Mortelmans, G., 'Une cause d'erreur en Préhistoire, la taille glaciaire', *Bull. Soc. Roy. B. Anthrop. et Préhist.*, LVIII, 1947, pp. 60–71.
5. Mortelmans, G., 'Le Quaternaire de l'Afrique Sud-Equatoriale. Essai de corrélation', *3e Co. Nat. Sc.*, Bruxelles, 1950, 3 pp., 1 Table.
6. Mortelmans, G., 'Vue d'ensemble sur le Quaternaire du Congo', *3e Co. Intern. Sc. Préhist. et Protohist.*, Zürich, 1950, pp. 114–26.
7. Mortelmans, G., 'Contribution à l'étude des Cultures pré-Abbevilliennes à galets taillés du Katanga: le site Mulundwa I', *Mélanges en hommage au Prof. Hamal Nandrin, Public. Soc. Roy. B. Anthrop. et Préhist.*, 1952, pp. 150–64.
8. Mortelmans, G., 'Les industries à galets taillés ('Pebble Culture') du Katanga', *2e. Congr. Pan-Afr. Préhist.*, Alger, 1952, pp. 295–8.
9. Mortelmans, G., 'La Pebble Culture Africaine, source des civilisations de la pierre', *Bull. Soc. Roy. B. Anthrop. et Préhist.*, LXV, 1953.
10. Van Riet Lowe, C., *The Pleistocene Geology and Prehistory of Uganda*, Part I: Prehistory, Entebbe, 1952.

34

Preliminary Report on a Chellean I Living Site at B.K.II, Olduvai Gorge, Tanganyika Territory

by L. S. B. LEAKEY

GENERAL

IN 1935 during our general survey of Olduvai Gorge, my wife and I located a very promising site on the south bank of the side gorge of Olduvai. This site was at the junction of Bed I and II and the wealth of material that was being washed out by erosion suggested that very extensive excavation would be worth while.

In 1952, these excavations were started as part of a seven-year programme of detailed study of the Olduvai Gorge culture sequence, following the completion of the general survey and the publication of the general report.

Work has now been carried out at site B.K. II for three seasons—1952, 1953 and 1955—and although much remains to be done it is now possible to make a preliminary report.

Excavations have revealed an old land surface which rests upon an unevenly eroded series of deposits of Bed I, subsequently buried beneath Bed II. On this land surface at B.K. II there is a living floor of Chelles-Acheul Stage I, with very numerous artefacts, and fossil remains of animals that were hunted and killed for food, by these Chelles-Acheul Stage I hunters.

The living floor adjoins a contemporary natural depression filled with bentonitic clay and which, at the relevant time, was clearly a clay-filled swamp. Within this clay there are the articulated fossil remains of numerous extinct animals. In some cases, whole skeletons occur, but in the main only articulated limbs, vertebral columns and skulls with horns. In other words, the heavier parts of large animals. In this bentonitic clay, too, we find very numerous natural round stones that clearly do not belong naturally with the clay but were thrown there by man. There are also numerous artefacts, especially artificially worked roughly cylindrical balls.

THE CULTURE

The artefacts that have been recovered from this living floor and from the bentonitic clay form a very large assemblage of thousands of specimens. In addition to very numerous waste flakes, that show that these tools were made on this spot, there are:

1. Very numerous pebble tools of evolved Oldowan type.
2. A few roughly-made hand-axes of Chelles I type, which provide the new element which shows that the Oldowan had given way to Chellean.
3. A certain number of very clearly worked *small* flake tools.
4. Numerous utilized flakes.

The assemblage is clearly of the type we have formerly classified as the first stage of Chelles-Acheul I, which is always found at the junction of Bed I and Bed II at Olduvai Gorge.

Owing to the vast quantity of artefacts found, it is possible to get a better idea of the total

217

assemblage, and the presence of numerous *small* flake tools is of special interest and will be the subject of a detailed report.

Immediately overlying the level at B.K. II, which is the subject of this report, is a deposit which contains a few tools of Chelles-Acheul Stage II.

The Fauna

The fossil animal remains of the living site of Chelles-Acheul I have not yet been studied in detail, but the preliminary examination reveals an archaic fauna typical of Bed II, Olduvai, including the following genera and species

1. *Palaeoloxodon antiquus*
2. *Sivatherium olduvaiensis*
3. *Serengetitherium*
4. *Metaschizotherium*
5. *Eurygnathohippus*
6. *Stylohipparion*
7. *Equus olduvaiensis*
8. *Pelorovis*
9. *Bularchus*
10. *Notochoerus*
11. *Mesochoerus*
12. *Tapinochoerus*
13. *Simopithecus*
    and many others

The majority of the fossil bones on the living floor have been broken open to extract the marrow, as have the skulls in order to obtain the brains. Jaws, too, are broken. On the other hand in the clay of the depression some perfectly preserved fossils occur.

It is of interest to note that there were quantities of fossilized ostrich eggshell fragments on the living floor. It is not yet clear whether these represent remains of eggs that were eaten by the Stone Age hunters, or whether they are the relics of eggshells used as containers for water.

35

The Sangoan Culture in Little Namaqualand

by O. DAVIES

DURING my tour of the Namaqualand coast with Mr R. C. Walsh in the winter of 1953, I was surprised to find many sites with a culture which can best be described as Sangoan. This widespread African industry occurs on the Zambezi and in Natal; but there is no trace of it on the high veld of South Africa, where its place is taken by the Fauresmith. The Bembesi culture of Matabeleland, while akin to Sangoan, seems to be an independent offshoot. It is thus not clear how the Sangoan industry reached Namaqualand; the only available route seems to have been near the inhospitable shores of South-West Africa.

Namaqualand, though now a zone of light winter-rainfall, apparently followed the climatic phases established for the Transvaal and Natal. At the mouth of the Doorn there are 70 feet of Younger Gravels, large pebbles with rolled Chelles-Acheul IV at the base, then silts and grits, at the top slightly rolled a cleaver and a hand-axe which could be Chelles-Acheul V and unrolled Fauresmith and Sangoan. The subsequent arid phase is represented on the Oliphants between Vredendal and Koekenaap. Overlying the Canal Gravels which were deteriorating before the end of Chelles-Acheul, are high calcified dunes on which is a scatter of pebbles with Sangoan tools. The deepening of river-channels in the Gamblian pluvial cannot be established so close to a fluctuating ocean save at the mouth of the Doorn. There are two levels of Older Gravels along the Oliphants below Clanwilliam, but without rolled artefacts.

On the Orange a mile below Goodhouse are traces of an Older Gravel at 40 feet, with one possible pebble-tool, and a Younger Gravel with one rolled flake at 15–25 feet, capped by a siltterrace. At Wallekraal, high enough up the Spoeg to be beyond the influence of fluctuating sealevels, is a gravel with rolled perhaps Kafuan material at 30 feet.

The greatest concentration of Sangoan types was found on the lower Oliphants. There is below Vredendal some admixture of Late Acheulian, but nothing of Fauresmith type was observed. On the surface of the Canal Gravels at Voorbeeld West is unrolled Late Acheulian. On the calcified dunes which cap these gravels near Koekenaap station are pebbles which must have been humanly transported, though some are of unsuitable material like quartz and tillite. Many of these pebbles have been made into Sangoan tools; in one collection there were cores and small cores, small and medium flakes, picks and miniature picks, straight-bladed choppers, segmental choppers or scrapers, and side-struck blades, one with a small notch. Sangoan material occurs unrolled also below Vredendal Narrows on the intermediate gravel and on a 30-foot gravel which must have been laid down after the Narrows were breached and the valley had assumed approximately its present form.

From Ebenezer at the Oliphants poort as far upstream as Vredendal Sangoan types seem to occur without admixture, for instance on the 170-foot terrace on the Van Rhynsdorp road. I had no time to survey the valley between Vredendal and the Doorn. Between the Doorn and Bulshoek there is a wide scatter of pebbles on the old 150-foot valley-floor. There is a great mixture of tooltypes, Acheulian, Fauresmith and Sangoan. Without excavation on sealed deposits it is difficult to identify a true Sangoan culture, or even to tell what material is coming from the rock-surface and what from the ten or twenty feet of capping sand. However, whereas Acheulian and Fauresmith forms are ubiquitous and scattered, the Sangoan seems concentrated in small patches. A mile or so south of the Doorn mouth we made a collection of picks with pebble-butts, scrapers, disc- and pyramidical-cores, one high-backed core. At Nardouws, on the same terrace at the bottom of the Bulshoek Rapids, two borrow-pits yielded the following assemblage of Sangoan appearance, made partly of pebbles from an eroded gravel and partly of land-rubble; three pieces are slightly rolled, the rest unrolled :

> 3 straight-bladed and 1 rounded pebble-chopper
> 4 elongated picks, 1 rounded pick made from half a pebble
> 1 miniature hand-axe, 1 small hand-axe with blade an inch long
> several flakes and cores, 1 blade-flake, 1 pyramidical core, 2 small disc-cores
> 1 end-scraper, 1 quartz polyhedral stone

The frontier of Sangoan types is sharply defined. Above Bulshoek Rapids none was found, and five miles north of Clanwilliam is a large Fauresmith factory-site. Nor is anything suggestive of the Sangoan known south of the lower Oliphants valley, between Clanwilliam and the sea.

The geological date of Sangoan forms can be closely defined. The Canal Gravels contain

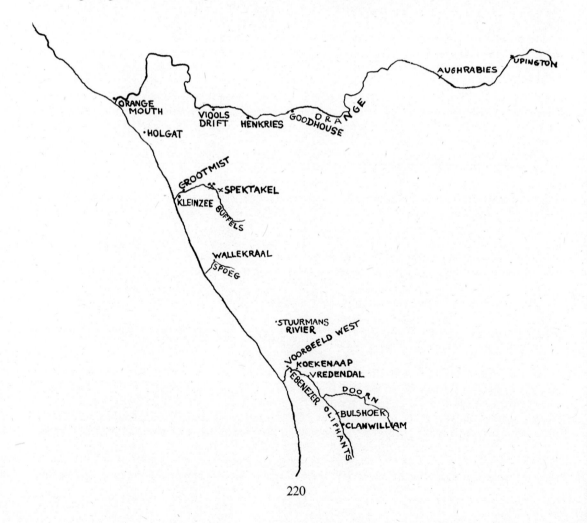

The Sangoan Culture in Little Namaqualand

Chellean material rolled. They were being drained and beginning to erode before the end of the Acheulian, which occurs unrolled on their slopes at Voorbeeld West. The erosion seems to have been the result of the 100-foot sea-level,[1] which broke a barrier near the mouth of the Oliphants; and this sea-level may reasonably be associated with the last northern interglacial. The subsequent low sea-level is reflected in the Intermediate gravel below Vredendal Narrows, which plunges beneath the present valley-surface near Koekenaap; it contains very rolled Acheulian and unrolled Sangoan. I did not see any reflection along the valley of the 50-foot sea-level, which is probably interstadial. The Sangoan is also later than the 'Kalahari' period of the Koekenaap dunes. A date after the 'Kalahari' stage and probably before the interstadial has been established also for the Natal Sangoan.[2] In colonial regions there has naturally been a time-lag; the Sangoan of central Africa starts in 'pre-Kalahari' times.[3] The rarity of Middle Stone Age types on the lower Oliphants may suggest that Sangoan forms lasted well into the Middle Stone Age.

Nucleated assemblages of Sangoan types were observed at several places between the Oliphants and the Orange. Near the surface of a silted vlei and round a small pan close by it at Stuurmans Rivier were collected rough cores and small flakes, picks, choppers, miniature picks, polyhedral stones and an end-scraper. Most of the material is made from slightly rolled pieces of vein-quartz. On the slopes above Wallekraal a large borrow-pit yielded quartz artefacts, mostly made on pebbles which seem to have been carried up from the River Spoeg: 4 large and 4 miniature picks, 2 large and 2 small choppers, 1 pyramidical core, nondescript cores and fragments, and in silcrete a T-shaped scraper. There are unrolled artefacts of similar types also on the 30-foot gravel at Wallekraal. The material is too crude for certain assignation to the Sangoan culture. We found unrolled pebble-picks, choppers and scrapers on the 45-foot terrace of the Buffels at Grootmist. Higher up the river at the copper-mine, quartzite pebbles have been chipped to form picks, choppers, trimming stones and cleaver-flakes, of generally Sangoan appearance.

A few unrolled picks and choppers made on pebbles, from various levels of the earliest beach at Orange Mouth (probably Villafranchian), resemble Sangoan rather than late Acheulian material; a high-backed core and one hand-axe might be of the same date. Choppers, miniature picks and a pyramidical core from the 40-foot terrace of the Orange (probably interstadial of the last glaciation) could not with certainty be identified as Sangoan or Fauresmith.

While collections from the Karasburg area suggested the dominance of Fauresmith material, two assemblages from the Orange gorge conform more to Sangoan type. On a delta-fan on the north bank 3¼ miles above Goodhouse we found many slightly rolled artefacts mostly of quartz, small picks, large scrapers, trimming stones, disc- and pyramidical-cores. Three assemblages were made near Viools Drift. In one were many artefacts made on pebbles; the other two contained tools from sandstone slabs. The statistics of one are:

> many flakes and large nondescript cores, pyramidical and disc-cores
> 2 large blunt-ended hand-axes, 3 piriform hand-axes
> 1 very large backed blade, 5 medium blades
> 2 cleaver-flakes
> 2 choppers
> 5 end-scrapers, 2 curved side-scrapers
> 3 large T-shaped redirecting flakes utilized in the hollows.

Considering the material, this assemblage is more closely akin to Sangoan than to Fauresmith, and has a strong suggestion of the Bembesi culture.

We observed the classic Vaal sequence of Older and Younger Gravels down the Orange as far as Upington. Sangoan material seems to intrude up the lower Orange valley to near the nickpoint at Aughrabies. The limits of the Sangoan seem set on the Buffels at Spektakel Pass, and on the Oliphants at Bulshoek nickpoint. The Sangoan culture in southern Africa has a predominantly waterside distribution, and the feeler which stretched down the Natal coast also extended up

Section Three

the Tugela and Pongola as far as important nickpoints.[4] Above these Fauresmith material begins.

The Little Namaqualand coast, bathed by the icy Benguela current, must have been arid desert during most of the Pleistocene. Chellean material is very scarce, we nowhere saw Oldowan remains. The principal period of admittedly scanty habitation seems to have been the end of the Kanjeran pluvial and the beginning of the Gamblian. There is Late Acheulian on the Oliphants and perhaps on the Orange, probably Middle Acheulian at Kleinzee. The classic Middle Stone Age cultures have not been found. There is some form of Magosian at Viools Drift, later material of Wilton affinities at Kliphoek and Holgat. In an area where sand-cover is unusually deep it is remarkable how consistently our survey yielded remains of Sangoan type, whether because the rainfall was more regular at that time, or the ecology of Sangoan man was adapted to existence in a desert through which rivers flowed.

REFERENCES

1. Davies, O. and R. C. Walsh (1954–5). *S. Afr. J. Sci.* li, p. 277.
2. Davies, O. (1951–2). *S. Afr. J. Sci.* xlviii, p. 212.
3. Davies, O. (1954). *S. Afr. J. Sci.* l, p. 273.
4. Davies, O. (1952), Natal Archaeological Studies (especially 'The Industry from Mfongosi').

36

The Term 'Middle Stone Age'

by B. D. MALAN

HISTORICAL

THE first attempts to classify the Stone Age Cultures of South Africa resulted in a two-fold classification. One with strong Lower Palaeolithic affinities was named the Earlier Stone Age, the other with strong Upper Palaeolithic affinities was named the Eastern Culture but soon came to be known as the Later Stone Age. The Earlier Stone Age included the industries characterized by hand-axes: the Stellenbosch, the Victoria West and the Fauresmith. The Victoria West industries have since been shown to have no independant status, but to constitute the third and fourth stages of the development of the Stellenbosch or South African Chelles-Acheul culture in the interior of the country. The Later Stone Age contained the Still Bay, Smithfield, Wilton and Kitchen Midden culture complexes.

In 1928 Prof. A. J. H. Goodwin[1] published a paper entitled 'An introduction to the Middle Stone Age in South Africa'. Influenced by Mr Miles Burkitt who had visited the Union in 1926 and by the late Rev. Neville Jones, he pointed out that the former 'Later Stone Age' group required further sub-division. He regarded the Smithfield and Wilton industries as 'Neo-anthropic' and assignable to the admittedly vague San or Bush-Hottentot physical type, while the Still Bay and allied industries were regarded as earlier and associated with the Boskop physical type. He pointed out the presence of the faceted platform technique with convergent flaking in the Fauresmith and, with Neville Jones, attributed it to 'the impact of the arrival of a "Mousterian influence" which mixed with elements already present to produce Fauresmith, but which evolved and spread in a purer state to lay the foundation of the Middle Stone Age'.

At that time Goodwin conceived of the Middle Stone Age as consisting of a number of cultural groups which he termed 'variations' namely Glen Grey, Pietersburg, Hagenstad, Alexandersfontein, Sawmills, Howieson's Poort, Mossel Bay and, of course, Still Bay. He concluded his paper by quoting stratigraphic evidence of the position of the Middle Stone Age intermediate in time between the Earlier and the Later Stone Ages.

In the next year Goodwin[2] elaborated this paper in the chapter on the Middle Stone Age in *The Stone Age Cultures of South Africa*, a joint work in which he and Prof. C. van Riet Lowe (1929) laid the foundation of much of the structure of our knowledge of the prehistory of South Africa. He now introduced a new concept, the distinction between 'Industry' and 'Variation'. He says: 'It is therefore, necessary to use two terms, the word *Industry* being employed where a group is certain and definable; but in cases where uncertainty may still exist either in our knowledge of the exact relationship to the other groups and industries, or where insufficient data have been collected to form a basis of a definite classification, the term *Variation* will be employed. This does not, of course, preclude our raising a 'Variation' to 'Industry' status should evidence of a sufficiently definite type accumulate to justify such action (pp. 99–100). Consequently he accorded the Glen Grey and Still Bay the status of 'Industries' and the rest remained 'Variations'.

Concurrently with this work of Goodwin's, our terminology was taken a step further by Burkitt[3] who defined the terms Industry and Culture in his book *South Africa's Past in Stone and Paint* (1928). *Industry* he defined as 'an assemblage of artefacts at a given site, when all are of the same age', while he defined *Culture* as a group of industries between which there is 'an evident connection, some common elements one with another', plus those intangible 'factors which help us to discover anything of the life and minds of the people'.

Applying this terminology, the Still Bay, Pietersburg and Mossel Bay have since those days been recognized as Cultures, the Howieson's Poort and Sawmills industries have been seen to be coastal and inland expressions of the South African Magosian Culture, while little has been heard of the Glen Grey, Hagenstad and Alexandersfontein so-called 'Variations' though they certainly exist as cultural entities and deserve thorough investigation and description. In addition, the Maselspoort Culture has been described (Cooke, Malan and Wells).[4] With full realization of the shortcomings of our knowledge of true interrelationships, I have nevertheless suggested[5] regional and chronological groupings which seem to present a logical arrangement of the main assemblages attributable to the Middle Stone Age.

CRITICISMS

The term 'Middle Stone Age', first introduced by Goodwin in South Africa, has been adopted in Rhodesia by Neville Jones[6] who was at least partly responsible for its invention, by Clark[7] in Northern Rhodesia and Somaliland,[8] by Janmart[9] in Angola and Wayland[10] in Bechuanaland. Surely this is proof enough of the need for the term and its usefulness. Nevertheless the term has come in for a good deal of criticism, mostly verbal, but formulated in print by Dr L. S. B. Leakey. Let us examine these criticisms.

1. 'The term "Middle Stone Age" has been used as a sort of "omnibus term" to embrace a whole series of cultures, the stratigraphical and cultural inter-relationship of which is still far from fully worked out' (L. S. B. Leakey[11]). This is true, and there is a place and a use for comprehensive terms, especially for a group of cultures and industries which so clearly forms a major division of the Stone Age. The fact that we have much to learn about the detailed stratigraphical and cultural inter-relationships does not invalidate the term; indeed it is this lack of detailed knowledge which makes the term convenient and necessary.

2. ' "Middle Stone Age" is an English translation of "Mesolithic" and would therefore seem to imply that all the so-called Middle Stone Age cultures of South Africa were post Upper Palaeolithic in date' (L. S. B. Leakey, loc. cit.). The term 'Middle Stone Age' is *not* a translation of 'Mesolithic'; it was, in fact, carefully chosen to distinguish it from 'Mesolithic'. It is only in recent years that a few English archaeologists have tended to translate 'Mesolithic' by 'Middle Stone Age' using the terms as synonyms. In doing this without regard to the well-established, pre-existing term in Africa they may have created some confusion where none existed before. If so, surely criticism should be directed at those people with a passion for translation who are responsible for the confusion. In any case, the meanings of 'Mesolithic' and 'Middle Stone Age' are so different that no-one interested in African prehistory can possible confuse them.

3. Dr Leakey's third criticism is that while some confuse our terms with 'Mesolithic' others confuse it with 'Middle Palaeolithic'. To equate 'Middle Stone Age' with 'Middle Palaeolithic' is to ignore the strong Upper Palaeolithic typological elements in the Middle Stone Age. But here again the answer must be the trite one: 'Middle Stone Age' is a different term with a different meaning.

4. 'It is very misleading . . . to use terms which have a "time significance" . . . as though they had a cultural significance' (L. S. B. Leakey, loc. cit.). This is true, but it is common practice amongst us to use terms both in a chronological sense and a cultural sense. In Leakey's book *Adam's Ancestors* there is a chapter headed 'The Upper Palaeolithic *Cultures*'* and in that chapter we read: 'During the *period** which we are now considering, the Upper Palaeolithic, the period from the beginning of the Würm glaciation in Europe (the Gamblian pluvial in

* My italics.

Africa) to the end of the Pleistocene . . . etc.' (p. 138). Again, Desmond Clark in his book on *The Horn of Africa*, has written: 'The Middle Stone Age in the Horn includes the Levalloisian Culture complex together with its ultimate development into the Somaliland Still Bay. The Middle Stone Age is co-terminate with the Upper Pleistocene. Transitional between the Middle and the Late Stone Age is the Somaliland variant of the Magosian and the intrusive blade and burin industries of the Hargeisan' (pp. 155–6). In both these instances the authors have been admirably precise in defining both the chronological and cultural meaning of their terms. When Goodwin originally introduced the term 'Middle Stone Age' he also made both meanings of the term quite clear. Confusion arises only when we use the terms loosely, not from inadequacies of the terms themselves. Surely our difficulties arise when we forget that 'Palaeolithic' and 'Middle Stone Age' are adjectives and not nouns and must qualify either the noun 'period' or 'culture' or their synonyms.

Some may argue that the word 'Age' in 'Middle Stone Age' restricts its meaning to a purely chronological one, but this is a pedantic quibble. Let us by all means beware of the dangers of inexact expression, but let us not deprive ourselves of a term which has proved useful and adequate in many parts of Africa when properly used.

GENERAL

The cultural meaning of the term 'Middle Stone Age' has been adequately defined for the various areas where it has been used. It connotes a group of cultures, differing from region to region and with different names, but all having a great deal in common with regard to technique and typology—the absence of hand-axes and cleavers, the faceted platform technique, convergent and parallel flaking on flake-blades and a variety of flake-tool forms. In most parts of Africa the relationships between these cultures is known, but in the Union of South Africa we have much to learn. The regional and chronological arrangement of some of these cultures which I suggested in 1949, is extremely tentative and rests too heavily on typological considerations, but forms a basis for further work and is reproduced here from the *S.A. Archaeological Bulletin*.[5]

Southern Mountain Region	O.F.S.-Natal	Transvaal	Griqualand West
S.A. Magosian (Howieson's Poort)	S.A. Magosian (Ladybrand, Dundee)	S.A. Magosian (Parma)	S.A. Magosian (Scattered)
↑	↑	↑	↑
Still Bay Mossel Bay	Natal Still Bay and Mazelspoort (incl. Vlakkraal, Utrecht)	Epi-Pietersburg (Border Cave)	Alexandersfontein (Various stages)
	↑	↑	
	Hagenstad	Pietersburg (Various stages)	

Not only do we lack sufficient stratigraphical evidence, but our difficulties are aggravated by the necessity of comparing industries of silcrete and quartzite in the Cape with those of indurated shale in the Karroo, Orange Free State and parts of Natal, felsite and vein quartz in the Central Transvaal, chert in Griqualand West and the Eastern Transvaal and rhyolites in Zululand. That these various materials had profound effects on the industries which used them is clear, but the interpretation of those effects is no easy matter.

Section Three

There is some lack of agreement as to whether the transitional Magosian should be included amongst the Middle Stone Age Culture. In the Union we have no evidence for a stratigraphic break between the Middle Stone Age cultures proper and the Magosian, but there is evidence for a break immediately after the Magosian. In Rose Cottage Cave[12] some seven feet of sterile water-laid sand separates the Magosian from the later Stone Age cultures, while at Skildergat Cave at Fish Hoek[13] there is a distinct unconformity between the Howieson's Poort (the coastal equivalent of the Magosian) and the overlying shell midden deposits. The faceted platform technique of the Magosian means a continuation of Middle Stone Age technical traditions. We in the South have therefore regarded the Magosian as falling within the Middle Stone Age cultural group. In Southern Rhodesia Neville Jones[14] also places the Magosian within the Middle Stone Age group. In Somaliland, in his book *The Horn of Africa*, Clark[8] places the Somaliland Magosian in the Late Stone Age and in his correlation tables published in the *S.A. Archaeological Bulletin* he places it in the Recent period.

When we turn to the chronological meaning of the Middle Stone Age period, it is elementary but necessary to point out that the term does not denote the same absolute interval of time wherever it is used. Clark's excellent correlation tables[15] show, for instance, that in the Zambezi area the Rhodesian Proto-Still Bay culture flourished during the latter two-thirds of the Gamblian pluvial of the Upper Pleistocene, the Rhodesian Still Bay during the succeeding Holocene dry period and the Rhodesian Magosian during the Makalian wet phase. On the other hand, in the Union the Middle Stone Age complex (*sensu stricto*) is placed during the oscillating Makalian and the Magosian during the subsequent wetter phase. In other words, in the Union the Middle Stone Age period is a considerably later absolute interval of time than it is in the Zambezi. But this is no new concept in prehistory, for we have long been familiar with the idea that the Stone Age covered different periods in different parts of the world. This fact offers no more difficulty than the fact that the Stone Age ended at different times in South Africa and Egypt.

One term used in connection with the Middle Stone Age in South Africa remains to be discussed—the term 'Variation'. As we have seen, Goodwin introduced this term to denote groups of assemblages of artefacts about which our knowledge was insufficient to enable us to regard them as cultures. Of Goodwin's eight original 'Variations', the Still Bay, Pietersburg and Mossel Bay are now recognized as cultures; Sawmills and Howieson's Poort are coastal and inland expressions of the Magosian, while little has been heard of the Glen Grey, Hagenstad and Alexandersfontein but Glen Grey and Alexandersfontein probably deserve status as cultures. In addition, the Mazelspoort Culture has been described. Although there are still other undescribed assemblages such as those which Goodwin called 'Variations', the need for this term has to a great extent disappeared and it may well be abandoned. A much more useful term is the word 'Variant' which is in common use by Clark, Leakey and others for localized assemblages which bear a clear relationship to a recognized culture and yet differ consistently from it. Thus Clark has described the Ogaden variant of the Wilton of Somaliland. When I described certain Middle Stone Age assemblages from the Eastern Transvaal and Swaziland I regarded them as a local expression of the Pietersburg Culture and ascribed the typological differences to the different material used. I might well have referred to these assemblages as representing an Eastern Transvaal variant of the Pietersburg Culture. The term is a useful one which will, I am sure, accurately reflect several cultural relationships within the Middle Stone Age cultural group when we come to know more about that complicated period and culture complex.

REFERENCES

1. Goodwin, A. J. H., 'An introduction to the Middle Stone Age in South Africa', *S. Afr. J. Sci.*, XXV, 1928.
2. Goodwin, A. J. H., 'The Middle Stone Age', in Goodwin and van Riet Lowe, *The Stone Age Cultures of South Africa*, Ann. S. Afr. Mus., XXVII, 1929.

3. Burkitt, Miles C., *South Africa's Past in Stone and Paint*, C.U.P., 1929.

4. Cooke, H. B. S., B. D. Malan and L. H. Wells, 'The Associated Fauna and Culture of the Vlakkraal Thermal Springs, O.F.S.', *Trans. Roy. Soc. S. Afr.*, XXIX, Part III, 1942.

5. Malan, B. D., 'Magosian and Howieson's Poort', *S. Afr. Archaeol. Bull.*, IV, 13, March 1949.

6. Jones, Neville, *The Prehistory of Southern Rhodesia*, C.U.P., 1949.

7. Clark, J. Desmond, *The Stone Age Cultures of Northern Rhodesia*, S. Afr. Archaeol. Soc., Claremont, Cape S. Africa, 1950.

8. Clark, J. Desmond, *The Prehistoric Cultures of the Horn of Africa*, C.U.P., 1954.

9. Janmart, J., *Stations Préhistoriques de l'Angola du Nord-est*, Museu do Dundo, Lisbon, 1946.

10. Wayland, E. J., 'Outlines of Prehistory and Stone Age Climatology in the Bechuanaland Protectorate', *Acad. Roy. des Sciences Coloniales, Mem.-Coll. in 8″*, T. XXV, Fasc. 4, 1954.

11. Leakey, L. S. B., *Adam's Ancestors*, Methuen, London, 1953, p. 138.

12. Malan, B. D., 'The final phase of the Middle Stone Age in South Africa', *Proc. First Pan-African Congress on Prehistory, Nairobi, 1947*, Blackwell, Oxford, 1952.

13. Jolly, K., 'The Development of the Cape Middle Stone Age in Skildergat Cave, Fish Hoek', *S. Afr. Archaeol. Bull.*, III, 12, December 1948.

14. Jones, Neville, loc. cit., p. 13.

15. Clark, J. Desmond, 'A Provisional Correlation of Prehistoric Cultures North and South of the Sahara', *S. Afr. Archaeol. Bull.*, 33, IX, March 1954.

37

A Re-Examination of the Industry from the Type Site of Magosi, Uganda

by J. D. CLARK

Description of Site

THIS rather insignificant waterhole in Northern Uganda has lent its name to what is now recognized to be a widely distributed complex of industries typologically transitional between the Middle and the Late Stone Ages, so that today there are recognized many regional forms of the Magosian Culture, though whether there is, in fact, any closer connection between them than the general similarity resulting from the continent-wide metamorphosis from macrolithic to microlithic industries still has to be proved. The discovery of the site in March 1925, and its partial excavation in November 1926, we owe to Mr E. J. Wayland, the pioneer of Uganda Prehistory who, in 1932, collaborated in a paper with Mr M. C. Burkitt describing the site and the industry. Only one industry appears to have existed at Magosi and the authors assigned it to a climatically dry period between the Late and the Middle Stone Ages.

In 1951 I was invited by Mr M. C. Burkitt to re-examine the collections from Magosi, which, with the exception of one implement, are all housed in the Museum of Archaeology and Anthropology at Cambridge. I am particularly indebted to Mr Burkitt for his kindness in putting these collections at my disposal and in giving me every facility for examining them. Out of this study a number of interesting points have arisen.

It is necessary to recapitulate briefly the nature and location of the site. Magosi is situated at approximately 2° 35′ North, 30° 25′ East in North-Eastern Uganda, some 5 miles to the West of the Rift escarpment forming the boundary between Uganda and the Turkana country in the Northern Frontier District of Kenya. For several months of the year the area is waterless and not far to the East true desert conditions are found. The site at Magosi lies at the foot of a granite cliff and was found to be a silted-up rock cistern. Such rock cisterns are common in the area as they are also in much of the granitic country of the Northern Frontier District of Kenya and Southern Somalia. They result in the first instance from decomposition of the rock by chemical agents, but their depth Wayland suggests may have been due to the artificial removal of the clay filling by human agency.

Wayland excavated three sections across the site (21 × 6 feet: 20 × 2 feet: 15 × 5 feet) and conclusively proved the nature of the deposit. A shallow pegmatite dyke divided the cistern into two parts, a comparatively shallow portion away from the rock face, and a deeper portion in the immediate vicinity of the rock, with a proved depth of 11 feet and width of 8–10 feet. The granite face sloped inward upon itself beneath the surface of the ground. The outer wall of the cistern similarly sloped steeply downwards, approximately parallel to the hanging wall of the cliff-face and at an angle of 45°. The cistern had become filled by a red brick-earth, which Wayland describes as an aeolian clay originating as very fine dust carried by wind into the water.

Anyone who has seen the amount of rain water running off one of these granite faces from one sporadic shower of rain in a semi-arid or arid region can readily appreciate that the cistern must, under similar climatic conditions, have contained water for several months of the year.

Down the steep slope of the outer edge of the cistern, up and down which man would have had to have followed the rise and fall of the water, was found an 18 inch layer of rock rubble, material that had fallen and rolled into the cistern, and in this, and in particular in the upper levels, occurred the fairly prolific stone industry. Below the rock rubble was a layer of sand resulting from the residual weathering of the rock, and this passed in turn into rotten and solid granite.

Wayland's Fig. 2 of the original publication shows clearly the nature of the site (Fig. 1). It is important to bear in mind that there is only one implementiferous layer which follows the steep slope of the side of the cistern, and that this is approximately of the same age at the bottom as at the top. The remainder of the filling of the cistern—the brick earth—was sterile.

The sections were excavated in two-foot layers and every worked piece of stone was kept, so that it has thus been possible to obtain a comparatively accurate picture of the technical processes behind the industry as well as a statistical analysis of the artefacts and debris.

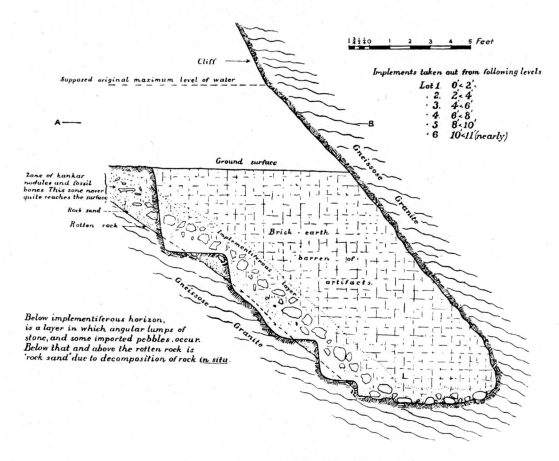

FIG. 1. Section through the Rock Cistern at Magosi

Reprinted from E. J. Wayland and M. C. Burkitt's *The Magosian Culture of Uganda*, by permission of the Royal Anthropological Institute

229

Section Three

Description of Industry

The microlithic industry was made largely from chalcedony, often banded and of a pure translucent variety, honey-coloured, grey, or brown; an opaque form of chert or jasper also occurs. Clear and cloudy quartz were also used, though less commonly. The material appears to have been collected in the form of small pebbles, and no doubt the chalcedonies were derived from the acid volcanic rocks of the north and east. A few coarse lava flakes, as well as five small fragments of obsidian, also occur, indicative perhaps of seasonal movements into the Turkana desert and Lake Rudolf areas to the east. Quartzite or fine-grained felsite, hornblende-gabbro and trachyte were also used for the macrolithic tools. I am indebted to Dr Agrell of the Department of Mineralogy and Petrology at Cambridge for identification of these rocks.

Not a little of the material, especially that from the 2–4 foot level, shows a glossy patina, due possibly to the implements having lain in water with fine clay in suspension. All implements are quite fresh but approximately 1% show signs of crackle due to fire.

The list of tool types is given below, sub-divided in accordance with the depth:

Inventory of Tools from Rock Cistern at Magosi

	0–2′	2–4′	4–6′	6–8′	8–10′	10–11′	Totals
Microliths—oblique truncation	2	9	11	2	14	—	38
lunates	22	7	10	8	4	—	51
triangles (isosceles)	2	1	1	1	—	—	5
triangles (scalene)	8	9	6	—	6	—	29
trapezes	5	—	1	—	1	—	7
eared	3	1	—	—	—	—	4
straight-backed	24	5	12	12	40	4	97
curved-backed	37	3	38	27	46	—	151
thick-sectioned	28	72	3	5	—	1	109
used bladelets—single-edge	54	89	60	14	171	12	400
double-edge	7	62	28	14	29	2	142
waisted	2	—	—	2	3	—	7
Saws	1	2	4	—	2	2	11
Burins	7	14	9	2	1	2	35
Points—unifaced (including fragments)	2	4	4	4	3	3	20
Points—bifaced (including fragments)	1	1	1	1	1	—	5
Awls and drills	6	3	6	2	13	2	32
Flakes—faceted	—	7	7	2	10	—	26
Flakes—plain	41	196	27	11	174	9	458
Redirecting	30	42	67	—	124	15	278
Flake-blades	52	362	226	10	230	21	901
Blades	44	530	351	17	5	16	963
Pestles	—	—	2	—	1	—	3
Muller	—	?	1	—	—	—	1
Stone Balls	—	—	—	2	—	—	2

A Re-Examination of the Type Site of Magosi, Uganda

	0–2'	2–4'	4–6'	6–8'	8–10'	10–11'	Totals
Bored Stones	—	1*	—	1	—	—	2
Ostrich eggshell	3	—	—	—	—	—	3
Scrapers—core and thick flake	6	6	7	3	17	1	40
thumbnail and short							
end	12	1	7	9	2	—	31
hollow	2	—	1	1	6	—	10
Outils Écaillés	3	26	3	2	7	1	42
Cores—bipolar	16	9	7	3	9	1	45
disc	7	2	4	2	6	1	22
nobbly	31	6	2	4	6	—	49
micro-blade	20	4	16	8	11	—	59
Waste	36	196	175	—	57	—	464
TOTALS	514	1670	1097	169	999	93	4542

Every artificially worked piece of stone has been classified and this gives a clearer picture of the industry. Of considerable interest is the fact that the site has yielded, besides the assemblage already briefly described by Wayland and Burkitt, several other tools, the inclusion of which was unknowingly omitted from the original publication. These implements, which consist of two stone balls, a muller or rubbing stone, and two bored stones, were not available to Burkitt when he carried out his examination of the industry. Because of their weight, they were not sent back from Uganda with the remainder of the material and were only later received in Cambridge. One of the bored stones, the heavier of the two, still remains in Entebbe and has not been available for examination. A note on these stones was published by Wayland in *Nature* on November 14, 1950.

Generally speaking it can be seen how the amount of material decreases with depth except for the apparent paucity of specimens from the 6–8 feet level. This is as might be expected with a site of this nature. The straight and curved-backed microliths and utilized bladelets, burins, points, awls, scrapers, *outils écaillés* and microlithic *débitage* occurs evenly distributed from top to bottom (though the lowest layer (10–11 feet) has yielded only a comparatively small series) and demonstrates clearly the homogeneous nature of the assemblage. Some of the more specialized forms of microlith seem to belong only to the period shortly before the cistern became completely silted up and may be indicative of some development in the industry.

There is a suggestion also that micro-flakes and flakes may become commoner than bladelets towards the lower levels and it may be that there is a slight increase in the average size of implements nearer the floor of the cistern. The inventory on the other hand provides additional confirmation for the homogeneous nature of the industry which Wayland and Burkitt ascribed to a single climatic episode—the dry period between the end of the Gamblian Pluvial and the first Post-Pluvial Wet Phase.

In the 0–2 feet level 14 pieces of comminuted fossil bone were found—derived from long bones, together with one fragment of tooth enamel. Additional fragments of fossil bone and two pieces of tooth enamel, all with kunkar concretions, also come from the 2–4 feet level. One piece of tooth enamel and a fossil bone fragment come from the 8–10 feet level.

The illustrations to this paper have been chosen to supplement those accompanying the

* Not examined. A bored stone said to be that from the 2–4 feet level at Magosi and examined by courtesy of Messrs Wayland and Burkitt has not been included in the inventory as there is some doubt as to its provenance. Also the previous descriptions of the specimen from the 2–4 feet level describe it as being heavier than that from the 6–8 feet level whereas this example is considerably lighter.

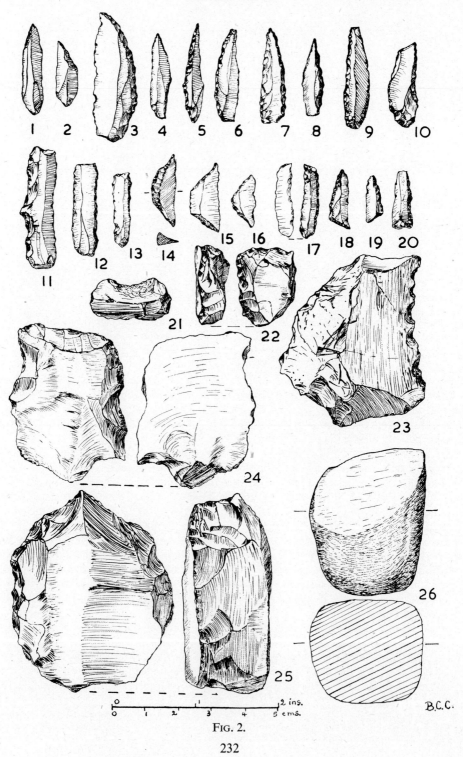

Fig. 2.

A Re-Examination of the Type Site of Magosi, Uganda

Fig. 2

1. Obliquely truncated microlith; bulb present but no platform: opaque chert or chalcedony: 0–2 ft.

2. Obliquely truncated microlith; translucent chalcedony: bulb present but no platform: 4–6 ft.

3. Large utilized curved-backed blade in honey-coloured translucent chalcedony: 8–10 ft.

4. Small blade backed at butt end and at tip only; cutting edge shows signs of utilization; honey-coloured translucent chalcedony: 8–10 ft.

5. Pointed backed microlith backed from both sides near the point in opaque grey chalcedony, glossy patina: 0–2 ft.

6. Curved backed microlith with blunt ends; bulb formerly at tip end; utilization down cutting edge. Opaque green chert, glossy patina: 4–6 ft.

7. Backed microlith with écrasé working down cutting edge on upper face; cream-coloured opaque chert, glossy patina: 0–2 ft.

8. Straight-backed microlith worked into an awl; translucent grey chalcedony glossy: 2–4 ft.

9. Straight-backed microlith with retouch at base on cutting edge and utilization on remainder of edge; tip broken, glossy patina, grey translucent chalcedony (some silica gloss): 8–10 ft.

10. Straight-backed microlith with retouch at base on cutting edge. Point broken, but some nibbling retouch; buff-coloured translucent chalcedony, glossy: 6–8 ft.

11. Straight-backed blade with boss in centre of backing; utilization and écaillé working on cutting edge; mottled red and grey chert, glossy patina: 10–11 ft.

12. Straight-backed blade with utilization on cutting edge; opaque red chert or jasper, some gloss: 2–4 ft.

13. Straight-backed blade with utilization on cutting edge and some nibbling on upper edge; red opaque chert or jasper: 10–11 ft.

14. Crescent backed from both edges, reddish-yellow translucent chalcedony, no utilization on cutting edge: 0–2 ft.

15. Trapezium with some utilization on cutting edge, glossy opaque brown chert: 0–2 ft.

16. Triangle glossy, mottled white and buff chert: 0–2 ft.

17. Straight-backed microlith with blunted end and Kasouga flaking, mottled red chert or jasper, glossy: 8–10 ft.

18. Scalene triangle; no utilization, glossy; mottled brown chert: 0–2 ft.

19. Scalene triangle; no utilization; opaque red chert or jasper: 4–6 ft.

20. Backed-blade with blunted end; some utilization, glossy, honey-coloured chalcedony: 0–2 ft.

21. Hollow scraper on earlier patinated micro-flake, red patina; honey-coloured, opaque chert, glossy: 0–2 ft.

22. Small core scraper or trimming stone in opaque green chert, glossy patina; resolved flaking: 2–4 ft.

23. Saw on a thickish primary flake. Opaque cream patina chert: 4–6 ft.

24. End and side scraper or trimming stone in brown honey-coloured chert: made on an earlier flake with hollow scraper or notch at butt end; resolved flaking: 8–10 ft.

25. Large core scraper or trimming stone on earlier thick flake in greenish-grey chert, patina purplish with some manganese staining in spots: 4–6 ft.

26. Pestle stone or rubber in hornblende-gabbro, well polished oblique rubbing surface made from a well-weathered sub-rectangular piece of rock; some faint trace of red staining in places on rubbing edge—perhaps used for grinding haematite: 8–10 ft.

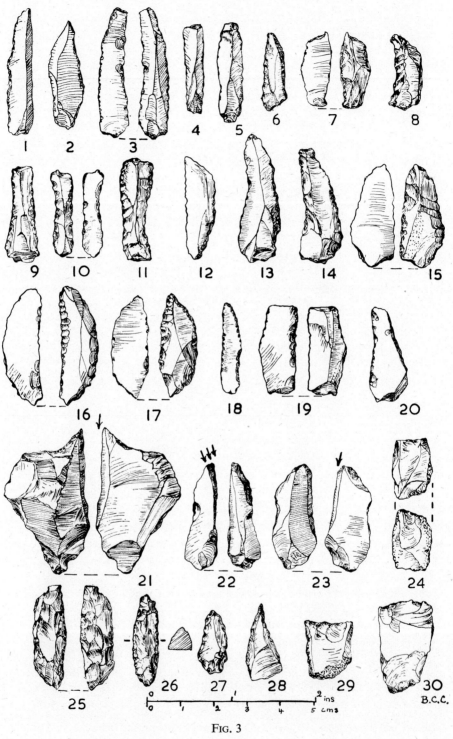

FIG. 3

234

A Re-Examination of the Type Site of Magosi, Uganda

Fig. 3

1. Blade utilized down one edge; honey-coloured opaque chert: 10–11 ft.

2. Blade utilized down one edge; grey translucent chalcedony, glossy patina; possibly the initial stage of a specimen like Nos. 13–15: 4–6 ft.

3. Blade utilized down both edges with some *écaillé* flaking in reddish-brown semi-translucent chalcedony, glossy patina: 4–6 ft.

4. Blade utilized down both edges; reddish translucent chalcedony, glossy patina: 2–4 ft.

5. Blade utilized down both edges; translucent chalcedony, glossy patina: 10–11 ft.

6. Micro-flake or blade with some vertical backing down one edge and typical fish-scale feather-edge flaking down opposite edge; bulb trimmed away; translucent chalcedony, glossy patina: 2–4 ft.

7. Micro-flake or blade with some vertical backing down one edge and typical fish-scale feather-edge flaking down opposite edge; bulb present; glossy chalcedony: 6–8 ft.

8. Micro-flake or blade with some vertical backing down one edge but fish-scale flaking somewhat steeper and slightly concave; no backing on opposite edge, whitish translucent chalcedony: 10–11 ft.

9. Double-edged bladelet with fish-scale or feather-edge flaking; translucent chalcedony: 8–10 ft.

10. Double-edged bladelet with fish-scale or feather-edge flaking; translucent chalcedony with gloss—mainly on the worked edge: 0–2 ft.

11. Double-edged bladelet with fish-scale or feather-edge flaking; translucent chalcedony with some gloss: 4–6 ft.

12. Backed bladelet with backing at lower end only; no utilization; purplish opaque chert: 6–8 ft.

13. Bladelet or flake with backing on lower half of one edge and utilization on cutting edge; glossy patina, translucent, greyish chalcedony: 8–10 ft.

14. Bladelet or flake—possibly a redirecting flake with backing at lower end and feather-edge flaking on cutting edge; glossy patina, translucent chalcedony: 8–10 ft.

15. Bladelet or flake—possibly a redirecting flake with backing at lower end and feather-edge flaking on cutting edge; glossy patina, whitish translucent chalcedony; shows crackle from fire: 2–4 ft.

16. Crescent, backed at lower end of one edge; feather-edge flaking on cutting edge; greyish-green glossy chert: 0–2 ft.

17. Crescent, with feather-edge flaking on cutting edge; glossy brown translucent chalcedony: 4–6 ft.

18. Bladelet with Kasouga flaking on both edges; translucent chalcedony, glossy: 2–4 ft.

19. Broken blade with Kasouga flaking on one edge in mottled grey patina, glossy: 0–2 ft.

20. Kasouga flake; glossy patina; red and grey chert: 6–8 ft.

21. Oblique straight angle-burin on a worked fragment of brownish translucent chalcedony; glossy patina: 4–6 ft.

22. Oblique straight angle-burin, honey-coloured translucent chalcedony, glossy patina: 0–2 ft.

23. Oblique straight angle-burin in mottled grey translucent chalcedony, glossy: 6–8 ft.

24. Double-ended bipolar core or *outil écaillé* in clear quartz: 0–2 ft.

25. Sub-triangular borer or drill, in brownish glossy chert: 8–10 ft.

26. Sub-triangular borer or drill, with signs of use, in reddish chert or jasper: 0–2 ft.

27. Borer or drill with signs of use; honey-coloured chert: 4–6 ft.

28. Awl or borer in brown chert: 0–2 ft.

29. *Outil écaillé*, one edge only, on fragment of honey-coloured translucent chalcedony: 2–4 ft.

30. Bipolar core or *Outil écaillé*, double-ended, translucent chalcedony: 8–10 ft.

original publication, and to amplify the description of certain other forms of tool which previously received only brief mention. For the complete range of tool forms, therefore, these illustrations should be viewed in conjunction with those accompanying Wayland's and Burkitt's paper.

Let us now examine the composition of the industry.

MICROLITHS (1040). These comprise the greater bulk of the implements and are subdivisible into a number of forms. The method employed for blunting the back is the flat 'curved over' retouch directed from the main flake surface and typical of that usually associated with the Magosian, though a few specimens, especially the straight-backed microliths, are blunted from both edges.

Microliths with oblique truncation (38) form a small but definite group, occurring in all but the lowest level (Fig. 2, Nos. 1 and 2).

Lunates (51) are commoner in the topmost two feet (Fig. 2, No. 14), as are also *isosceles triangles* (5) (Fig. 2, No. 16), *trapezes* (7) (Fig. 2, No. 15) and *eared microliths* (4). An interesting and charac-teristic form is a small *scalene triangle* (29) (Fig. 2, Nos. 18–20) which appears to be a form of diminutive straight-backed microlith with abrupt truncation. These tools appear at first glance rather out of place in a general non-geometric microlithic industry such as that from Magosi.

The greater part of the microlithic element, however, consists of three main forms. Firstly *straight-backed bladelets* (97) (Fig. 2, Nos. 8–13), sometimes with the cutting edge showing signs of utilization (15), and sometimes showing retouch on the lower end of the cutting edge to facilitate hafting (Fig. 2, No. 9). Secondly *curved-backed bladelets* (151) (Fig. 2, Nos. 3, 5–6), again with the cutting edge sometimes showing signs of deliberate retouch (17) (Fig. 2, No. 7; Fig. 3, Nos. 16, 17). With this second group must be included a number of usually but not always coarse, thickish, rather clumsily curved specimens (109) blunted on the lower part of the back only, and which show varying degrees of use of the cutting edge. Thirdly *used bladelets* in which sometimes the one edge (400) sometimes both (179) are used. These last are an interesting series and the second-ary work shows a graduation from the nibbling resulting from use for cutting, through feather-edge flaking to a typical rather fine, sometimes flat, sometimes steep, form that is very character-istic of the secondary work on some neolithic-type tools from the Horn and the Sahara and which give the implements the appearance of half-finished diminutive 'slugs'. Fig. 3, Nos. 1–5 show the usual kind of utilized blade. Fig. 3, Nos. 6–8 show feather-edge flaking down one edge to form a kind of scraper or pressure flaked knife-blade, while Nos. 9–11 show a development of this type of flaking from both edges, to form a waisted tool and giving it a somewhat 'neolithic' appear-ance. Fig. 3, Nos. 12–15 and Fig. 2, No. 4, show examples of the thick-sectioned bladelets blunted on the lower half of the back, and with secondary working developing into full feather-edge flaking due to pressure along one, sometimes both edges. Kasouga retouch also occurs (Fig. 3, Nos. 18–20). Of note also is the fact that not a few of these microliths and used bladelets have been snapped off or intentionally blunted at one or both ends which suggest that this was done to facilitate hafting several together in sequence.

Saws (11). A few flakes and blades showing serrated edges, classified as saws, are also found (Fig. 2, No. 23). No evidence of silica gloss was apparent on these however.

Burins (35). These are usually approaching microlithic proportions but show undoubted burin facets (Fig. 3, Nos. 21–23). The forms found include angle, bec-de-flute and single-blow burins, together with one 'pointed' specimen. Not a single example of the microburin occurs.

Points (25). These are never a common tool but they occur evenly distributed from top to bottom of the cistern. The unifaced examples (20) are commoner than the fully bifacial form (5). They are all with one exception diminutive. Only one or two of these tools show anything like the fine degree of secondary work attained by the Middle Stone Age Still Bay people, and for the most part retouch is confined to the point or edges of the tool.

Awls and Drills (32). These tools are well represented at Magosi. The awls are of the usual kind worked along both edges (Fig. 3, No. 28), but the drills (Fig. 3, Nos. 25, 26, 27) conform to a type well known in the Nile Valley and the eastern Sahara as well as in the Horn, and in the Nachikufan Culture of Northern Rhodesia. Nos. 25 and 26 also resemble crude unifaced 'slug' points of the Somaliland Doian industries.

Flakes (762). These are usually small and approximately 1–1½ inches long, though a few larger specimens occur. Only 26 of these show faceted striking platforms, while the remainder (458) all show plain platforms. A fairly high proportion of redirecting flakes occur (278), most of which are of the long core-sharpener variety, removed down the length of a micro-core.

Flake-Blades (901). These grade imperceptibly on the one hand into flakes and on the other into blades. For the purposes of classification it has been taken that the width of a blade is not more than approximately ¼ its length and of a flake-blade approximately ½ its length.

Blades (963). These are almost all fully microlithic and show no evidence of use.

Pestle Stones (3). Two are made from hornblende-gabbro while the third is in quartz. The one illustrated from the 8–10 feet level (Fig. 2, No. 26) shows an oblique rubbing surface, not unusual in such tools.

Muller or Rubbing Stone (1). This is made from a fine-grained trachyte and shows patches of a manganese crust. Some fine shallow groovings exist on one face, such as might have been made by a sharp stone or sharp-edged bone but not from rubbing bone. The edge has been evenly rounded by rubbing and pecking. The specimen is derived from the 4–6 feet level (Fig. 4, No. 2). It is a type of implement more commonly associated with the Later Stone Age.

Stone Balls (2). These are made from quartz and typical of the Middle Stone Age form of missile stone. The first specimen (Fig. 4, No. 1) shows somewhat flattened battering on two opposing surfaces, otherwise it has been carefully rounded by pecking. Slight signs of a manganese crust are present. It is 7·4 centimetres in diameter.

The second specimen is 6·9 cms. in diameter and well rounded by pecking; it shows little or no manganese crust. Both were found in the 6–8 foot level.

Bored Stones (2). Only one of these was available for examination. It is made from a coarse-grained trachyte and shows a manganese crust in places, particularly in the bore. It weighs 3 lb. ½ oz. and one face is flattened, suggesting use as a hammer. The maximum width is 14·05 cm. and the internal diameter of the bore is 3·2 cm. The average height of the specimen is 6·8 cm. It shows typical hour-glass perforation and came from the 6–8 feet level.

The second specimen—the larger and heavier of the two—is still in Uganda. It came from the 2–4 feet level. The dimensions are not known.

Ostrich Eggshell (3). Three fragments, but showing no decoration or piercing, come from the 0–2 feet level.

Scrapers (81). Hollow scrapers (Fig. 2, No. 21) account for a small proportion of the scraper forms, but the main types are small core scrapers, whether on cores, thickish nodules (Fig. 2, No. 22) or thickish flakes (Fig. 2, No. 24), together with thumbnail and diminutive end-scrapers on short bladelets; these are already well illustrated in the original publication. One quite typical and two not so good examples of core scrapers of the type known in South Africa as 'trimming stones' occur (Fig. 2, No. 25).

Outils Écaillés (42). These are usually found on small bipolar and single-ended cores and show the typical *écrasé* work at one or both ends. Not a few specimens occur also on flakes and broken fragments, however, and in the writer's opinion there can be little doubt that these tools are more than mere worked out cores and represent a definite tool—probably a type of adze-flake (Fig. 3, Nos. 24, 29, 30).

Cores (175). The greater proportion are small single platformed and bipolar cores for the production of punched micro-blades. Of the former the majority show a straight or gently curved striking platform, but 16 small, circular-platformed conical cores also exist. A smaller proportion of micro-cores (7) show two or more platforms. A number of specimens classed as 'nobbly' also occur. They presumably represent worked out multi-platformed cores. It is of interest to note that

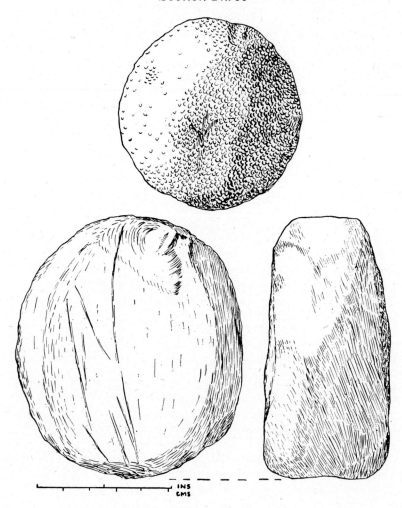

Fig. 4

1. Stone Ball: 7·4 cm. diameter. Somewhat flattened battering on two opposing faces, otherwise well rounded by pitting. Slight trace of manganese crust. Material—quartz. From 6–8 ft. level.

2. Muller or rubbing stone: maximum diameter 10·05 cm. minimum diameter 9·3 cm. Thickness at centre point 4·85 cm. Material grained trachyte with manganese crust in places. Fine groovings on one face might have resulted from stone or sharp bone, as if the specimen might have been used as a chopping block but not for rubbing bone; hollow at one end, probably due to the accidental removal of a flake and later rubbed smooth. Other face is flat and smooth, no evidence of a dimple scar, but some fine scratches apparent. From 4–6 ft. level

the number of disc cores is only 22 and when this is considered in relation to the number of faceted flakes (26) it will be seen that the micro-blade element far exceeds the prepared core element.

DISCUSSION AND CONCLUSIONS

Taking the industry as a whole, it is apparent that it is predominantly microlithic but with a few late Middle Stone Age forms added. Those elements which anticipate the Late Stone Age industries are the bored stones, muller and perhaps the pestle stones, together with the variety and nature of some of the secondary work on the microliths and used bladelets and the drills. The Middle Stone Age elements are, of course, the points and disc-cores and the stone balls. As the former greatly predominate over the latter, it might be suggested that the Magosi industry is fairly late in what has now come to be called 'The Magosian Complex'.

Let us now see whether it is possible to be more precise in this matter. After examining the Magosi industry, the writer was struck by the similarity of some of the techniques and forms to elements of the Doian Culture of Southern Somalia. Incidentally the environment in which this culture existed is very like that of Magosi and the sites are usually found grouped round the granite inselbergs of the Southern Somalia coastal plain. Here also rock cisterns exist and in fact are

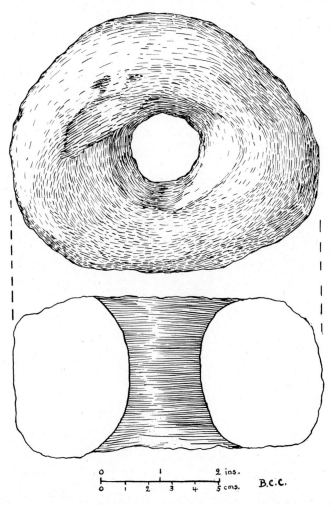

FIG. 5. Bored Stone: maximum width 14·05 cm. minimum width 11·65 cm. Obverse external diameter of bore 5·05 × 5·4 cm. Internal diameter of bore 3·2 cm. Reverse external diameter of bore 6·45 × 6·25 cm. Internal diameter of bore 3·1 cm. Average thickness 6·8 cm. Material coarse grained trachyte: manganese crust adhering in places, especially in the bore. The stone has been flattened somewhat on one face suggesting that this may have been caused by hammering. Weight 3 lb. ½ oz. From 6–8 ft. level

regularly cleaned out and used as a water supply by the present day Rahanwein and Dighil Somalis. The spoil thrown out from these cisterns has similarly yielded Doian artefacts and *débitage*. The Magosi industry finds its closest comparison with the transitional Magosio-Doian industries of the Southern Somalia rock shelters and open sites situated on approximately the same parallel of latitude between 3° 0′ North, 40° 20′ East. These industries are also assigned to a dry period subsequent to the Gamblian Pluvial, i.e. that separating the Makalian from the Nakuran wet phases. They post-date the Magosian proper of the Horn assigned to the Makalian and the pre-Makalian dry period in which a preponderance of small sub-triangular bifaced and unifaced points occur associated with a proportionately small microlithic element, and antedate the Doian which contains a high proportion of points, 'slugs', trihedral rods, etc. which have close parallels in the Sahara and Egyptian Neolithic industries.

In regard to the chronological position of the Magosi industry it would seem more likely that it should be assigned to the post-Makalian and not to the pre-Makalian dry period on the Somaliland evidence, though on correlation with Kenya the earlier position is preferable. On the other hand no early Wilton without pottery has yet been found in Uganda to my knowledge, and it may be that in these dry regions to the north of the Kenya high plateau climatic belt the development of the microlithic industries was retarded.

The points of especial similarity between the Magosi industry and the Magosio-Doian are to be found in the straight-backed microliths, often with the characteristic basal retouch; in the utilized and waisted bladelets; in the curved backed microliths with flat Neolithic retouch (occasional specimens of which are of the nature of diminutive asymetric 'slugs'), and in the micro-drills. The lunates, thumbnail and short end-scrapers, burins, *outils écaillés*, pestles and mullers are all common to both as they are, for that matter, to most other transitional and Late Stone Age industries of East and North-East Africa. I do not, however, know of any industry from Kenya which shows on bladelets the characteristic controlled pressure flaking of Neolithic-type that occurs at Magosi. The microliths of scalene triangle-form do not occur in the Horn before the Doian-type industries of the Mudug, though they are present, of course, in the Capsian and later cultures of Kenya. This form of microlith is therefore by no means confined to the geometric industries practising a micro-burin technique, for they also occur commonly, for example, with the Ibero-Maurusian of North-West Africa, in which the micro-burin is only rarely present, as well as in some of the Sahara Neolithic and in the Bedouin Neolithic of Kharga Oasis. It is of considerable interest however that the Magosio-Doian industries of Somalia also contain rare hollow-based and triangular arrow-heads of Eastern Sahara form, which leave little doubt that these industries are approximately contemporary with what Breuil believes may be one of the earlier phases of the Eastern Sahara Neolithic. The similarities between the specimens from the Somalia sites and the examples from Taferjit and Tamaya Mellet in the Nigerian Sahara, and with those from the Ténéré, as well as with Kharga for example, preclude any suggestion of autochthonous development in the various regions.

Thus on the evidence of the microlithic element there is every indication that the Magosi industry is late in the Magosian Complex and we have through the Magosio-Doian industries in Southern Somalia a possible correlation with probably the earlier part of the Eastern Sahara Neolithic. The presence of the bored stones argues in favour of such a date, while the rare Magosian-type unifaced and bifaced sub-triangular points are occasionally present also in the Somalia industries with which the Magosi industry is compared. The stone balls are perhaps the only discordant element, being essentially, so far as is known at present, a Middle Stone Age tool. It may be, however, that their use continued later in this part of Africa than it did in other regions, and in this connection it is of interest to note that it is in East Africa, among the Jaluo, Nandi, Embu, Meru, Theraka and Kamba peoples that the stone-headed club was, until very recently, still in use. Also almost the only surviving evidence to suggest that the bolas was ever used in Africa comes from a toy bolas used by children at Toro in Uganda.

A Re-Examination of the Type Site of Magosi, Uganda

We may, in conclusion, suggest therefore that the industry from Magosi is the probable contemporary of the Magosio-Doian industries of Somalia and of an early phase of the Neolithic in the Eastern Sahara. It probably belongs in time to the post-Makalian dry phase. Thus, for the first time, we have an approximate correlation between a later industry from the Equatorial climatic belt with industries from the Sahara, which if fresh investigations should be carried out in Uganda's North-Eastern Province may well result in a firm correlation being established between these two regions.

REFERENCES

Wayland, E. J. and M. C. Burkitt (1932), 'The Magosian Culture of Uganda', *J.R.A.I.*, LXII, pp. 369–90.
Wayland, E. J. (1950), *Nature*, 14 October 1950.
Clark, J. D. (1954), *The Prehistoric Cultures of the Horn of Africa*, pp. 203–18 and Plates 22, 23 and 25.
Van Riet Lowe, C. (1952), 'The Pleistocene Geology and Prehistory of Uganda', Part II, *Prehistory*, pp. 98–101.
Kelley, H. (1934), 'Harpons, objets en os travaillé et silex taillés de Taferjit et Tamaya Mellet (Sahara nigérien)', *Journ. Soc. Africanistes*, IV, pp. 135–43.
Joubert, G. and R. Vaufrey (1946), 'Le Néolithique du Ténéré', *L'Anthropologie*, 50 (1941–6), pp. 325–30.
Caton-Thompson, G. (1952), *Kharga Oasis in Prehistory*, pp. 32–6, 145–64, Plates 94–9.
Clark, J. D. (1955), 'The Stone Ball: Its Associations and Use by Prehistoric man in Africa', *Actes du Congrès Pan-Africain de Préhistoire*, Algiers, 1952, pp. 403–17.

38

Découverte de nouveaux instruments en os dans l'Ouest Africain

par TH. MONOD et R. MAUNY

PUBLIANT il y a quelques années 'Un harpon du territoire du Tchad,' l'un de nous passait en revue les instruments en os préhistoriques trouvés à ce jour en Afrique occidentale.[1] La liste en était courte: une pointe et un stylet de Tagant Keina (Roulet); des harpons et hameçons du Ténéré de l'Ouest, Taferjit, Tamaya Mellet, etc. . . . et d'In Guezzam (Le Rumeur, Kelley, Marchand, Lhote); harpons, hameçons et poinçon d'Akreijit, du Taokest, de Guir et d'Asselar (Th. Monod, F. Roman), (Fig. 4); poinçons de Karkarichinkat et Gao (Cap. Gérin-Jean, Lt. Bouesnard, R. Mauny). Enfin quelques objets: une hache, sans doute votive, trouvée près de Saint-Louis (J. Joire),[2] un poinçon à Seigaboun (H. Bessac) et un autre à Ouakam-plage près Dakar (A. Villiers), sont probablement post-néolithiques.

C'est donc fort à propos que de nouvelles trouvailles viennent d'être enregistrées au cours des dernières années, en plusieurs points du Soudan (Fig. 1).

A. NORD-OUEST D'ARAOUANE

Lors de la tournée que l'un de nous (Th. Monod) fit dans le Sahara occidental il fut rencontré, le 5 janvier 1955, à quelque 50 km. Nord-Ouest d'Araouane, des fonds lacustres avec ossements humains, d'Hippopotames, de Crocodiles, de Poissons, des Coquillages d'eau douce (*Melania tuberculata*, etc.) et, au milieu des débris de cuisine de toutes sortes, quelques harpons en os entiers ou brisés (Coll. IFAN. Dakar, SO 55–64). Ces pièces (pour leur nomenclature, nous suivons celle de A. Leroi-Gourhan, 1946, p. 328) sont les suivantes (Fig. 2, Nos. 1 à 10):

1. Harpon intact, de 125 mm. de long, 18 de large et 9 d'épaisseur à hauteur de la perforation de ligature. Section ovoïde. Perforation de 6 mm. de long et 4 de diamètre. Deux barbes et une amorcée à hauteur du trou.

2. Harpon de 125 mm. de long, 15 de large juste au-dessous de la perforation et 8 d'épaisseur au même endroit. Section ovoïde. Perforation de 7 mm. de long et 5 de diamètre. 5 barbes (une manque ainsi qu'une partie du harpon, entre les deux dernières barbes).

3. Harpon de 95 mm. de long, 14 de large au renflement du talon, 9 mm. d'épaisseur au même endroit. Section ovoïde. Perforation de 7 mm. de long sur 3 de diamètre. 4 barbes, dont 2 manquent.

4. Fragment de harpon de 83 mm. de long, 10 de large et 4 d'épaisseur vers la base. La face non visible sur la photographie est profondément corrodée, sans doute par l'érosion éolienne et une coche à la base montre que cette pièce avait au moins une barbe de plus. Le talon manquant, on ne peut dire s'il comportait une perforation.

5. Harpon de 66 mm. de long, 14 de large et 6 d'épaisseur à hauteur de la perforation qui a elle-même 4 mm. de long sur 4 de diamètre. Section concave, la pièce ayant été taillée dans une portion d'os peu épais, à la courbure intérieure très visible. Deux barbes brisées aux extrémités et une ébauchée à hauteur de la perforation.

6. Fragment de harpon de 49 mm. de long, 7 de large et 4 d'épaisseur vers le talon. La partie invisible sur la photographie montre que ce fragment a perdu la moitié environ de son épaisseur. Une barbe au sommet et l'insertion d'une autre visible à mi-hauteur. Le renforcement du talon est l'amorce d'une troisième.

7. Fragment de harpon de 46 mm. de long, 13 de large et 7 d'épaisseur au talon. Section ovoïde. Perforation de 4 mm. de long sur 5 de diamètre. La partie supérieure manque. Une barbe et l'amorce d'une autre à hauteur de la perforation.

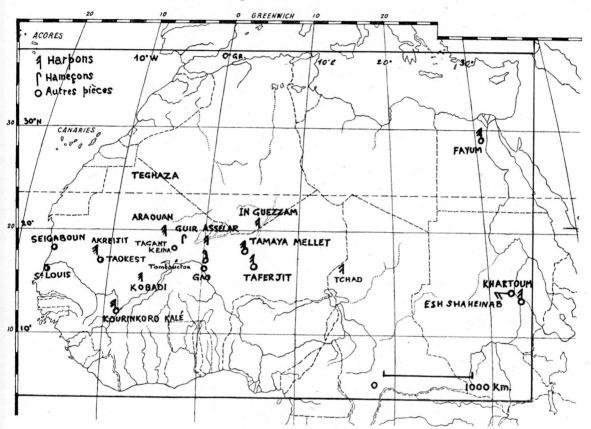

FIG. 1. Sites du Sahara occidental ayant fourni de l'outillage en os

8 et 9. Fragments trop petits et trop abimés (27 × 8 × 5 mm. et 23 × 8 × 7) pour qu'on puisse se faire une idée des harpons d'origine.

Toutes ces pièces, trouvées sur le même gisement, sur une surface d'environ 100 × 50 m., présentent une patine allant du jaune foncé au brun foncé.

10. Un autre fragment fut trouvé à 2 km. 500 environ plus loin, le même jour. Il s'agit d'un fragment d'os — vraisemblablement de harpon dont ne subsiste que le talon — de 56 mm. de long, 11 de large et 8 d'épaisseur, dont l'un des bords de la perforation manque, laissant voir que la pièce fut perforée des deux côtés.

B. Kobadi (Fig. 2, Nos. 12 à 13)

Le gisement néolithique de Kobadi (15° 20′ N., 5° 30′ W.) à une dizaine de kilomètres au Nord-Est de Nampala (Nord Macina) se compose d'un affleurement argileux de 500 m. de long

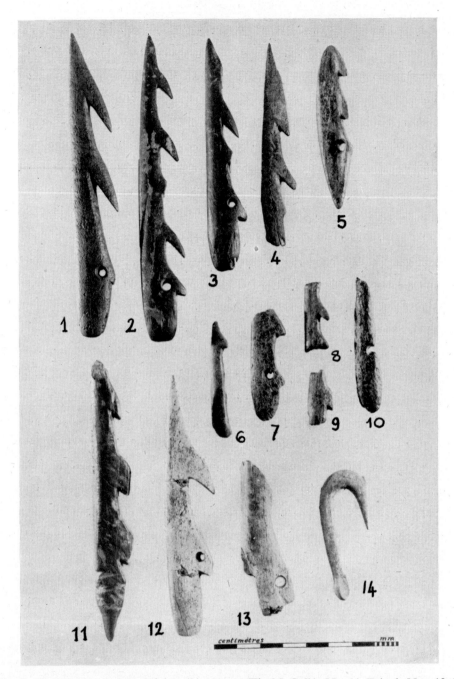

Fig. 2. Harpons Nos. 1 à 10. Région d'Araouane (Th. M. Coll.); No. 11, Tchad; Nos. 12–13,
Kobadi; No. 14, hameçon de Karkarichinkat-Sud

Découverte de nouveaux instruments en os dans l'Ouest Africain

sur une trentaine de large, à 500 m. à l'Est du village du même nom. Il fut découvert par M. Giengier, Chef de la Subdivision de Nioro, en 1954.

Un abondant matériel fut récolté tant par l'inventeur que par l'un de nous (R. Mauny) qui y passa le 4 décembre 1954 : ossements humains et d'animaux — Hippopotame, Ongulés, Crocodile, Poissons — , matériel néolithique peu abondant à part les débris de meules et de poteries et quelques pièces en os, les seules qui nous intéressent ici. Notons que c'est le seul gisement ancien connu à 180 km. à la ronde, le delta central du Niger n'ayant pas fourni jusqu'ici de matériel préhistorique.

12. Harpon brisé en 4 morceaux et reconstitué, de 108 mm. de long, 14 de large et 8 d'épaisseur au talon. Section ovoïde. Perforation de 6 mm. de long et 4 de diamètre. Deux barbes, dont une à hauteur de la perforation.

13. Fragment de harpon de 65 mm. de long, 8 d'épaisseur. Section ovoïde. Perforation de 4 mm. de long et 6 de diamètre. Deux barbes au moins.

A noter deux autres fragments d'os, l'un de poinçon vraisemblablement, l'autre indéfinissable (Coll. IFAN SO 55. 30).

C. Karkarichinkat-Sud (Tilemsi) (Fig. 2, No. 14)

Le gisement néolithique de Karkarichinkat-Sud, dans la zone d'épandage du Tilemsi au Nord de Gao, doit être publié prochainement.[3] Il n'avait fourni, comme pièces en os au moment où fut écrit l'article le concernant, que deux fragments, vraisemblablement de poinçons (Coll. SO 51–141–203 et 204).

Or depuis, le Lieutenant Bouesnard y a découvert un magnifique hameçon (Coll. SO 53. 1).

Cette pièce a 53 mm. de long et un diamètre de 7 mm. La base comporte un léger étranglement et se termine sur une partie renflée, ovoïde, oblique par rapport au plan général de la pièce, et une de ses faces a été évidée intentionnellement, formant une surface concave sans doute pour le passage du fil. La pièce est intacte, sauf une esquille à la base de la pointe dont la cicatrice (5 × 4 mm.) laisse à penser qu'il y avait là soit un crochet d'arrêt offrant la particularité curieuse de se trouver sur la partie extérieure de l'hameçon, soit un renflement dont on ne voit pas bien l'utilité et qui ne se retrouve pas sur les hameçons connus.[4]

D. Kourinkoro-Kalé

Les fouilles de l'abri sous roche de Kourinkoro-Kalé au Sud-Est de Bamako par M. G. Szumowski, de l'IFAN, dont la publication est en cours, a fourni plusieurs instruments en os, dont deux harpons et un fragment de harpon (Fig. 3). Le premier (No. 1) est perforé et le second (No. 2) ne présente qu'une ébauche de perforation. [4 bis]

*   *   *

Quelles conclusions tirer de ces nouvelles découvertes de matériel en os de l'Ouest Africain?

D'abord, la confirmation, s'il en était besoin encore, du fait qu'au Néolithique tout le Sud du Sahara, en des points aujourd'hui complètement arides, présentait des régions lacustres et des fleuves aujourd'hui à sec dont les populations se livraient à la pêche et à la chasse aux animaux aquatiques.

A quelle époque rapporter toutes ces découvertes?

A notre avis, compte tenu du matériel qui leur est lié, au néolithique déjà évolué.

Il est intéressant de comparer à ce point de vue les harpons en os découverts au Soudan égyptien et en Afrique occidentale. Il y a en effet plusieurs formes bien nettes à distinguer ici :

(*a*) ceux portant des rainures pour la fixation à un manche ou à un fil: Khartoum [4 bis], Tchad[5];

(*b*) ceux dont la base ne comporte pas de rainures mais une perforation pour la fixation du fil qui reliera le harpon à la main du pêcheur ou à un flotteur : Shaheinab,[6] Araouane, Kobadi, Kourinkoro-Kalé ;

(c) ceux dont le talon porte un renforcement, permettant la fixation d'un fil : Khartoum,[7] Taferjit,[8] Azaouak et In Guezzam[9] ;

(d) ceux auxquels il ne semble pas qu'un fil ait été attaché et qui devaient donc seulement blesser l'animal sans le fixer, le harpon à talon pointu ou simplement conique semblant avoir été conçu pour tuer ou blesser sans chercher à retenir la proie, le harpon devant se détacher et le manche rester dans la main du pêcheur : Shaheinab,[10] Kourinkoro-Kalé (Fig. 3, No. 1).

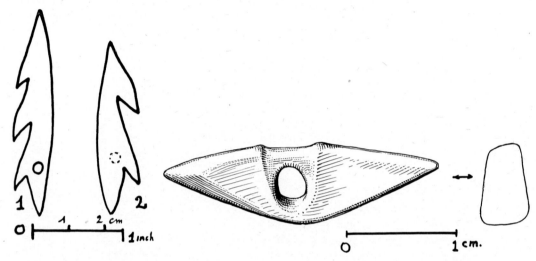

FIG. 3. Harpons de Kourinkoro Kalé   FIG. 4. Hameçon d'Akreijit (Th. M. Coll.)

Dans tous les cas, il s'agit de ce que A. Leroi-Gourhan appelle harpons mâles.[11]

L'hameçon de Karkarichinkat ne peut pas être comparé à notre connaissance, à d'autres pièces. A côté des hameçons de l'Azaouad, de l'Aouker,[12] de l'hameçon droit de Teghaza, il représente un stade plus évolué, se rapprochant de celui de Shaheinab.[13]

C'est en conclusion à ce néolithique de Shaheinab que ressemble le plus l'ensemble de ces pièces nouvelles du Soudan : néolithique évolué mais non final, que des déterminations récentes par le Carbone 14 rapportent à 3300 environ avant notre ère.[14] La parenté indéniable de ces objets en os, ainsi que bien des pièces lithiques, est une observation à verser au dossier du groupe industriel de culture néolithique saharien soudanais, allant de l'Atlantique au Nil par le Tchad proposé par Mlle H. Alimen.[15]

NOTES

1. Mauny, R. (1952), pp. 469–71. Voir également la bibliographie jointe.
2. Joire, J. (1947), pp. 236–7. Le site de Shaheinab en a fourni plusieurs à A. J. Arkell.
3. Mauny, R. (1955), 'Les gisements néolithiques de Karkarichinkat (Tilemsi, Soudan Français), *C.R.2° Congrès panafr. de Préhistoire*, Alger, 1952, pp. 617–629.
4. Gruvel, A., *La pêche dans la préhistoire, dans l'Antiquité et chez les peuples primitifs*, Paris, Soc. Édit. Géogr. Mar. et Colon., 1928, 232 pp., pp. 91–112 ; Leroi-Gourhan, A., *Milieu et techniques*, Paris, Albin Michel, 1945, 512 pp., pp. 79–84 ; Thomazi, A., *Histoire de la pêche des âges de la pierre à nos jours*, Paris, Payot, 1947, 645 pp.
4 bis. Arkell, A. J. (1949), Plate 49.

Découverte de nouveaux instruments en os dans l'Ouest Africain

5. Mauny, R. (1952), Fig. 3.
6. Arkell, A. J. (1953), Plate 25 (trois harpons à trous).
7. Arkell, A. J. (1949), Plates 47, 3 (harpon de droite).
8. Kelley, H. (1934), Plate VIII, No. 4, 13, 14.
9. Lhote, H. (1950), p. 170; (1951), Fig. 39, p. 197 et H. Marchand (1936), p. 679.
10. Arkell, A. J. (1953), Plate 25, première pièce en haut à gauche.
11. Leroi-Gourhan, A., 'Archéologie du Pacifique-Nord', Paris, *Trav. et Mém. de l'Inst. d'Ethnol.*, XLVII, 1946, 542 pp., pp. 325 seq. *Milieu et techniques*, Paris, A. Michel, 1945, pp. 54–62.
12. Monod, Th. (1937), Pl. XI, Nos. 22–3.
13. Arkell, A. J. (1953), Pl. 27, 9.
14. Arkell, A. J. (1953), p. 107.
15. Alimen, H. (1955), p. 492.

BIBLIOGRAPHIE

Alimen, H., *Préhistoire de l'Afrique*, Paris, Boubée, 1955, 578 pp., 155 Figs., 11 Tableaux, XXVIII Pl.

Arkell, A. J., *Early Khartoum*, Oxford Univ. Press, 1949, 145 pp., ill. pp. 75–8, Plates 46–54; *Shaheinab*, Oxford Univ. Press, 1953, 114 pp., 43 Plates, 57 Figs.

Joire, J., 'Amas de coquillages du littoral sénégalais dans la banlieue de Saint-Louis', *Bull. de l'IFAN*, Dakar, 1947, pp. 171–340, 3 Pl., pp. 236–8.

Kelley, Harper, 'Collections africaines du Departement de préhistoire exotique du Musée d'Ethnologie du Trocadéro. I-Harpons, objets en os travaillé et silex taillés de Taferjit en Tamaya Mellet (Sahara nigérien)', *Journ. Soc. des Africanistes*, IV, 1934, pp. 135–43.

Lhote, H., *Les Touareg du Hoggar*, Paris, Payot, 1944, pp. 56–7; *La Chasse chez les Touareg*, Paris, Amiot-Dumont, 1951, 245 pp., pp. 196–7; 'Le gisement néolithique d' In Guezzam (Sahara central)', *Bull. Soc. Préh. Fr.*, 1950, pp. 165–71.

Marchand, H., 'Harpon et aiguilles néolithiques du Sahara nigérien', *Bull. Soc., Préh. Fr.*, 1936, pp. 678–80.

Mauny, R., 'Un Harpon en os du territoire du Tchad', *Bull. Soc. Prh. Fr.*, 1952, pp. 469–71.

Monod, Th., *Méharées*, Paris, Je sers, 1937, 300 pp., p. 111.

Notes Africaines, 'Où la pierre polie peut être de l'os', *Not. Afr.*, Dakar, No. 3, juillet 1939, pp. 2–3.

Roman, F., 'Sur une faunule de Vertébrés et sur des pièces néolithiques du Sahara occidental', *Bull. Assoc. région. de Paléontologie et de Préhistoire*, Lyon, juin 1935, 13 pp., 4 Pl.

Szumowski, G., 'Fouilles de l'abri sous roche de Kouroun Korokalé (Soudan français)', *Bull. de l'IFAN*, ser. B., 1956, pp. 462–508.

Y . . . [G. Le Rumeur], 'Les témoins d'une civilisation ancienne dans le cercle de Tahoua', *Bull. du Comité d'Études Hist. et Scient. de l'A.O.F.*, 1933, pp. 299–318.

39

Préhistoire et Protohistoire de la région d'Akjoujt (Mauritanie)

par R. MAUNY et J. HALLEMANS

Histoire

Du fait même de la pacification relativement récente de la Mauritanie du Sud (1902 à 1909), les études de préhistoire de ce territoire ne commencèrent que fort tardivement : en 1912 Mme Crova pouvait encore intituler un de ses articles : 'Y a t-il du paléolithique en Mauritanie?' En 1920 le Capitaine Augieras signalait le premier gisement acheuléen de ce territoire, à Oum Mouchyate (Maqteir). Il fallut attendre les découvertes faites en 1934 par M. Monod, à El Beyyed en particulier, pour se rendre compte de la richesse surprenante de la Mauritanie en paléolithique : le néolithique, lui, y avait été decelé dès 1907 par MM. Gruvel et Chudeau, puis en 1908–1909 par Mme Crova et en 1909 par le Lt. Danzegler dans la région de Port-Etienne ; parmi les pierres récoltées par ce dernier, quelques unes provenaient de la région d'Akjoujt.*

Quelques trouvailles sporadiques seulement sont à signaler dans cette dernière région — qui seule nous occupera désormais — jusqu'à la magnifique découverte en 1940 par le Lt. Bayard du gisement acheuléen de la daya de Sbekhat. A. Villiers trouvait en 1948 des nouveaux gisements paléolithiques à Khat Takfoil.

Le néolithique est présent un peu partout, sans qu'on y ait à proprement parler trouvé de gisement intéressant. Par contre, une bonne partie des découvertes de flèches de cuivre faites en Mauritanie proviennent de la région, ainsi que les deux seules monnaies antiques trouvées en A.O.F.

Le cadre géographique et géologique

Le cercle d'Akjoujt se trouve tout entier en zone saharienne, à cheval sur le 20° N., entre l'Adrar et l'Atlantique.

La région offre 3 aspects :

1. Une vaste plaine de cailloutis (reg) hérissée de petits pitons isolés (guelbs). C'est la topographie en inselberg qui caractérise ici le précambrien. Ces terrains s'enfoncent à l'Est sous le primaire et à l'Ouest sous le quaternaire. Les roches composantes sont, au Nord de l'Akchar, des granites post birrimiens et, au Sud de l'Akchar, des orthogneiss et leptynites. Les collines de la région d'Akjoujt sont constituées en majorité de roches peu métamorphiques : chloritoschistes et quartzites ferrugineux rubanés, attribués au précambrien moyen ou birrimien. Sont à signaler d'importantes venues basiques : gabbros, dolérites, chloritoschistes ortho. et des filons de dolérite récente, de quelques mètres de large sur des kilomètres de long. Enfin, au Sud-Est d'Akjoujt, du quartzite micacé.

---

* Gruvel et Chudeau, *A travers la Mauritanie*, Paris, Larose, 1911, Vol. II, pp. 363–83, 3 pl. ; R. Verneau, 'Ethnographie ancienne de la Mauritanie d'après les documents de MM. Gruvel et Chudeau', *Actes Soc. Linné*, Bordeaux, t. 65, 1 fasc., 1912 ; Mme B. Crova, 'Notice sur les instruments néolithiques de la presqu'île du Cap Blanc (Maur.)', *Bull. Soc. Préh. Fr.*, juillet 24, 1909, pp. 369–75, 1 carte, 3 pl. ; Danzegler, Lt., R., pp. 217–20. Nous appelons dans cette étude 'région d'Akjoujt' toute l'étendue du cercle du même nom et ses abords immédiats.

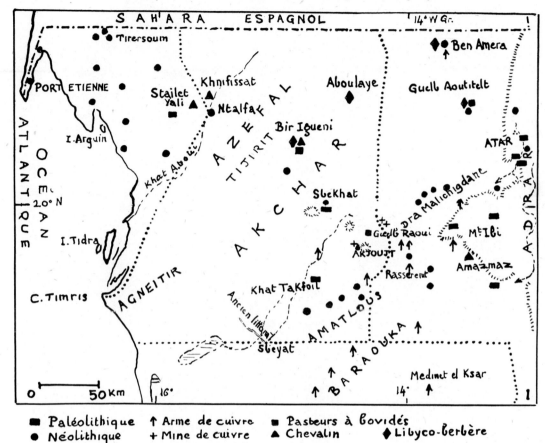

Paléolithique   ↑ **Arme de cuivre**   ■ **Pasteurs à Bovidés**
● **Néolithique**   + **Mine de cuivre**   ▲ **Chevalin**   ◆ **Libyco-berbère**

FIG. 1. Carte de la région d'Akjoujt

2. Le Quaternaire, se terminant en biseau sur le précambrien, suivant une ligne N.W.–S.E., à 50 km. au S.W. d'Akjoujt. Il comprend de bas en haut : les grès bigarrés de Tirersoum (peut-être fin du Tertiaire?) ; une latérite fossile ; un calcogréseux à mollusques marins pouvant passer à une lumachelle ou à un conglomérat ; un grès ou calcogréseux hamadien (formation continentale, lacustre et dunaire, consolidée) ; une plage soulevée à *Arca senilis*.*

3. Des alluvions récentes et de puissants massifs dunaires tous allongés dans la direction des vents dominants, N.E.–S.W. : Azefal, Akchar, Amatlich-Treïna, Lahbara, etc. . . . Entre les dunes, des dépressions de reg et parfois des dayas (cuvettes formant des mares temporaires). Le néolithique se trouve sur les dunes mortes (medina) apparaissant par places au bord de la dune vive.

INDUSTRIES LITHIQUES

A. Paléolithique

A part quelques pièces trouvées sporadiquement† le paléolithique de la région d'Akjoujt est représenté surtout par deux gisements, celui de Khat Takfoïl et celui de la daya de Sbekhat.

(*a*) Khat Takfoïl (Fig. 2).

Ce gisement fut découvert en 1948 par A. Villiers, de l'IFAN, sur la piste Coppolani-Akjoujt,

---

* Monod, Th., 1945, p. 13.
† Mauny, R. et A. Villiers, 1950, p. 1010.

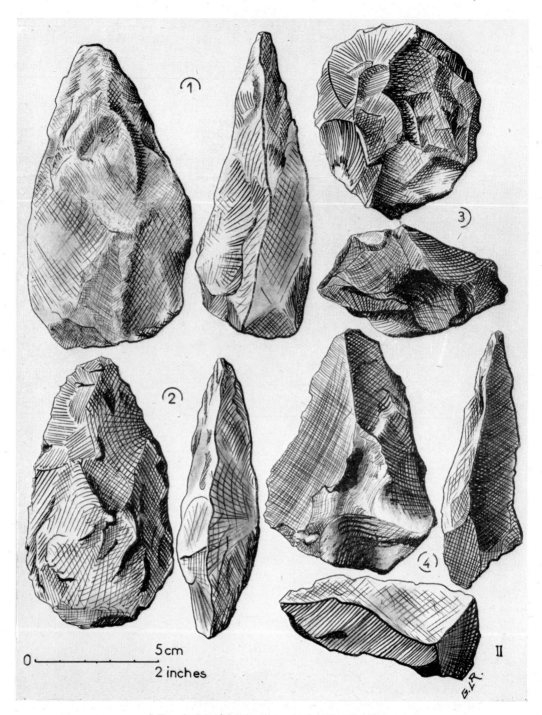

Fig. 2. Matériel du gisement de Khat Takfoïl

à une cinquantaine de kilomètres de ce dernier centre. Il s'étend sur les deux côtés d'une dépression peu marquée, aux abords d'affleurements quartzeux qui fournirent la matière première à l'homme paléolithique. Le matériel est épars sur le reg. Des récoltes y furent effectuées à diverses reprises : A. Villiers, 1948 (M-48. 165 et M-49. 225); Th. Monod, 1950 (M-50. 153); R. Mauny, 1953 (M-53. 10).

On a récolté à Khat Takfoïl :

33 petits bifaces (100 × 60 × 30 mm. en moyenne), en quartzite blanchâtre recouvert d'une patine jaune-rougeâtre, en général de faciès archaïque, aux tranchants ondulés, avec de nombreuses irrégularités dues à la consistance de la pierre (Fig. 2, No. 1); mais certains bifaces ont un tranchant presque rectiligne (No. 2).

14 disques retouchés sur les deux faces (No. 3), à arête médiane tranchante, circulaire, ovaloïdes ou quelconques, en moyenne de 75 × 70 × 65 mm., mais dont l'un d'eux mesure 125 × 90 × 60 mm.

Diverses pièces aux bords tranchants (ébauches, déchets de fabrication).

1 pointe de type mousteroïde, de 92 × 67 × 30 mm., préparé selon la technique bloc sur bloc, dont le plan de frappe est de même patine que les bifaces, tandis que le reste de la pièce est de patine plus fraîche. Sans doute une pointe très postérieure (paléolithique moyen?) à l'ensemble (No. 4).

(*b*) Daya de Sbekhat (Fig. 3).

En 1940, le Lt. Bayard trouva, à quelques kilomètres au Nord-Est du massif de Tourarine, le très important gisement de la daya de Sbekhat. Sbekhat est une vallée dunaire (aïn) qui, partant de Tourarine, remonte sur une 15° de kilomètres en direction Nord-Est, le long d'une chaine de dunes rougeâtres nommées 'Alelb El Homar'. Le fond de cette vallée laisse apercevoir par places une couche d'argile consolidée souvent recouverte de concrétions blanches. Les sondages effectués en divers points montrent que le sable reparait en profondeur sous l'argile : ils ne fournirent aucun matériel.

Les trouvailles faites par le Lt. Bayard en 1940 et par l'un de nous (R.M.) le 21 janvier, 1953 ont été effectuées en surface tout autour de la grande daya.* Le matériel, très épars, est mis à jour par l'érosion. En plusieurs points aux abords de la cuvette affleurent les roches qui ont servi de matière première : roches noires compactes et quartzites blanchâtres et gris verdâtres, ces derniers constituent la presque totalité du matériel récolté.

Les trouvailles furent très abondantes : outre ce qui a été rapporté pour les collections de l'IFAN, le Lt. Bayard dit (*in litt.* 7 octobre, 1940) avoir récolté plusieurs centaines de bifaces, qu'il a laissés sur place en deux dépôts.

Le matériel en collections rapporté par le Lt. Bayard (M-45. 11) comprend :

> 40 bifaces + 10 ébauches ou ratés de ces pièces
> 5 hachereaux
> 6 disques

Celui rapporté par R. Mauny (M-53. 15) comprend :

> 112 bifaces acheuléens + des ébauches ou des ratés
> 10 petits bifaces
> 16 bifaces au tranchant ondulé
> 8 hachereaux
> 19 spheroïdes
> 35 disques et discoïdes

Les bifaces sont, soit ovaloïdes, soit à pointe.

* Alors complètement à sec, trois mois seulement après la fin de l'hivernage.

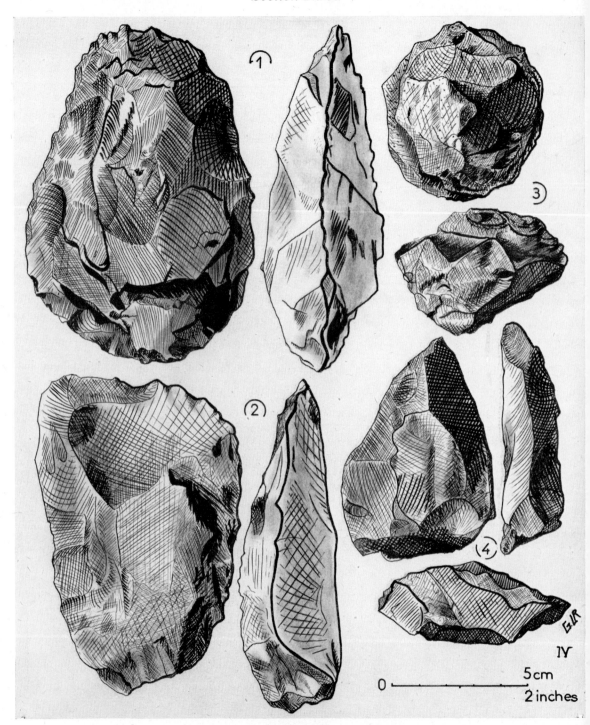

Fig. 3. Matériel du gisement de Sbekhat

Leurs dimensions sont variables (85 × 45 × 25 mm. à 245 × 110 × 60 mm.) et forment un tout relativement homogène, bien que le tranchant de certains soit ondulé et celui d'autres à peu près rectiligne.

Les hachereaux (No. 2) sont nettement plus rares. Leurs dimensions vont de 120 × 60 × 35 mm. à 185 × 105 × 35 mm. Les spheroïdes de fabrication grossière (sans doute des percuteurs), ont de 50 à 90 mm. de diamètre. Les discoïdes (No. 3) présentent un plan médian tranchant. Ils ont de 55 × 50 × 25 mm. à 110 × 95 × 40 mm.

A part quelques pointes de flèches et quelques rares fragments de poterie recueillis aux alentours, l'ensemble industriel de Sbekhat est homogène : c'est du paléolithique de technique acheuléenne évoluée, le seul gisement de ce faciès dans la région.

Au milieu des centaines de pièces et d'éclats jonchant le sol, prouvant surabondamment que Sbekhat était un atelier de fabrication, je n'ai trouvé qu'une seule pièce de facture moustérienne : une pointe de 80 × 55 × 20 mm. (No. 4), au plan de frappe non préparé. Il est à noter que sa patine est la même que celle des autres pièces.

A part ces deux gisements, il n'a été fait dans l'état actuel de nos connaissances, que des découvertes sporadiques de paléolithique dans la région : il faut arriver dans le massif gréseux de l'Adrar pour retrouver de grands gisements de cette époque : Hamdoun, Aguinjob, Chinguetti, Ouadane, Nouezzine, El Beyyed, etc . . . .

Pas de paléolithique supérieur ni de mésolithique à notre connaissance.

B. *Néolithique*

Le cercle d'Akjoujt, placé pourtant entre deux régions où les industries de cette époque sont bien représentées, celle de Port-Etienne et l'Adrar, est pauvre en néolithique.

La zone de dunes mortes du Dra Malichigdane est la seule qui ait fourni un nombre appréciable de pièces et où les habitats semblent avoir eu une certaine densité. Ailleurs, sauf à Rasseremt, il ne s'agit que de trouvailles sporadiques : à vrai dire, la prospection méthodique du pays est loin d'être finie et c'est surtout au fait qu'elle est longée par la piste Akjoujt-Atar qu'il faut attribuer notre connaissance de la richesse relative du Dra Malichigdane en néolithique.

Ces dunes, 'medina' rapprochées, s'étendent sur quelque 80 km. de long sur quelques kilomètres de large seulement, le long de l'ancienne zone d'épandage de l'Oued Seguelil, qui lui a donné naissance, au milieu d'une région pierreuse où affleure la roche et assez peu propice aux hommes. Seules ces dunes constituaient un habitat favorable. Ces gisements furent découverts par J. Hallemans, puis prospectés par Mlle O. du Puigaudeau d'une part et A. Villiers de l'autre.

L'homme néolithique était fixé sur la dune elle même et c'est l'érosion éolienne qui met les gisements à jour.

Le matériel en collection qui se distingue par la rareté des pointes de flèches et l'existence de beaux et lourds broyeurs ovoïdes en dolérite, parfaitement polis et réguliers recueilli par diverses personnes* est le suivant (Fig. 4).

> haches polies 8 (Nos. 2, 4, 5)
> haches non polies 2
> gouge 1 (No. 6)
> herminettes 2 (No. 3)
> ciseaux à section rectangulaire 2 (No. 1)
> molettes 3
> pointes de flèches foliacées 3 (No. 10)
> pointes de flèches à base concave 1 (No. 9)
> pointe de flèches à pédoncule 1 (No. 8)
> demi-lunes 4 (Nos. 11 à 13)
> grattoirs 28 (No. 14)

* O. de Puigaudeau, 1950, M-51. 48 et M-51. 78 ; P. L. Dekeyser et A. Villiers, 1951, M-51. 96 ; R. Mauny, M-53. 16 et M-53. 58.

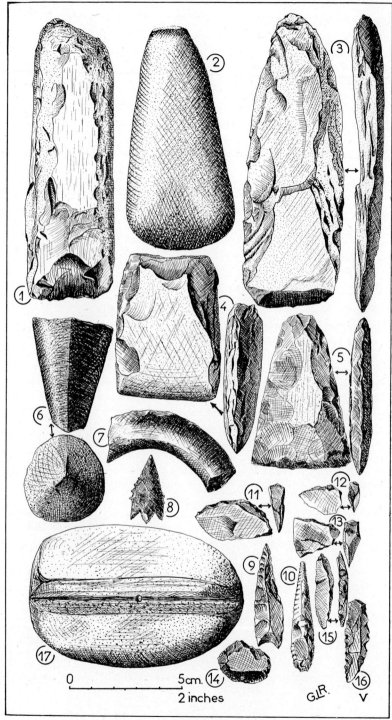

FIG. 4. Matériel des gisements de Dra Malichigdane

lames à dos rabattu 7 (No. 15)
fragments de bracelets 33 (No. 7)
polissoirs à rainures 3 (No. 17)
perle de pierre verte 1
fragments de meules, de broyeurs, de poterie,
    d'œufs d'autruches

Nous avons affaire à un néolithique très évolué (avec des pièces de technique ibéromaurusienne) presque final comme nous le prouve la qualité de certaines pièces. Il en va de même pour les autres rares gisements néolithiques de la région, par exemple celui des environs de la daya de Sbekhat (M-45. 11. 6) avec ses fines pièces denticulées et quelques pièces de silex rappelant celles de la région de Port-Etienne.

D'autres belles pièces isolées sont à signaler : à Rasseremt, un grand bracelet dentelé (M-54. 16) de 170 mm. de diamètre et 67 d'ouverture (Fig. 5, No. 1); une houe agricole (?) brisée en 5 fragments, de 285 × 145 mm., de schiste violet, également de Rasseremt (No. 2); une belle coupe de 190 mm. de diamètre extérieur sur 63 mm. de haut, de roche noire, trouvée à Benichab (No. 3); un repoussoir (?) à contreforts de dolérite (poids Okg., 860) de 180 mm. de long, 52 de large et 72 de hauteur maximum, trouvé à Saboun Lefta au début de l'Akhchar au Nord d'Akjoujt* (No. 4); un ciseau long, de quartzite beige, de 410 mm. de long, de section rectangulaire de 74 × 29 mm. maximum d'Aguelt en Nage (No. 5); une hache à gorge légèrement esquissée, de 150 × 82 × 30 mm., ayant servi postérieurement de pierre tombale, provenant de 200 m. au Nord du puits de Bou Rabrah (No. 6); un fragment de pierre décorée d'un quadrillage, à section ovalaire, provenant de la région dunaire au Nord de Tourarine (No. 7); un fragment de bracelet orné, trouvé au Sud de Dhelet el Ahmar, région de Kahouat El Hamra, au S.E. d'Akjoujt (No. 8); un pic de mineur, trouvé dans une exploitation ancienne de cuivre, à Sainte Barbe à 25 km. au N.E. d'Akjoujt, de 482 mm. de long et 60 de diamètre, en gabbro ou dolérite (No. 9), d'un poids de 3 kg. 700 environ.† Une seule poterie entière, sphéroïde, sans décor, trouvée par le Cap. Chaon à Legleitat, de 110 mm. de diamètre et 25 d'ouverture (M-54. 36), vraisemblablement néolithique, sans qu'on puisse l'affirmer.

PROTOHISTOIRE

Pour des raisons que l'un de nous a eu l'occasion d'expliquer ailleurs,‡ nous estimons que le monde sud-saharien est passé lentement du néolithique à l'âge du fer (− 300 av. J.C. à + 100 J.C. environ). Mais en Mauritanie occidentale, il se peut que l'âge du fer ait été précédé par un âge du cuivre.§ Les découvertes d'objets en ce dernier métal se sont multipliées depuis 1951, toujours dans la Mauritanie du Sud. Sont connus actuellement comme instruments en cuivre, au total :

4 haches (Fig. 5, No. 10)‖
1 lance (No. 12)
5 pointes de flèches à longue soie (No. 11)
33 pointes de flèches extra plates, à pédoncule et ailerons
1 pointe de flèche plate, à soie et sans ailerons
1 poignard

* Cette pièce, unique pour l'instant en A.O.F., ressemble à l'herminette à gorge de l'Alaska, de date récente, décrite par A. Leroi-Gourhan, *Archéologie du Pacifique Nord*, Paris, Institut d'Ethnologie, 1946, 542 pp., ill., p. 217, Fig. 206 et 207.

† Toutes ces belles pièces isolées, sauf la première qui fait partie des collections de l'IFAN (M-54. 16), appartiennent à la collection J. Hallemans.

‡ Mauny, R., 1952, pp. 586–92.

§ Beaudouin, Dr M., 1911, pp. 67–8 et 1919, p. 167–71; Crova, Mme B., 1912 [1913], pp. 702–4; Monod, Th., 1944, p. 11; Mauny, R., 1951, pp. 168–80, 1952, pp. 545–95; *contra*, Saez Martin, B., 1949 [1951], pp. 111–18.

‖ Toutes les pièces représentés sur la Figure 5 sont inédites.

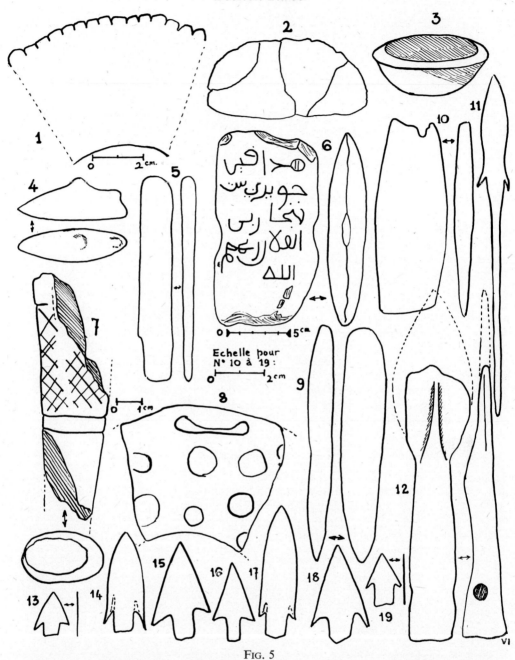

Fᴵɢ. 5

Matériel néolithique de pierre : 1. Bracelet de Rasseremt ; 2. Houe ? de Rasseremt ; 3. Coupe de Benichab ; 4. Repoussoir à contreforts de Saboun Lefta ; 5. Ciseau d'Aguelt en Nage ; 6. Hache à gorge épigraphiée de Bou Rabrah ; 7. Pierre décorée de Tourarine ; 8. Bracelet décoré de Dhelat el Hamar ; 9. Pic de Ste Barbe

Matériel de cuivre : 10. Hache et 12. Lance, de Medinet el Ksar ; 11. Flèche à soie de Medinet Jleilet ; 13 à 19 : flèches extra plates ; 13. Akjoujt ; 14. Lemdenat ; 15. Kahouat el Amra ; 16–17. Ntomi ; 18. Aguelt en Naje ; 19. Guichrié

Préhistoire et Protohistoire de la région d'Akjoujt

Tout ce matériel provient de Mauritanie, entre le 18° et le 22° Nord, sauf les pièces suivantes :

> 1 hache (Sud de Tabelbalat, coll. Terrasson)
> 2 pointes de flèches extra plates : 1 de l'Erg Er Raoui*
> et l'autre de Villa Cisneros.†

1 pointe de flèche plate, à soie et sans ailerons, trouvée à Sidi Messaoud (Maroc).‡
1 poignard (Erg Chech),§ sans compter une épée du bronze atlantique, venant de Larache.∥

Une bonne partie du matériel sud mauritanien énuméré plus haut provient de la région d'Akjoujt qui, ne l'oublions pas, comprend plusieurs mines de cuivre, toutes d'exploitation ancienne.

Le minerai se présente sous forme de veines et mouches de malachite et chrysocolle dans un amas d'hématite.

La découverte dans l'une d'elles d'un pic de mineur en pierre (Fig. 5, No. 9) laisse supposer que cette exploitation peut remonter à une période relativement ancienne. Les pièces retrouvées peuvent donc fort bien être de fabrication locale, hypothèse qui prend corps, en attendant la possible découverte d'ateliers anciens de fonte de cuivre.

Rappelons enfin que, précisément dans la région au Sud d'Akjoujt, d'où proviennent plusieurs flèches de cuivre ont été trouvés récemment deux deniers d'argent du premier siècle avant J.C., les deux seules monnaies antiques recueillies à ce jour en A.O.F.**

RUPESTRES

Les sites rupestres sont relativement rares dans la région car les roches s'y prêtent peu : l'homme a préféré graver les grès de l'Adrar voisin.

Ils sont tous de découverte récente et pratiquement inédits : aucun d'entre eux ne figure dans l'inventaire de Th. Monod†† et ils ne sont mentionnés que sommairement dans celui de R. Mauny.‡‡

Voici des précisions à leur sujet :

Aboulaye

Guelb à 150 km. W.N.W. d'Atar, dans le Tijirit. Au sommet du piton, quelques gravures se trouvant sur le sol d'un abri ouvrant vers l'Est, furent découvertes et relevées par le Cap. Bayard en 1942.

Il s'agit de trois séries de 8 rayons partant d'un cercle central, le dernier étant orné de deux cercles concentriques (Fig. 6, No. 1), tous trois placés sur un même rocher. Le trait est régulier et soigné, la patine, ferrugineuse, très foncée, couleur roche : la gravure paraît très ancienne.

Bir Igueni

Très importante station, trouvée en mars 1943 par le Cap. Trancart, dans le Tijirit à 190 km. Ouest d'Atar. Les innombrables dessins sont gravés sur le granit des guelbs (pitons) ou peints sur les parois d'une caverne située dans un guelb à l'Ouest du puits. L'ensemble appartient aux groupes 'pasteurs à bovidés', 'chevalin' avec un peu de 'lybico-berbère' et a fait l'objet d'un relevé relativement complet (Doc. IFAN, XV-3, Mauritanie) de la part de son inventeur.

---

* Ruhlmann, A., *Contribution à la préhistoire sud-marocaine*, La Collection Terrasson (Paris, Larose, 1932, 41 pp., 1 carte ; pp. 22–3 ; Mauny, R., 1951, p. 170.
† Saez Martin, B., [1951], p. 112.
‡ Antoine, M., 'Répertoire préhistorique de la Chaouia', *Bull. de la Soc. de Préh. du Maroc*, V, 1931, p. 32, Fig. 1 ; Mauny, R., 1952, p. 563.
§ Gautier, E. F. et Reygasse, M., 'Le monument de Tin Hinan', *Ann. Acad. Sc. Colon.*, t. VII, 1934, 12 pp., XVI Pl. ; Mauny, R., 1951, pp. 169–70.
∥ Saez Martin, B., 1949 [1951], p. 112.
** Ziegler, Lt., Hallemans, J. et Mauny, R., 1954, p. 476–7.
†† Monod, Th., 1938, 158 pp.
‡‡ Mauny, R., 1954 : Aboulaye, p. 50 ; Bir Igueni, p. 54 ; Guelb Raoui, p. 60 ; Khnifisset, p. 63 ; Takoust, p. 69.

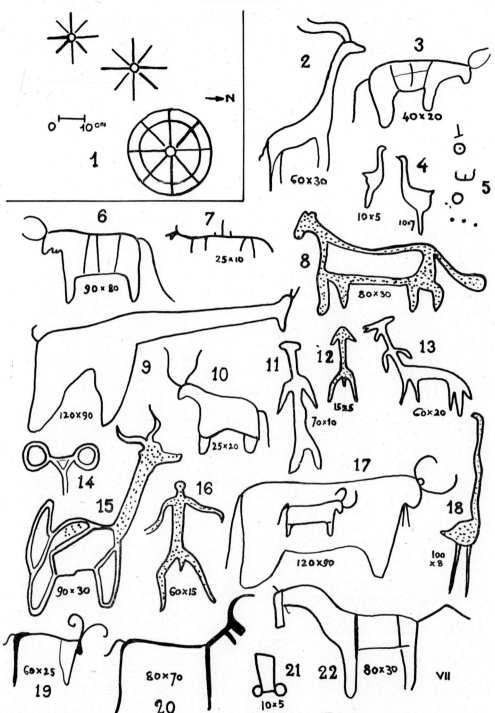

FIG. 6. Rupestres : 1. Aboulaye ; 2 à 22. Bir Igueni

Parmi les gravures, une bonne partie se rapporte aux bovidés (Fig. 6, Nos. 3, 6, 9, 17, 19, 20) ; certaines à des autruches (Nos. 4, 18), des chevaux (No. 22), des chars? (Nos. 14, 21),* des personnages (Nos. 11, 12, 16), des girafes (No. 9), des antilopes (Nos. 2, 15), etc. . . . Les peintures, groupées dans une grotte et particulièrement au plafond, sont en majorité indéchiffrables : animaux, dessins géométriques, quelques tifinar (No. 5). A part les peintures, l'ensemble est ancien, précamelin.

Guelb Raoui

Piton à 10 km. environ au Nord-Est d'Akjoujt. Les gravures furent découvertes par J. Halle-mans en 1953, sur des blocs arrondis de dolérite récente au Nord et au Sud du guelb. Elles repré-

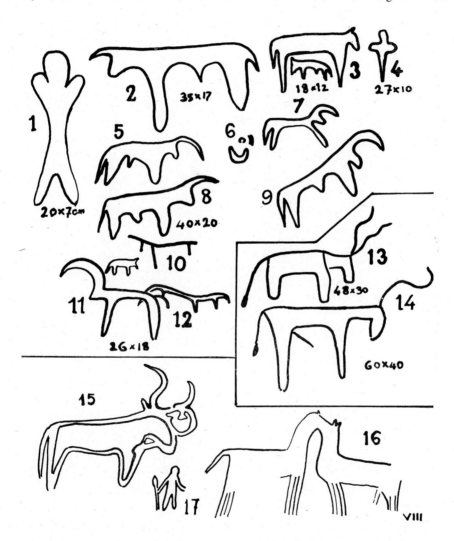

Fig. 7. Rupestres : 1 à 12, Guelb Raoui ; 13–14, Takoust ; 15 à 17, Khnifissat

* Rappelons qu'une route préhistorique jalonnée de chars rupestres passait à proximité. Voir R. Mauny, 'Une route préhistorique à travers le Sahara occidental', *Bull. de l'IFAN*, 1947 [1950], pp. 341–57 ; Th. Monod et R. Mauny, 'Nouveaux chars rupestres sahariens', *Notes Afric.*, No. 44, octobre 1949, pp. 112–14.

sentent des personnages (Fig. 7, No. 1), des bovidés (Nos. 2, 3, 5, 7 à 11), quelques animaux filiformes indéterminables (No. 12). Le No. 4 est soit une arme, soit un personnage stylisé.

Khnifissat

Site trouvé par P. Lacroix en septembre 1953 en même temps que celui tout proche de Steilat Yali, sur les bords du Khat Atoui, dépression riche en monuments préislamiques. Les gravures représentent surtout des bovidés (Fig. 7, No. 15) et des chevaux (No. 16).

Takoust

Le site rupestre découvert en 1950 par le Cap. Noël, se trouve à une 30° de km. à l'Ouest Sud-Ouest de ce guelb, dans une série d'alignements rocheux fortement ensablés.

Il ne présente que deux bovidés gravées superposés (Fig. 7, Nos. 13 et 14), de patine couleur roche.

Conclusions

Nous avons choisi la région d'Akjoujt comme sujet d'étude car elle est typique d'une zone sud saharienne dont les conditions d'habitat ne sont pas améliorées (comme c'est le cas pour l'Adrar, les Iforas, l'Aïr, le Tibesti) par l'existence d'un massif montagneux formant château d'eau.

Le pays, ici, est plat, non fertile et l'influence de la mer s'y fait peu sentir.

Il est symptomatique dans ces conditions de noter :

(*a*) La très grande rareté du matériel d'allure chélleo-acheuléenne archaïque : à Khat Takfoïl, le mélange avec les disques et la taille relativement petite des bifaces milite plutôt pour le rattachement de ce gisement à la période de transition du chelléen à l'acheuléen. Notons que dès que l'on aborde l'Adrar, le faciès archaïque, de grande taille, est présent, parfois en très importants gisements.

(*b*) L'existence d'un seul grand gisement abondant du chelleo-acheuléen évolué, à Sbekhat, lié à une dépression offrant le double avantage de la présence de l'eau et de roches aptes à être taillées. La région devait être alors beaucoup plus humide qu'aujourd'hui et le système dunaire, déjà en place.

(*c*) Absence presque totale de paléolithique moyen. Absence totale d'atérien.

(*d*) Rareté relative du néolithique. La richesse des sites rupestres en bovidés montre qu'à cette époque la région était occupée par des pasteurs et non, comme sous la même latitude le long du dhar Tichitt-Oualata par exemple, par des agriculteurs noirs.

(*e*) Relations à la fin du néolithique avec le Maghreb (piste transsaharienne de l'Ouest parcourue par des chars) au moment où ce dernier connaissait une protohistoire rattachée à l'âge du bronze ibérique (armes de cuivre). Ces relations durent se maintenir jusqu'à l'arrivée des Arabes dans l'Adrar (734 J.C.), comme le prouvent la trouvaille des monnaies romaines de Rasseremt et le fait que les Arabes, dès qu'ils furent dans le Sous, poussèrent au Soudan occidental, certainement sous la conduite de guides berbères.*

BIBLIOGRAPHIE

Beaudouin, Dr Marcel, 'Les haches plates en Vendée', *Mém. Soc. Préh. Fr.*, Paris, t. I, 1911, pp. 1–133, 31 + 4 Figs.

Beaudouin, Dr Marcel, 'Hache plate et flèche en métal de Mauritanie', *Bull. Soc. Préh. Fr.*, Paris, t. XVI, 1919, pp. 167–71, 1 Fig.

Crova, Mme B., 'Vestiges de l'âge du cuivre en Mauritanie', *Huitième Congr. Préh. de France*, Angoulême, 1912 [1913], pp. 702–4, 1 Fig.

Danzegler, Lt. R., 'Notice sur la préhistoire de la Mauritanie occidentale Saharienne', *Bull. Soc. Préh. Fr.*, 1911, t. VIII, No. 3, pp. 217–20 ; 1 carte.

* Comparer avec le fait qu'au Kawar, les habitants ne semblaient pas avoir de relations avec le Sud (Ibn Abd Al Hakam, *Conquête de l'Afrique du Nord et de l'Espagne*, trad. A. Gateau, Alger, Carbonel, 1942, pp. 119 et 59).

Préhistoire et Protohistoire de la région d'Akjoujt

Mauny, R., 'La préhistoire [de l'Ouest africain]', *Encyclo. Mar. et Colo.*, vol. AOF, 1949, T. I, pp. 23–34.

Mauny, R., 'Une route préhistorique à travers le Sahara occidentale', *Bull. de l'IFAN*, 1947 [1950], pp. 341–357, 4 Figs., 1 carte.

Mauny, R., 'Un âge du cuivre au Sahara occidental?' *Bull. de l'IFAN*, janvier 1951, pp. 168–80.

Mauny, R., 'Essai sur l'histoire des métaux en Afrique occidentale', *Bull. de l'IFAN*, avril 1952, pp. 545–95.

Mauny, R., 'Gravures, peintures et inscriptions rupestres de l'Ouest africain', Dakar, IFAN, *Init. Afr.*, XI, 1954, 93 pp., 12 Figs., 8 phot., 7 cartes, 3 Tableaux.

Mauny, R. et A. Villiers, 'Contribution à la préhistoire de la Mauritanie occidentale' (Mission A. Villiers, 1948–1949), *Bull. de l'IFAN*, octobre 1950, pp. 1007–14, 5 Figs.

Monod, Th., *Contribution à l'étude du Sahara occidental (Gravures, peintures et inscriptions rupestres)*, Public. Com. Ét. Hist. et Sc. AOF, Paris, Larose, 1938, 158 pp., VIII Pl.

Monod, Th., 'Sur quelques pointes de flèches sahariennes', Dakar, *Notes Afric.*, No. 24, octobre 1944, p. 11 et Fig, p. 13, Nos. 22–3.

Monod, Th., 'La structure du Sahara atlantique', *Trav. de l'Inst. de Rech. sahar.*, Alger, t. III, 1945, t. à p. 31 pp.

Saez Martin, B., 'Sobre la supuesta existencia de una edad del bronce en el Sahara occidental y Africa Menor', *Cuad. Hist. Primit.*, Madrid, 1949 [1951], pp. 111–18.

Ziegler, Lt., J. Hallemans et R. Mauny, 'Mauritanie: Trouvaille de deux monnaies romaines', Alger, *Libyca, Série Archéologie-Epigraphie*, T. II, deuxième sem., 1954, pp. 476–7, 2 Figs.

40

Some Notes on the Neolithic of West Africa

by M. D. W. JEFFREYS

Stone Age Africa by Dr L. S. B. Leakey was published in 1936 and a perusal of it revealed the paucity of information available on the Stone Age cultures of West Africa and of Nigeria in particular, for, beyond a passing reference to Mr Braunholtz's paper of 1926 describing some stone implements from Nigeria, there is no further reference to stone implements in Nigeria. Yet, as I shall show, scattered through the literature on West Africa are a number of early references to stone artefacts in West Africa and there is evidence that the use of Neolithic stone implements survived in West Africa until the beginning of this century.

I (1948, III, 1–8) have shown that some of the iron workers of the Bamenda province in the British Cameroons regard iron merely as a form of stone. This view is by no means novel, for according to Richard the Eskimo attitude to copper is the same. Describing a group of Eskimo who, finding metalic copper in its native state used it for making metal implements by hammering it, Richard (1938, No. 213) writes: 'He is right: the copper is to them a soft kind of stone, as is the steatite, or soapstone, of which they make their seal-oil lamps and other containers. Mr Stefanssen tells me that they do not use stone artefacts, except a little black slate, which they break in pieces and then grind the edges on granular rock, to make knives. It appears that formerly they knew how to chip hard stone, such as quartzite, but now finding the copper more amenable, on account of its malleability, they have rejected the use of stone. The slate knives and spear points found in the Copper Eskimo region belong to an earlier period of Eskimo life, to the Thule culture, which extended from northern Alaska to Greenland. So Mr Diamond Jenners informs me. These earlier Eskimos used hard stone as well, whereas the Copper Eskimos used soft stone only, soapstone and copper, except the unshapen stones employed for pounding the copper and for cracking marrow bones.

'This use of native copper therefore does not belong to any stage of culture intermediate between the use of stone and the use of metal; on the contrary, and definitely, it belongs to an early phase of the stone age.'

One can now understand why elsewhere the first metal tools were fashioned to conform with the shapes of the old stone implements. The early artificers knew only the stone technique, consequently when they found a new kind of stone, native copper or meteoric iron, and hammered out from this new kind of stone metal tools, these tools took the conventional shapes, the only shapes these artificers knew. Petrie (1898, I, 206) has drawn attention to this fact. He wrote: 'Two types of axe were known in both Egypt and Palestine. One was developed from the stone axe and is longer from back to edge than it is across.' [This type is the ordinary polished stone celt reproduced in iron.] 'The other type was purely metallic, and was developed from a sharp edge of metal inserted into a stick, as seen in early Egyptian forms. Probably the first type was used as a tool, the second as a weapon.' These new tools are not necessarily Neolithic, as Richard has shown and Clark (1949, 42) writing of the Neolithic Maori says: '. . . stone tools were simple, the basic implement being a stone adze which was morphologically a hoe but functionally an axe.' I will show the same features in some of the Neolithic stone implements I have picked up in the British

Cameroons. To return from the Eskimo to the iron workers of Isu, Bamenda province, the point to note about these present-day metal workers is that they use only stone as tools. No metal tools of any description were used by these men who, as I (1948, III, 1–8) have pointed out, shaped from local iron ore, iron hoes, spears and knives and in this respect the Neolithic age still persists in the British Cameroons because it was Neolithic man who first invented the use of metals and must, at the start, have had only stone tools to work with. Bent (1896, 272) describing the iron workers of Mashonaland and noting that all their tools were stones remarked: 'They are still in the Stone Age here, using for anvils and hammers pieces of hard diorite.'

These Isu iron workers are interesting from another point of view because one beholds in them the abrupt transition from stone age to the iron age without any of the intervening ages of copper or of bronze.

I shall now give the information that I have collected about stone implements in West Africa before proceeding to describe some of the Neolithic material that I have collected. Most of this summarized material is from British sources. The French have published a good deal but I am not conversant with their material.

Major Ellis (1885, 250, 204) remarked on the reputed use of stone implements among the Guanche of Teneriffe. 'According to the history, as narrated by the priests, the image (of Our Lady of Candelaria) arrived in the island (of Teneriffe) in the year 1390, that is to say about one hundred years before the Spanish conquest. . . . The other goat-herd . . . went towards the image and tried to cut off its hand with his obsidian knife. . . . When preparing their mummies, the islanders (of Grand Canary) opened the body at the side, as did the Egyptians, with the same kind of sharp stone that was used in Egypt.' Here then is evidence of the persistance of Neolithic stone implements in use for a custom that started in Neolithic times, namely mummification.

Crone's translation of Cadamosto shows that Cadamosto in 1456 mentions the use of stone implements among these islanders for he (1937, 13) wrote: 'They have no other weapons than stones and sticks like spears, which are tipped with a sharpened horn in place of iron.' The Friar Epinosa in 1594 remarked, according to Markham's translation, that the Guanches of Teneriffe's manner of effecting 'a cure was by bleeding on the arms, head and forehead with a *Tabona* or obsidian knife'. One does not know whether *tabona* is a Guanche word or a word that the Friar had picked up elsewhere, for a stone knife. The reason for this query is that on the Gold Coast the vernacular word for a polished stone axe is *abonua*.

A description in the fifteenth century of the inhabitants of Grand Canary translated by Miall (1936, 227) says: 'They have no gold or silver, nor any money, nor jewels, nor anything else artificial, save that which they make with the stones that serve them as knives. . . . They shave themselves with stones.'

The earliest mention of the use of Neolithic stone implements in West Africa comes from the American missionary, Bowen, who writing of the Yoruba in 1857 (nearly a hundred years ago) remarked: 'Shango, the Thunder God of the Yoruba, is often called Jakuta, the stone-caster, and certain old stone hatchets (leather dressers) like those found in America, are picked up in the fields and are venerated as thunderbolts.'

Bowen's remark is interesting because he recognized:

(*a*) these polished stone axes as similar to ones found in the Americas;
(*b*) nearly a hundred years ago, because it was only in April 1859 that Charles Lyell and other members of an English mission went to France and confirmed Boucher de Perthes's stone implements as human artefacts;
(*c*) and because of his remark that these polished stones were really leather dressers.

This last remark is of great interest because Migeod (1924, 136) when visiting the indigo dye pits of Ngala near the southern shore of Lake Chad, writes: '. . . I was greatly surprised to see lying there a very large neolithic axe head, measuring some 6 by 4 inches at least. I inquired what it was for, and was shown how it was rubbed on the cloth like a flat iron to give it a final polish. This use almost throws doubt on the assumption that these larger implements of axe shape were axes at all. Of course, it may have simply been a case of putting an unknown handy object which had been found to some use for which it was reasonably suitable. Still, against this must be set the conservatism of technical craftsmen who like their accustomed tools and nothing else.' Then there is also Bowen's remark that such stones were known as leather dressers.

Hutchinson (1858, 192) who was British Consul for the Bights of Biafra and Benin wrote: 'I have been informed that at a locality named Bassakatoo near Ballipa (Fernando Po) there are stone hatchets in the keeping of one of the kings. This fashion of instrument was used for splitting wood and separating bunches of palm-nuts from the trees, before they became acquainted with iron. The knowledge of this metal was first communicated to them through their exchanging vegetables and stocks for iron hoops in the early visits of European traders.'

This fact intrigued Mary Kingsley, the intrepid woman explorer who visited Western Africa in the early eighteen nineties. She (1897, 65) remarked: 'But what adds another difficulty to the matter is that the Bubi is not only unlearned in iron lore, but he was learned in stone, and up to the time of the youth of many Porto-negroes on Fernado Po, he was making and using stone implements, and none of the tribes within the memory of man have done this on the mainland. It is true that up the Niger and about Benin and Axim you get polished stone celts, but these are regarded as weird affairs—thunderbolts—and suitable only for grinding up and making into medicine. . . . The Bubi stone implements I have seen twice, but on neither occasion could I secure one. . . .'

There is evidence that within living memory of today, Negroes on the mainland were, in places, using stone implements. Thus, two of the Basel Missionaries in the Cameroons reported some twenty years ago the use of stone axes among tribes lying to the north of the Bamenda province, while the natives of the Age tribe in Bamenda are reported to have been using stone axes for tree felling at the turn of this century. In 1924 Mr Pleass, now Sir Clement Pleass, as District officer, Obudu in the Ogoja province, stated in a private conversation to me, that the natives of Atanga village which lies between the Songkwala hills and the Mamfe border, were using stone hoes of a broad shape.

The Government anthropologist, Northcote Thomas, in 1910 gave the following Edo words for stone tools:

Oghara	a stone axe
Isavang	a long stone axe

It is quite evident that one does not have names for things unknown to one.

The next earliest reference to neolithic stone implements in Western Africa is by the traveller Winwood Reade (1873, II, 168) in 1868 who mentions that while at Akropong in the Gold Coast and at other mission stations he procured a quantity of stone implements, called 'god-axes' or thunderbolts by the local natives. He also procured a couple of round, perforated stones. Sir John Lubbock supposed that these were ornaments worn round the neck. Reade thought that they were spindle-whorls. Reade gives a number of illustrations of these stone implements which clearly depict neolithic axes or chisels. He remarked that this collection had been presented to the Christy collection.

Burton who was also on the Gold Coast in 1883 writes (1883, II, 106–108): 'I was fortunate enough in collecting stone-implements before unknown to Europe. My lamented friend, Winwood Reade, was the first to bring them home from the eastern regions, Akwapim, Prashu and the Volta river. Arrived at Axim, I nailed to the walls of our sitting room a rough print showing the faces and profiles of worked stones. The result was a fair supply from the coast both up and down till I had secured thirteen. All were of the neolithic or ground type; the paleolithic or chipped was wholly absent, and so were weapons proper, arrowpips [*sic*, tips?] and spearpoints.

'Mr Carr, the able and intelligent agent of Messieurs Swanzy, brought me sundry pieces and furnished me with the following notes. The "belemnites" are picked up at the stream-mouths after freshets; but the people, like all others call them "lightening stones" (*osráman-bo*) or *abonua*, simply axe. They suppose the *ceraunius* to fall with the bolt, to sink deep in the earth, and to rise to the surface in the process of time. The idea is easily explained. All are comparatively modern, and consequently thinly covered with earth's crust; this is easily washed away by heavy rains: and as thunder and lightning accompany the downfalls, the stones are supposed to be the result.

'The *osráman-bo* are used in medicine; they "cool the heart"; and water in which they are steeped, when given to children, mitigates juvenile complaints. One of my collections owes its black colour to having been boiled in palm-oil by way of preserving its virtues; it resembles the básanos of Lydian Imolus; but the Gold Coast touchstone is mostly a dark jaspar imported from Europe. The substance of the thunderstone is the greenstone-trap everywhere abundant, and taking with age a creamy patina like the basalt of the Haurán. I heard, however, that at Abusi, beyond Anambo (Bird Rock), and other places further east worked stones of a lightish, slatey hue are common. About New Town and Assini these implements became very plentiful. Mr S. Cheetham informs me that the thinner hatchets, somewhat finger-shaped, are copied in iron by the peoples of the Benin river. These expert smiths buy poor European metal and, like other West Africans, turn out a first rate tool.

'Axim seems to have been a great centre of stone manufacture. Mr Carr showed us a dozen huge boulders of greenstone, chiefly at the eastern angle of the wart that bears, in dangerous proximity to his stores, his powder-magazine. The upper surfaces are scored and striped with leaf-shaped grooves, formed like old Greek swords; some of them are three feet long by three inches wide and three deep. I made a sketch of the place; Cameron photographed it, and on return carried off a huge slice of the block, which is now in the British Museum. We afterwards found these striated stones on the sea-ward face of St Anthony Fort, in northern Axim, and on other parts of the seaboard.'

One wonders whether these grooves were moulds for casting bronze swords and one is reminded of the recent discovery, at Stonehenge in England, of designs of swords and daggers engraved in the monoliths there. Burton adds that he read 'a paper upon these stone implements (July 11, 1882) before the Anthropological Society at the house of my friend, the President, General A. Pitt-Rivers; and made over to him my small stock. It will find a home at Oxford'.

Desplanges (1907, 28, 29) drew attention to the discoveries in French West Africa of iron, pottery and polished stone implements in the same strata. Thus he writes of the stone age sites among the Noumans in the lacustrine regions of the Niger as follows: 'Mais ces stations se distinguent des précédentes, par la présence de laitiers de haut-fourneaux, de fragments de fer, et une abondance extraordinaire de poteries ornementées de dessins extrêmement variés et originaux, poinçonnés en creux. L'aspect des amas de débris que les indigènes de Koulikoro nomment "de vieux ateliers de Noumaus (forgerons)" nous présentent également ce même mélange de fer et poteries avec des instruments en pierre. . . . Toutefois il est certain que l'usage des instruments en pierre a dû se conserver très longtemps dans la région nigérienne et se prolonger en plein âge du fer. Car dans les grand tumuli nigériens à côte d'une grande variété d'instruments, d'armes et de parures en cuivre ou en fer, on trouve toujours quelques instruments néolithiques. . . . Les campements de cette nature que j'ai pu visiter pendant mon voyage au Niger sont ceux de Sumpi, de Gourao et de Koulikoro.' Rattray in 1911 discussing the neolithic stone implements found in the Gold Coast came to the same conclusion namely that neolithic stone implements and iron implements functioned side by side and that stone implements were only ousted by iron ones quite recently. Thus he (1923, 322) writes: 'In the year 1911 it was my good fortune to be in Ashanti during the latter part of the construction of the Coomassie-Ejura main trunk road and to have obtained a collection of celts which were then unearthed. . . . The Ashanti generally call them *Nyame akuma* or *Nyame asoso*, i.e. the Sky-God's axes or hoes. . . . Nevertheless I have been informed by several old men that, according to traditions handed down to them, the so called "God's axes" were really tools used by their ancestors in the past, not only previously to, but contemporaneously with, a period when the smelting of iron was practised.

'Kakari, an exceptionally intelligent Ashanti, gave me the following statement, before I was aware of the existence of the very long celts.

' "My grandfather, Kakari Panyin, once told me that he had been told by his grandfather, who himself had heard of, but had not seen them in use, that very long ago the Ashanti used the stone hoes which are now called *Nyame akuma*. My grandfather also told me our ancestors formerly wore a girdle with leaves before and behind. He said these axes were not originally the short things now found but were very long, and that they used them for hoeing, holding them in both hands and digging between their open legs." Kakari could not say clearly whether they were hafted or not. He picked up a stick lying against the verandah, to show the length and held it about $1\frac{1}{2}$ to 2 feet up the shaft.* Later, and after I had seen the long celts, another old man, Kobina Wusu, between seventy and eighty years of age told me that his grandfather once told him that very long ago the Ashanti used hoes made of stone a cubit long, demonstrating this by holding out the right arm, fingers pointing and touching the elbow-joint with the left hand. When asked why they did not use iron, he replied that they also used it but that it was scarcer and more difficult to work than stone, and was only used for making *nabuo* (iron money). These statements were made independently, and neither informer had ever had any intercourse with Europeans, and neither had been told by me the real origin of these celts. The points of interest in these statements are:

'I. The fact that a definite tradition still survives of a stone age;
'II. The statement in each case that the celts were long (a foot or more);
'III. The fact that in one case iron-working was stated to have been practised contemporaneously with the use of stone.'

So much then for Ashanti tradition over the use of neolithic stone implements within living memory. Rattray himself found celts, pottery and a tuyère associated together. Thus he (1923, 325–7) writes of the sites of Government bungalows on the tops of hills at Obuasi. 'It is no exaggeration to say that there is hardly a square foot of ground on the tops of some of these hills which does not contain fragments of pottery; and I am informed many celts had also been found there. The pottery bears an endless variety of designs, herring bone, bands, elliptical punch marks, contiguous and detached circles, etc. A celt was also found by me about six inches below the surface. A few yards from it and in the same strata were unearthed two curious objects of clay, one apparently unbaked, the other having been subjected to intense heat. These seemed to be fragments of a pipe. . . . For some time I could not obtain any explanation of these objects; later, however, on my showing the collection of pottery to an old Ashanti, he singled out these fragments at once and said they were *nsemua* (i.e. tuyères). . . . I think enough has been said to indicate that these *nsemua* found associated with a celt, are relics of an iron-smelting age in Ashanti, and would seem to show that the Stone Age in Ashanti survived into comparatively recent times and overlapped the Iron Age'. Here then is conclusive proof of the but recent eclipse of the neolithic by the Iron Age in the Gold Coast.

Sir Harry Johnston in 1908 drew attention to the wide area in Africa over which, at that date, neolithic stone implements were distributed. He (1908, II, 499) wrote: 'In the cataract region of the Congo stone implements are fairly abundant and consist of axe-heads with one end broad, spear heads or javelins (some with barbs), and double-headed axes pointed at both ends . . . but in common with the stone implements of the Zambesi basin, they are said to be of late *paleolithic* character; whereas the stone axes and other implements discovered by various explorers in the eastern valley of the Mubangi-Wele (especially near the Bomokandi river) along the north of Congo land, and in the Bahr-al-Ghazal are similar to those found in the Valley of the Nile and of the Shari-Chad region and are of a decidedly *neolithic* character, in any case, greatly superior (as

* A celt of this length, from the Gold Coast, is now in the British Museum.

Some Notes on the Neolithic of West Africa

evidence of culture) to the stone implements of the cataract region of the Congo.* These last are not restricted in their distribution to the western Congo regions, but are also found in the coast region of Angola as far south as Mossamedes and along the coast region of Guinea.

Tremearne (1912, 93) gives first-hand evidence of the use of stone by local natives of Northern Nigeria. 'The Kagoro say that they came long ago from Bauchi country westwards to Nimbia, near to where Jemaan Dororo now is—though it was not in existence at that time—and from Nimbia they passed after a short stay, to the site of the present Fada Kagoro. . . . There they found the ruins of a former forgotten people, perhaps the makers of the stone-axes said to have been discovered in the vicinity. . . . The Agwan (chief) of Ogbon, said that one of them was an axe, and this was very strange, for the other chiefs all swore that nothing of the kind had been used within their memory. He, however, was a good deal older than the others, and it is just possible that he knew that stones may have been used before iron became available, a metal which must always have been somewhat difficult to obtain, for the ore is not found in the Kagoro country, and only Hausa blacksmiths seem able to work it when brought there.'

Here then is evidence of the recentness of stone as a tool in the use of man and this man is the Sudanic Negro. Sir Harry Johnson has pointed out that the Bantu Negro had early abandoned stone tools for iron ones and it is remarkable how little neolithic culture is associated with the Bantu Negro as against the Sudanic Negro. Thus Mr Roger Summers (1955, 44) writes: 'There is now ample evidence to show that iron was known and widely used in southern Rhodesia before the building of the stone structures known as "Rhodesian Ruins". The evidence collected by Miss Caton-Thompson at Zimbabwe twenty-five years ago has been confirmed at many other sites and it is safe to affirm that iron was known in Central Africa prior to the building of Zimbabwe, for part of which C-14 tests give a date about the 8th century A.D. . . . For the introduction of iron on the sub-Saharan fringe of West Africa Mauny suggests a date of about the 5th century B.C. by which time it had already penetrated from Upper Egypt to Napata and Meroe.'

Al Biruni, writing *circa* A.D. 900, mentions that high grade iron was being exported from Sofala to India, and Dr Desmond Clark informs me that a reliable carbon dating for some iron slag found in remote Barotseland places this slag at the end of the first century of the Christian era. Such evidence goes a long way to explain the absence of neolithic culture among the Bantu. Hence the evidence for the Bantu Negro using iron *circa* the beginning of the Christian era and continuing to use it to modern times is good; the evidence for the Sudanic Negro at about the fifth century B.C. as some people aver is still to seek.

So far as the forest Negroes are concerned they remained in this stage, without knowledge of metal, using stone and also horn, bone, stick, thorn and shell.

I may say that I myself found among the Ibo of Nigeria where no iron ore exists, an extensive use of wood: wooden swords, fighting sticks, wooden hoes besides the usual extensive use of wood for domestic utensils and for ceremonies.

Ames (1934, 18) drew attention to the recentness of the Neolithic in Nigeria when he wrote: 'The neolithic implements have obviously been in use in historical times and many of them are used as sacred objects even now. It would therefore be incorrect, as far as present knowledge goes, to assume that these neolithic implements have dates corresponding with those of similar objects found in other parts of the world. Present knowledge points to a more recent period. Some of them have been found at much higher levels in the subsoil than those at which iron implements and pottery have been discovered, while others have been found side by side with modern things. For example at Kassa three pots, iron knives and a neolithic implement were all found together at

---

* These indeed are of much the same character as the stone implements found in Ashanti. Sir Harry Johnston (1919, I, 26) reverts to this subject and remarks that: 'With the exception of the Bube or Fernandian indigenes, no Bantu people has been found living in an age of stone implements, though there are abundant evidences to show that nearly all Negro Africa (except perhaps the innermost forests of the Congo basin) went through ages of using flaked, chipped, bored and polished stone weapons and tools. The Bushmen and Hottentots had remained in this stage, without knowledge of metals, using stone and also horn, bone, stick, thorn and shell. Most of the forest Negroes apparently adopted—or reverted to—wood before they were introduced to copper.'

twenty feet below the surface. In fact the nature of the soil has resulted in modern things often finding their way down to depths of twenty feet.

'All this, together with a few finds of neolithic implements on the actual surface, points to their relatively recent use. This in its turn, together with the fact that the inhabitants of the plateau are not aboriginal but have migrated from distant places, makes it possible that some at least of these were not made anywhere near the district in which they were found.'

Among the inhabitants of the Bauchi plateau concerning whom the above remarks were written are the Birom, and of these Suffie (1943, 179) writes: 'This spirit (*chee*) is also the spirit of the woods. It is an offence to *chee* to cut timber in the sacred grove with a metal instrument, or even to lay a metal instrument on the ground within this grove. Chee is still in the stone age, so trees may be cut with a stone axe without giving offence.' There is thus much evidence to show that the neolithic has persisted in West Africa well into this century and Dr Leakey's (1936, 136) remarks thereon are not inappropriately quoted here. 'Polished stone axes as well as long stone chisels, are common, and some of these apparently were in use long after metal was introduced.'

So far as I am aware the only reference to the finding of human remains with polished stone axes comes from the vicinity of lake Fitri, east of lake Chad. There Gaden and Verneau (1920 XXX, pp. 513–43) found polished celts and three associated crania and remarked that the discovery of a greater amount of osteological material in a better state of preservation would have confirmed their opinion of the presence of a neolithic race differing from the present day inhabitants in somatic traits. One wonders whether in these skeletal remains one is not witnessing the diffusion of the neolithic from the valley of the Nile to the Negro by means of these carriers who are not of negro stock.

So much then for the historical evidence of the neolithic in West Africa. I shall now give what evidence for it that has come my way.

The following areas in Nigeria have been searched by me for stone artefacts: the Warri province, the divisions of Onitsha and Awka in the Onitsha province, the Calabar province, the Bamenda province and the districts of Victoria and Mamfe in the Cameroons province and part of the Dschang province in the French Cameroons. I found nothing in the Warri province but from the neighbouring one of Benin I was informed that part of the sacred relics of the Oba are at least two polished stone axes; whence they arose is not known.

I found no stone implements during the year I was in the Onitsha province at Awka but on letting the local natives know that I would buy 'thunderbolts' (*okwute-igwe-nni*) two much worn down, polished stone celts were procured. Since then others have been reported.

In 1926 when at Opobo, in the Calabar province, I was shown by old chief Cookey Gam a polished stone axe with lugs as shown in Fig. 1. On it he had written the word God, and refused to part with it. He stated that it had come from the far northern interior and that it with others similar to it had such magical properties that it could fell a tree at a single stroke. One is reminded of the Birom pagans who until recently felled trees in sacred groves with stone axes only. Some years later Mr D. A. F. Shute while District Officer at Ikot Ekpene, found at Ikpe Ikot Nkun, the most northerly Ibibio town in the Calabar province a similar polished stone lugged axe.

In 1928 I discovered at Itu on the Cross river in the garden of what was once the Medical Officer's bungalow a flaked stone axe or adze in quartzite, with a polished cutting edge. Further search revealed a large number of flaked stone implements on the high ground on the right bank of the Cross river, made from local quartzite which was by no means plentiful. These implements were cores that had been processed by flaking or chipping. Polishing was rare. Their shapes and types puzzled me because they did not fit in with any of the paleolithic material with which I was acquainted.

In April 1935 I was back in Itu and occupied the old Medical bungalow in whose garden I had found in 1928 the polished stone adze. In the backyard which measured about 20 yards square and which by now had been eroded down by rain and sweeping I found the remains of a pot, and

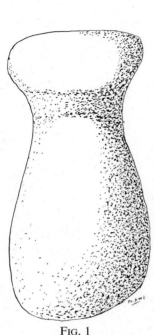

FIG. 1   FIG. 2

beside it a quartz bead which had an hour glass bore and in it a small piece of rusted iron in the last stages of fragmentation.

Some 10 feet away lay a stone implement marked as No. 120 while not far from where I picked up the polished adze I found implement No. 122. I then found another stone implement No. 129 with fragments of pottery alongside it. Thus in the compound of the Medical bungalow I had found a polished adze, two other stone implements, a quartz bead, the base of a pot with a piece of rusted iron in it. The general impression I then had was that I was dealing with a neolithic culture. The wide variety of types that I had picked up—some 800 specimens—in and around the district which did not fit into any known paleolithic categories supported the conclusion and I realized that the techniques and tools of the old stone age would be carried on into the neolithic just as neolithic tools had persisted into the iron age. To the local Ibibio these implements were just stones. There was no tradition that stone tools had ever been used among them and though they have a word, *itiat obuma*, for a thunderbolt, none of the stone implements I picked up was so regarded. Some of these implements that I picked up in 1928 are now in the British Museum. Some I handed over to my tutor in Anthropology, Professor C. G. Seligman. He (1927, I, 218) wrote of them as follows: 'A collection of Neolithic implements from Calabar include stone axes, unusual in that they possess a definite tang for hafting.'

Those that I picked up in 1935 were sent on May 29, 1935 to the Wellcome Museum, Euston Road, London. Case No. 8 contained, according to my records, the fragments of the base of the pot, the white quartz bead and the bit of rusted iron as well as the more recent stone implements that I had found in and around the Medical bungalow at Itu. As my collection, made for the Wellcome Museum with funds kindly provided by the Wellcome Foundation, was transferred to the Pitt Rivers Museum, Oxford, I have given in this article the field identification numbers of these stone implements so that they may be traced because unfortunately I took no photographs of the stone implements I collected in the Calabar Province. There was one unusual one (Fig. 2). The groove suggests that it was lashed to something with a thong or rope.

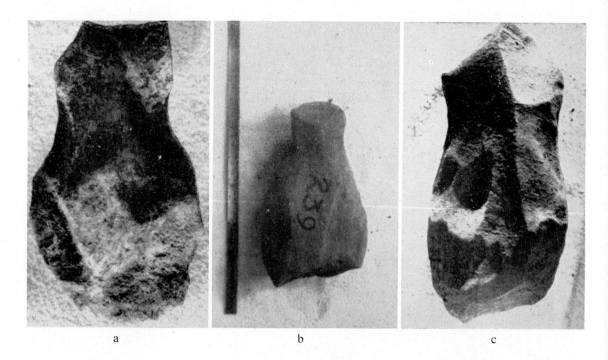

a   b   c

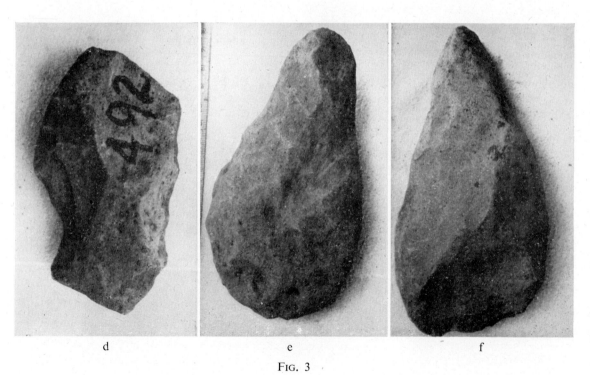

d   e   f

Fig. 3

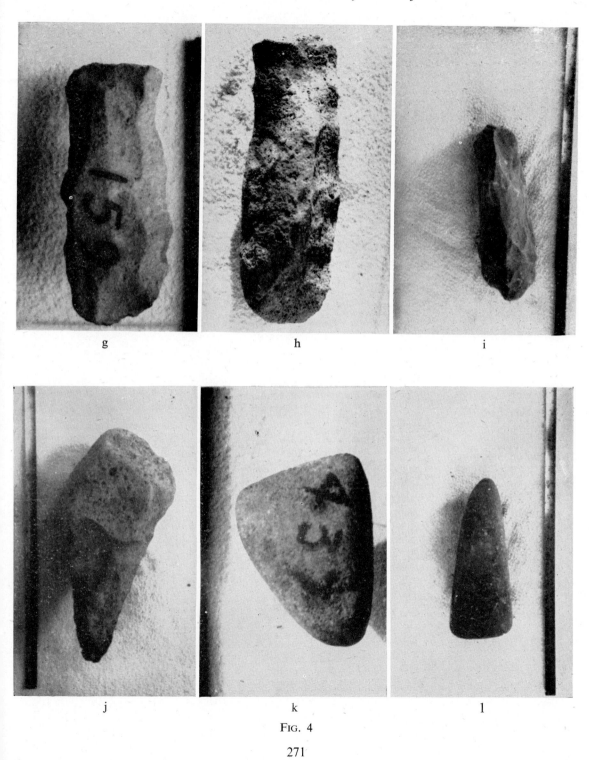

g   h   i

j   k   l

FIG. 4

Section Three

In 1936 I found myself stationed at Bamenda in the British Cameroons on whose eastern boundary rises the Cross river. In the Bamenda province there is a wide range of rocks but for the purpose of this paper attention will be drawn to the presence of quartzite and of blue basalt.

Stone implements had been reported in these regions by Migeod when he passed through in 1923. He labelled them paleolithic, a conclusion I do not accept. He (1925, 253) wrote: 'The stones had been hacked or hammered to produce a shape that was required and the result was a paleolithic type of instrument. . . . The variety of shapes produced indicate different usages, and would further indicate that the makers were a race with considerable intellect and with a variety of arts which curiously enough is not indicated by the neolithic people.' I was soon picking up at Bamenda all the types I had found at Itu but other types as well and I realized that Migeod was wrong in referring these artefacts to the paleolithic and that they were really recent neolithic. He (1925, 256) had however pointed out that: 'There is plenty of evidence all through West Africa that the neolithic people inhabited the dense forest, and accordingly there is no reason to assume that they did not so inhabit the grassland, for stones of this type have been found in both.'

After ten years in Bamenda I realized that out of the many thousands of artefacts I had picked up I had found only two in quartz, none in flint, obsidian, or what was more astonishing any in quartzite, though quartzite was abundant. All the rest were of blue basalt. It seemed then that *vis-à-vis* those of Itu which were in quartzite, the only material available, one could conclude that the Itu ones were more recent than the Bamenda ones. The argument runs as follows:

If the Neolithic peoples of the lower reaches of the Cross river, where they used quartzite, had migrated up the river and peopled Bamenda they would have continued to use quartzite in Bamenda and I would have found some quartzite tools. If on the other hand the basalt-using people of Bamenda had migrated down the Cross river then as quartzite is the only stone available around Itu they would perforce have had to use it, and this appears to be what has happened thus making the Bamenda blue basalt neoliths older than the Calabar quartzite neoliths.

During the ten years that I was in charge of Bamenda—the size of Wales—I found less than a dozen polished stone celts but then I also found only about the same number of cleavers. The presence of cleavers in an essentially Neolithic milieu means that this important tool had persisted into Neolithic times.

Migeod (1924, XXIII, 186) remarked after his journey from Buea in the south to Yola in the north, through the British Cameroons, that he collected both paleolithic and neolithic implements. Unless the implement was polished Migeod regarded it as paleolithic. Thus he (1925, 101) remarks: 'Just beyond Bafreng (a few miles from Bamenda station) I picked up a pecked stone implement, $4\frac{1}{2}'' \times 3''$ with a wrist or waist at the haft end. I had not seen such a type before but later found others.' This type of implement, according to Migeod's illustration of it, is shown by the following specimens which I have picked up (Fig. 4, a and b). There are certain points to note about these artefacts. The first is that they all have blunt butts and waists, or wrists. These butts indicate that they functioned either as hoes or as adzes. No. 4 (b) exhibits the 'tang' referred to by Professor Seligman. No. 4 (a) resembles the polished specimen I picked up at Itu in 1928. In the Itu specimen the cutting edge was polished on both sides. Nos. c, d and f are of the same shape as the preceding two specimens with the exception that the butts of these last four are V-shaped. This shape of the butt indicates a different type of hafting. The hafting required shows that these last four specimens were used as axes.

Then there is the type represented in Fig. 4 g and h. How these were hafted decides their function and that is difficult to say. They are not hand-axes as can be seen by a comparison with Fig. 4 j which is a hand-axe.

Figs. 4 k and 4 l show two of the polished celts that I picked up in the Bamenda province. There are other implements with different shapes, while cleavers are occasionally found. I never had an opportunity to do any excavating, but with the exception of the polished stone celts, hand-axes and cleavers, all the other types were found around Itu in the Calabar province. The conclusion I reached, from studying over two thousand stone artefacts that I picked up in the Bamenda province, is that they represent a recent neolithic culture. How recent I was unable to ascertain because none of the locals had any tradition of a stone age. As the art and craft of iron smelting reached the Bamenda division from the north east it is most likely that these grassland people were introduced to iron at a considerably earlier date than people to the west of them, for instance the Birom of Nigeria, or further west, the Ashanti of the Gold Coast.

Enough evidence has now been marshalled to show that among the Sudanic Negroes the Neolithic has lasted into this century whereas the Bantu negroes appear to have passed from a stone age to an iron age more than a thousand years ago.

The preparation and part of the research of this paper was defrayed by a Research Grant from the University of the Witwatersrand, Johannesburg, for which I am most deeply grateful.

REFERENCES

Ames, C. G., *Gazetteer of the Plateau Province, Nigeria*, Jos, 1934, pp. 18, 19.

Braunholtz, H. J., *Stone Implements of Paleolithic and Neolithic Types from Nigeria*, Occasional Paper No. 4, Geological Survey Nigeria, Lagos, 1926, p. 6.

Bent, J. T., *The Ruined Cities of Mashonaland*, London, 1896, p. 272.

Bowen, J. T., *Central Africa*, Halifax, 1857.

Burton, R. F., *To the Gold Coast for Gold*, Vol. II, London, 1883, pp. 106–8.

Crone, G. R., *The Voyages of Cadamosto*, Hakluyt, London, 1937, p. 13.

Clark, A. H., *The Invasion of New Zealand by People, Plants and Animals: The South Island*, New Brunswick, 1949, p. 42.

Desplanges, L., *Le Plateau Central Nigérien*, Paris, 1907.

Ellis, A. B., *West African Islands*, London, 1885, p. 250.

Gaden, H. et R. Verneau, 'Stations et sépultures néolithiques du territoire militaire du Tchad', *L'Anthropologie*, XXX, Paris, 1920, pp. 513–43.

Hutchinson, T. J., *Impressions of Western Africa*, London, 1858, p. 192.

Jeffreys, M. D. W., 'Stone-Age Smiths', *Archiv für Volkerkunde*, III, 1948, pp. 1–8.

Johnston, Sir H. H., *George Grenfell and the Congo*, Vol. II, London, 1908, pp. 499–500.

Johnston, Sir H. H., *A Comparative Study of the Bantu and Semi-Bantu Languages*, Vol. I, Oxford, 1919, pp. 26, 27.

Kingsley, M., *Travels in West Africa*, London, 1897, p. 65.

Leakey, L. S. B., *Stone Age Africa*, London, 1936.

Markham, Sir Clements, *The Guanches of Teneriffe*, Hakluyt, London, 1907, p. 34.

Miall, B., *Conquests and Discoveries of Henry the Navigator*, London, 1936, p. 227.

Migeod, F. W. H., *The Languages of West Africa*, Vol. I, London, 1911, p. 18.

Migeod, F. W. H., *Through Nigeria to Lake Chad*, London, 1924, p. 136.

Migeod, F. W. H., *Through British Cameroons*, London, 1925, p. 101.

Rattray, R. S., *Ashanti*, Oxford, 1923, pp. 322–7.

Reade, W., *The African Sketch Book*, London, 1873.

Richard, T. A., 'The Chalcolithic Eskimos', *Man*, 213, November 1938.

Seligman, C. G., 'Africa, Archaeology', *Encyclopedia Britannica*, Vol. I, London, 1927, p. 314.

Suffill, T. L., 'The Biroms', *Farm and Forest*, Vol. IV, Ibadan, December, 1943, p. 179.

Summers, R., 'Possible Influences of the Iron Age in Southern Africa', *S. Afr. Jn. of Sci.*, September 1955.

Thomas, N. W., *Report—Edo Speaking Peoples*, Part II, London, 1910, pp. 221, 246.

Tremearne, A. J. N., *The Tailed Head Hunters of Nigeria*, London, 1912, p. 93.

41

Los Trabajos de los ultimos quince Años sobre la Prehistoria del Africa Española

par L. PERICOT GARCIA

Eℓ estudio de la Prehistoria de los territorios españoles en Africa, se encuentra en pleno desarrollo. Durante varios años se han sucedido las expediciones al Sahara español y a la Guinea española. A la expedición del profesor Martínez Santa-Olalla siguieron las de los profesores Almagro y Alcobé, luego la del profesor Alcobé con A. Panyella, a la Guinea, y finalmente las de Caro Baroja y Jordá al Sahara. Ello ha permitido reunir materiales muy considerables que están ahora en estudio, tanto en útiles como en placas grabadas, y la publicación de algunas notables obras. [1]

Más importantes son las campañas realizadas por el Museo Arqueológico de Tetuán bajo la dirección de nuestro discípulo Miguel Tarradell. Aparte las importantes excavaciones de las antiguas ciudades púnico-romanas de Lixus y Tamuda y de otros vestigios de esta época tardía, hemos de señalar sus estudios del túmulo de Mezora, y las excavaciones en yacimientos aterienses y neolíticos. [2]

Pero el más importante para nosotros de los estudios realizados por Tarradell es el de la cueva de *Gar Cahal*, cerca de Ceuta, a pocos kilómetros de una bahía que pudo ser excelente lugar de desembarco trás atravesar el estrecho de Gibraltar.

Los niveles fértiles son los siguientes:

De 0·6 a 1·40 ms.	Bronce II y siguientes
1·40 a 2·05	vaso campaniforme
2·05 a 2·70	Neolítico con cerámica escasa y abundante sílex
4·30 a 4·80	casi estéril

La presencia del vaso campaniforme del mismo tipo que la de la vecina región andaluza, es un hecho trascendental. Sobre todo por confirmar lo que la cazuela hallada por Ruhlmann en Dar es Soltan había ya indicado. De una importancia cronológica que no puede desconocerse es el hecho de que debajo del nivel con vaso campaniforme se encuentre el de la cerámica pintada (reticulados y motivos geométricos). Se encuentran también fragmentos de cerámica cardial y varios esqueletos.

Un nivel inferior es claramente un Neolítico de tradición iberomauritánica, con toscos instrumentos de cuarcita.

La relación con el vaso campaniforme andaluz parece ser comercial. La cerámica cardial parece hallarse entre la pintada y la campaniforme, pero es demasiado escasa para sacar consecuencias.

En todo caso, la cueva de *Gar Cahal* señala el primer avance serio que hemos realizado respecto del neolítico del Marruecos español y se enlaza con los hallazgos de los últimos años en la costa atlántica marroquí. Al darnos una cronología relativa, segura, de las cerámicas pintada y campaniforme, ha aclarado un punto capital en la Prehistoria del Occidente del Mediterráneo.

Trabajos sobre la Prehistoria del Africa Española

Otros yacimientos iberomauritánicos, en la región de Melilla (Kerker, Gurugú, etc.), han sido estudiados por el profesor Posac.

No podemos dejar de citar las pinturas rupestres de Magara Sanar que el profesor Martínez Santa-Olalla dió a conocer.[3] Sin duda la exploración del Marruecos español dará resultados abundantes en los próximos años.

Mucho más interesante, pues hace tiempo que se inició, es el estudio de la Prehistoria de las Islas Canarias, cuyo misterio ha atraído siempre a los especialistas y a los aficionados. Desde hace quince años la Prehistoria de las Canarias ha recibido un impulso decisivo por parte de los investigadores locales apoyados por los peninsulares. En especial la Comisaría General de Excavaciones, en sus primeros tiempos, animó grandemente tales trabajos. Por vez primera tenemos un cuadro algo completo de todas las islas del archipiélago. Luis Diego Cuscoy para Tenerife y J. Jiménez Sánchez para Gran Canaria han sido los arqueólogos más destacados.[4]

El cuadro que en conjunto nos ofrecen las Canarias es el de una población de agricultores y ganaderos que aprovechaban las mesetas y zonas altas para el pastoreo y las anfructuosidades costeras para su habitación.

Cada isla tiene sus particularidades arqueológicas pero dentro de una cierta unidad se aprecian dos grandes grupos, el occidental y el oriental.

La habitación más frecuente es en cuevas, que también se utilizaban con fines funerarios, depositándose en ellos las momias envueltas en telas y pieles, al lado de las vasijas con ofrendas.

El trabajo de la piedra era tosco, no conociéndose las puntas de flecha. Las lascas de obsidiana (llamadas *tabonas*) servían para armar palos, a manera de espadas. Son frecuentes los hallazgos de bolas de piedra así como de molinos, cuentas de collar, incluso segmentadas, punzones de hueso, etc. De gran interés son los ídolos que ofrecen varios tipos: placas de barro, figuras de hombre y animal, betilos, figuras femeninas con una especie de capucha, y otros. Todos estos elementos encuentran su paralelo en las culturas del Norte de Africa y del Mediterráneo. Los ídolos recuerdan a veces tipos egeos, las cuentas de collar segmentadas, a las egipcias, las lascas al Sahara, la cerámica al círculo hispano-mauritano e incluso a la cerámica de los dólmenes norte-europeos. Hay objetos claramente importados como unas hachas de cloromelanita halladas en Gran Canaria.

El tipo de momificación y de enterramiento señala también las culturas mediterráneas. El uso de la trepanación sigue el mismo camino que las estructuras megalíticas, con su exacto paralelo en el Norte de Africa y Sahara.

De gran valor para establecer relaciones son los grabados rupestres. De ellos hay en las islas tres tipos. El más moderno está en relación con la escritura tifinagh. Otro tipo tiene círculos, óvalos, cruces, meandros y otros signos esquemáticos. Un tercer tipo, el más interesante y probablemente muy antiguo, contiene espirales, figuras laberínticas y meandros y ofrece un curioso paralelo con los petroglifos atlánticos (Irlanda, Bretaña, Galicia).

Enigmática es la posible relación entre las *pintaderas* canarias y las americanas, caso parecido al de la trepanación. Con otros vagos indicios que la distribución de algunas plantas nos proporcionan, parece apuntarse la posibilidad de esporádicos contactos entre ambas orillas del Atlántico.

Desde el punto de vista antropologico es seguro, después de los trabajos del profesor Vallois, que los guanches, primeros pobladores de las islas, pertenecen a la variante africana de la raza de Cro-Magnon, o sea el tipo de Mechta-el-Arbi, que llegaron tal vez durante el Mesolítico. Después llegaron los mediterráneos con elementos culturales del Neolítico norteafricano, probablemente bereberes. Más tarde llegaron los elementos negroides y los braquicéfalos.

En conjunto la Prehistoria canaria ha entrado en una fase del mayor interés por reflejar la sucesión cultural de las costas africanas vecinas, siendo sólo de lamentar la dificultad de obtener una cronología de sus yacimientos.

Section Three

NOTES

1. M. Almagro, *Prehistoria del Norte de Africa y del Sahara español*, Barcelona, 1946.
2. L. Pericot, *Prehistoria de Marruecos. I. El Paleolítico y Epipaleolítico*, Tetuán, 1953. M. Tarradell, 'Noticia sobre la excavación de Gar Cahal', *Tamuda*, II, 2, Tetuán, 1954, p. 344.
3. J. Martinez Santa-Olalla, 'Las primeras pinturas rupestres del Marruecos español', *Atlantis*, XVI, Madrid, 1941, p. 438.
4. La bibliografia sobre las Islas Canarias y el estado actual de sus problemas puede verse en L. Pericot, 'Algunos nuevos aspectos de los problemas de la Prehistoria canaria', *Anuario de Estudios Atlánticos*, I, Madrid, 1955, p. 579. L. Diego Cuscoy, 'Paletnologia de las Islas Canarias', *IV Congreso Internacional de Ciencias Prehistóricas y Protohistóricas*, 1954. S. Alcobé, 'Biodynamik des Afrikanischen Kontinents', *Historia Mundi*, I, Basilea, 1953.

[RÉSUMÉ]

L'étude de la Préhistoire de l'Afrique espagnole se trouve en plein essor. Pour le Sahara et la Guinée espagnole, les expéditions et recherches de Martínez Santa-Olalla, Almagro, Alcobé, Panyella, Caro Baroja et Jordá ont recolté du matériel très riche (silex, dalles gravées) mais publié seulement en partie.

Pour le Maroc espagnol il y a les fouilles de gisements iberomaurusiens par M. Posac dans la région de Melilla et la découverte des peintures de Magara-Sanar par le professeur Martínez Santa-Olalla. Mais les fouilles les plus importantes ont été entreprises par M. Tarradell, directeur du Musée Archéologique de Tetuán. En dehors de Lixus, Tamuda et d'autres gisements punico-romains, on doit signaler des gisements atériens et néolithiques et surtout la grotte de *Gar Cahal*, près de Ceuta, avec des niveaux néolithiques à vas caliciforme, preuve des intenses relations avec l'Andalousie. En dessous de ces niveaux apparaît la céramique peinte, apparentée à celle de la Méditerranée centrale et orientale.

Les fouilles dans les Iles Canaries sont encore plus nombreuses et sont dues surtout à M. L. Diego Cuscoy et à M. J. Jiménez Sánchez, pour Ténérife et la Grande Canarie respectivement. Plusieurs éléments en relation avec les cultures atlantique et méditerranéenne ont été découverts. Ainsi la poterie, le type d'inhumation en grottes avec mommification, les ornements (*segmented beads*), les idoles, les types de constructions en pierre, montrent la dérivation du continent voisin et la relation avec la culture hispano-mauritanique et même avec la lointaine Égypte et l'Égée. Des trois types de petroglyphes qu'on trouve dans les Iles, le plus caractéristique, avec des motifs circulaires et spiraliformes, sont ceux de l'île de la Palma, clairement liés à ceux de la Galice, Bretagne et Irlande. En même temps, quelques éléments comme les pintaderas et la trépanation signalent un énigmatique chemin vers l'Amérique. Après les études de Vallois on est sûr que la première population des Canaries, les *guanches*, sont des gents de la variété africaine du Cromagnon (type de Mechta-el-Arbi) arrivés peut-être pendant le Mésolithique. Après sont venus des méditerranéens, des negroides et des éléments brachycéphales.

42

The Rock Paintings of Basutoland

by JAMES WALTON

BASUTOLAND is situated largely in the mountainous areas of the Drakensberg and the Maluti, which have been carved out of thick masses of the Drakensberg lavas. Around the western margin and along the deep river valleys, notably the Orange, the underlying beds of Cave Sandstone, Red Beds, Molteno Beds and Upper Beaufort Beds are exposed. Apart from the prominent Cave Sandstone, beds of buff and yellow sandstone occur throughout this series and all have hollowed-out shelters which were occupied by Smithfield-Wilton and Bush peoples. Large numbers of these shelter walls provided canvases on which the primitive artists worked.

The rock paintings of Basutoland, numbering well over 400, can be divided into four fairly distinct periods as follows:

Group D. Post-European Period. After about A.D. 1830

Crude polychromes in pigments which are easily removed. Blue, black, white and red are the predominant colours. Horses (which did not appear in Basutoland until A.D. 1825), Europeans (not earlier than about A.D. 1830), umbrellas, iron sickles and iron 'kaffir pots' are depicted. Some of these were certainly painted by Bantu.

Group C. Between about A.D. 1800 *and* A.D. 1830

Polychrome paintings in fast pigments but without shading. Domestic cattle replace the elands of Group B. Pictures of Nguni invaders.

Group B. Bantu Period. From about A.D. 1620 *to* A.D. 1800

Shaded polychrome paintings.

Sub-group B3. Between A.D. 1750 *and* A.D. 1800

Shaded polychrome animals. Human figures, including Bantu in peaceful occupations and at war, painted in a single colour, usually reddish-brown, but sometimes black and, more rarely, white. Figures frequently display great activity.

Sub-group B2. Between about A.D. 1700 *and* A.D. 1750

Shaded polychrome animals showing foreshortening. Very tall human figures in stiff postures; frequently shaded or outlined and often wearing animal head masks.

Sub-group B1. Between about A.D. 1620 *and* A.D. 1700

Shaded polychrome animals with dark outlines and fine detail. Human figures, often in brown and ochre, shaded and with fine lines radiating from the head. Usually depicting initiation ceremonies.

Group A. Pre-Bantu Period. Before about A.D. 1620

Human figures of a gaunt type and monochrome animals, usually in reddish-brown or maroon.

Section Three

Group A. Pre-Bantu Period

The pre-Bantu paintings are represented by usually indistinct human figures and animals in a reddish-brown or maroon colour. Neither from the character of the paintings nor from archaeological associations has it been possible to determine the age of such paintings. Bushmen continued to live in the Maluti until less than seventy years ago and artefacts of Smithfield-Wilton type such as are found in the shelter floors were still being made by them. The animals depicted are all those which were plentiful throughout South Africa a century ago and no extinct forms have been recognized. Such evidence as is available indicates that paintings of this group belong to the period before the arrival of the Bantu but not to any very remote period. Underlying fragmentary patches of colour may, of course, be much older.

Group B. The Main Bantu Period

The introduction of the beautiful shaded polychrome paintings of Group B, during which period parietal art reached its greatest heights, almost coincided with the arrival of the Bantu. To what extent, if any, the new invaders were responsible for this development cannot be determined but it is unlikely that they exerted any direct influence on the artists, other than providing them with fresh models. No early Bantu artistic representations comparable to the shaded polychromes are known and many such paintings are found in remote valleys which were not occupied by the Bantu.

The first Sotho tribes to reach the Caledon valley were the Phetla, Polane and Phuthi who crossed the Drakensberg from the upper Tugela valley about A.D. 1600. They had settled earlier in Swaziland and Natal, from where they were driven by the Ngwane. Almost at the same time bands of Fokeng reached the Caledon from the north after comparatively long stays in the vicinity of Zeerust and in the Magaliesberg. These early Sotho tribes left Southern Rhodesia as a result of the arrival of the Karanga and Shona and they did not have an opportunity to absorb any elements of these later cultures. Their settlement in the Caledon was a peaceful infiltration and ultimately they intermarried with the Bush.

Materially the culture of the new settlers was meagre and impoverished but their ritual and particularly their initiation ceremonies proved subjects of great interest to the rock artists. The Sotho normally destroy all traces of their initiation ceremonies, although baked clay figurines have remained, but the Bushman artist had no such inhibitions and he delighted in portraying the decorated figures of the Sotho initiates. These are the earliest polychromes and the shaded human figures and detailed animals of this Sub-group B1 represent a high artistic development.

The use of brown shading to ochre, as at Moyeni, Ha Khotso and Tandjesberg, is characteristic of this period, although other colours are employed. Detailed body patterns (Plate I*a*), karosses with pointed fringes (Plate I*b*) and thin lines radiating from the head (Plate I*b*) are also common. At Tosing four tall figures, one of which has wings, are painted entirely in white with red outlines. The red lines radiating from the heads of these figures are extremely thin and straight; too thin to have been painted on rock by means of a crude brush. The artist engraved lines and rubbed colour into them and here and there the colour has been removed, leaving only the engraved lines. These figures are recognized by the Sotho as the 'owls' of the initiation school. At night it was the custom for boys to paint their bodies white and to run around the countryside screeching like owls and frightening the women and uninitiated.

The animal figures of this sub-group, notably elands, are painted in dark brown and white (Plate II*a*), the brown serving as a bold outline which often remains after the white infilling has been removed. They are remarkable for their fine detail, an excellent example being the head from Ha Khotso (Plate II*b*). Of particular interest also are birds (Plate III*b*) and large insects (Plate III*a*) at Ha Khotso which, in their linear treatment, are similar to another later bird from a boulder shelter at Furumela (Plate III*c*).

In the Sub-group B2 paintings, tall, erect figures carrying bows and sometimes ostrich plumes,

278

march in long stiff processions (Plate I*d*). Arrows are usually secured in a head-ring as a crest after the manner depicted by Daniell in his painting of 'Bushman Hottentots'. The presence of bows, and especially 'triple-curved bows', has been regarded by the Abbé Breuil as evidence of an invasion by a Mediterranean people thousands of years ago. I have already shewn elsewhere that the 'triple-curved bow' of these paintings can be linked more directly with the Tswana, Chewa and other tribes of southern Africa rather than with the remote, in both space and time, early Egyptian bows. It is often assumed that the Sotho-Tswana knew nothing of the bow and relied entirely on the assegai. This is not the case. The Polane, according to their own traditions, used the bow and the presence of iron arrow-heads in the middens of early Sotho-Tswana settlements in the Free State and the Transvaal indicates that its use was widespread.

Considerable speculation has arisen over the elongated manner in which these figures are depicted. To the Bushmen watching the arrival of fresh Sotho-Tswana waves of people who had not already intermarried with the Bush the newcomers would obviously appear extremely tall in comparison to themselves and it is only natural that the artists exaggerated this very striking feature. Animal heads are also often added to these figures (Plate I*d*). These were worn for a number of purposes; hunters assumed the disguise of animals in order to approach nearer to their quarry and they were also worn by medicine-men and witch-doctors, as they still are today by the Southern Sotho.

Two very striking groups belonging to this period are depicted at Advance Post, in the Berea District, and at L'Esperance, in the Ladybrand District of the Free State (Plate IV). Both would appear to represent a medicine murder, but in different stages. The L'Esperance group is painted in black with deep red shading and depicts a tall figure with an animal's head standing beside another figure without a mask and carrying a spear. At their feet is a prostrate figure, remarkable for the delineation of the feet which are usually badly represented. The head of this figure is confused by a mass of colour and cannot be recognized. At Advance Post, where the group is painted in red, shading to ochre, all the figures are masked. Two of them, with blood dripping from their mouths, are kneeling over the third which is lying on the ground. Both these scenes represent a medicine-man, with the murderer, preparing to remove or removing blood, and probably flesh, from the victim. The scene is so similar to that of the present-day *liretlo* murders that it seems safe to conclude that such murders are actually depicted.

Animal representation differs little from that of the previous sub-group except for a change in colouring from brown and white to red and white (Plate II*a*) and the use of shading and foreshortening (Plate II*c* and *d*). Technically animal rock art reached its most advanced form in this period although the human figures lack the elaborate detail of the previous sub-group. The use of shading, which is confined to Basutoland and the surrounding area, appears to have been invented accidentally by using the same brush to apply both red and white pigments.

The human figures of Sub-group B3 are small and full of activity. The Sotho were no longer strangers to the artists and their comparative tallness was no longer a striking feature, for the Bush had hybridized with the Sotho for well over a century. The Sotho are now depicted following their normal occupations; running at top speed, carrying bows and arrows, typical Sotho shields, spears and short stabbing assegais; making head-dresses of porcupine quills; fitting battle-axe heads into the shafts; and so on. These figures are always monochromes, usually in reddish brown. Animals show little change from the earlier sub-group.

From about A.D. 1800 for the next thirty or forty years art of a high pictorial standard continued but foreshortening and shading are no longer evident and cattle, instead of elands, become the favourite animal subject (Plate II*e*). It was during this period that the Nguni hordes from east of the Drakensberg swept down the Caledon Valley and over the Free State. An excellent pictorial record of this upheaval is portrayed in the famous 'Cattle Raid' scene at Mountain View, Wepener, where tiny Bushman archers are defending their cattle from black Nguni figures, armed with assegais and carrying black and white oval shields (Plate I*f*).

Section Three

Although Bushman artists have been encountered in the more remote valleys of Basutoland even within living memory, rock art in this area began to decline after about A.D. 1830. After that time the paintings, some of which were painted by Sotho copyists, are much more crude (Plate I*g* and II*f*). Colours are no longer permanent and can be easily washed off, indicating a change of medium. Some fixative was undoubtedly employed by the earlier artists and various suggestions have been made, including urine, honey, aloe latex and animal fat, but only an analysis of the pigments will throw any light on this problem. Black and white were increasingly used during this period for both human and animal figures.

The paintings from Basutoland and adjoining territories, apart from the early indistinct, crude monochromes, all belong to the period following the arrival of the Bantu early in the seventeenth century. Not a single feature is represented which cannot be identified as either Bush, Hottentot or Bantu and the theories of Mediterranean influence, submitted by the Abbé Breuil, cannot be substantiated in Basutoland.

Stylistically the paintings are closely linked with those of the eastern part of Southern Rhodesia and with those of South-West Africa. There is a striking similarity in treatment between the early paintings at Ha Khotso and Makhetha in Basutoland, the so-called 'White Lady' group in the Brandberg, and the later paintings, notably the 'Dying King' at Diana's Vow, near Rusape, in Southern Rhodesia. Any attempt, on stylistic grounds alone, to connect areas so far removed geographically would be most unscientific but it is highly probable that similar influences in these different areas resulted in similar forms of artistic expression. If such a premise is accepted, then the paintings at Ha Khotso and Makhetha in Basutoland would be roughly contemporaneous with those of the 'White Lady' group in the Brandberg; that is, early seventeenth century. Those of Mtoko and Diana's Vow, in Southern Rhodesia, would date from a period several centuries earlier; between A.D. 1200 and 1500.

Artefacts from the floors of the rock shelters in Basutoland throw little light on the problem of age determination. In many shelters, where the whole range of paintings is displayed, implements of only Smithfield-Wilton type are found. In others the range extends back to the Magosian but, in Basutoland, Magosian and Smithfield-Wilton type of implements continued in use after the arrival of the Sotho and these have been found in early Fokeng middens in association with typical Fokeng pottery.

BIBLIOGRAPHY

Battiss, W. W., *The Amazing Bushman*, Red Fawn Press, Pretoria, 1939.
Battiss, W. W., *The Artists of the Rocks*, Red Fawn Press, Pretoria, 1948.
Bleek, D. F. and G. W. Stow, *Rock Paintings in South Africa*, Methuen, London, 1930.
Bleek, D. F. and J. and M. van der Riet, *More Rock Paintings in South Africa*, Methuen, London, 1940.
Brodrick, A. H., *Prehistoric Painting*, Avalon, London, 1948.
Breuil, Henri, 'Les Roches Peintes de l'Afrique du Sud', *France Abroad*, 3, 1945, pp. 6–10 and 31–2.
Breuil, Henri, 'South African Races in the Rock Paintings', *Roy. Soc. S. Afr. Robert Broom Commemorative Volume*, 1948, pp. 209–16.
Breuil, Henri, 'The White Lady of the Brandberg and Her Companions', *S. Afr. Archaeol. Bull.*, III, 1948, pp. 2–11.
Breuil, Henri, 'Les Roches Peintes d'Afrique Australe, leurs Auteurs et leur Age', *L'Anthropologie*, 1949, pp. 377–406.
Breuil, Henri, 'Remains of Large Animal Paintings in South-West Africa, Older than all the other Frescoes', *S. Afr. Archaeol. Bull.*, IV, 1949, pp. 14–18.
Breuil, Henri, 'Some Foreigners in the Frescoes on Rocks in Southern Africa', *S. Afr. Archaeol. Bull.*, IV, 1949, pp. 39–49.
Breuil, Henri, 'Further Details of Rock-Paintings and other Discoveries', *S. Afr. Archaeol. Bull.*, VI, 1951, pp. 46–50.
Breuil, Henri, 'Carbon Test and South-West African Paintings', *S. Afr. Archaeol. Bull.*, 1954, p. 48.
Breuil, Henri, *The White Lady of the Brandberg*, Trianon, London, 1955.

c.
Group B1
Moyeni

e.
Group B3
Phamong

a.
Group A
Thabana Morena

f.
Group C
Mountain View

b.
Group B1
Ha Khotsa

g.
Group D
Phamong

d.
Group B2
Ha Khotsa

Human Figures

James Walton
1955

PLATE I: Rock Paintings of Basutoland

(*By courtesy of The Wilkie Foundation*)

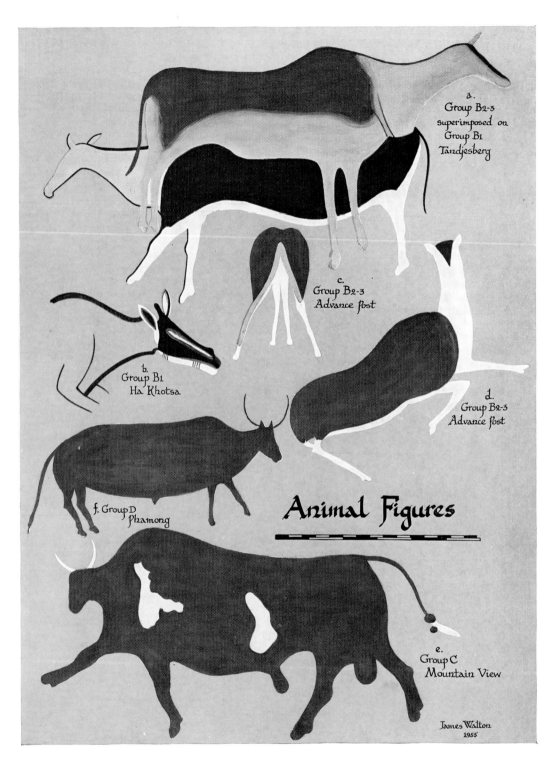

a.
Group B2-3
superimposed on
Group B1
Tandjesberg

c.
Group B2-3
Advance post

b.
Group B1
Ha Khotsa

d.
Group B2-3
Advance post

f. Group D
Phamong

Animal Figures

e.
Group C
Mountain View

James Walton
1955

PLATE II: Rock Paintings of Basutoland

(By courtesy of The Wilkie Foundation)

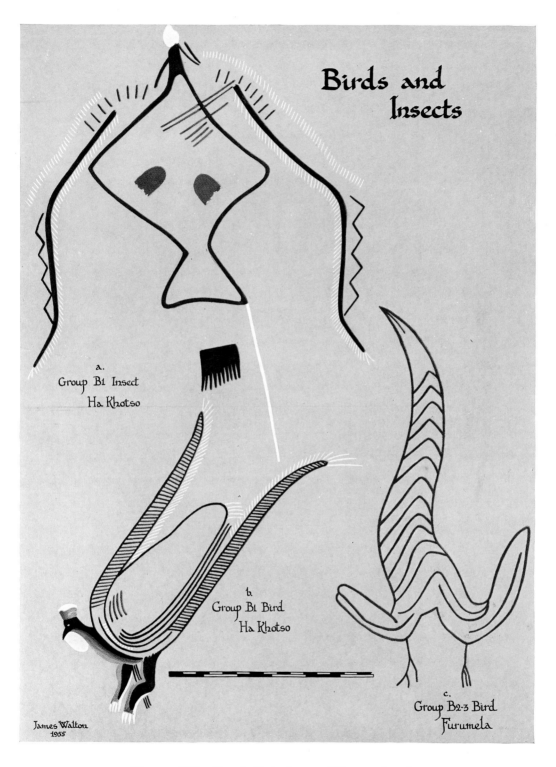

Birds and Insects

a.
Group B1 Insect
Ha Khotso

b.
Group B1 Bird
Ha Khotso

c.
Group B2-3 Bird
Furumela

James Walton
1955

PLATE III: Rock Paintings of Basutoland

(*By courtesy of The Wilkie Foundation*)

L'esperance

Advance Post

"Medicine Murder" Scenes

James Walton 1955

PLATE IV: Rock Paintings of Basutoland

(*By courtesy of The Wilkie Foundation*)

Frobenius, Leo, *Madzimu Dsangara*, Atlantis, Berlin, 1931–2.

Frobenius, Leo, *Kulturgeschichte Afrikas*, Phaidon, Berlin, 1933.

Frobenius, Leo, *Erythräa*, Atlantis, Berlin, 1939.

Goodwin, A. J. H., 'A Fishing Scene from East Griqualand', *S. Afr. Archaeol. Bull.*, IV, 1949, pp. 51–3.

Goodwin, A. J. H., *Our Early Artists*, Cape Town, 1946.

Harding, J. R., 'A Remarkable Rock Painting in the Bethlehem District, O.F.S.', *S. Afr. Archaeol. Bull.*, V, 1950, pp. 51–4.

Harding, J. R., 'Paintings of Robed Figures in Basutoland', *S. Afr. Archaeol. Bull.*, V, 1950, pp. 133–6.

Harding, J. R., 'Painted Rock-Shelters near Bethlehem, O.F.S.', *S. Afr. Archaeol. Bull.*, VI, 1951, pp. 14–29 and 39–45.

Harding, J. R., 'Notes on Some Rock-Paintings in the Eastern Free State', *S. Afr. Archaeol. Bull.*, VI, 1951, pp. 116–19.

Van Riet Lowe, C., 'Rock Paintings near Cathedral Peak', *S. Afr. Archaeol. Bull.*, IV, 1949, pp. 28–33.

Newnham, C. D., 'Two Painted Rock Shelters in the Eastern Free State', *S. Afr. Archaeol. Bull.*, IX, 1954, p. 110.

Schofield, J. F., 'Four Debatable Points', *S. Afr. Archaeol. Bull.*, IV, 1949, pp. 98–106.

Schofield, J. F., 'The Age of the Rock Paintings of South Africa', *S. Afr. Archaeol. Bull.*, III, 1948, pp. 79–88.

Tongue, H., *Bushman Paintings*, Clarendon, London, 1909.

Walton, James, 'Kaross-clad Figures from South African Cave Paintings', *S. Afr. Archaeol. Bull.*, VI, 1951, pp. 5–8.

Walton, James, 'South-West African Rock Paintings and the Triple-Curved Bow', *S. Afr. Archaeol. Bull.*, IX, 1954, pp. 131–4.

Willcox, A. R., 'The Shaded Polychrome Paintings of South Africa, Their Distribution, Origin and Age', *S. Afr. Archaeol. Bull.*, X, 1955, pp. 10–14.

43

The Prehistoric Artist of Southern Matabeleland: his Materials and Technique as a Basis for Dating

by C. K. COOKE

THE date of the rock paintings in this part of the country, and in all other parts has never been established satisfactorily. The methods so far employed have brought the whole question to a dead end, unless a new approach is attempted there is little hope that any further progress can be made.

It is for that reason that I am endeavouring on a basis of materials and techniques combined with what archaeological evidence we have, to open up another way, or at least to try and circumnavigate the barrier which has held up progress for so long.

An enormous amount has been written on this subject but little consideration has been given to the fact that the artists carrying out the work were individuals and therefore must have had individual preferences, in expression, the choice of colour and technique. Whilst it is admitted that in any 'school of art' a similarity of design and method is apparent giving to that work a basic conformity of approach, there are also tricks of draughtsmanship and other individual characteristics which stamp the artist within his group.

Although the art of the prehistoric painter is not very complex, there are in his work the same human variations which appear in the later and more ambitious studies of man. Except in the case of the very stylized representations when the artist will to the best of his abilities draw the conventional form that is required, it can be said that the first attributes of any graphic artist are the abilities to observe and by the best means available to him to transfer his observations to his 'canvas'. He will firstly do this so that he himself is achieving the object of his desire, whether it be for sympathetic magic, religion or his self-satisfaction. And secondly for the use magical, religious or the aesthetic pleasure of his fellow-man.

The percentage of first-class artists in any modern community or among such people as the Australian Aborigine is never high; although all may learn to paint, only some reach a high standard. That being so it is more than probable that every shelter did not have a really competent artist, and therefore the prehistoric master painter was of necessity itinerant, painting in other shelters belonging to families in the same tribal group, a man who did not starve in a garret, but a man who lived by his art, not only by hunting and trapping, but on the goodwill of his less gifted fellows. The size of the shelters make it certain that large numbers of people did not live in them, possibly in most cases only one or two families and then only completely in times of inclement weather, moving to different shelters within their hunting area from time to time, but each important shelter would in all probability be the headquarters of a family or tribal group and would be used for meetings and ceremonies by the whole tribe.

It is a very noticeable fact that every painting of any particular style is painted with an almost equal degree of skill, there is no hesitation in draughtsmanship, no smudging of outline, and no patchiness of colour, except in the final decadent styles. Obviously no beginners were allowed to paint in the shelters, even today nobody except an accomplished artist could equal the skill by which the animals are portrayed. It may be presumed that the students and incompetent artists practised their art on such things as skins or wood, materials which have not survived, and not until they had graduated were they allowed to paint in the permanent 'art galleries'.

In the Matopo Hills there are paintings in widely separated shelters which appear to have been executed by the same artist. The individual portrayal and technique is as easily recognizable in some of these paintings as it is in the works of later artists. To my mind there is no doubt that artists were commissioned to paint in shelters belonging to the tribe in which their families did not normally shelter. Yet there are outcrops of painting, usually away from the main painted shelters, which show unusual expressions of the artist's skill; some have the gay abandon of the impressionist, and some a stylization which can only be compared with the work of a caricaturist, but nevertheless they show that the artist was as he always has been, an experimenter. Possibly he was not allowed free rein to his imagination when commissioned, but every now and then gave vent to his imagination and broke the fetters of convention on some uninhabited rock. Some of these differing styles might be admired and thus start a 'new school of art' which would become acceptable to the ordinary man.

The artist is after all a person somewhat apart from his fellow-man, and can always be expected to do something which does not conform with accepted standards, therefore it is dangerous to confine his works to the narrow limits set by the scientist who would place him in the same category as his fellows, who were only hunters, and expect him to abide by a system laid down possibly thousands of years after his death. There will always be paintings which cannot be fitted in with any of the accepted styles because of the uncontrollable urge to improve and change which has been the basis of all art throughout the ages.

Therefore in an endeavour to classify these paintings we must examine them from an artistic angle as well as an archaeological one. Firstly the methods of painting, then the materials used for their production.

During a number of years of study it has become obvious to me that there are several groups each following one on the other, and within these groups there exist individual styles, yet there are in the main standard methods which help these groups to be separated.

The earliest paintings by superposition are faded and many are underneath the later paintings; it is therefore difficult to decide exactly the method used for their production. They are on the whole lifelike although the animals lack much movement and the human figures are stylized. The animal figures appear to have been drawn without a preliminary outline, charcoal may have been used but if so it has long since disappeared. The paint is thin, and there appears to have been a preliminary rubbing down of the rock surface to make it smooth prior to painting. The human figures are painted with simple direct brushstrokes. All colours of pigment from chrome to dark red have been used, but each figure was completed in one colour only, for although a lighter tone of the same colour occasionally appears in a figure, this would appear to be fortuitous or the result of uneven fading or oxidation.

In the next group there are several methods of approach in the animal silhouettes. In an unnamed shelter in the Gwanda District the artist outlined the figure using a fine brush; then filled in the whole figure with a mastic, finally overpainting with a liquid paint whilst the gum was still wet. I cannot decide what this white mastic or gum was or how it was applied, but it appears that the colour applied afterwards was liquid and not a powder. It is possible that if the pigment was hot when applied that the mastic or gum would melt and give a very smooth and varnished appearance to the painting. This method probably accounts for the glossy finish which is apparent in this style of painting. In this shelter there are fortunately three figures only one of which is completed, one which is filled with mastic, the third a mere outline. These three figures of kudu are almost identical and were obviously done by the same artist at the same time. It is interesting to note that the rock was not rubbed down and that the mastic filled in the slight irregularities in the granite, a definite step forward from the previous style. This was not the only method employed by this group; there is in the same shelter a freize of over twenty animal heads, which has been painted using only four brush strokes for each figure, one for the head, two for the ears, and one for the neck, yet each a recognizable head of a kudu cow. The human figures are stylized and painted without any apparent preparation. The pigment used was usually, but not always, chocolate in colour. These were painted at the height of the skill reached in the mixing of colour and media; they are therefore likely to be the most permanent and often appear brighter than others which were painted later.

The next step forward is to the delightful drawings of animals in outline. Possibly this style is the expression of rock engraving in areas in which the rock was too hard for that form of artistic expression, but it is more likely to have been a direct development from the outlines used in the previous style as a preliminary to the silhouette. They show a masterly control of the brush and very easy and confident draughtsmanship, the clever use of the thick and thin line gives an appearance of rotundity to the animal showing the clear appreciation that the artist had of every bone and muscle in the animal's structure.

The style following this is somewhat decadent, more in the media used to mix the colour than in actual skill in drawing, but yet shows further progress and is full of what can only be termed interesting experiments. The animals vary from pure silhouette to shaded outline drawings, an advance on the previous outlines, and from monochromes to polychromes. Animals are depicted as running, jumping and performing natural functions, many of them fleeting impressionistic sketches. The human figures are very stylized and also in a semi-naturalistic style with ornaments. The silhouettes were drawn in outline either with a brush or sometimes with a crayon then filled in with the main colour; as the colour did not flow easily, the outline can usually be seen and there are often gaps in the body colour. The bichromes were done by the same method but the whole or part was subsequently outlined in white, in some cases the bottom half of the legs was not painted in the main colour but in white directly; this has often disappeared, and some of the silhouettes which appear to be monochromes are in fact bichromes from which the white the most fugitive of their colours has disappeared. The polychrome figures have been painted in solid colour, the lighter colours being painted on top to give the desired effect. In the human figures the ornaments are outlined in white over the original colour or colours; whilst the faces were usually overpainted in the same manner, they were sometimes left blank and filled in afterwards with white. The first real landscape compositions appear in this group, being the record of scenes appreciated for their beauty.

This phase would certainly appear to be one of disturbance of the artists and their people; the art although developing is hurried and sketchy, as is always the case during times of upheaval, as if the artists felt the urgency and troubles of the times and unconsciously transmitted it to their work.

The latest are the crude paintings done mainly in white or in charcoal, sometimes copies of the earlier works but more rarely original and including native huts and cattle. They are usually badly executed, the animals being boxes with legs, having no movement and except in very rare instances not recognizable as any particular species. These do not belong to the general developing art in the previous styles and do not in all probability belong to people living in the stone age.

It has long been established that the colours used were obtained from the local rocks and earths mainly haematite, limonite and other iron ores giving the range yellow, yellow-brown, chocolate, light red, dark red, and brownish-red. The purplish-blacks may have come from manganese ore, whilst the white pigment may have been either bird droppings or of vegetable origin. The white pigment in the very late paintings is not the same, it may be kaolin, or some similar substance. The late blacks are mainly in charcoal. The media which they used is a matter for conjecture, tree gums, animal fats, water, hyrax urine, were all probably used, but to keep the pigment liquid with fat or gum must have been a problem. The evidence of spilt paint on rocks within some shelters shows that a very liquid paint was used, and by the way that it adheres to the rock that some other medium than water was used. The distillation of spirits must have been beyond their means, so that it is more than a possibility that the paint was kept liquid by the application of heat. A tree sap which is very slow drying may have been used, but all with which I have experimented coagulate too quickly. The crayons of haematite were either ground to shape, or manufactured from powdered material using a greasy substance as a binding agent, probably fat from marrow bones.

By the skill and precision by which a great deal of the line work was done there is no doubt in my mind that the artists used a form of multiple hair brush, or a piece of fibrous wood frayed to form a brush. Stiff feathers could have been used for the main infilling. The observers of the painters in historic times in South Africa stated that some used a flexible piece of bone, rather like a small palette knife; something of this nature could have been used for the last prehistoric styles in which strokes can be observed in the paintings, but not for the line drawings or when using very liquid paint.

Nearly all the methods of comparative dating so far laid down have been based on colour sequence and superposition; unfortunately the colour sequence cannot be established conclusively, nor is superposition always present. In the earliest paintings recognized the artists used any colour that they happened to have available, some used two or more colours in the same group to give an impression of depth. The pigments they used are found both in the Middle Stone Age deposits as well as in the middens of the Later Stone Age people. We are left therefore with superposition where it exists as the only other means of comparative dating, without consideration being given to the technique of painting and the variations in approach.

It is a matter for conjecture how or where the first paintings or drawings were produced on the cave walls; they may have been a development from decorations on skins or even from tribal marks or totems. It is probable however that the first drawings were done with impermanent materials, and those which are still in existence were a development. Once the paintings became permanent they would take on a meaning for others beside the artist, sometimes magical or ritual but often recording a scene of importance, a successful hunting trip, the burial of a chief or the appearance of other humans not of the same cultural group.

It has always been assumed that people of differing cultural groups were responsible for the differing styles of painting. I feel that this art as we can still see it is the result of a continuous unbroken development by people having the same pattern of living. There are really no differences in the main approach, only improvements in drawing materials and technique. Art must develop or die; this form of art lasted for a considerable period and it is only logical to state that it must have developed.

It is apparent from the foregoing that strictly speaking it is impossible to separate these paintings into different styles, but there were changes both in materials and technique that make it possible to divide the paintings into separate headings although each style is in effect only an improved continuation of the previous one, there being no actual dividing line.

Taking superposition and combining it with the technicalities of the artists the following is suggested as the relative dating of the main styles, and a means of recognizing the styles where no superposition exists.

1. The silhouette in all colours, stylized human figures, true animal portrayal but little movement shown in the animals. The human figures not of the matchstick type but having some shape, no faces or features depicted.

2. Small stylized human figures, of the matchstick type, grouped to convey an idea, mainly in chocolate colour but not always. Some human figures have shape but usually only in the lower limbs. Finish usually glossy especially the animal figures. The animals beginning to show some movement.

3. Line drawings, the animals usually of large size, but occasionally a few small ones are seen. Some large outline human figures.

4. Naturalistic, including bichromes and polychromes as well as monochromes, large and small human figures, the line drawings partially shaded. The bichromes in silhouette outlined in white. Landscape designs and complicated patterns. Mythological animals.

285

5. Stylistic, patterns and animals mainly in white or black usually decadent and badly executed. Unlikely to belong to the Stone Age.

Other Styles not Included in the General Classification

(*a*) Light patches on the granite from which all pigment has disappeared, usually crude in shape but recognizable as definite animal species. Usually of large size and depicting such animals as the elephant or lion. These may represent an earlier period than Style 1.

(*b*) Purplish-black paintings, some mythological animals, fishes but few humans, not seen in superposition with other paintings, but by method of execution most likely to belong to Style 1.

(*c*) Outline figures of humans not stylized, with rudimentary features, so far only seen in isolated shelters, no superposition, should connect with Style 3.

(*d*) The paintings of the little people sometimes with boot-like appendages on their feet, crowns and other head-dresses. The female figures showing definite steatopygia. Not seen in superposition. But by pigment and glossy finish probably belong to Style 2.

(*e*) Patterns of dots and dashes, circles, etc. These appear to belong to Style 4 but are often painted enclosing figures which belong to that Style.

It has been suggested that the paintings are the equivalent of 'doodling' time wasting in times of inclement weather. I would personally not place any of the existing paintings, except the final historic series, as work done to pass an idle hour. The development from single unrelated figures to landscape compositions show that this was in the main 'art for art's sake', an endeavour by the artist to record scenes and events, sometimes the results of suffering either the loss of a ruler, or even the pangs of hunger, but often a scene of beauty remembered for its aesthetic qualities.

I have carefully avoided both in the text and in the list of styles mention of the animal-headed human figures. These appear in a lesser or greater degree in all styles, and for that reason are part of a tradition and not a separate expression or style. This fact helps to prove my contention that

Fig. 1. Bambata Cave, Matopo Hills
Black = Faded Light Red
Dotted Area = Chrome Yellow

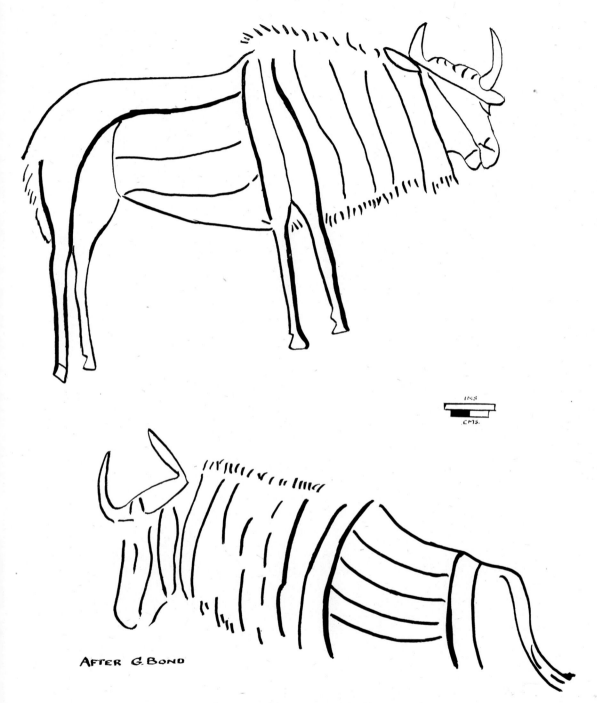

FIG. 2. White Rhino Shelter, Matopo hills
Outline drawings. Colour: brownish-red

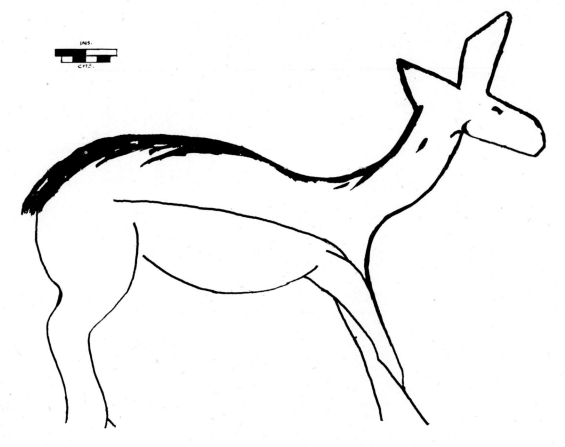

Fig. 3. Amadzimba Cave, Matopo hills.
Caricature. Colour: reddish-chocolate

the rock art in Southern Matebeleland is a developing one and not differing styles by people of differing cultural groups.

In writing of these animal-headed human figures in our cave art many writers have drawn parallels to the gods of Egypt and other Mediterranean cultures. Whilst a diffusion of cultures must have taken place in Africa, I am very loathe on the evidence so far brought forward to draw any conclusion from the apparent similarity to gods and other supernatural beings, other than that it is probable that these likenesses are accidental, although the possibilities of some 'memory culture' cannot be dismissed willy-nilly. Ritual figures and signs have often been adopted by people of different cultural groups or religious groups, but in the passage of time have come to mean something entirely different from the original conception. Therefore it would be dangerous to attempt to draw any conclusions either religious or cultural from these similarities even if it could be proved that they had the same basic source.

I believe that these animal-headed human figures, sometimes with musical instruments, represent the ritual dances and ceremonies of the people themselves. The heads would seem to be masks, similar to and possibly the forerunners of the 'Bantu' dances of today. The Makishi dancers of Northern Rhodesia provide an example which immediately comes to mind.

1

2

3

4

5

PLATE V: Prehistoric Artists of Southern Matabeleland

1. Other styles not in general classification. 'C' connecting with Style 3. From un-named shelter near Nswatugi Cave, Matopo Hills.

2. Style 4. Polychrome and bi-chrome animals and humans. Nswatugi Cave, Matopo Hills.

3. Style 5. White copies of earlier paintings. Amadzimba Cave, Matopo Hills.

4. Style 2. Outline figures filled in firstly with white and then coloured pigment. Near Ififi, Matopo Hills.

Scale 2 inches = 1 foot.

5. Other styles not in general classification: the little people: small shelter Gwanda district. May connect with Style 2. Female figures dressed like Hottentots.

Scale 2 inches = 1 foot.

(By courtesy of The Wilkie Foundation)

The Prehistoric Artist of Southern Matabeleland

Having dealt with the comparative dating it is now necessary to endeavour to arrive at a feasible absolute date for the various periods of development. The earliest series which can still be seen is far too advanced to be the first expression. Somewhere, perhaps here, there must have been more primitive styles but these have long since disappeared. An agricultural people are depicted in some paintings, as are also their weapons and shields, they are however a late occurrence. The modern 'Bantu' do not on the whole practise any form of art except the modelling of clay figurines for playthings, and in connection with initiation ceremonies. A certain amount of wood carving is also done by the males, the females doing what linear decoration there is on pots and ornaments. All the natives I have questioned do not admit to their forefathers having executed these paintings, except the very late scribblings; on the whole they regard the paintings with a certain amount of awe. It is safe to assume that their ancestors were not the artists. The fact that the very late paintings in black or white are attributed to the 'Bantu' in no way alters this contention; they are mostly imitative, and an unusual occurrence caused by their proximity to the paintings during periods of invasion by the Nguni people from the South. They had time on their hands, so this phase can certainly be classed as 'doodling'. The rare occurrence of an original study of this period also shows that there were people among the 'Bantu' who could have developed an art, but that it would not have been a continuation of the older school.

There is no evidence to support the suggestion that the Hottentots were the artists, but on the other hand there is little evidence which suggests they were not, except that there is no archaeological evidence so far to suggest that the Hottentots ever lived for any length of time in Southern Matabeleland. We are left therefore with a people living in the Stone Age. We have evidence from

FIG. 4. Amadzimba, Matopo hills
Impressionistic: outline filled in with visible brush strokes
Colour: brownish-red

South Africa of Bush people painting during historic times. The nearest cultural group is therefore the Wilton. From archaeological evidence we know that they had the materials for painting and that they occupied the shelters, by the evidence of pottery sherds some way down in the middens that they had contact either visual or actual with the Iron Age people. But the Middle Stone Age people also had colouring matter and therefore could have painted, not necessarily on the cave walls, but perhaps only on skins or their own bodies.

The Middle Stone Age Culture is materially different from the Later Stone Age suggesting that they were people of a different group and therefore it is very unlikely that their art would be basically the same as the later people, any more than the 'Bantu' art is the same as that of the Later Stone Age.

Another reason which does not rest on artistic appreciation is that in most shelters there is a definite break between the middens of the Later Stone Age and the granitic sands which contain the implements of the Middle Stone Age, showing a cultural hiatus of a considerable length of time; if, as I think, the art is a straightforward development, then these Middle Stone Age people must be excluded.

Dr Neville Jones on purely typological grounds divided the Wilton into two periods, the earliest being Bambata Wilton followed by the Nswatugi Wilton. The excavations recently carried out at Amadzimba in the Matopo Hills show a further development within the Wilton which in my opinion is a later phase than the others; there is a very large number of bone tools and a reduction in the numbers and types of stone implements. It is hoped that C.14 tests on material from this cave will confirm this opinion. This all fits in very well with my contention that all the existing paintings belong to the Wilton, except the very late 'Bantu' ones. Styles 1 and 2 are found in the greatest number at Bambata, whilst in Nswatugi Styles 2 and 4 are the most numerous although earlier ones do appear. At Amadzimba except for a few early paintings all can be considered as Style 4, some of which are overpainted with the historic Style 5.

The estimated age of the Middle Stone Age as over 5,000 years ago makes it very unlikely that any paintings would have survived to the present day, especially as they are painted on granite, which exfoliates in thin sheets and slabs, and also weathers by a process of attrition into coarse sand grains. The shelters on the whole are not weatherproof, the damp mists of winter blow into nearly all of them. So far no paintings have been discovered below the top of the Wilton middens. The earliest type of paintings are often on the highest part of the shelter walls. In Bambata this would mean that if they were executed by the Middle Stone Age people at the lowest level at which pigment was found they would have been painting some 25 feet above the floor level at that time. Not impossible but rather unlikely. If they were all done during Later Stone Age times then 10 to 12 feet would be the maximum, a height which could be reached with reasonable ease using a felled tree as a ladder. This applies in other shelters, but none so far excavated has the depth of deposit found at Bambata.

There are still isolated pockets of people who are probably descendants of the rock painters, mainly living in areas where there is no granite, but they no longer paint; they still engrave ostrich egg shells with figures which bear some resemblance to the figures in the painted shelters. Ever since they became disturbed firstly by the 'Bantu' from the North and East they became, instead of a people settled in their own hunting areas, a people of no home, now entirely nomadic, gradually being exterminated by the ever rising tide of civilization on all sides of them. Their only home is where they kill a large animal, moving on when it is necessary to replenish the larder to the next kill.

Although historically it is known that the Bushman was almost exterminated because he would not leave his ancestral hunting grounds, I firmly believe that this was because he was hemmed in and does not compare with the earlier forced migrations when most of the country was free of all but his own people.

Not having had the opportunity to study at any great length the paintings in other areas of the Colony or in the Union of South Africa I am not prepared to draw any parallels to paintings exist-

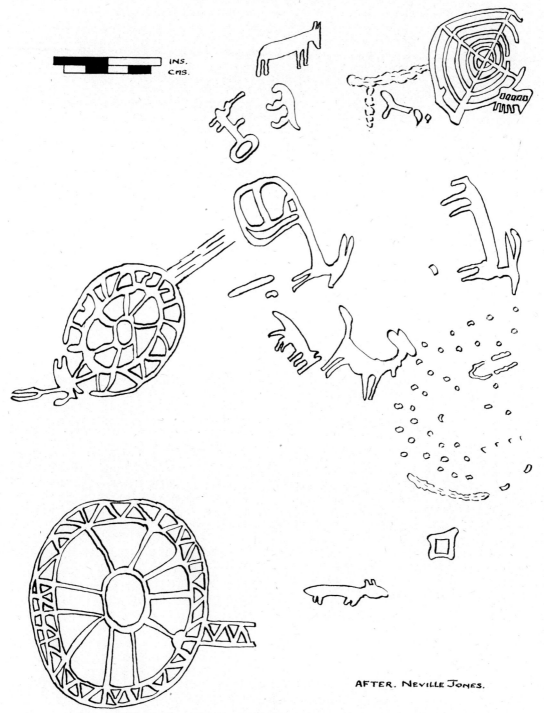

INS.
CMS.

AFTER. NEVILLE JONES.

FIG. 5. Protohistoric original
Painted in white outlined with black. Chinymbwe no. 1. Copied by Neville Jones

ing in those areas, except to say that it is fairly evident that a further development took place south of the Vaal River in South Africa giving rise to the shaded polychrome paintings which are a logical step forward from the polychromes and partially shaded outlines of Style 4 in Southern Matabeleland; these Style 4 paintings also show the beginnings of foreshortening. New elements also entered the Wilton Stone Age assemblages to the South. In Mashonaland there is also a development that does not appear in this part of the country; it is fairly evident that Southern Matabeleland was disturbed by invaders prior to the areas further north and east, but the migrations from Southern Matabeleland were to the South and the natural development from these styles took place there and not to the North. The Mashonaland paintings seem to be more akin to some in South-West Africa than to those in the South, the human figures and burial scenes being far more complex.

Without the aid of any further archaeological evidence it can be assumed that the following is a fair basis to work on for the absolute dating of the various styles.

Style 5. There can be little doubt that these were painted about the time of the Nguni invasions i.e. A.D. 1820 onwards. Some are still being done by herd boys sheltering from the rain.

Style 4. The final phase of the prehistoric painting in Southern Matabeleland. With the evidence of painted shields, some akin to the Zulu/Matabele type, Bantu-like figures, groups showing activities which do not belong to the Stone Age, the occurrence of early Iron Age pottery in the middens, all make it possible that these people were painting almost in historic times, and were certainly painting during the time of the arrival of the first strangers either Hottentot or 'Bantu', between 1,000 and 2,000 years ago.

Style 3. Earlier than the last, but could be almost contemporary, a style which did not last for a very long period and which is the forerunner of the shaded outline drawing.

Style 2. A style which is earlier than 3 and 4 but shows the beginnings from which they developed. Possibly between 1,000 to 2,000 years old.

Style 1. Preceding the previous styles and possibly going back to the earliest Wilton in this part of the country. The earliest date possible would be somewhere after 4000 B.C. the date established by C.14 for the Nachikufu 1 of Chifubwa in Northern Rhodesia, the woodland/forest equivalent and the contemporary of the Wilton of Northern Rhodesia, which is earlier than the Wilton of Southern Matabeleland.

In conclusion I think that the period of 5,000 years covered by these suggested classifications is far too long and would more than account for the development which took place; after all superposition does not mean necessarily that any great length of time elapsed between one painting and another. Five thousand years is too long for any of the existing paintings to have survived under the conditions which exist and have existed during the whole of the Wilton period, and preclude the possibility that any other culture than the Wilton was responsible for any of the existing prehistoric paintings.

Except for colouring matter, grindstones and some possible pallettes none of the painting materials has survived, no painted stones, painted or engraved ostrich egg-shells, or other materials have so far come to light in an excavation. Therefore although there is no doubt in my mind as to who was responsible for these paintings, nothing concrete has yet been brought to light that will clear for all time this very controversial subject.

In writing this paper I have had to read everything available on the subject, it is therefore impossible to refer to every book chapter and verse. For that reason I have included a bibliography instead of the usual references. If I have left out any names, some books I read years ago, I would like to tender my apologies now to the author or authors.

Finally I would like to thank Mr Roger Summers and Dr Desmond Clark for their very valuable help and criticisms during the time that I have been preparing this paper, without their help and encouragement I very much doubt that I would have ever completed it.

The Prehistoric Artist of Southern Matabeleland

Mr K. R. Robinson after reading my paper gave me the following note; this is taken from his excavation notes during the work which he carried out for the Inyanga Research Fund during July 1950. This work although in the hands of the publishers has not been printed.

Site XIX B on Ziwa Mountain

A black series seems to be the oldest in this shelter, and dark red the latest, but in an adjacent shelter there is an earthy yellow series which overlies the dark red.

The walls and the roof of this shelter show evidence of much exfoliation of the granite at some time previous to the execution of the paintings. This fact may be of interest in view of the exfoliated granite layer between the Wilton and the late Still Bay or Magosian which occurs in the cave deposit.

Site XIX Lower Shelter

(*a*) Three kudu bulls in earthy yellow painted over figures in dark claret and plum colour. In these figures where the body was not painted in entirely there were stripes in the same colour as the rest of the figure.

(*b*) Hartebeeste bull in dark claret done over a figure in very faded light red.

(*c*) Sable bull in dark red painted over dashes in dark red.

(*d*) Two human figures in dark red with white ornamentations.

In view of my contention that all the paintings were by people living in the Wilton period the information stating that exfoliated granite was between the Middle and Later Stone Age deposits is of very great interest, especially as his description of the paintings make it evident that at least two and in all probability all four of my styles are represented at these shelters. This shelter is in Mashonaland and not in the area with which I have dealt, but nevertheless it is very interesting to get this information which points to a very similar development in the paintings on the Eastern borders of Southern Rhodesia.

Although an isolated occurrence of this nature cannot be taken as definite proof that the painters of all the existing works were living during Wilton times, it can be said that it is very strong circumstantial evidence.

My thanks are due to Mr Robinson for allowing me to use this note.

BIBLIOGRAPHY

Armstrong, A. L., 'Rhodesian Archaeological Expedition (1929): Excavations in Bambata Cave and researches into Prehistoric Sites in Southern Rhodesia', *J.R.A.I.*, LXI, 1931.

Adam, L., *Primitive Art*, Pelican Books, 1949.

Battiss, W., *The Artist of the Rocks*, Red Fawn Press, Pretoria, 1948.

Battiss, W., *The South African Paint Pot*, Red Fawn Press, Pretoria, 1946.

Bleek, D., W. Rosenthal and A. J. H. Goodwin, *Cave Artists of South Africa*, Balkema, Cape Town, 1953.

Bleek, W. and G. Stow, *Prehistoric Paintings*, Avalon Press, 1948.

Breuil, H. and L. Frobenius, *Afrique*, Cahiers D'Art, Paris, 1931.

Broderick, A. H., *Prehistoric Painting*, Avalon Press, 1948.

Burkitt, M. C., *South Africa's Past in Stone and Paint*, Cambridge University Press, 1928.

Burkitt, M. C., *Bushman Art in South Africa*, Ipok, 1929.

Cole, Sonia, *The Prehistory of East Africa*, Pelican Books, 1954.

Cooke, C. K. and K. R. Robinson, 'Excavations at Amadzimba Cave located in the Matopo Hills Southern Rhodesia', *Occ. Pps. Nat. Mus. S.R.*, Vol. 2, No. 19, 1954.

Goodall, E. (E. Mannsfeld), *Frobenius, Catalogue of South African Paintings*, 1930.

Goodall, E., 'Some observations on Rock Paintings illustrating burial sites', *Pro. R.S.A.*, XII, p. 63, 1946.

Section Three

Goodall, E., 'Domestic Animals in Rock Art', *Pro. R.S.A.*, XII, p. 57, 1946.

Jones, Neville, *Stone Age in Rhodesia*, Oxford, 1926.

Jones, Neville, *The Prehistory of Southern Rhodesia*, Cambridge University Press, 1949.

Jones, Neville, 'Excavations at Nswatugi and Madiliiyangwa and notes on new sites located and examined in the Matopo Hills Southern Rhodesia', *Occ. Pap. Rhod. Mus.*, No. 2, 1933.

Mannsfeld, E., see Goodall, E.

Patterson, Canon E., *The Bantu as Artist*, Cyclostyled, 1948.

Schofield, J. F., 'Weathering of Granite in relation to the Age of the Bushman Paintings', *S.A.J.S.*, XXIX, 1932.

South African Archaeological Society Bulletins, Vols. 1 to 9. Various articles by A. J. H. Goodwin, C. van Reit Lowe, W. Battiss, H. Breuil, J. F. Schofield, C. K. Cooke, K. R. Robinson, E. Goodall, M. Schoonraad, 1945–55.

Stow, G., *The Native Races of South Africa*, Macmillan, New York, 1905.

44

Styles in Rock Paintings*

by E. GOODALL

AN attempt has been made to bring the numerous stylistic periods of Rhodesian rock art into a classified system. A beginning is made with the foremost example provided by the Makumbe cave paintings, in the Chinamora Reserve. One section of this is particularly instructive as the paintings include examples of nearly all styles, from the beginning to the decadent periods. Nowhere else have so many different layers been observed (Fig. 1). Fifteen superpositions can be counted, whereas most cave paintings show only up to five or six layers superimposed.

The earliest paintings are the large elephants. The colour is a dark mauvy brown, now very pale. The next artists painted in a similar, but a little darker, colour. To this group belong the smaller elephant, the sable and some finely drawn antelopes, all done in full flat wash; the latter belong to the best animal style. The third style is done in a deep, subdued, reddish colour. The fourth style is pale red and is of lesser quality.

New people came and painted in yellow or yellow-brown, a colour which did not last so well as the earlier dark brown. One of the antelopes is extraordinarily well done, with great sensitivity, but others less so; they lack the finer details, such as hooves, of the second style. In layer six are human figures, the best style being represented by a standing man (centre top of the frieze) and by the 'mourner' (bottom right), both in dark Indian red. No. 7, the rhino, belongs to an important group, a later recurrence of larger animals; the body is drawn in outline, but filled in with a pale yellow colour. Style 8 shows a small, thin man, a thin tree and two baboons, all in a brown colour. Style 9 is represented in nearly all caves and shelters: human beings in vivid movements—here a row of people dancing, including women—all full of life, but the end of the fine style. Style 10 is represented by large yellow ovals which occur in other caves from Nos. 8 to 11. No. 11 is represented by a leaf motif in dark brown. No. 12 is a rather crude style consisting of human beings, carelessly done and clumsy in form. No. 13 is a medley of fairly bright red lines, angular and geometric; it is inconceivable what they may represent. No. 14 consists of massive, crude, white animals, sometimes humans, sometimes angular forms. Nos. 13 and 14 occur in other parts of the Makumbe frieze.

Besides these successive styles, there are occasionally examples of the true profile method, recalling the earliest French cave drawings; each animal has only one front leg and one hind leg, as instanced in the large Mrewa cave. Such representations are the beginning of the art and it is apparent that the style is more primitive than the Makumbe elephants. There are fragments of stiff, outline animals in other sections of the Makumbe wall which seem to be the earliest art in that cave. So much has disappeared from the walls that it is extremely hard to find the true beginnings. Fragments of the earliest art are tentatively called Styles 01 and 02. The colour is always a dark red. Many caves and shelters were first occupied at a later time; in such cases no early art exists and we begin with Style 5, or 9 and 10. The true profile method can be found also, but very rarely and small proportioned, among the later 'classical' style animals.

The fifteen sections of Makumbe can be further elaborated upon and compared with examples

* This paper appears in an abbreviated form, having been submitted originally with 45 illustrations.

from other sites. No. 1 Style is well represented in the Domboshawa Cave by several large rhinos. There are also large old outlines, representing parts of elephants, with a very vivid hunting scene in Style No. 7 superimposed upon them. The large outline elephants are well represented at Gomokurira, in the Chinamora Reserve, where there is a wall with five of them, up to 9 and 12 feet in length. They can be found also at various open shelters in the vicinity of Salisbury.

In the Umvukwes, there are well drawn, large buffalo, of a similar period as the rhinos from Domboshawa; they are the nearest in Rhodesia to the fine Perigordian bulls of Lascaux in France, heads and legs being in full colour and slightly modelled, other parts in outline.

The large Mtoko cave, with a kaleidoscope variety of motifs, has three enormous elephants as the earliest, painted in full colour, in a pale greyish-brown shade, with Styles 3 and 6 to 11 superimposed upon them; they do not resemble others in any known cave. A recurrence of the large animal style, No. 9, of a later period, is represented by several examples from the Chikupu cave in the Masembura Reserve. Below the legs and neck of one elephant is a rectangular motif in multi-colour outline, rather reminiscent of similar forms from Nswatugi cave in the Matopo Hills, and belonging to Style 10 of Makumbe.

The finest period within this art has been referred to as that of the 'classical style' (layer 6 of Makumbe). It is the 'wedge style' of Frobenius, comprising human figures with broad shoulders, thin waists, standing or sitting in a somewhat stylized, calm attitude. The term 'classical style' is used here instead, as it includes the representations of animals. They are drawn and painted with sensitivity and knowledge, true to life in rest and in movement. Fine examples are in evidence in all caves and many of the shelters throughout Mashonaland and in the magnificent caves of the Matopo Hills.

The paintings afford a glimpse into the changes of social conditions. There is no more the purely hunting existence. Communal interchanges have occurred; gatherings of people are depicted, men and women engaged in different occupations, and in some cases women are portrayed with children.

In the classical style, a greater variety of animals is portrayed, not only the great pachyderms and antelopes. Zebras are often most skilfully depicted by drawing the dark stripes, with only a few indications of outline or none at all. Birds are sometimes drawn with a background of dashes, indicating their habitat—a very great advance—exemplified at Kisanzi Farm, Darwendale. Even a python has food value and the writhing of a mortally wounded snake is most admirably depicted at Enkeldoorn, Mangene Reserve. All the carnivores can be found on the cave walls; a leopard depicted in the pointillé manner at Mazoe, Ndobe Hills, shows great accomplishment.

At the culminating point of this art the subjects become most varied; there are ceremonially seated people holding insignia of some kind and being adorned with shoulder and arm ornaments (seen in Zwimba Reserve). The figures in the classical style are usually red monochromes. At the Eighty Miles cave, Mtoko, the medicine man is depicted, clearly marked by a strange hairstyle; it is a singular achievement to have portrayed an old man with folds of flesh as on the body of an aged person. In this case the medicine man has drawn a magic circle round fruits of some kind. The animal world was not the only source of food supply; the people became food-gatherers, having learned from the animals to dig for roots, etc. Nearly every shelter or cave has some special variety of edible root exhibited amongst its paintings and great care is often taken in depicting the fine shoots or tendrils by which the varieties can be recognized. Landscape painting is shown by finely drawn trees, hills and lakes; all expressed through fine dashes and dots.

In the happiest and most productive period, the late classical (also representing a distinct cultural epoch), is expressed the beginnings of mythology and, within it, fully established personalities of myths and legends. All these curious creatures are as a rule monochromatic. At Carolina Farm, Salisbury West District, are examples of locally restricted mythic creatures of predominantly reptile character. Eight examples have so far been located in an area between Lake McIlwaine and Macheke. Two groups of these 'crocodile men' occur at Glen-Norah Farm, Salisbury South.

1

2

4

3

PLATE VI: Styles in Rock Painting

1. Mrewa Cave, Mangwende Reserve. Fine reproduction of a Sable Bull in bi-chrome style, portraying the white markings on face, chin and underparts of body. The upright mane is correctly contoured. The splaying hooves are shown, also the annulations of the finely-curved horns.

2. 'Impey's Cave', Fort Victoria area. Polychrome style. Assembly of nine male figures, with bodies painted in various colours, possibly representing an initiation ceremony.

4. Chikupu Cave, Masembura Reserve. A funeral scene, with row of people in a curious simplified style.

3. Mucheka Cave, Mrewa area. Gracefully drawn tree, with marked naturalistic understanding.

(By courtesy of The Wilkie Foundation)

Apparently they were creatures held in great esteem, as four normal shaped men bow low before them.

Elongated people at Arlington Estate, Salisbury South, seem to display a similar prodigious head. One of these strange figures is in a lying position, with knees drawn high up and surrounded by dozens of antelope heads. Apart from the mythic character of the assembly, near rocks and animals, the scene may be connected with a sacrificial rite.

Another type of sub-human and mythic figure is represented at Mshaya Mvura cave, Mtoko, of the type called the 'lady with streams'. It is a round-bodied female creature, possibly connected with myths concerning the 'primeval mother of all things', a motif found in the Macheke, Enkeldoorn and Salisbury districts.

A development during the extensive era of this very distinctive form of art is the introduction of bichrome and polychrome paintings. Often the face markings of animals are finely and distinctly drawn, also stripes over the bodies of antelopes, belly markings and leg contours (Plate VI, 1). In processions, hunting and meeting scenes, white, pink, red and all ochreous shades are used very effectively (e.g. at Dengeni cave, Zaka). At Mucheka cave, Mrewa, two lively 'cave ghosts' are sketched in red, yellow, white and black. One much discussed meeting scene, at 'Impey's cave', Rumwanda rock shelter, Ndanga, is multi-coloured and most likely represents an initiation ceremony. Nine male figures are participating and the bodies seem to be coated with white paint or ash. As the sex is indicated in all figures, it may be conjectured that the bodies were meant to be painted in various colours over the white, instead of being draped (Plate VI, 2).

Paintings concerning the vegetable kingdom are also influenced by elaborations of this style. Some trees are ornamented by fine white or pink dots (Plate VI, 3). The large ovals or rocks, as pertaining to landscapes, are chiefly polychromatic, having different coloured edges and dots with, very often, white tops or 'caps'.

Concurrent with the polychrome art exists a distinct style, the human figure in outline, though examples are not numerous. One, in Makumbe Cave, portrays two women running vigorously, sketched in a graphic way. More stiffly drawn are two long-legged men (Epworth Mission, Salisbury East). Outstanding are the drawings of two unusually large men in Gonye Cave, Mtoko, where an attempt was made to achieve life size. The large man from the Kanyoni rock shelter, Fort Victoria area, may have been painted at a similar time.

The late, outline style is prolific in the representations of animals; the White Rhino shelter, Matopo Hills, is a good example. The animals in this style are usually medium or small in size and can never be confused with the early large animals. The late, large-animal style, in bicolour, has its place in this more decadent period. The cycle of evolution, having passed its zenith, produces a variety of crude, yet delightful and often humorous renderings of individual styles. People are drawn in striped technique (Carolina Farm), some with ear-like protrusions. Such details are frequently met with at this later stage. Another example (Chikupu Cave) shows a row of people at the bottom of what may be a crude funeral scene. The little procession is typical of the period in losing its balance but not its temperament. There is also a curious variant in which heads are drawn in outline with one or two vertical dashes inside the head circle to express a countenance (Plate VI, 4). There is also the tendency for a geometric perception of the human figure, a clear indication of the approaching termination of this art.

Some drawings appear to have been made in a hurry; there is not much anatomical feeling and sometimes the style becomes a schematized pattern, with body and limbs equally wide, like ribbons. The bizarre and grotesque is often expressed. A very late, schematic style is indicated by a group of archers in the Lower Mawanga rock shelter, Makumbe. Although fully geometric, it is very descriptive and singular, the arrow being depicted at the moment of leaving the bow: a fine snapshot illustration.

Style No. 14 of the Makumbe cave is represented on several cave walls. It consists of large white, rather clumsy, animals or such forms reduced to rectangles or squares; Makumbe and

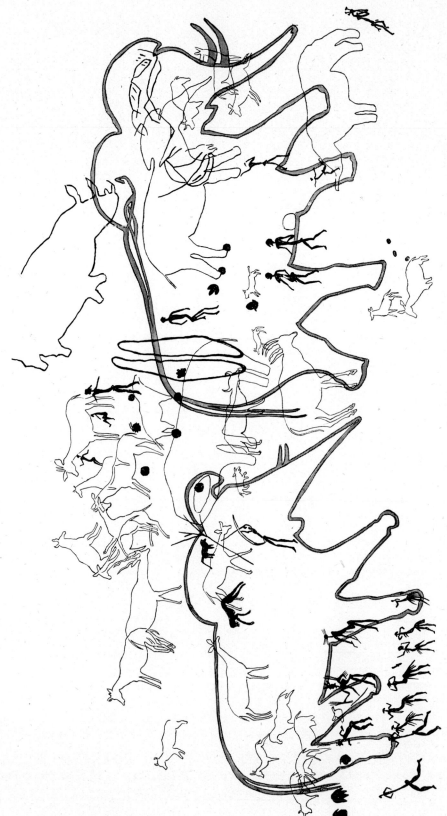

Fig. 1. Makumbe Cave. Portion of the large frieze, which is composed of at least 14 superpositions

Styles in Rock Paintings

Silozwane cave, Matopos, have clear examples. It may be represented also by the large crude human figures at Chikupu, where the more or less schematic forms may be finger drawings.

It is seen that prehistoric man was capable of illustrating his life and social conditions; glimpses are captured of his religion and philosophy. Grouping and compositions occur in a variety unparalleled in any rock art of the world.

The age grouping may, in the future, be supported by correlating finds in cave floors. Dr N. Jones, like Professor Armstrong, found pieces of yellow ochre at a depth of 5 and 7 feet, together with material of the Middle Still Bay (as it was then called); but, in digging further, he found a piece of red haemetite at a depth of 16 feet, at the base of the Proto-Still Bay. This is an indication that the dark red is indeed the earliest painting.

In studying the various styles as they follow each other, it is convincing that the core of the art lies in the animal and not the human figure. Intensified studies of this great animal art will contribute towards a clearer understanding of prehistoric man.

45

The Geometric Motif in Rock Art*

by E. GOODALL

SOME recently discovered rock engravings in the Eastern Districts of Southern Rhodesia, representing various distinctive geometric designs, prompted the writing of this paper. Rock engravings are a rarity in S. Rhodesia; therefore this newly found area with scattered engraved rocks may be introduced by a number of examples and compared with similar motifs occasionally found in rock paintings.

There are over 35 carved rock drawings on a hill in the Melsetter area. The patterns are made by removing the surface of the rock by fine peckings to a depth of 2 to 4 mm. Several series of designs can be distinguished. One notable feature is the 'rosette' motif, a circle of dots or 'roundels' enclosed in a larger circle (Fig. 1A and E). Sometimes rays emerge from a circle (Fig. 1C). Two circles are frequently connected by a straight or curved line, assuming the shape of dumb-bells (Fig. 1B). Curious bulbous patterns are found, one of which may represent a primitive human form, an important variant (Fig. 1F). Others seem to represent elements of plant life (Fig. 1G and H). Several rocks have nothing but two or more rows of dots; one has dots in the rough shape of a cross.

One rock, with a design different from all others, seems to be made with particular care. It may be compared with the representations of animal spoors: the foot at rest and splaying out when running (Fig. 1D).

Wavy-linear motifs occur on a few Melsetter rocks. They are also very conspicuous on a larger rock surface, further north, on the Inyanga Downs. In the so-called 'labyrinth', a large rock painting in the Umtali District, we find spirals, meanders and wavy lines, profusely displayed by carefully painted treble lines. The wavy lines of the French caves, known as 'macaroni', also have their parallels in Rhodesian paintings (Fig. 2, from Masembura Grave Cave).

Circles and concentric circles occur only occasionally in the paintings, but seem to be important and devised to express cosmic or abstract subjects. In a painting near Salisbury three such motifs appear to represent clouds and rain. Near Macheke are found concentric circles giving the impression of water. Meandering lines have been painted on a wall-surface near Mrewa, as well as in a cave to the south, near Zaka.

Animal spoors are found in rock engravings and paintings in several parts of S. Rhodesia. They may well be classified under the geometric signs; in their simple style they may have conveyed messages to others. One example shows spoors leading to an antelope. In another, a hunter seems to follow spoors. There are also some short dashes which may represent water. Quite unique is the large spoor of a hippopotamus near Lake McIlwaine.

The carved animal spoors at Bumbusi, Wankie area, include also human feet, but this is a rare and late idea, frequently found in S.W. Africa. Far more important are human hands, which occur as very early signs in French and Spanish cave art, notably those at Gargas and Castillo. There is a 'Cave of Hands' at Wilton, Cape, and a similar one in Australia. North of Domboshowa is a single hand in connection with some alignments of dots. Hands are not often found in Rhode-

---

* This paper appears in an abbreviated form, having been submitted originally with 50 illustrations.

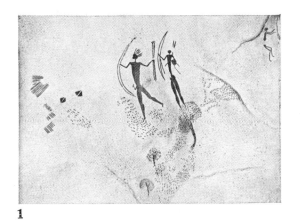

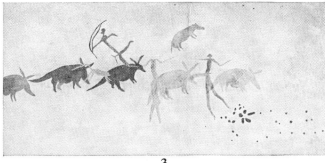

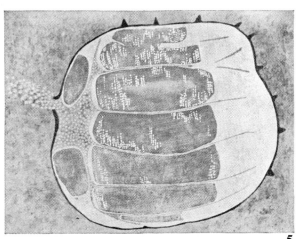

1

2

3

4

5

PLATE VII: The Geometric Motif in Rock Art

1. Saffron Walden Farm, Salisbury West. Hunters in hilly country. An impression of distance is created by massed rows of dots. To the left is an angular geometric motif.

2. Elladale Farm, Lake McIlwaine. Water is often represented by dashes: to the left they are arranged like a bird in flight, to the right in the form of fishes.

3. Makumbe Cave, Antbears and other animals with splashes like a flower motif.

4. Ruchera Cave, Mtoko. A variation of the 'formling' motif. These may be boulders, piled up or standing. They are often dotted, sometimes striped, and often have white 'caps'.

5. Zombepata Cave, Sipolilo area. Another variation of the 'formling' motif. Oval or brick-like forms surrounded by a curved outline, with 'arrow-heads' or 'birds' feet' moving in and out between the yellow oblong shapes.

(By courtesy of The Wilkie Foundation)

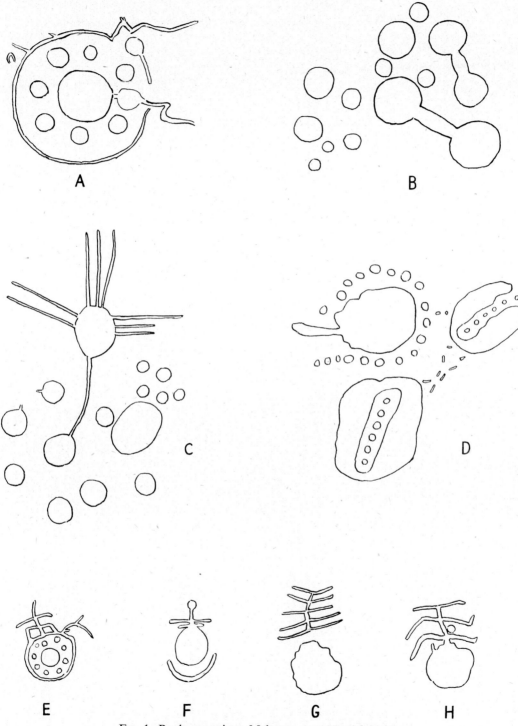

FIG. 1. Rock engravings, Melsetter area, Heathfield farm

sian cave art, but some massing of hands was observed in the richly painted Chikupu cave, where over 70 are arranged in several rows; but they are much obliterated and barely visible.

Animal spoors and short dashes often go together. Such dashes may mean various things; sometimes, as at Glen-Norah Farm, Salisbury South, where they are drawn in conjunction with a fish, they clearly represent water. They can also depict grass or the panorama of hilly country (Plate VII, 1). To the left of this painting is an unique geometric sign: two pairs of clearly drawn triangles next to various parallel lines.

At some sites in Mashonaland one can observe a curious development when the artist sees living forms in the massing of dashes and then arranges them in the shape of animals (Plate VII, 2). Here some of the dashes are sketched in the shape of a bird with open wings, and further to the right are two fishes sketched in stippled manner. In the lower part of this painting are many rows of dots, apparently an important motif which is often painted in the Union of S. Africa, where it is described as game tracks. In Franco-Cantabrian cave art this motif is sometimes quite conspicuous.

In Makumbe Cave, Chinamora Reserve, a procession of antbears passes a neatly drawn arrangement of dots and splashes which possibly represent animal droppings, as important as spoors to guide the hunter to his quarry (Plate VII, 3).

Mention should be made here of the 'formling' motif, introduced under that name by L. Frobenius; and quite a good word it is, as one cannot always understand these peculiar forms. Many of them are truly geometrical: the commonest forms are rectangles, ovals, segments and many variations of these. A graceful variation of ovals, some lying as if piled up, others rigidly standing, is apparent in Plate VII, 4. The 'formling' or 'sausage' motif appears late in the development of Rhodesian rock art and is in most cases done in bichrome or polychrome. At Concession, Howick Estate, is an elaborate composition belonging to the formling category. Quite possibly, most of these geometric forms represent piled-up rocks, with cliffs and shelters. Occasionally

Fig. 2. Rock painting, Masembura Grave Cave, south of Bundura.
A style resembling the 'macaroni' motif of the French caves

someone is pictured standing on top and, in some instances, an antelope is so portrayed. But looking at a motif from Chikupu Cave, resembling 'dancing legs' (which can only be a link in the great family of these variable patterns), one is at a loss where to place it.

Piled up brick-like forms are occasionally surrounded by a curvilinear outline, which usually has an 'entrance' where tiny white 'arrow-heads' seem to move in and out; this is quite an individual concept only observed in the Umvukwe area. A fine example is reproduced in Plate VII, 5. In this same area one also sees on the rocks irregular ovals filled with white dots which are extremely carefully arranged within these ovals; sometimes the dots move across their periphery or are carefully filing out of a little entrance towards the neighbouring circle. These signs may have a relationship with the cloud-and-rain motif of Epworth Mission, Salisbury, and there is the possibility that the idea for this motif arose from the importance water played for the cave man and his observations of rain clouds.

An extreme angular and quadratic variety was found at Ruundzi Farm, Wedza; the colours are red, brown and yellow. There are surprising counterparts in the French caves, as at Lascaux (Fig. 3); these chequered figures, painted in red, black, brown and mauve, also called blazons, were tentatively linked with tribal signs. We find in Rhodesian paintings all the geometric devices which occur in Franco-Cantabrian rock art, with the exception of angular drawings representing huts, roofs or tents, and despite the vast difference in age.

Fig. 3. *Left:* Painting, Ruundzi Farm, Wedza, Southern Rhodesia
Right: Painting of 'blazon', Lascaux, France

Spoors and hands were included in this study, although they do not strictly rank in the geometric group, since there seems to have been a similar purport as with dashes, dots, waves, circles and other motifs. We find these symbols in all stylistic periods, but in Southern Africa more at the culminating point of the art and lasting until the end. They are seemingly of secondary importance, but of immense value to those who strive to solve some of the problems involved in the study of prehistoric art.

46

Techniques of Recording Prehistoric Art

by L. S. B. LEAKEY

ANY worker who is attempting to record prehistoric art will naturally have certain ideas of his own as to the best technique to adopt and the best materials to employ; but, nevertheless, a knowledge of techniques used by others can often be very helpful and, as a result of the experience gained by my wife and myself in recording the prehistoric paintings of 186 sites in Tanganyika Territory, we feel that the following notes may be of use to others.

For the actual tracing material, we have found that thick, good quality, cellophane sheets are as serviceable as the more expensive, fully transparent, polyethylene products and, where a large number of paintings have to be traced, the use of the latter is obviously prohibitive.

The sheets of cellophane are fastened to the rock face with sellotape and should be fixed not only at corners and sides but, if large sheets are being used, hinged sections (like stamp mounts for affixing stamps in albums) should also be made and applied in the centre of the underside of the sheet. If this is done, there is much less likelihood of wind getting in between the cellophane and the rock and tearing the tracing material.

We have found that the best medium with which to make the tracings on the cellophane is that known as 'glass ink', which can be obtained in a wide range of colours. It is better applied with a very fine camel-hair brush than with a pen. It dries very quickly, does not run and can be used even for tracing a painting on a ceiling.

We do not use glass ink of colours comparable to those of the original paintings, finding it much more satisfactory to employ colours which do *not* appear at all on the rock face, such as greens and blues, since thus it is far easier to see what part of any figure has already been traced and what remains to be done.

Where paintings are high up on the face of the cave or rock shelter, we have discovered that ladders are unsatisfactory and that the best method is to take light-weight (preferably aluminium alloy) builders' scaffolding rods and couplings, since these can be erected firmly, no matter how uneven the floor, and provide one with a really satisfactory stand from which to carry out the tracing work. Reflectors of white cardboard and also of sheet aluminium are useful for lighting difficult corners.

Whereas many workers take their field tracings back to the laboratories and there carry out the processes of reduction to half or quarter size and the transference to a paper medium, we have found that this often leads to inaccuracy. We, therefore, take into the field large 8 feet × 6 feet trestle tables and upon these lay the cellophane tracings and then cover them with sheets of perspex, which have been ruled into 2 inch and 1 inch squares. This makes it possible to reduce very rapidly to either half or quarter natural size.

When the tracings have been accurately reduced to squared paper, these reductions are placed upon a drawing board and taken back to the original site, where they are carefully compared with the originals that were traced in order to eliminate any inaccuracy.

The next stage of the work is to transfer, by means of *white* carbons, the reductions on the

304

squared paper to drawing paper. This must be as nearly as possible the colour of the original rock and, where necessary, tinted before the outlines of the tracings are transferred to it.

The coloured sheets with the *white* carbon outlines of the reduced tracings are then placed on the drawing board and set up on an easel at the original site; the final colouring is done on the spot, carefully matching the colours used with the originals at every stage.

Some advice may be given about the medium used for this final work. Water-colours serve best in some cases, but frequently crayon has to be used and later 'fixed'. We have also discovered that to reproduce the *texture* of certain types of prehistoric painting a mixture of water-colours with powdered crayon is the most successful medium.

47

The Cave Paintings and Rock Gongs of Birnin Kudu

by B. E. B. FAGG

THE first discovery of rock paintings in Nigeria was made when the chief of the town of Birnin Kudu reported a small painted rock shelter to a touring administrative officer early in 1954. Birnin Kudu is an important District headquarters in Kano Emirate and is situated about 84 miles east-south-east of Kano on the new main arterial road to Bornu and the Sudan. Two years ago the town was moved from its old site two miles away and re-sited on the main road in the middle of a group of small granite hills extending over an area of two or three square miles. These outcrops of the so-called Younger Granite Series happen to have weathered in such a way that many shelters have been formed and huge boulders, exfoliations and rock spalls lie in great disorder and show a striking contrast to the gently undulating plain.

Work at Birnin Kudu has so far been confined to half a day in January and two days in December 1954, one day in April and three and a half days in June this year, and six days' work kindly undertaken by Professor A. J. H. Goodwin in April of this year on his way back from carrying out excavations in Benin City for the Nigerian Antiquities Service.

The first group of paintings, on the hill known as Dutsen Mesa, was always known to the people of Birnin Kudu for they are only about a hundred feet from the old motor road and were clearly visible to pedestrians (and one might have thought to motorists) who passed along the road. The new arterial road passes within about 300 feet of this rock shelter, which is therefore particularly vulnerable to damage by vandalism. Its protection by a masonry and steel structure was completed in April this year (see Fig. 1).

The rock shelter is formed by the weathering of the granite face below a gently sloping cleavage plane which causes the rain water draining from the rocks above to drip off three or four feet clear of the paintings, which are thus well protected, except from occasional driving rain. The annual rainfall is between 25 and 30 inches and humidity is therefore relatively low, even at the height of the rains. The subjects of the paintings are exclusively of domestic cattle with the exception of a single enigmatical drawing, which may possibly be a sketch plan of a cattle kraal. An identical design has been recorded in two places in the area of Dermel-Tal, near Colomb-Béchar in Algeria.

The paintings are without movement and usually without composition. There are no human figures. The cattle are of two main types, a long-bodied, long-legged humpless breed with long spreading or converging, sometimes lyre-shaped, horns (see Fig. 2) and a short thick-bodied short-horned humpless breed (see Fig. 3). These two species are tentatively identified as the Hamitic long-horn, now extinct in Nigeria though perhaps leaving its mark on the characteristic long-horned *zebu* cattle of the present day, and *brachyceros*, the short-horned humpless cattle known today as *muturu* and confined, or nearly so, to the tsetse-infested rain-forest regions of the south of Nigeria and parts of the riverain provinces, while a few herds survive among the pagan tribes inhabiting the hills of the Jos Plateau and similar hill regions of Northern Nigeria.

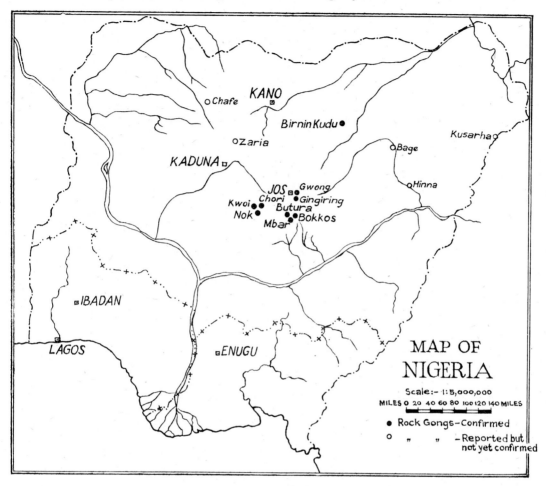

There appear to be three main styles of painting and four substyles at Birnin Kudu. The only superposition so far identified is a succession of three main styles at Dutsen Mesa.

Style A Large humpless long-horned cow in red outline. The line of the back is partly executed in black.

Style B (overlying Style A) Large solid white humpless long-horned cow.

Style C (overlying Style B) Solid red humpless *brachyceros* cow.

Similar to Style A there are:

*Style A*1 Humpless long-horned cattle in solid red.

*Style A*2 Humpless long-horned cattle in red outline with faded white body, more stylized than A1 and with convergent horns, tentatively placed here on account of the condition of the pigment.

The latest paintings appear to be solid white *brachyceros* (many have patches without pigment) and these have been called *Style D*.

There is, elsewhere, a single red outline *brachyceros* (at present without horns) which can conveniently be called *Style D*1.

FIG. 1. The Rock shelter at Dutsen Mesa (B.K.1) near Birnin Kudu: (*a*) and (*b*) are rock gongs; (*c*) is the entrance to a cave in which there are three rock gongs

FIG. 2. Two Hamitic long-horn cows painted in solid red on the ceiling of the rock shelter at Dutsen Habude (B.K.2). In the foreground is part of a large exfoliation used extensively at its other extremity as a rock gong. Note chatter-marks on the paintings where they have evidently been struck with stones in an effort to obliterate them

FIG. 3. White *brachyceros* cows at Dutsen Mesa (B.K.1)

Within ten feet of Dutsen Mesa, which is the main site at Birnin Kudu and known as B.K.1, there is a gap varying from nine to twelve inches between a roughly horizontal earth floor and a horizontal ceiling, which gave reason to expect that a habitable cave of convenient proportions might have existed before it became choked with soil and débris. Professor Goodwin began the excavation of an approach trench to put this theory to the test. He was able to complete about half of it in spite of great difficulties through the excessively hot weather, which was aggravated by the incidence of fasting in preparation for the Mohamedan feast of Ramadan. The excavation of this trench was completed by me in June. The trench yielded some 600 sherds of which 90 were decorated, a dozen iron objects including arrow and spear points, 90 stone flakes and a single core, and a dozen lumps of stone which could have been used as ingredients for the pigments used on the wall. In addition there was a fragment of a stone bangle and a quartz lip-plug which may prove to link this assemblage with the Epineolithic culture of Nok, which stretches 300 miles across the valleys of the Benue and Niger Rivers. It is not possible to identify the stone industry. The probability however is that these rock paintings belong to the period of transition from the neolithic to the metal age when the introduction of iron working, perhaps from the Nile valley, made possible the unification of culture and language over a wide area in much the same way as the trade which followed the British flag in Nigeria is tending inevitably to destroy the rich diversity of material culture of the very numerous tribes living in Northern Nigeria and to replace their languages with Hausa, which has already become the *lingua franca*.

In April this year I noticed that a slab of granite lying close to one of the less accessible paintings had apparently been heavily struck by some kind of a hammer and deep troughs and cup-shaped holes had resulted from this percussion. When struck this rock vibrates with a dull bell-note. This was followed by the discovery of other hammered rocks, but lack of time prevented the following up of this clue at the time.

In June however I returned to Birnin Kudu with a set of 13 tuning forks. Very extensive

FIG. 4. View of rock shelter at Dutsen Habude (B.K.2) from below, showing a rock gong which has been struck heavily on the edge and also underneath, on the right hand side. The paintings shown in figure 2 are faintly discernible just below the x

exploration of the granite hills revealed the existence of large numbers of these hammered rocks, which I think can best be described as rock gongs. They consist of huge natural spalls or exfoliations of rock which happen to rest or be wedged in a position favourable to the production of musical notes (see Fig. 4). No less than ten groups of rock gongs were found within a hundred feet of Dutsen Mesa. While rocks which ring when struck are very common in these hills, due to the quite extraordinary way in which the rock fractures, those which have been hammered are very significantly clustered around the painted caves, and it is difficult to believe that they are not connected with the paintings. It seems highly probable that in most cases they were used as *ensemble instruments* by several players.

After experimenting with the tuning forks on several of the rock gongs and finding that the notes could be identified, I had my attention drawn to a group of rocks where the boys of the town have been known to play at making the rocks ring by striking them with stones. Here under a large overhanging boulder and just within the drip line we found a fine, though faded, representation of a *brachyceros* bull. There were also several other paintings. About five yards behind this painted rock we found a group of rock gongs, most of which were under the cover of overhanging boulders.

These seemed to make such a homogeneous group that we tuned all the parts which had been struck and marked the notes and semi-tones on the rocks. Having completed tuning all the deeply struck specimens we checked and found that eleven of the thirteen available notes were present. Returning to the largest of the multiple gongs (see Fig. 5) on which five notes had already been identified, we found the other two notes on parts of the rock which had been only slightly used. All the identifications had been made with the help of the two best drummers in the town.

Although many of the rock gongs have recently been bruised by hammering they all have a patina which in the case of those placed out of the reach of children is intact. It is evident from their condition that they were extensively used in antiquity. Their distribution makes it probable that they were intimately connected with the rock paintings and may conceivably have provided music for some religious cult.

The Cave Paintings and Rock Gongs of Birnin Kudu

The cave with the short-horned bull, where the complete range of musical notes was found, is about two miles from the old walled city of Birnin Kudu, whose inhabitants are strict Muslims. In spite of this no girl born in Birnin Kudu is ever married without, on her wedding day, going to this cave at dawn and sitting there alone or with other brides until the late afternoon when she returns to the town for the marriage ceremonies. No one in Birnin Kudu can explain this custom which is apparently unknown elsewhere in the Emirate of Kano. It is very difficult not to see in this the vague folk-memory of a long-forgotten and, no doubt, prohibited ceremony. Similar survivals exist in England and elsewhere of pagan customs whose purpose has long been forgotten.

The paintings themselves are somewhat similar to some Algerian and Nubian groups and superficially to those in south-east Abyssinia. They portray humpless long-horned cattle which are now extinct, and short-horned cattle which are now only found far to the south. The latter may have arrived in West Africa early in the Christian era following perhaps the introduction of the camel to the Saharan region. The cultural remains in the cave deposits, though not necessarily associated with the paintings, suggest a possible link with the Epineolithic culture of Nok, whereas

FIG. 5. Large multiple rock gong at Dutsen Murufu (B.K.5) from which at least seven different notes can be produced. The left hand of Mallam Abati, the custodian, is resting on the most heavily worn edge

FIG. 6. Rock gong at Bokkos on the Jos Plateau. This huge boulder is in the open air, unlike most of the others which are in caves or rock shelters where the resonance is increased. The depressions at the bottom are in current use; one at the top left corner of the photograph is covered by a patina, and lichen

the design on the ceiling of the cave at Dutsen Habude (B.K.2) leaves no doubt that the paintings of some, if not all, periods are linked closely with those described by Frobenius and Obermaier in the region of Colomb-Béchar in Algeria.

NOTE

On my return from Livingstone, I began to search for rock gongs in likely places as opportunity offered and soon found good specimens in the vicinity of the village of Bokkos (at Mbar, Bokkos itself (see Fig. 6), and Batura), near Jos (at Gwong and Gingiring) and around Nok in Southern Zaria Province (Kwoi, Nok and Chori).

I have also noted sites reported by reliable informants over a wide area stretching across Northern Nigeria through the Provinces of Sokoto, Zaria, Kano, Plateau, Bauchi and Bornu, to the Northern Cameroons. Some are used to this day in initiation rites for the dances prior to circumcision (Bokkos area). Many are used by young girls and boys purely for entertainment though many of the gongs are closely connected with groups of small grinding grooves used for practise by young girls before marriage (Birnin Kudu, Nok, Bokkos, etc.), and some with rock slides used by the young boys (Birnin Kudu, Kwoi, etc.). Some again (e.g. at Nok) were used during wartime to warn the farmers of enemy attack, and many are even said to be connected with religious beliefs about which my informants were reluctant to give information.

48

Protohistoric Pottery in Uganda*

by E. C. LANNING

IN Uganda our knowledge of protohistoric pottery has been enhanced to some extent as a result of collections made at major sites at Ntusi, Bigo, Mubende Hill and Munsa. These are the most important and elaborate of the group of ancient earthworks and occupation centres that stretch from the south of Lake Albert down to the Uganda-Tanganyika border, in the vicinity of Lake Victoria. According to legend these sites are all associated with a highly skilled people known as the Bachwezi who, coming from the north, subjugated a large area as far as Kavirondo in Kenya in the east, the Congo in the west and Tanganyika in the south.

Smaller collections and records of pottery have been made in the past outside of the area of Bachwezi sites but mainly within the boundaries of the kingdoms of Bunyoro and Buganda.

The ware to which it has been possible to give some detailed attention comes mainly from Ntusi, which is an ancient settlement covering approximately ¾ of a square mile, in Masaka District, Buganda; other Bachwezi sites are, of course, also included.

Ntusi and associated ware may be considered in three classes. A, a friable rough red undecorated ware; B, brown undecorated ware, vessels having no form of rim lip; C, the most common and characteristic ware of the Bachwezi culture, being a coarse brown ware, normally incised or elaborately decorated with punch-marks or geometric patterns, often gritty with quartz particles and badly fired.

It is with class C that this paper deals in the main. The rims of vessels in this classification have everted lips, and are sometimes completely decorated with square or round impressions. The decoration usually ends with a wide band round the neck though, in some cases, small pots were completely covered with rouletted or string-impressed patterns. The normal colour is brown but varies from red-brown to grey. A red paint, as well as other colours, has been used in different ways.

Decoration with paint took the form of complete coloration of interiors of vessels or the reddening of the exterior of smooth undecorated rims. Another method was to daub the roulette-patterned exterior of a pot with red spots.

An interesting application of colour was by means of the fingers, leaving an impression or smear for the length of the three joints overlapping the rim, the finger tips, in some cases, having been pressed just below the neck of the vessel (Fig. 1). Sherds have been recovered having this smear in black, blue and brown as well as in red. The only known instance of this type of design being present on an almost complete vessel is where three associated finger marks, which overlap the neck, have been impressed at intervals around the rim.

Most of the hilltops in the environs of Kampala have yielded broken pottery, mainly bearing string or grooved roller as well as scratched patterns.

A number of objects, patterned, rounded and elongated from the Bachwezi sites, might well

* Most of the pottery referred to in this paper is either in the Uganda Museum or the author's present collection. Certain specimens are in the British Museum and the National Museum of Southern Rhodesia.

The Babemba initiation utensils referred to are in the Rhodes-Livingstone Museum, Northern Rhodesia.

have been handles of heavy vessels or, in some instances, legs of pots. The former type, and the use of stout clay handles, is unknown in pottery fashioned since the beginning of the century. Pots raised on supports are likewise unknown with the exception of a four-legged pot found at a shrine at Luzira.

Large looped handles have been recovered from Ntusi and Mubende Hill; also pots with perforated bases which suggest their use as strainers.

Looped handles for small bowls were evidently in common use not only at these and other Bachwezi sites but elsewhere as well. A small complete bowl with handles, from a rock shelter in Mubende, was probably in use at the latest one hundred years ago and is believed to be of a type kept by women for the storage of perfume. Another interesting bowl, from Ankole in the West, is also remarkable for its small looped handles as well as the unusual impressed patterns of decoration arranged in zig zag form that encircle it below the neck. Nothing is known of the usage of this pot.

Vessels, jars, pots, etc. have evidently played part in worship and burial. It is of interest to note that ware, originally designed as fumigators, appears in certain cases to have been used purely for purposes of ritual.

Jars with narrow necks 4 to 6 inches long were in use, as well as semi-oval pots perforated by a central hole in the base, but whether for ritual or domestic purposes it is impossible to say.

Unusual complete vessels have come to light at apparently abandoned centres of worship. The purposes that they fulfilled are, in most cases, unknown. The Mubende Hill occupation site, covering 12 acres, had at its centre a woodland shrine presided over by a priestess of the spirit of smallpox. Two flat-bottomed beakers from there come in this category of doubt. The reconstructed specimens have four inch-wide bands of oblique cross-hatching below their rims. Likewise, large globular vessels, some over two feet high, were in apparent use at the same centre. Possibly they were originally designed for the storage of grain or beer. However, their position *in situ* at the actual centre of worship, the presence of pierced cowrie shells and smooth stones known to have been used in witchcraft, as well as animal and bird bones usually the result of sacrifice, does suggest the vessels' sole use in some form of ritual. They are plain except for rows of indentations below the rims made by pressure of the finger-nail or a flat rounded spatula.

From an excavation further north, at Semwema near the Munsa earthworks, it is probable that this large type of vessel has also been associated with burial. It is known that the bodies of twins, together with small pots, were placed inside such a large vessel, which was then buried near the hearth of a fire in an inverted position.

Small pots, inverted over mounds of ritual offerings or grave goods, have also been excavated at Ntusi.

During recent years small pots with pointed bases have been recovered in western Uganda from swamps and sites fifty miles and more apart.

Mention should be made of a burial urn bulldozed to the light of day at Nkongora in Toro (Fig. 2). This urn was rescued and reported on by the Government Archaeologist, Mr K. Marshall, in 1953. Available evidence is insufficient to date it. It appeared that it had been inverted in a pit. The contents were parts of two human skeletons, one adult and an infant as well as a saucer and a broken bowl in red ware, the latter burnished. The urn itself has a flat base and is $45\frac{1}{2}$ cm. in height, the maximum diameter of the mouth being 31 cm. Though about two-thirds larger, it is similar in many features to the two flat-bottomed beakers from Mubende Hill. Four more pits containing pottery, unavoidably smashed by the scraper, were also revealed close by. It seems probable that the cutting passed through the edge of an area containing ceremonial burials.

An unusual sherd excavated on the Mubende Hill site bears two moulded bosses stuck on side by side, immediately below the rim which is broad and undecorated (Fig. 3). This sherd calls to mind certain of the moulded decorations found on pottery in Southern Rhodesia. Similar bosses which indicate female breasts have been recorded on pottery connected with the significance of

FIG. 1. Sherd from Mubende Hill showing finger smears of paint

FIG. 4. The Ntusi Cylinder

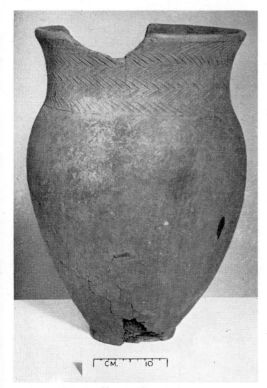

FIG. 2. The urn from Nkongora

FIG. 3. Sherd with applied moulded bosses from Mubende Hill

315

married life. Such moulded decoration is extremely rare in Uganda and, I am given to under-stand,[1] is unknown in Kenya.

Since this is the only sherd of its kind recovered up to date, comparison is justified with another isolated object, the cylinder covered with bosses found at Ntusi some years ago (Fig. 4). Un-fortunately the provenance of this cylinder within the area of the settlement is unknown. The purpose that it fulfilled is still open to conjecture. A comparison has been drawn to the Rosette Cylinder from Zimbabwe which has similar characteristics. The Rev. G. Mathew, in a preliminary observation after his visit to the site in 1952, considered that it may well be a cult object with some form of fertility worship. But it is interesting to note that in Northern Rhodesia such knobs appear on the ritual utensils used by the Babemba in the Chisungu initiation ceremonies.[2] Similar bosses, I have been informed by Mr B. E. B. Fagg, are also prominent on certain Nigerian ritual vessels.

The only other known examples of moulded decorations on pottery are those on the Luzira Head, in the hair, and on a *kiganda* clay pipe said to have belonged to a warrior chief, Nsimbi (*circa* 1814). In this latter case the moulds appear to represent cowrie shells and drums.

The terracotta head found at Luzira in 1930 has been given close attention. In his study of this head Mr H. J. Braunholtz commented that nothing analogous to the figure could be suggested in African art.

In recent years, following on the exhibition of a plaster cast of the finds at the Uganda Museum, Dr K. P. Wachsmann, the Curator, drew attention to a number of similar features in one of the Djenne figures from the river Niger which set the Luzira head into some perspective.

He has found numerous points of close resemblance, for instance, in the heads being pyramid-shaped, the eyes protruding and the treatment of the hair in applied pellets; in the squat shape of both trunks; in the hands, the treatment of the fingers including a heavy bracelet on the wrist.

Further, a four-legged pot or vessel was found close by in each case. Also the Djenne heads were recovered from above the seasonal flood of the Niger, whilst the Luzira head was discovered on a hill-top close to Lake Victoria. Cylindrical fragments of pottery were found at both sites.

Mr R. Mauny has drawn attention to the five figures recovered at Mopti, likewise on the Niger, but has also pointed out that even closer comparisons can be drawn with the sculptures excavated at Sao in the Tchad region.[3]

Whether fertility cults of protohistoric times ever resulted in the modelling of figurines or not, it is still too early to say. One or two small unidentified objects from Bachwezi sites as well as from Kanyanya Hill near Kampala have given cause for thought on these lines. Only the recovery of associated objects, however, can throw further light on the question. In passing, mention should be made of the isolated instance of two small clay figures, apparently of some antiquity, which come from Lango in the Northern Province. They were presented to the Uganda Museum ten years ago as being definitely fertility figures. Unfortunately further data is not available.

It has recently been established that certain clay objects, recovered during the past two years, once formed part of the bowl-bellows of blacksmiths. Their purpose was apparently decorative, symbolizing human male and female genitalia. It has, as yet, been impossible to throw any light on the purpose and origin of this custom.

Worthy of mention are the middens of Kibiro, on the eastern shore of Lake Albert. These are easily accessible situated as they are only a few miles from Hoima, the District Headquarters of Bunyoro.

They constitute an immense wealth of stratified pottery. The salt deposits of this area had been one of the major sources of revenue at least to the ancient kingdom of Bunyoro-Kitara and prob-ably to its forerunners. The area, at the foot of a steep escarpment, always administered by a senior ranking chief, has supported a sizeable population for centuries.

No systematic excavation of this site has ever been carried out. In the top layers sherds, bearing roller patterns similar to those found on pottery from inland sites, as well as fragmentary smoking pipes, are common. Only smooth sherds appear to rest in the lowest layers. Animal bones appear numerous throughout the stratification.

Mr E. J. Wayland considers that wide and flat dishes were probably used for the purpose of evaporation much as somewhat similar pots are used today. He has also recorded finding small grinding stones, whilst in the bottom layers he discovered a perforated cowrie shell. The upper layers have also yielded a number of glass and disc beads.

These middens which are up to twelve feet deep must have a compact story to tell of the mediaeval period they cover and their early attention is fully warranted.

The pottery under discussion covers a considerable period, a period of which very little is known. In the absence of detailed explorations at the major sites and the lack of excavation no attempt at dating can be made. There is little doubt that the area alone of the Bachwezi sites has much to reveal and to tell. Its careful study would undoubtedly fill much of the gap that still exists in our knowledge of the protohistoric period.

NOTES

1. Personal communication, Mrs M. D. Leakey, 1954.
2. A close similarity is evident between the Babemba initiation pot Mundu, which has four mouth-pieces, and a multi-mouthed pot recovered from the ritual centre at Masaka Hill, Mubende District.
3. Personal communication, 1955.

REFERENCES

Bequaert, M. (1949), 'The Masaka Cylinder', *Uganda Journal*, 13, p. 23.
Braunholtz, H. J. (1933), 'Archaeological Discoveries at Luzira', *Man*, 29.
Cole, S. M. (1954), *The Prehistory of East Africa*, Pelican Books, Harmondsworth, Middlesex, pp. 280–4.
Goodall, E. (1946), 'Rhodesian Pots with Moulded Decorations', *Native Affairs Dept. Annual, Southern Rhodesia*, No. 23, pp. 37–49.
Lanning, E. C. (1953), 'Some Vessels and Beakers from Mubende Hill, Uganda', *Man*, 283.
Lanning, E. C. (1953), 'Ancient Earthworks in Western Uganda', *Uganda Journal*, 17, pp. 51–62.
Lanning, E. C. (1954), 'Masaka Hill—An ancient centre of worship', *Uganda Journal*, 18, pp. 24–30.
Lanning, E. C. (1954), 'Genital Symbols on smiths' bellows in Uganda', *Man*, 262.
Lanning, E. C. (1955), 'The Munsa Earthworks', *Uganda Journal*, 19, pp. 177–182.
van Riet Lowe, C. (1952), *The Pleistocene Geology and Prehistory of Uganda*, Pt. 2: 'Prehistory', pp. 102–3.
Marshall, K. (1953), 'Preliminary Report on Archaeological Discoveries near Nkongora Camp', Geol. Survey Dept., Uganda, unpublished.
Marshall, K. (1954), 'The Prehistory of the Entebbe Peninsula', *Uganda Journal*, 18, pp. 44–57.
Mathew, G. (1953), 'Recent Discoveries in East African Archaeology', *Antiquity*, 28 (109), pp. 214–17.
Mauny, R. (1949), 'Statuettes de Terre Cuite de Mopti', *Notes Africaines*, 43, pp. 70–2.
Trowell, M. (1945), 'A Rosette Cylinder of Clay from Uganda', *Man*, 100.
Trowell, M. (1953), *Tribal Crafts of Uganda*, Oxford University Press, p. 276.
Vieillard, G. (1940), 'Sur quelques objets en terre cuite de Dienné', *Bulletin de l'IFAN*, 2 (3–4), Paris, p. 347.
Wachsmann, K. (1950), 'A Comparison between the Luzira and the Dienne finds', Uganda Museum, unpublished.
Wayland, E. J. (1920), *Some facts and theories relating to the Geology of Uganda*, Govt. Press, Uganda.

49

Early Iron Age Sites in Tanganyika relative to Traditional History

by H. A. FOSBROOKE

NORTHERN Tanganyika represents a borderland where several ethnic stocks meet and mingle. Firstly, there are the Nilo-hamitic pastoralists, represented by the Masai and the Tatog; secondly, an unidentified stock, possibly Hamitic, of whom the Iraqw of Mbulu form the largest tribe: and, finally, the Bantu, typified by the Pare, Chagga and Meru.

All these tribes possess one feature in common; none claims autochthony, all having arrived, according to their own and neighbouring tribes' traditions, in recent centuries into their present habitat. The pastoralists arrived with their language and culture much as they are today; there is a considerable body of evidence to support this traditional belief. Much the same applies to the Iraqw group, though modification has probably been greater here.

With the Bantu, however, no tribe possesses a tradition or belief in a mass migration; all admit to entering their present areas in dribs and drabs, drawing their component elements from various tribes, and not always Bantu. There is no traditional record of the new inhabitants replacing previous agricultural folk. The Chagga record dwarf hunters in the forest (Dundas, 1924), as do the Mbugwe (Gray, 1955). The Chagga (Dundas, ibid.) also record another tribe, the Umbo, but it appears from the record that these were transitory and not settled inhabitants of the area. A remnant group, the Ngassa, is found amongst the Chagga but I have shown elsewhere (Fosbrooke, 1955) that these were probably precursors of the Nilo-Hamitic Masai. Another remnant group, the Mbugu, were more numerous amongst the Pare in the past, but are today found mostly amongst the Sambaa; the latest assessment of their language (Whiteley and Gutkind, 1954) indicates that they are more likely of Iraqw, rather than of Nilo-Hamitic origin. The latter stock, however, was early in the area, as, in addition to the Ngassa mentioned above, the present-day hunters, the Dorobo, of the Ruvu Valley, speak a language of the Nandi group (Maguire, 1948), whilst early German records mention the existence of Tatog in the Kilimanjaro area.

Thus there is much evidence of comings and goings in the past but two features are noticeable; the goings seem to concern pastoral and hunting folk, the comings the agricultural Bantu, who settled in the mountain areas. There is no traditional evidence of the Bantu replacing other agriculturists in these forest areas; confirmation of the accuracy of this is available from sociological sources. Time and again a study of the clan and lineage structures of the various tribes reveals an expanding population taking up more and more unoccupied forest land till eventually the area was completely filled and the surplus population had to move elsewhere.

There is, however, a considerable body of archaeological evidence coming to light that at some time in the past there were sedentary, agricultural iron-age folk living on the plains. It is with these sites that this paper deals. In the first place they were sedentary, as proved by the fact that the mud of their wattle and daub houses has at times been turned to brick—presumably by the house catching fire—with a result that burnt brick clots of varying size are to be picked up on the site today. As shown in Fig. 1, the impression of the withies is still preserved on the internal surfaces, whilst on the outer surface is sometimes to be discerned the imprint of the plasterers' fingers. It is a matter of conjecture whether these huts were roofed with thatch, or with the flat mud roof of *tembe* type, characteristic of Central Tanganyika today. Further research will answer this problem for us, for it has been observed that different techniques are today used in applying the wall plaster and the mud to the roofs. The former is well puddled with water, and slapped onto the wooden framework in a very plastic state. The roof, however, is covered with dry crumbly clay, which is left in that state till the first rain falls. When thus naturally moistened it is then worked with the hands to form an unbroken surface. Internally the clay, not having been puddled, retains its crumbly appearance, and on this evidence it is possible to differentiate roof clay from wall clay. The technique of identification requires further study, but is, I am convinced, capable of being perfected.

Further evidence of the sedentary nature of the population is to be found in the size of the kitchen middens. In one case the heap of refuse was 45 yards by 15, but of no great height—probably much of the ash had been removed by wind action. I am unaware whether anyone has studied the output of refuse by a subsistence agricultural community, but it should be possible to ascertain a factor of x cubic feet per person per year. From this the period of occupation could be ascertained.

There is thus sufficient evidence available to prove that the people concerned were sedentary. Some village sites must contain up to 100 house sites; this is my own estimate as I have not got down to detailed survey. The sites are distinguished from the neighbouring bush by a change in vegetation type. Not all the sites are open; some in Pare are, in fact, very thickly covered, but the ash heaps give freer drainage and varying soil composition, thus leading to different vegetational types, so that the inhabited area can be recognized.

The fact that the inhabitants were agricultural is proved by the presence of grindstones, Fig. 2. The fact that the granite is worn through testifies to the period of use. A line worth taking up is the varying techniques employed when grinding. In Northern Tanganyika today there are tribes who use an elongated upper stone whose ends protrude beyond the sides of the lower: this means that the latter eventually wears into a saddle shape. Others use a small upper stone which results in a bowl formation, as illustrated, whilst others again practise a technique of grinding such that the lower stone wears evenly and continues to present a flat surface until it is worn out. So side by side with any archaeological work undertaken in the area I commend a study of existing grinding methods and their relations to the grain being ground.

That the people were iron-age is undoubted, as slag and broken *tuyères* are to be found in all the villages, varying from isolated occurrences to profusion. I distinguish these villages from known iron-smelting sites used till recently by the Rangi and the Pare; I have recently described (Fosbrooke, 1954) one such site where 800 *tuyères* were found on the surface, with indications of many times that number underground. In the villages the profusion is not so great, but enough to indicate that the ironworking took place in the village. This disposes of one misconception held by the Pare who equate the inhabitants of these village sites with the Galla. For the Galla, in common with the Somali, Masai, Tatog, etc., regard their smiths as belonging to a lower caste; though Huntingford (1955) does not specifically say so, by implication and analogy we may conclude that the smiths lived apart in villages of their own. Thus evidence of ironworking would not be found in the centre of the villages—that is, unless they were specifically smiths' villages; and if so, where did the rest of the Galla live?—for evidence of ironworking occurs in practically every site. In one case two anvil stones have been found. Their use for this purpose is proved by the underpinning stones placed so that the anvil presents a level surface. This technique is used today by the local Rangi; in fact, further work is necessary on this site which, although now uninhabited, may prove to be the work of the Rangi and not their predecessors.

With the exception of one tiny iron ring, such as might have been used for decorating a bow tip, no iron work has yet been found, but this is understandable as all evidence so far consists of surface finds and any iron objects must have by now oxidized away; but not so the potsherds and shell beads which are the main indicators of sites.

The potsherds, to be found in considerable numbers on the sites, present features absent from the adjacent areas today. The double rim from Pare (Fig. 3) is something unique, as is the massive construction of the vessel which carries it. Pierced lugs are also common in this area and thereby hangs a tale. The early Pare lived side by side with the 'Galla', the latter having a repulsive habit of catching young Pare girls and cutting their breasts off. These they stewed up in pots; one such sacrificial site is pointed out today where elders still alive remember a complete pot standing as left by the 'Galla'. The association between lugged pottery and a breast legend is very suggestive of a rationalization.

Many of the patterns are very distinctive and show greater richness than anything to be found in the area today. The zigzag pattern (Fig. 4) occurs frequently and the technique of its application is plain. A fragment of curvilinear material, probably gourd, is impressed edgeways on the damp clay. It is then pivoted on one end and again pressed, pivoted on the opposite end and pressed, and so on till the rim of the pot is reached. The wavy-line specimen (Fig. 5) is almost identical in pattern with an example of Khartoum Mesolithic reproduced by Sonia Cole (1954) but too much significance must not be placed on this, for, as Mrs Cole herself says, 'Pottery is the favourite artifact of many archaeologists; from a handful of sherds they work out zones of contact, spheres of influence, migration routes over half a continent, and many other things besides. All this could not be plotted on a map if individual pot makers departed from the accepted pattern of their culture; if they did not, they must have been very dull fellows.'

Beads are a line which should help to date the sites, though the surface finds reveal the inhabitants as depending more on their own resources than on trade beads. A profusion of shell beads is to be found on all Pare sites: their occurrence gets less the further west one goes. Ostrich shell is used (Fig. 6, upper row), though snail shell is the more common material (Fig. 6, lower row). Beads, other than shell, are illustrated in Fig. 7. These are mostly stone, but the varying materials have not yet been identified so their origins are uncertain. At the left hand end of each row is illustrated a glass bead, the lower a half section. These are so patinated as to present the appearance of stone.

One pendant of snail shell has been found (Fig. 8, top row, centre), whilst the occasional cowrie indicates contact with the Coast. But they are few and far between, and being surface finds might have been dropped by the traders or the Masai who are known to have passed through the area in the nineteenth century. In fact the technique of cutting out the back of the cowrie (Fig. 8, top row right) is that practised by the Masai today when sewing cowries on to leather garments or gourds. The hole drilled in the top (second from right) is a non-Masai feature.

Two pieces of pigment have been recovered (Fig. 8, top left), pieces of haematite obviously shaped by rubbing on stone. These come from Pare and the fact that there are no rock paintings, save some Late Whites, in the area indicates that the pigment was more likely used for personal adornment than for rock painting.

The association between the sites and the 'Late White' style of rock painting, as defined by Fosbrooke et al. (1950) seems to be more than fortuitous. In Pare the only known rock paintings are of Late White style at Tusa Hill, within 10 miles of two or three iron-age sites. One of the two painting sites, both Late White, known in Masailand is within a few hundred yards of the Lerug occupation site. As can be seen in Fig. 9, one or two of the designs are modern, e.g. the shield device, but that is merely illustrative of the fact that painting attracts painting. In general the designs and styles are identical to the Kondoa Late Whites, which again occur in close proximity to the iron-age sites in the vicinity.

Though just outside the area here dealt with, the association between Late White paintings and the inhabitants who preceded the present tribes is recorded by Culwick (1931) at Bahi in Gogo country, at a point about 100 miles south-west from the Kondoa sites. Mnyampala (1954) describes the evidence of these pre-Gogo inhabitants as consisting of hut sites, grindstones, pot-

FIG. 1. Clay from wattle and daub structure turned to brick. Note: grooves indicate position of woodwork

FIG. 2. Push quern from Kondoa site, worn through with prolonged use

FIG. 3. Fragment of massive pot with double rim of type not found today. Section reveals thickness as approximately one inch

FIG. 4. Potsherd from Pare bearing zigzag pattern not now used

FIG. 5. Potsherd from Pare with wavy-line
pattern, also not used today

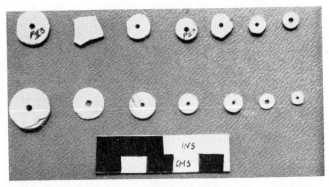

FIG. 6. Shell beads from Pare site. Upper row ostrich, lower
row snail shell

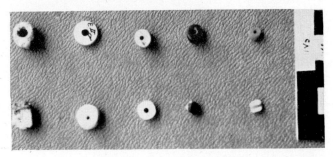

FIG. 7. Glass and stone beads from Pare sites

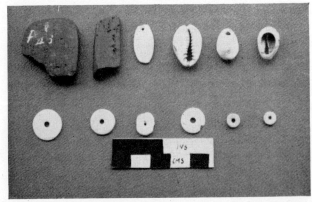

FIG. 8. Pigment, pendant, cowries and shell beads from Pare sites

sherds, etc. The circumstantial evidence is thus considerable that the Late White paintings were the work of the iron-age folk who preceded the present Bantu inhabitants.

I have not yet described the positions of the sites, but considerable significance attaches thereto (see map, pp. 328–9). In the case of the Pare group all lie at the eastern foot of the South Pare range, associated with the permanent streams which flow therefrom. But the significant feature is this; whilst the present day villages straddle the streams, the pre-Pare iron-age sites occur in the arid interstices between the rivers, in country which is today unattractive to agriculturists. Some is bush, whilst other portions have been taken up by non-Africans for sisal production. Thus the assumption is that when the sites were occupied the environment was more favourable than at present, whilst the present village sites were less attractive, damper, heavily forested and liable to flooding. Unfortunately none of the old sites has a rain gauge situated on it, but the southernmost, and admittedly the most arid, Kihurio, is in very similar country to Mkomasi Railway Station, 10 miles distant; here the rainfall is 13·67 inches over a fourteen-year average.

In the Masai group the siting is also significant. At Lerug there is a small seepage in the hill, but no agriculture in the area. Tradition has it that in the past a section of the Burungi tribe settled in the area for a short while, but was driven out by drought. The same fate befell an alien agriculturist who tried to settle in the area in German times. At Makami and Londergess both settlements must have been dependant on the deep wells described in the paper which follows. Neither area supports agriculture today: there are no rain gauges at these places; there are, however, several stations within a radius of 30 or 40 miles, in very similar country, which give averages varying from 16 to 23 inches per year. Lest it be thought that the Masai, rather than the paucity of the rainfall is the deterent to agriculture, I must emphasize again, as I have done frequently in the past, that the Masai, far from being antagonistic to agriculturists, welcome them in their midst as producers of cereals, of which commodity the Masai produce none but consume much.

Finally, in the Kondoa District, though some of the sites occur adjacent to water and in country which carries cultivation today, the main site, Chubi, is in arid country *about 10 miles distant from the nearest permanent water.*

Thus the majority of the sites in Pare, Masai and Kondoa all indicate that the climate was more favourable when they were in use than that enjoyed today. Further evidence of the process of desiccation is to be obtained from another Iron-Age site in the area, Engaruka, which I have not described as I have done no original work there. I was, however, instrumental in having the area photographed from the air. Sections of the mosaic are produced as Fig. 10. The photo covers a portion of Leakey's North Ruins. The dwelling sites stand out clearly, terraced into the steep base of the Rift Wall (top left) whilst the pattern of irrigated agriculture can be discerned on the plain at the base of the scarp (lower right). There are today a few Swahili type agriculturists at Engaruka presenting a pattern very different from that of the earlier inhabitants.

So there is irrefutable evidence that the Engaruka Ruin folk produced their own food. Leakey reckons: 'The population figure was probably between thirty and forty thousand, and I think this may be an underestimate.' Allow each individual just over 1 lb. of cereals per day, say 400 lb. per year. With the unlikely crop yield of 2,000 lb. to the acre, each person would require $\frac{1}{5}$ acre to feed him; in other words, there must have been about 8,000 acres under cultivation if Leakey's population figure is correct. Under present conditions this grain could not have been produced on rainfall alone, as the average rainfall is 14·76 inches, with maximum of 23·65 inches (1951) and a minimum of 8·00 inches (1946). Consequently, today irrigation is the only means of cropping the area, and even in the assumed better conditions of the past irrigation must have been resorted to to supplement the rainfall. The evidence of this is as pictured above; in addition, it is significant that the Sonjo tribe enjoy 5 inches more rainfall than Engaruka (ten-year average at Samunge 19·75 inches) and yet are largely dependent on irrigation for their food crops.

In parenthesis it should be explained that the Sonjo are a small tribe of Bantu-speaking agriculturists who live in five fenced villages at the foot of a scarp to the west of Lake Natron some 50

FIG. 9. Late White painting from Lerug, South Masai—
entrenching tool, 1′ 4½″ handle, denotes scale

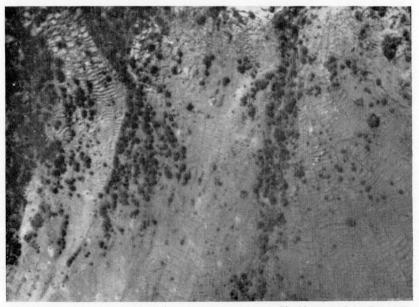

Photo by Survey Dept., Tanganyika

FIG. 10. Engaruka from the air: the North Ruins with terraced dwelling sites top left, at base of
scarp, and irrigation basins on right

miles north of Engaruka. Though not linked with the late inhabitants by legend or by physical type—for no skeletal material has yet come from Engaruka—there are points in Sonjo culture suggesting that they were picked up from Engaruka. The position of the villages, the terraced house sites and paths, the stone fireplaces and the irrigation system are examples of this.

Back then to Engaruka, with 8,000 acres under cultivation to feed its 40,000 inhabitants. The duty of irrigation water varies tremendously according to the crop, the nature of the soil and the time of year. Figures given in the authorities are as low as 40 acres per cusec for sugar-cane or rice and up to 250 for general crops when merely supplementing rainfall. A reasonable figure for Engaruka conditions would be 100 acres. The hydrologists of the Tanganyika Department of Water Development and Irrigation have measured the Engaruka stream and find that at minimum flow it carried eight cusecs. This would irrigate 800 acres or precisely a tenth of the area required to feed the estimated population.

It must be borne in mind that Engaruka is in an area of tectonic disturbance, at the base of the Rift Wall, with an active volcano, Oldonyo Lengai, only 25 miles to the north. Thus it might be argued that water which previously flowed on the surface has been lost through some fault or crack appearing. To set off against this, 72 cusecs is an awful lot of water to lose, about 36 million gallons every 24 hours, sufficient to serve a town of nearly one million inhabitants in Europe.

Further evidence of desiccation is available in the form of glacier recession on Kilimanjaro, reduction of lake levels and the shrinkage of forests on mountain tops. But these points cannot be developed here: suffice it to say that on archaeological grounds alone a strong *prima facie* case is made out, which only further research, including careful excavation of the sites already discovered, can confirm or refute.

It is the arid nature of the country in which these sites are found which has so far preserved them from agricultural activity and consequent destruction. But population pressure and modern technological progress—drilled or piped water supplies, sisal production, etc.—is leading to the utilization of these marginal areas and the destruction of this evidence, hence the urgent necessity for excavation.

REFERENCES

Cole, Sonia (1954), *The Prehistory of East Africa*, Pelican Books.
Culwick, A. T. (1931), 'Ritual Use of Rock Paintings at Bahi', *Man*, 1931, 41.
Dundas, C. (1924), *Kilimanjaro and Its People*, London.
Fosbrooke, H. A. (1938), 'Rift Valley Ruins', *Tanganyika Notes and Records*, 6, pp. 58–60.
Fosbrooke, H. A. *et al.* (1950), 'Tanganyika Rock Paintings. A Guide and Record', *Tanganyika Notes and Records*, 29, pp. 1–61.
Fosbrooke, H. A. (1954), 'Further Light on Rock Engravings in Northern Tanganyika', *Man*, 1954, 157.
Fosbrooke, H. A. (1954), 'A Note on the Ngassa', *African Studies*, 13, pp. 153–4.
Gillman, C. (1944), 'An Annotated List of Ancient and Modern Indigenous Stone Structures in Eastern Africa', *Tanganyika Notes and Records*, 17, pp. 44–55.
Gray, R. F. (1955), 'The Mbugwe Tribe; Origin and Development', *Tanganyika Notes and Records*, 38, pp. 39–50.
Huntingford, G. W. B. (1955), *The Galla of Ethiopia*. Ethnographic Survey of Africa. North-Eastern Africa, Part II, International African Institute, London.
Leakey, L. S. B. (1935), 'Preliminary Report on Examination of the Engaruka Ruins', *Tanganyika Notes and Records*, 1, pp. 57–60.
Maguire, R. A. J. (1948), 'Il Torobo', *Tanganyika Notes and Records*, 25, pp. 1–27.
Mnyampala, M. E. (1954), *Historia, Mila na Desturi za Wagogo wa Tanganyika*, Eagle Press, Nairobi, p. 5 (in Swahili: 'The History, Manners and Customs of the Gogo of Tanganyika').
Whiteley, W. H. and A. E. Gutkind (1954), *A Linguistic Bibliography of East Africa*, Supplement No. 1, p. 3.

50

Prehistoric Wells, Rainponds and associated Burials in Northern Tanganyika

by H. A. FOSBROOKE

THE Masai Steppe in Northern Tanganyika is remarkable for the existence of water works un-explained by history and indicating that their constructors had a considerable knowledge of hydrology and a capacity for organization.

THE WELLS

First the wells; Naberera may be taken as the type site of a group of six well-fields scattered over an area about 40 miles by 30. At Naberera over 50 wells occur in an area of about half a square mile. The geological formation is crystalline limestone. It is remarkable that the wells are not in a depression but on sloping ground, so that within a few hundred yards the ground level is lower than the level of the water in the wells, although these are 30 to 40 feet deep. This fact encouraged an enterprising District Commissioner to devise a syphon system for drawing water for the cattle but unfortunately he neglected the altitude factor, Naberera being over 4,000 feet above sea level—so the scheme failed. The surrounding country is arid (Naberera's ten-year rainfall average is 16·10 inches) and the nearest permanent water, apart from wells of a similar nature and one or two hill-top springs, is the river Ruvu or Pangani, about 40 miles distant.

Originally the wells were narrow shafts, presenting a small circular opening at ground level. One such well-mouth is shown in Fig. 1; this is at Londergess where, exceptionally, the well is in a granitic type rock and in consequence has retained its shape. The general pattern is that subsequent to the sinking of the well-shaft a narrow adit has been driven from ground level to a point 20 or 30 feet below ground (as Fig. 2) so that instead of the water being drawn to the surface for the cattle, they descend into the ground and drink at a point close to the water table (Fig. 3). The remaining lift is met by a team of water drawers—sometimes only two, but as many as eight are employed—wearing nothing but a leather head-dress (Fig. 5) to protect their ochred hair. They stand on cross-bars at vertical intervals of about six feet and throw a leather bucket from hand to hand. The number of buckets employed is one less than the number of drawers; the empties are not passed down from hand to hand but thrown direct to the bottom of the shaft. They are always dropped in such a way that the open mouth strikes water first. This enables the bottom man of the chain gang, who is standing waist deep in water, to grab the handle under the water surface and by a flick of the wrist fill and pass up the bucket in one motion without fumbling. The leather buckets striking the water mouth first make a characteristic 'boom' which acquaints everyone within a mile or more that water drawing is in progress.

In some cases the original well-head is intact—suspended in mid-air as it were—in the roof of the watering cavern. In other cases the line of the original shaft can be traced in the wall, running from the surface to the present well-mouth. The troughs are cut out of the living rock and at times —particularly at Ndedo—a partition of rock has been left between the well-mouth and the watering chamber, to prevent the well from being fouled.

FIG. 1 (*top left*). Mouth of well at Londergess. The figure is bending to receive bucket from companion immediately below. The cylindrical object on the back of the head is a tied-up pig-tail

FIG. 2 (*above*). Narrow adit leading to well at Namalulu; figure indicates scale

FIG. 3 (*left*). Cattle watering from trough cut out of solid limestone 30 feet below ground level

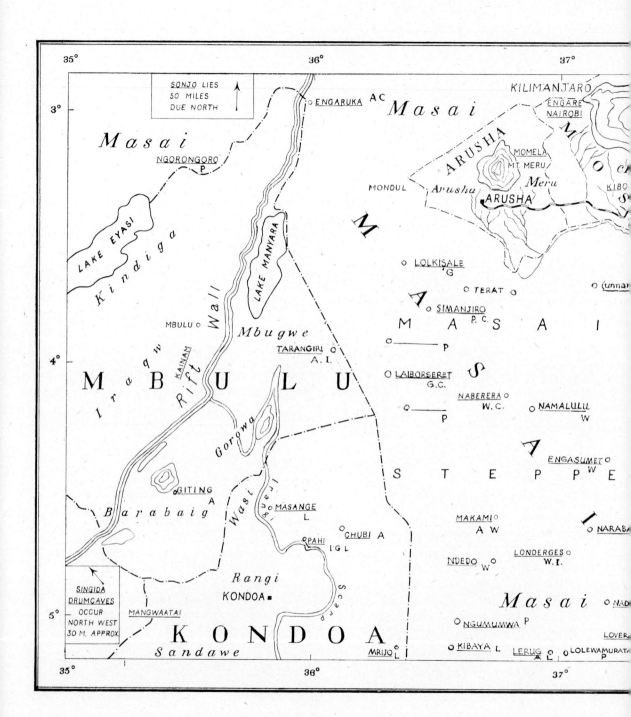

SONJO LIES
50 MILES
DUE NORTH

35°   36°   37°

3°

Masai

NGORONGORO
P

ENGARUKA   A C   *Masai*

KILIMANJARO

ENGARE
NAIROBI

ARUSHA

MOMELA
MT. MERU

Meru

MONDUL

Arusha

ARUSHA

KIBO

M

Masai

LAKE EYASI

Kindiga

Iraqw

Rift Wall

MBULU O

Mbugwe

TARANGIRI
A. I.

LAKE MANYARA

KAINAM

M   B   U   L   U

A   S   A   I

LOLKISALE
'G

TERAT

(unna

SIMANJIRO
P. C.

P

LAIBORSERET
G.C.

S

NABERERA
W. C.

NAMALULU
W

4°

Gorowa

P

STEPPE

ENGASUMET
W

GITING
A

Barabaig

Wasi

Iren

MASANGE
L

PAHI

CHUBI   A

I G L

MAKAMI
A W

NARABA

LONDERGES
W. I.

NDEDO   W

SINGIDA
DRUMCAVES
OCCUR
NORTH WEST
30 M. APPROX

MANGWAATAI

Scarp

Rangi

KONDOA ■

5°

K   O   N   D   O   A

Sandawe

MRIJO   L

Masai

NGUMUMWA   P

KIBAYA   L

LERUG   L

LOLEWAMURATA

NAD

LOVER

35°   36°   37°

328

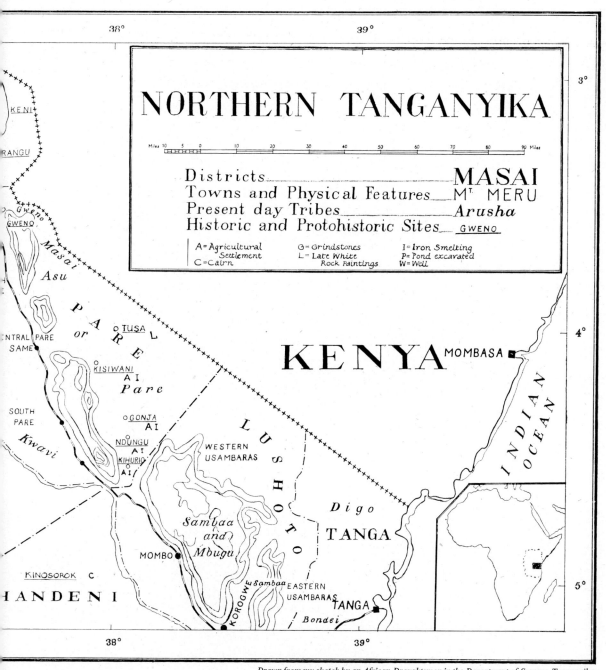

NORTHERN TANGANYIKA

Miles 10   5   0   10   20   30   40   50   60   70   80   90 Miles

Districts..MASAI
Towns and Physical Features____Mᵗ MERU
Present day Tribes_____Arusha
Historic and Protohistoric Sites____GWENO

A=Agricultural   G= Grindstones   I= Iron Smelting
   Settlement   L= Late White   P= Pond excavated
C=Cairn   Rock Paintings   W= Well

KENI

RANGU

Gweno
GWENO

Masai

Asu

NTRAL PARE
SAME

SOUTH
PARE

Kwavi

KINOSOROK C

HANDENI

P A R E
or
Pare

TUSA

KISIWANI
A I

GONJA
A I

NDUNGU
A I
KIHURIO
A I

WESTERN
USAMBARAS

KENYA MOMBASA

L U S H O T O

Digo

TANGA

Sambaa
and
Mbugu

MOMBO

KOROGWE Sambaa

EASTERN
USAMBARAS

Bondei

TANGA

INDIAN OCEAN

3°

4°

5°

38°   39°

Drawn from my sketch by an African Draughtsman in the Department of Surveys, Tanganyika

Section Three

The problem of keeping the watering chamber clean is a considerable one; at Engasumet (Fig. 4) the problem has been met by plastering the dung on the walls of the approach ramp. In other cases the donkeys are given the task of removing the dung. As befits their lowly status, they water last, and whilst they are drinking, large pats of cow dung are slapped on their backs, which they then carry up to the surface.

Naberera has been mentioned as typical; so is Namalulu—only two wells—and Makami, about 20 wells. Ndedo with a dozen or more wells is characterized by greater depth—some 30 feet to the watering chamber and another 30 feet to the water table; the cross walls are also more in evidence here than elsewhere. At Londergess two sets of wells occur, two in the east and two in the west. The different nature of the rock has caused a deviation from type. No chambers are—or could be—excavated, and the shafts instead of being perpendicular, meander to left and right down the strikes of softer rock.

Engasumet, illustrated in Fig. 4, is entirely atypical. Presumably owing to the softer nature of the rock, the vertical sides of the excavations have collapsed so that eventually each well has been converted into an inverted truncated cone. The cattle walk down the slope of the cone, their tracks becoming wider and wider till only a narrow wall remains between one track and the next, and between one well and its neighbour; this shows clearly in the illustration.

Although they form such a striking feature in an otherwise arid bit of country very little has been written about these wells, and what is on record is mostly nonsense. Koenig (1951) gives us four good photos of Engasumet, but spoils these by an inappropriate article which assumes that the shape is not fortuitous, but a matter of design. From this he goes on to draw comparisons with the water tanks of Aden, and to consider Phoenician influence, and looks for support to the Abbé Breuil and his Rock Painting theories! Gillman (1944) gives the first recorded reference as Sir Edmund Teale, writing in the Annual Report of the Tanganyika Geological Survey for 1927. Considering Gillman's intimate acquaintance with the German literature, it is unlikely that he has overlooked any earlier descriptions; it is remarkable that none of the earlier geographers or geologists who left so many detailed records of northern Tanganyika ever visited these wells. That they were known at the time is proved by their appearance on German pre-1914 maps. The probable explanation is that after the rinderpest and famine of *c.* 1890 the Masai were still impoverished, and only a few wells in use; in those circumstances they would not have attracted the attention that they excite today. Gillman, usually so sound, allows himself to be misled by an anti-Masai bias, as when he states: 'Unfortunately, they have since been spoilt by the Masai who, too indolent to draw the water to the surface, have used Chagga workers to dig inclined lateral trenches through the rock so that cattle can now descend to the bottom of the wells for the double purpose of drinking and fouling an otherwise clean and clear water supply.' Gillman, too indolent to walk to Naberera, paid a hurried visit by car, and so did not give himself time to reflect on the increased efficiency which the Masai device gives to this water supply. The delivery rate of the Masai must be ten times as great as could be achieved by drawing up a bucket to the surface on the end of a string.

Another misconception of Gillman's occurs when he says the wells 'must once have formed an adequate supply for a sedentary population'. Even if a sedentary agricultural population had inhabited the area—assuming that the rainfall was at that time better than the present 16–17 inches —no agricultural village would have required 40 or 50 wells within a quarter-mile radius for domestic purposes. Excluding such improbable arguments that for *tabu* reasons each house had to have its own well, this large number of wells can only have been dug for the purpose of watering a considerable stock population. Taken in conjunction with the excavated rainponds described below, to be found throughout the area, the pastoral origin of the wells is undoubted.

The traditional history of the Masai, which can be dated with some accuracy by the age group system (Fosbrooke, 1948, p. 11) claims that the wells were captured from the Kwavi about 125 years ago. The Kwavi are Nilohamitic pastoralists of the Masai Cluster whom poverty and defeat drove to agriculture from time to time. The Kwavi in turn assert that they found the wells when

FIG. 4. The wells at Engasumet. Photo by P. R. O., Tanganyika

they first penetrated into the area, not many years in advance of the Masai, who were slowly driving them southwards. There is no record concerning whom, if anyone, the Kwavi displaced. The Masai allege that it was the Kwavi who first excavated the underground watering chambers and point to certain wells that have not been altered since Kwavi times. Each well is owned by a particular Masai clan, such ownership being attributed to ancestors who assisted in driving out the Kwavi and claimed a well for the clan at the time of taking over.

There is little evidence of pre-Masai habitation in the neighbourhood of the wells. The cairns of Naberera are dealt with below, whilst I have recently described (*Man*, 1954, 157, and especially the footnote thereto) the evidence to indicate a trade in iron conducted at the Londergess wells. In the vicinity of Makami (about 2 miles from the wells) there is evidence of a considerable agricultural settlement (grindstones are evidence of this) where iron smelting was extensively practised —as witnessed by the large amount of iron slag to be found. In the absence of other water supplies, the inhabitants must have been dependent on the wells, but that is not to say that they were responsible for their construction.

THE RAINPONDS

Turning now to the rainponds, the first point to stress is the distinction between certain natural depressions and those which exhibit obvious evidence of man's handiwork. Certainly many natural rainponds exist; probably starting from a tiny puddle, the wallowing game must over the centuries have performed a double service. Their puddling would make the bottom more and more impervious, whilst every time an elephant walked away with a few pounds of mud sticking to his hide, by that amount would the excavation be deepened. But the characteristic of these natural ponds is that they exhibit no adjacent spoil heaps.

Not so the excavated ponds, where the excavation is matched by corresponding heaps of debris around the periphery. Fig. 6 shows the size of the spoil heaps. The ponds vary very much in size but taking a medium-sized pond 100 yards in diameter and an average of 6 foot in depth, this represents an excavation of about 15,200 cubic yards. At task work African labour today can excavate up to 4 cubic yards of soil when for instance side-cutting a road. But in such case no carrying is involved. In excavating the ponds a cubic yard probably represents a day's work in digging and carrying, so a medium-sized pond represents 15,000 man-days. In other words a gang of 50 labourers would take nearly a year to construct one pond.

It must be emphasized that these works are not dams in water courses or drainage lines, nor are they the centre of obvious natural depressions. More work remains to be done on their actual siting; detailed survey work is required. The general impression one gets is that they were served by only small catchment areas and that water entered through more than one of the breaks which characterize the form of the spoil heaps.

The ponds are much more numerous than are shown on the map. There are a considerable group round Talamai in the south-eastern corner of Masai District, and many more farther south in Mpwapwa and Dodomo Districts. Many of these only came to light when the Groundnut Scheme cleared the thick deciduous thorn bush. This must have grown up since the ponds were constructed, as no pastoralist would be attracted to a country where the grass growth is suppressed by the thick bush through which no animal with a hide less thick than a rhino can possibly penetrate. Thus one can certainly postulate a recent change in environment, which might well be caused by desiccation; but it would be dangerous to attribute the change to this cause alone, as misuse of the grazing might have led to the suppression of the grasses and the dominance of the woody shrubs, finally reaching the present climax of impenetrable bush.

One must assume the pond diggers to have been pastoralists, supplementing their permanent water supplies by temporary wet season supplies. For none of the ponds are so deep as to provide a permanent supply of water. Even if the rainfall were greater and more regular when the ponds were constructed, evaporation must have been much the same as today. Though no figures are available for the area concerned, Mr C. K. Cooke tells me that similar conditions at Khami near Bulawayo yield an evaporation rate of about 84 inches per year. So this rules out the possibility of the ponds being the basis for permanent agricultural settlement. It is most likely that the ponds were constructed on open grazing plains, rather than the bush that surrounds the majority of the ponds today. A few examples of ponds on plains remain today.

So far few artefacts have come to light in connection with the wells or ponds; but no excavation has been undertaken. Masai tradition has it that when clearing out certain wells which on first arrival they found choked up, they recovered spears of a non-Masai type, but these were thrown

FIG. 6. Close-up of earthworks surrounding rainpond near Talamai. Figures illustrate proportions

FIG. 8. Two skeletons *in situ* in one cairn (not that illustrated in Fig. 7). Gloss on bones due to preservative

FIG. 5. Masai warriors wearing leather 'sou-wester' to preserve red ochred pigtails as seen emerging under head-dress in figure on right

FIG. 7. Burial cairn at Naberera formed of limestone nodules

away, so cannot be adequately described. In one case on the spoil of a rainpond a type of pottery has been recovered which differs from anything in use in the area today; it differs also from any pottery found on iron-age dwelling sites in Northern Tanganyika. The distinguishing characteristic is decoration on the internal as well as the external surface in the vicinity of the lip, consisting of lines (in one case two external and four internal) of contiguous punched triangles encircling the vessel.

THE CAIRNS

Cairns are found throughout the area where the wells and ponds occur. Again Naberera is taken as the type, though cairns occur far from wells as at Simanjiro in the vicinity of ponds, at Terat near permanent water and near the Ruvu River.

At Naberera are located 18 cairns, scattered through an area of thick bush (so I may have missed some) about ¾ mile by ¼ mile lying to the north-west of the wells: the nearest well is only about 200 yards distant. The cairns are heaps of limestone nodules piled up without any attempt at masonry construction. In one case termites have built in the interstices, providing in effect a mortar which has preserved the original shape of the cairn. This shows that the sides were originally more vertical than the hump shape which the rest of the cairns exhibit. The example illustrated in Fig. 7 is typical for shape but not for size, it being much larger than the average. Some are little more than 18 inches high. Weathering and the passage of cattle has caused the stones to spread over a greater area than that originally occupied.

Galloway (1933) must have been misled by the finder of the first skull from the area. Thompson by name, he was a prospector, a type notoriously given to exaggeration, who opened one of the 'tombs' (*sic*) in search of treasure, but only found a skull. At least he was conscientious enough not to throw this away but saw that it got into the proper hands. However, if there had been, as Galloway reports him as saying 'a tomb 20 deep and 63 paces across' I could not have failed to find it on my numerous visits to Naberera. Likewise Thompson appears to have taken for 'mine workings' the wells which I describe above. If at the time some were disused and silted up, no water would be in evidence so the mistake is understandable.

The largest cairn which I located, that illustrated, was about 25 feet in diameter and 5 feet in height. This gives an approximate capacity of 50 cubic yards. It requires no great feat of organized labour to construct such a heap in an area where the nodules of limestone to be found on the surface are so numerous as to make walking unpleasant, so any correlation between the size of the 'tomb' and the importance of the inmate is of dubious validity. On the Masai analogy however, the fact that the body was buried at all is of significance, as the present day pastoralists of the area typically expose the dead to carnivora.

This brings us on to the inmates, of whom five have been recovered to date. I will not attempt to touch on the physical anthropology aspect, but summarize what is known concerning age, sex, burial position, etc. Of the first find Galloway (1933) states: 'The body was found in a crouching position facing the East.' Crouching normally indicates a vertical position but might be used, as I suspect it was, in this case, for an ultra-contracted burial on one side. For the rest Galloway says: 'Apart from stating that it is the skull of an elderly person it is impossible to age and sex the skull.'

The next skeleton examined was by myself in 1939. The skull and bones were too friable to recover, but were photographed and published (Fosbrooke, 1950). The main point of interest was position—contracted, not ultra-contracted, and the orientation—facing east. No funerary furniture or artefacts were found in the grave.

Some time later a Field Officer (Tsetse) G. E. Clausen opened one of the numerous cairns at Terat. Unfortunately he neither removed or photographed the skeleton he found, but reported on the typical contracted position and on the lack of funerary furniture.

In 1953 I recovered two skeletons from a single cairn at Naberera. One was ultra-contracted, the other in a contracted position, both facing slightly north of east (Fig. 8). They were young adults, one male and the other female (Galloway, 1955). Again no funerary furniture was found.

Prehistoric Wells, Rainponds and Burials in Tanganyika

Meanwhile, J. G. Stephenson, District Commissioner Handeni, had excavated a couple of cairns in the north-western corner of his district; though politically separate, the area is geographically a portion of Masailand. Of the two skulls recovered one was of a middle-aged female, the other an unidentifiable adult (Galloway, 1955). In one case the remains of an iron anklet was found on the skeleton and a single glass bead was recovered. I have no information whether the position of the bead indicated that it had been buried with the body or had dropped into the grave fortuitously. J. S. Kirkman, of the Kenya Royal National Parks, in a letter on the Handeni files, states that the bead is an Arab green cane glass bead such as was manufactured from the thirteenth to the seventeenth centuries. Such beads occurred at Gedi in the fourteenth-, fifteenth- and sixteenth-century levels, most frequently in the fifteenth century.

CONCLUSIONS

Such then are the facts. What conclusions can be drawn from them? Firstly that the wells were dug by a pastoral people, as no agriculturalists would have required so many sources of water in so small an area. Secondly that the rainponds were also the work of pastoralists as they could not provide a permanent water supply such as an agricultural community would require. Considering their juxtaposition it is logical to assume that the same pastoralists constructed both the wells and the rainponds, and utilized them on a basis of transhumance such as the Masai practice today, using these same wells and ponds.

Associated with the wells at Naberera, with permanent water at Terat and elsewhere throughout the area, are to be found numerous cairns. Though the association of the cairns with the pastoralists cannot be proved with certainty, it is very probable indeed. It is known that certain agricultural iron workers lived in the vicinity of two well-fields, but neither of these have cairns adjacent. Further, it is difficult to conceive of the agriculturists burying their dead many miles from the nearest permanent water, in which position some of the cairns in fact appear. Hence the cairns must be the work of a pastoral people and most probably those responsible for the wells and ponds. It is of course just conceivable that one lot of pastoralists who did not bury their dead dug the wells and ponds whilst another succeeding tribe took over the wells and ponds (just as the Masai have done) and erected the cairns in the vicinity.

However that may be, the skeletons prove to be of similar physical type to those found at Mapungubwe (Fouche, 1937; Gardener, 1955), where, as in central Masailand, the forerunners of the Bantu inhabitants showed skill and organizing ability sufficient to leave a permanent memorial to their passing.* It may not be without significance that both prove to be of the same physical type.

REFERENCES

Fosbrooke, H. A. (1948), 'An Administrative History of the Masai Social System', *Tanganyika Notes and Records*, 26.

Fosbrooke, H. A. (1950), 'A Proto-Historic Burial, Naberera Masai District, Tanganyika Territory', *South African Archaeological Bulletin*, V (19), pp. 105–7.

Fosbrooke, H. A. (1954), 'Further Light on Rock Engravings in Northern Tanganyika', *Man*, 1954, 157.

Fouche, Leo (1937), *Mapungubwe, Ancient Bantu Civilisation on the Limpopo*, Cambridge University Press.

Galloway, A. (1933), 'The Nabarara Skull', *South African Journal of Science*, XXX, pp. 585–96. (The more common spelling is Naberera.)

Galloway, A. (1955), 'Proto-Historic Skeletal Remains from Tanganyika Territory', Paper read to the Third Pan-African Congress on Prehistory, Livingstone, N.R., 1955.

Gardner, G. A. (1955), 'Mapungubwe 1935–1940', *South African Archaeological Bulletin*, 4 (39), pp. 73–7.

Gillman, C. (1944), 'An Annotated List of Ancient and Modern Indigenous Stone Structures in Eastern Africa', *Tanganyika Notes and Records*, 17, pp. 46–55.

Koenig, O. (1952), 'The Wells of Engasumet', *Tanganyika Notes and Records*, 31, pp. 53–4.

Wilson, G. E. H. (1932), 'The Ancient Civilisation of the Rift Valley', *Man*, 287 and 323.

* I have unfortunately been unable to consult Wilson (1932) when drafting this paper, but to my recollection he records little that would assist in the present discussion.

51

Some Features of the Monomotapa Culture

by JAMES WALTON

ASSOCIATED with the ruins of Southern Rhodesia are a number of objects which have figured prominently in discussions on the origin of these ruins. Notable among them are the soapstone birds, soapstone bowls, conical towers, monoliths, cross-shaped ingots and double gongs and it is mainly on account of these that earlier workers, such as Bent and Hall, linked Zimbabwe directly with the Sabaeans and the Phoenicians. Later archaeologists, notably Masey, Summers and Caton-Thompson, whilst regarding the ruins as essentially African, considered that some external influence was responsible for at least certain of these features.

Masey concludes: 'So we may see in these ruins the remains of an ancient *African* rude civilization, but affected by foreign influence, perhaps contemporary with, and not more unaccountable in its features, than those of Mexico or Peru, and the study of which, as Mr M'Iver points out, should be rather more, than less, interesting on account of its parentage, in view of the relations which seem to have existed between it and the Mediterranean civilization during one of the most interesting epochs of the world's history.'

Similarly Miss Caton-Thompson states emphatically that: 'Examination of all the existing evidence, gathered from every quarter, still can produce not one single item that is not in accordance with the claim of Bantu origin and mediaeval date.' Yet elsewhere in the same book, when discussing the conical tower, she writes: 'My suggestion therefore that certain peculiarities of the ruins may owe something to the foreign coastal settlements, is based, not on the assumption that foreigners from those settlements directed the building (for in my opinion had they done so, their recognizable national mark would tell the tale), but that the natives themselves in the course of trade relations with those settlements seized, with the quick imitative instinct which characterizes them, upon a feature such as the minaret which, owing to familiarity in a more homely context, particularly impressed them, and which it was within their technical capacity to imitate.'

Summers expresses a similar idea when he says: 'For myself I am convinced that our great monuments are African in execution and that the dwellers therein were akin to our modern natives; on the other hand some of the *ideas* underlying the culture probably had a foreign origin and may have been introduced by non-Africans.'

In this paper I intend to discuss the distribution and typology of those features which have demanded the introduction of outside influence for their explanation in order to determine their origin.

THE SOAPSTONE BIRDS OF ZIMBABWE

From the ruins of Zimbabwe, particularly from the 'Eastern Temple' of the 'Acropolis', a number of carved soapstone birds mounted on pedestals have been recovered. These were first described by W. Posselt who reached Zimbabwe in 1888. He records that: 'There (on the "Acropolis"), in an enclosure which served as a cattle kraal, I saw four soap stones each carved in the image of a bird and facing east; one stone shaped like a millstone and about nine inches in diameter; and a stone dish, broken, about eighteen inches in diameter, with a number of figures carved on the border. The "bird" stones were planted in an old ruined wall within the enclosure.' After some considerable opposition from chief Andizibi, Posselt eventually managed to obtain one specimen which is now preserved in the Groote Schuur collection.

Three years later J. Theodore Bent recovered four birds on pillars (Fig. 1, *a* and *b*), one fragment (Fig. 1*d*) and two miniature birds. 'From the position in which we found most of them', he writes, they 'would appear to have decorated the outer wall of the semi-circular temple on the hill'. He adds that, 'though they are different in execution, they would appear to have been intended to represent the same bird; from the only one in which the beak is preserved to us intact, we undoubtedly recognize that they must have been intended to represent hawks or vultures', and he concludes that they 'are closely akin to the Assyrian Astarte or Venus, and represent the female element in creation'.

Discussing these four birds, R. N. Hall states that they, together with another beam which had previously supported a bird figure, 'were standing more or less erect and fixed in granite cement on the Eastern Temple on the Acropolis'. Three stood on a raised platform on the west side of the interior immediately on the left-hand side on entering at the western entrance, and the fragment of another was found by Bent among the loose stones surmounting a small platform on the left-hand side of the eastern entrance. On his plan Hall shows two more birds on pillars standing on a platform on the right-hand side of the eastern entrance. It would thus appear that these six birds stood on platforms on the inside of the boundary wall of the 'Eastern Temple'. In 1902–3 Hall discovered the upper portion of another bird on the 'Acropolis' and in 1903 he found, 'on the east side of a high and massive wall and at the south side of a small conical tower in the North-East Enclosure of Philips Ruins', the very fine soapstone bird which has since become emblematic of Southern Rhodesia.

Examples of carved soapstone birds mounted on pedestals are unknown outside Zimbabwe but birds in earthenware or carved in wood and mounted on poles have been recorded from many Bantu tribes. In 1951 I saw a number of bird effigies carried on tall poles surrounding the *lelapa* of a witch-doctor in the Dilli Dilli valley of South Basutoland. Among the Sotho, as among many other Southern Bantu tribes, lightning is regarded as a giant bird and these carved figures are intended to deceive the lightning bird. The same belief is maintained by the Venda who place the image of a bird on the hut roof and Miss Earthy has collected from Portuguese East Africa a wooden bird which had four legs for securing it more safely to the roof. In 1918 J. S. Trevor found three carved wooden birds and a carved animal mounted on poles, 18 feet high, surrounding an enclosure belonging to headman Maraba of the Roka tribe in the Lydenburg district of the Transvaal. At Vukwe, in the Tati Concession, Wieschoff discovered two complete earthenware birds and a fragment of a third in a midden near the western wall, and each had a socket underneath suitable for mounting the figure on an upright pole. Wieschoff concludes: 'It is certain that the Vukwe birds, like those of Zimbabwe, once crowned the top of a wall.'

In all these cases, where any association can be proven, the bird figures on posts served as a protection against lightning and invariably surrounded the *lelapa* of a witch-doctor or headman. At Zimbabwe, where they were found in association with phalli and soapstone bowls, they undoubtedly fulfilled a similar function and the 'Eastern Temple' was probably the *lelapa* of a witch-doctor. The agitation caused by Posselt when he attempted to remove one of the figures suggests that they were still regarded by Andizibi and his followers as having some important significance and Schofield states that the natives in the vicinity of Zimbabwe still regard the Bateleur eagle as a sacred bird and greet it with hand-clapping whenever it is seen.

The bird revered as the lightning bird varies from tribe to tribe: among the Southern Sotho it is the hamerkop, among the Venda it is the bird of prey, Raluvimbi, and among the tribes of the north-west Transvaal it is the flamingo. The soapstone birds from Zimbabwe also represent two distinct species. One is a naturalistic representation of a bird of prey of the hawk or eagle type

(Fig. 1, *a* and *b*); the other is a more conventionalized bird with a fan-shaped tail and square-cut wings, resting on a raised ring (Fig. 1, *c* and *d*). No complete example of the second type of bird is known but a head and neck found by Hall (Fig. 1*e*) seems to belong to one of the fan-tailed bodies. A noticeable feature of this type is the pronounced flange or ridge down the front and back exactly as one would find in a metal casting and Masey has already suggested that this type of bird 'is evidently a copy of a bronze original, the jointing of the metal at the back and front being carefully reproduced, whilst the treatment of the eyes, mouth, etc., is distinctly a metallic one'.

The soapstone birds indicate, on stylistic grounds, that they were made by the same people who first produced the soapstone bowls, about A.D. 1400. Later the craftsmen produced a second type of bird based only on a metal model which suggests that when Monomotapa was overthrown by the Kazembe people in A.D. 1560 the new overlords ordered the carvers to produce their own bird effigies and provided them with a metal model. The uniformity in treatment of these birds and the universal presence of the ring indicates a copy from a single model. Whether this represents the true nature of events or not it is certain that the two types of bird, depicting the lightning birds of two different peoples, were executed by the same carvers and that the one type was modelled from nature and the other from a metal prototype.

SOAPSTONE BOWLS

Among the many interesting cultural features of the Southern Rhodesian ruins the soapstone bowls or trays probably provide the greatest problem. These are shallow, flat-bottomed trays varying in diameter from 1 foot $1\frac{1}{2}$ inches to 1 foot 9 inches and having an outer depth of from 2 to $3\frac{1}{2}$ inches. The sides usually have upper and lower rounded rims, the space between being occupied by geometrical or pictorial patterns. A few bowls are quite plain and one of these has a flanged rim. Bent, in his efforts to prove their Mediterranean origin, found the diameters of seven of these bowls to be identical, 19·2 inches or two Egyptian spans, but re-measurement of Bent's material does not indicate any such uniformity.

As with most of the early finds, reports of the occurrence of these bowls are extremely vague and lacking in detail either as regards locality or horizon. Thus Hall states that: 'The fragments of bowls with carved processions of horned animals . . . were found only on the lowest floors, and these only on the Acropolis,' yet in the same volume he records the finding of 'fragments of the rim of a soapstone bowl carved with a procession of horned animals' in Enclosure No. 5 of the Elliptical Building.

The majority of the soapstone bowls have been recovered from the 'Acropolis' and the Elliptical Building at Zimbabwe but others have been found in the Mauch, Maund, Philips and Renders Ruins and, contrary to Caton-Thompson's assertion that they 'appear to be confined to Zimbabwe alone', they have also been recorded from Dhlo Dhlo, Umnukwana and Mundie. Bent's bowls were 'most of them deeply buried in the immediate vicinity of the temple on the fortress' and Hall states that 'the best-made soapstone bowls are found on the lower granite cement floors of the ruins and far below any native clay floors'.

A few specific records of horizon have been published. In Enclosure 6 of the Elliptical Building the succession was as follows:

Ground level
	mould
1 ft.	red foundation of hut, iron hoes, iron assegais, and pottery of no great age
	filling-in of blocks and soil
2 ft. 9 ins.	gold crucibles, iron pincers, iron gong, soapstone amulet
3 ft. 6 ins.	large soapstone bowl carved with herring-bone on cord pattern

From her excavation Test A1 below the west wall of the 'Acropolis' Miss Caton-Thompson found

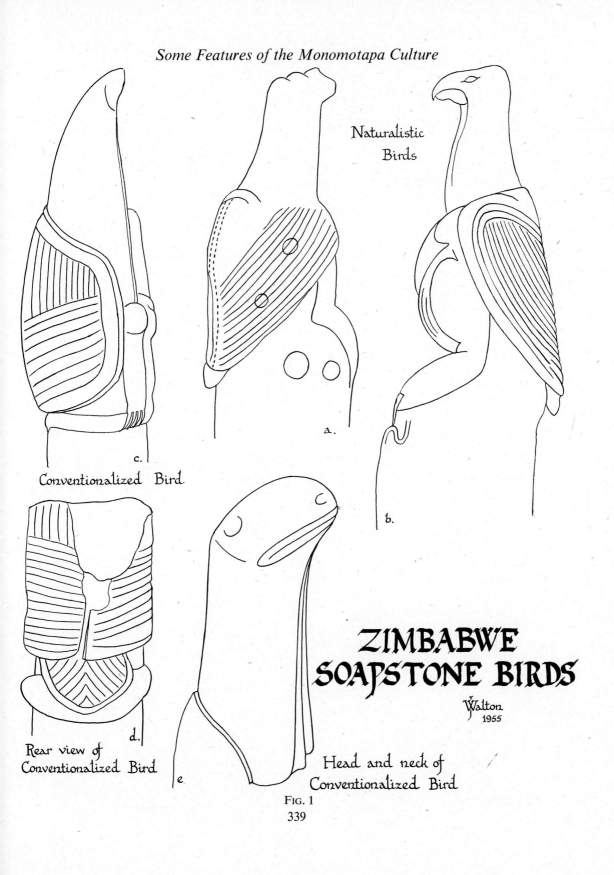

Naturalistic
Birds

Conventionalized Bird

a.

b.

c.

Rear view of
Conventionalized Bird

d.

e.

ZIMBABWE
SOAPSTONE BIRDS

Walton
1955

Head and neck of
Conventionalized Bird

FIG. 1

two fragments of a handled bowl, one at a depth of 3 feet 6 inches and one at a depth of 5 feet, associated with Class C and Class B pottery, iron arrow-heads, an iron hoe-head and a spear-head.

At No. 1 Enclosure, Renders Ruins, the bowls occurred in a position comparable to that of Enclosure 6 at the 'Acropolis'. There they were associated with Arabian glass, thin green glass and china, all attributable to the thirteenth or fourteenth centuries:

Ground level

        copper, crucibles, hoes, axes, chisels and two double gongs

4 ft.   Arabian glass, thin green glass, china, pottery with a green glaze and a large soap-stone bowl.

Caton-Thompson's bowls from the Maund Ruins were found in association with iron arrow-heads, spear-heads and Class B and Class C pottery in humus overlying the cement floor whilst at the Mauch Ruins a bowl fragment was obtained, together with an iron spear-head, from below the cement pavement.

At Camp Ruins No. 1 Willoughby found 'several phalli; fragments of soap-stone bowls; fragments of painted glass, which have since been pronounced to date from the thirteenth century; an iron dagger; a slab of soap-stone, with scooped depressions similar to those required for a game which is even now played by natives upon bare ground; many fragments of pottery, some with embossed patterns and far superior to any Kaffir pottery of the present day; iron chisels or wedges; and the copper fittings of a box, suggestive of a modern date, though they were found beneath a cement flooring and on bed rock itself at a depth of six feet'.

From these stratigraphical records it is apparent that the soapstone bowls at Zimbabwe are normally associated with Class B and Class C pottery, which Caton-Thompson found in levels above the lowest floor and which Schofield ascribes to the 'Shona supremacy and the Empire of Monomotapa'. Summers places Class B and Class C pottery in his Iron Age Group B1 which he also considers belonged to the 'Empire of Monomotapa' and reached Southern Rhodesia during the fourteenth or fifteenth century. The association of the soapstone bowls with Class B and Class C pottery on the one hand and china of the thirteenth to fourteenth centuries on the other strongly supports the hypotheses of Summers and Schofield whereby Class C pottery is associated with the Monomotapa culture.

The patterns on the bowls vary considerably and may be classified into eight groups:

1. Bowls decorated with long-horned cattle
2. Bowls decorated with zebras, hunting dogs, baboons and huntsmen
3. Herring-bone and cord pattern
4. Guilloche pattern
5. Studded pattern
6. Sunken disc pattern   ⎫
7. Diamond panel pattern ⎬ known only from references by Hall
              ⎭
8. Plain

These various patterns are distributed as follows:

1.	2.	3.	4.	5.	8.
'Acropolis'	'Acropolis'	'Acropolis'		'Acropolis'	'Acropolis'
'Elliptical Temple'		'Elliptical Temple'			'Elliptical Temple'
			Maund		
					Mauch
		Dhlo Dhlo			
		Umnukwana			
		Mundie			

6 and 7 are known from 'Zimbabwe' only.

Some Features of the Monomotapa Culture

Bowls with herring-bone or cord pattern are the most widely distributed and these usually have sides with a well-pronounced rounded upper rim and a much narrower lower rim. The space in between is occupied by bands of herring-bone or cord pattern, frequently divided into panels by blank bosses (Fig. 2, *j, k, l*) which Bent described, without any justification, as 'a representation of the round tower'. These patterns are of little diagnostic value and Caton-Thompson points out that the 'double row of herring-bone' is a simple basketry motif.

Of much more importance are the bowls bearing carved processions of lyre-shaped horned cattle (Fig. 2, *c, d, e*). Although these cattle are portrayed in side view both horns are shown and the exceptional length of the horns as well as the unusual shape are marked features. Margaret Trowell notes that: 'The cattle which the Hima-Tusi brought to the Lakes plateau (of Uganda) belong to a type with very long, lyre-shaped horns; the same breed is still reared in southern Abyssinia and the Galla countries. This characteristic type of cattle is found associated with the Hima-Tusi over the greater part of the inter-lacustrine region.' On the basis of tribal genealogies and traditions Cjekanowski has concluded that the Hima-Tusi reached the northern half of the Lakes plateau as far back as the first centuries of the present millenium.

'The Hima-Tusi culture', according to Margaret Trowell, 'is characterized by a complex pattern of customs, beliefs and taboos, clustering about the occupation of cattle-rearing.' Stayt has pointed out that: 'The bull is symbolically represented on all Venda magic bowls, and plays an important part in the religious life of the Bavenda, who in common with some of the Karanga groups possess a highly developed bull cult, which is I think unknown elsewhere in Southern Africa.'

Edward Muller discovered in a cave some ten miles from Zimbabwe a wooden platter or dish, 38 inches in circumference, which is very similar to the Venda divining bowl and bears a carving of a bull. As Caton-Thompson has already observed: 'We have only to compare the rudely carved figure of a bull upon the bowl with the bull on the soap-stone bowl found by Bent on the Acropolis to see the family resemblance, accentuated by the curious error common to both, though not unusual in primitive art, in the perspective of rendering the creature's horns.'

The other patterns throw little light on the origin of either the bowls or their makers. The hunting scene with the huntsman and his dog surrounded by baboons and zebra (Fig. 2b) indicates little more than the fact that dogs were used for hunting, a practice followed by many African tribes and of no diagnostic value. Bent suggested that the huntsman 'is obviously a Hottentot' presumably on account of the steatopygy portrayed. The guilloche pattern (Fig. 2, *m, n*) depicted on bowls from the Maund Ruins is also too widespread to afford us any help.

Analogies for the soapstone bowls of Zimbabwe and other Southern Rhodesian ruins are by no means plentiful. It is apparent that the Zimbabwe craftsmen rendered in stone objects which elsewhere in southern Africa were carved in wood and that they developed the technique to a high standard of workmanship. Both the soapstone bowls and birds point to this conclusion. Large bowls have been reported from two sites outside Rhodesia but in both cases detailed information is lacking. From the vicinity of Bigo, on the south bank of the Katonga, circular dishes up to 4 feet in diameter were found some thirty years ago but these have been lost and it is not known whether they were of soapstone or earthenware. In 1948 Mr W. de Vos gave a lecture to the Northern Transvaal section of the South African Archaeological Society on a soapstone bowl manufacturing site which he discovered in the Harmonie Block in 1942 but I have so far been unable to obtain any description of these bowls. The closest parallels are to be found in the carved wooden divining bowls of the Venda and Karanga and in the circular wooden feeding platters of the same peoples.

The only clue to the origin of these bowls lies in the carvings of the long lyre-horned cattle which point to a Hima-Tusi origin and an earlier association with southern Abyssinia. They were introduced into Southern Rhodesia at the beginning of the Monomotapa Period, about A.D. 1400, and continued in use until after A.D. 1700.

Section Three

Records of Soapstone Bowls

Zimbabwe. Camp Ruins No. 1

1. 'Two large fragments of a big soap-stone bowl or tray, bearing a double row of the Zimbabye herring-bone design' (F.E.Z.).

Zimbabwe 'Acropolis'

1. A bowl with 'three zebras, two hippopotami, a sportsman in the centre who is obviously a Hottentot and is shooting a zebra with one hand and holding in the other an animal by a leash. To fill up a vacant space, a bird is introduced flying' (R.C.M.). Fig. 2*b*.
2. A fragment of another bowl with zebras, similarly treated, though somewhat higher and coarser (R.C.M.).
3. Fragments of a large bowl with a procession of bulls (R.C.M.). Fig. 2*h*.
4. A fragment of a large bowl representing what 'must have been a religious procession' (R.C.M.). Fig. 2*g*.
5. A fragment with a design representing 'probably an ear of corn' (R.C.M.).
6. A fragment of a lip of a large bowl, over 2 feet diameter, around which ran 'an inscription' (R.C.M.).
7. A fragment with cord pattern (R.C.M.). Fig. 2*k*.
8. A fragment with 'a herring-bone pattern alternating with what would appear to be a representation of the round tower' (R.C.M.). Fig. 2*j*.
9. A large plain bowl, external diameter 2 feet and internal diameter 1 foot 8 inches (R.C.M.).
10. Fragment of a plain bowl with a hole (R.C.M.).
11. Fragment of a plain bowl of reddish soapstone (R.C.M.).
12. Fragment of a studded bowl (R.C.M.). Fig. 2*a*.
13. Fragment with two horned cattle. Western Temple (G.Z.). Fig. 2*f*.
14. Fragment with horned bull. South Enclosure (G.Z.). Fig. 2*i*.
15. Fragment with herring-bone on cord pattern. South Enclosure (G.Z.).
16. Fragment of rim. Cord pattern. South Enclosure (G.Z.).
17. Fragment of rim. Cord pattern. No. 10 Enclosure (G.Z.).
18. Seven fragments of bowls. 'Acropolis' and Elliptical Building (G.Z.).
19. Case of sections of soapstone bowls, plain and decorated. 'Acropolis', Elliptical Building and Philips Ruins (G.Z.).
20. Fragment of soapstone bowl with handle from 3 feet 6 inches in excavation Test A1, 100 feet from 'Acropolis' west wall and 25 feet below level of its ground course (Z.C.). Fig. 2*p*.
21. Fragment similar to preceding. Same site. From 5 feet 'These two bowl fragments are in a pink talc-schist, and almost certainly belong to the same dish.' Associated with Class C and some Class B pottery, iron arrow heads, hoe head and spear head (Z.C.).

Zimbabwe Elliptical Building

1. Collection of seven bowl fragments. See 'Acropolis' No. 18.
2. Fragment with herring-bone pattern on cord. No. 1 Enclosure (G.Z.).
3. As No. 2. No. 6 Enclosure (G.Z.).
4. Fragment, carved. No. 7 Enclosure (G.Z.).
5. Fragment, cord pattern. No. 6 Enclosure (G.Z.).
6. Fragment of large bowl, carved. No. 6 Enclosure (G.Z.).
7. Fragments of rim of a soapstone bowl carved with procession of horned cattle. Pieces fit together. No. 5 Enclosure (G.Z.).
8. See 'Acropolis' No. 19.

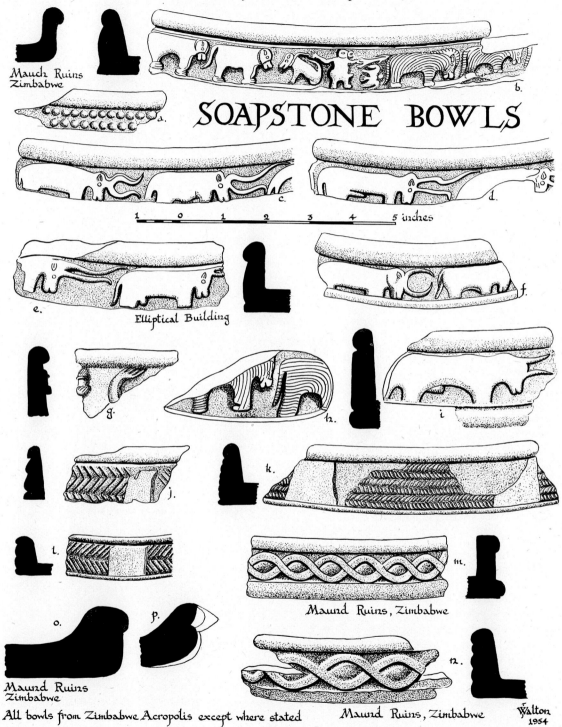

SOAPSTONE BOWLS

Mauch Ruins Zimbabwe

Elliptical Building

Maund Ruins, Zimbabwe

Maund Ruins Zimbabwe

All bowls from Zimbabwe Acropolis except where stated

Maund Ruins, Zimbabwe

Walton 1954

FIG. 2

Section Three

Zimbabwe, Mauch Ruins

1. Fragment of bowl in pink talc-schist. Found with iron spear head below cement pavement (Z.C.).

Zimbabwe, Maund Ruins

1. Fragments of rim of bowl covered with 'ring pattern' (guilloche). Fragments fit together (G.Z.). Fig. 2*m*.

2. Fragment of bowl decorated with guilloche pattern in low relief. From humus overlying cement (Z.C.). Fig. 2*n*.

3. Fragment of undecorated bowl. Associated with Class B and Class C pottery, an iron spear head and an arrow head (Z.C.). Fig. 2*o*.

4. Two fragments of a stone bowl with guilloche pattern as in No. 2. Probably the same bowl although the fragments do not fit. From humus overlying cement floor. Associated with Class B and Class C pottery and with iron arrow head (Z.C.).

Zimbabwe, Philips Ruins

1. See 'Acropolis' No. 19.

Zimbabwe, Renders Ruins

1. A large soapstone bowl (G.Z.).

Dhlo Dhlo

1. Portions of soapstone bowls with herring-bone pattern (A.R.).

Umnukwana

1. Portion of soapstone bowl with single herring-bone pattern (A.R.).

2. Portion of soapstone bowl with double herring-bone pattern. 18 inches across and $2\frac{1}{2}$ inches deep (A.R.).

Mundie Ruins

1. Soapstone bowl with herring-bone pattern (A.R.).

References

F. E. Z. Willoughby, Sir John, *Further Excavations at Zimbabye*, 1893.
Z. C.   Caton-Thompson, G., *The Zimbabwe Culture*, 1931.
R.C.M. Bent, J. T., *The Ruined Cities of Mashonaland*, 3rd Ed., 1902.
G. Z.   Hall, R.N., *Great Zimbabwe*, 1905.
A. R.   Hall, R.N. and Neal, W. G., *The Ancient Ruins of Rhodesia*, 2nd Ed., 1904.

MONOLITHS

The presence of monoliths at Zimbabwe and other Southern Rhodesian sites has been used as evidence by Wainwright and Jensen to link these ruins with south-western Abyssinia and the Gala, where monoliths have a phallic significance. The monoliths of Southern Rhodesia cannot, however, be regarded as all serving the same function nor, in most cases, can they be shewn to have any phallic significance. They can, however, be correlated with similar monolithic cultures in southern Abyssinia from where they apparently spread southwards.

In Southern Rhodesia and northern Transvaal the monoliths may be divided into five distinct groups:

1. Flat monoliths used as back-rests at meeting-places.
2. Monoliths, often associated with small stone towers, surmounting patterned walls.
3. Monoliths, sometimes decorated, placed on or around daga mounds.
4. Monoliths standing upright on stone mounds covering graves.
5. Isolated monoliths adjoining cattle kraals, which served as tethering posts.

Some Features of the Monomotapa Culture

Among the Budja from the north-eastern part of Southern Rhodesia a flat monolith, *dare*, stands in front of the headman's hut and serves as a back-rest to a stone slab seat (Fig. 3*b*). Identical seats have been recorded by Jensen from the Konso area, on the southern shore of Lake Chamo in southern Abyssinia, where they are arranged inside a stone-walled meeting-place (Fig. 3*a*). In the same district miniature phalli are worn on the foreheads of the councillors and stone-faced cultivation terraces, like those of Inyanga, are constructed. A very similar seat, in which flat monoliths are backed by a stone wall (Fig. 4*a*), is reserved for the installation of the headman at Mandeya, in the Inyanga district. Flat monoliths, set vertically as back-rests, are known also from the Rhodesian ruins, notably the Elliptical Building at Zimbabwe (Fig. 3*c*) and the Webster Ruin near Melsetter (Fig. 3*d*). The monoliths at Zimbabwe stood in Enclosure 5, which was apparently the meeting-place of the men. The one still remaining in the standing position is 3 feet wide, 3 inches thick, and rises to a height of 6 feet 9 inches above the ground. Similar monolithic back-rests are recorded by Andrews from the Webster Ruins, where they are arranged in a circle. At this site sufficiently wide slabs appear to have been rare and the required width was obtained by placing two monoliths close together. All these flat monoliths are identical in construction and arrangement and were undoubtedly the seats of the headman and his councillors at the meeting-place. They indicate a cultural diffusion or transference from southern Abyssinia to eastern Mashonaland.

An entirely different type of monolith is found surmounting the walls of several ruins in Southern Rhodesia, the best known examples being those on the outer girdle walls of the Elliptical Building and the 'Acropolis', where they alternate with small round towers (Fig. 4*d*). Similar monoliths have been recorded from Gombe, Matendere, Nalatali, where they are mounted on stone bases (Fig. 4*c*), the Webster Ruins, and from the old Venda sites of Machemma Kop and Dzata in the northern Transvaal. Where the monoliths are placed the walls are usually better built, thicker and often decorated.

At Dzata are three short lengths of slightly curved walling built of stones quite different from the remainder of the walls and which tradition asserts the chief forced his Karanga vassals to carry from north of the Limpopo. In each wall is a niche which served as a seat for the chief; one used when he was conducting a meeting, one when he was drinking beer and so on. One of these walls is decorated along the crest by a row of upright monoliths and, when I asked their purpose, Chief Mphephu's headmen informed me that formerly the chief's councillors sat on this wall on each side of the chief and that the monoliths served as back-rests (Fig. 3*e*). At Verdun there is a similar niche seat in a short length of walling and this type of seat, set in a wall screen, seems to be a later development of the Shona seat with its monolithic slab back-rest. Monoliths, sometimes decorated with engraved concentric circles (Fig. 4*b*) are still placed on walls enclosing the settlements of Venda headmen or in the courtyards in front of the huts and monoliths placed on walls generally appear to be indicative of the chief's quarters, as also is patterned walling.

At Dzata one seat is quite different from the rest. It is the one which the chief occupied when he watched his cattle and it consists of a circular mound of rubble covered with daga and surrounded by a number of monoliths, all of which have fallen. There is a striking similarity between this seat, with its associated monoliths, and the so-called 'altars' from the 'Eastern Temple' of the 'Acropolis' and the Elliptical Building (Fig. 3*f*). Both these daga-covered platforms supported soapstone monoliths, some of which were decorated with geometric patterns. No direct parallels with this type of monolith have been established outside Southern Rhodesia and northern Transvaal.

Stone mounds covering graves are widespread and in certain instances these are surmounted by monoliths but examples of this are too few to allow of any definite conclusion. One example has been recorded by Frobenius from Inyanga (Fig. 4*e*) which Jensen compares with a similar grave from Burdji, in southern Abyssinia.

Monoliths are also found in association with the Inyanga pit settlements and have been dealt with in some detail by Mrs Finch. She writes: 'This Hut Stone, or Yard Stone is found always in a direct line with the pit entrance, the distance varying from 30 feet to 40 feet. These stones, roughly

(a) Monolithic back-rests. Konso (*after Jensen*)

(b) Budja *dare* (*Photo: J. Walton*)

(c) Monoliths. Enclosure 5, Elliptical Building, Zimbabwe (*after Hall*)

(d) Monoliths. Webster Ruin (*after Andrews*)

(e) Wall with monoliths. Dzata (*Photo: J. Walton*)

(f) Daga platform with monoliths. Elliptical Building, Zimbabwe (*after Hall*)

Fig. 3

a. Mandeya's Seat, Inyanga

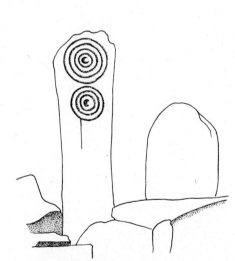

c. Nalatali

d. Zimbabwe Acropolis

b. Venda, Milaboni (after Stayt)

MONOLITHS

Walton. 1955

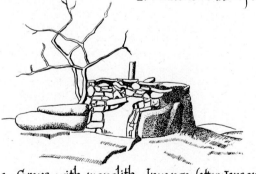

e. Grave with monolith, Inyanga (after Jensen)

Fig. 4

rectangular, though not necessarily squared at the top, stand three to four feet above ground, embedded about 18 inches. Some are quite slender, being only 11 inches by 5 inches. They have apparently no practical use, standing as they do isolated in an open space some distance from the hut mound. They are therefore only explained as some tribal totem or of some magical signi-ficance.' As these pits are now almost generally accepted as kraals for small cattle, the position of these monoliths in front of the entrances to the kraals indicates, however, that they were most probably tethering posts to which the cattle were tied when being milked. Some of them are notched near the top to secure the rope. Among the Sotho of Basutoland a similar stone is placed a little distance in front of the cattle kraal, on the smooth area where salt is sprinkled, and this also serves as a milking post.

None of the monoliths can, then, be directly associated with phallic cults and in certain cases they certainly served such utilitarian functions as seat back-rests and tethering posts. Almost parallel monolithic constructions can be found in Mashonaland and in southern Abyssinia and it is highly probable, therefore, that these particular uses of monoliths had their origin in Abyssinia.

HANDA INGOTS

The uncertainty and confusion which surrounds the early finds at Zimbabwe is particularly noticeable in the case of the cross-shaped ingots, referred to by Frobenius as *handakreuze* and by Bent as *astragali*. In a cave on the 'Acropolis' at Zimbabwe Bent 'dug up an ingot mould of soap-stone of a curious shape, corresponding almost exactly to an ingot of tin found in Falmouth Harbour. This ingot of tin was undoubtedly made by Phoenician workmen, for it bears a punch mark thereon like those usually employed by workmen of that period; and Sir Henry James draws attention to the statement of Diodorus, that in ancient Britain ingots of tin were made in the shape of astragali or knuckle-bones. Probably this shape of ingot was common in the ancient world, for Sir John Evans has called my attention to an ingot mould somewhat similar in form, found in Dalmatia, and the Kaffirs far north of the Zambezi now make ingots of iron of a shape which might easily be supposed to have been derived from the astragalus; but at the same time the find-ing of two ingots in remote places where Phoenician influence has been proved to be so strong is very good presumptive evidence to establish the fact that the gold workers of ancient Zimbabwe worked for the Phoenician market'.

At Little Umnukwana Hall and Neal discovered a copper 'cross-bar five inches long, in the form of a double-headed claw hammer', together with double iron gongs and a soapstone bowl. Two similar ingots had been discovered previously; one, in 1891, in some 'ancient ruins (not Zimbabwe) near Victoria' and one in the Mazoe district.

In 1902–3 Hall found a fragment of a soapstone mould in No. 7 Enclosure and two fragments in No. 6 Enclosure of the Elliptical Building, all of which were similar to that found by Bent and conjectured by Hall to be of 'Makalanga origin'. No horizon or association is given but Hall states that they 'were cut into the broken section of an ornamented beam. Moulds of this shape are not, therefore, necessarily ancient, though the form may have been handed down from ancient times. Mr Selous some years ago, discovered considerable quantities of copper ingot moulds in actual use by the natives of Katanga, and these were almost the identical shape of the ingot mould discovered by Mr Bent at Zimbabwe. The Administrator of North-Eastern Rhodesia reported in March, 1900, that ingots of copper in the form of a St Andrew's Cross were common articles of trade in the Katanga district. It must also be recollected that three such ingots have been found in Southern Rhodesia. Though old, their appearance does not in any instance suggest antiquity. The author, taking these points into consideration, does not believe that the ingot mould discovered by Mr Bent can be any evidence of the occupation of this country by the Phoenicians, and this opinion is confirmed by the locations of the moulds found'.

In 1891 Neal discovered 'a St Andrew's cross-shaped copper ingot in a grave within a ruin' and Hall records that 'similar ingots have also been discovered in the graves of much later squatters in the ruins, but these do not relate to the time of the original builders, but to a very much later time'. Hall concludes that: 'Possibly these cross-shaped ingots of later times are but in general form a survival of the old pattern of mould found at Zimbabwe, and used by the people who sank the ancient gold mines to depth in the rock of Rhodesia. This pattern is undeniably the oldest pattern mould ever discovered in the country.'

Three distinct varieties of *handa* ingot are discernible and these have a vague regional and probably a chronological distribution. The earliest are of the small narrow type found at Zimbabwe and Umnukwana in association with soapstone bowls and dating from the beginning of the Monomotapa period. Similar examples are known also from the Katanga region of the Belgian Congo. These ingots have a relatively long central portion and only bifurcate at each end (Fig. 5a).

The second variety is somewhat similar to the first but the connecting bridge is much shorter,

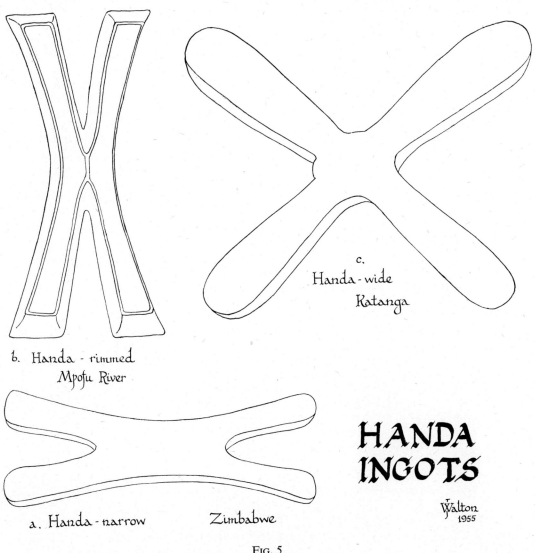

c.
Handa - wide
Katanga

b. Handa - rimmed
Mpofu River

HANDA
INGOTS

Walton
1955

a. Handa - narrow   Zimbabwe

Fig. 5

349

each limb is surrounded by a narrow raised rim and the finish of the casting is well executed (Fig. 5*b*). An ingot of this type has been recorded from Mpofu River, Miami Mica Fields, Lomagundu, whilst twelve soapstone moulds of the same pattern were found in ancient workings at the Star of the Congo mine near Elizabethville and another was obtained from ancient workings in Northern Rhodesia.

In Katanga and east and south Kasai the *handa* takes the form of a St Andrew's Cross (Fig. 5*c*), which varies in weight from 9 oz. to as much as 8 lb. 5 oz., and is used as a form of currency. In 1516 d'Almada reported that beyond a certain river (the Hunyani, according to Tracey) were people who were more white than black living in the land of Ambar, which adjoined Monomotapa. 'D'Almada declared that Fernandes had seen them patronising the fairs of the district. The people of Ambar sold *aspas* (windmill-sails) of copper; this copper came from "the rivers of Manicongo"— North Rhodesia. Fernandes had made detailed mental notes regarding the size and value of these bars of copper, so d'Almada suggested that they might be made and supplied by Portugal.'

Ingots of this type were made by the Sanga until 1891 and the Rev. F. S. Arnot has left a brief account of their craft. 'Not many traces of caste are to be found in Africa,' he writes. 'There is of course an aristocracy of mighty men, and the richer members of society rule over the poorer, but some trade castes exist among the Ba-Sanga. The copper mines were wrought and the copper smelted out of the malachite ore by certain families. This business is handed down from father to son and the instructions of forefathers are followed with the greatest accuracy; at one place the copper is cast in the form of a very wide capital H, at other mines it is cast in the sand by the workers with their fingers.'

Dr Livingstone mentions the same ingots when he writes: 'The cross has been used—not as a Christian emblem certainly, but from time immemorial as the form in which the copper ingot of Katanga is moulded—this is met with quite commonly and is called Handiplé Mahandi. Our Capital I (called Vigera) is the large form of the bars of copper, each about 60 or 70 lb. weight, seen all over Central Africa and from Katanga.' Cameron, writing in 1877, stated that copper came to the Waguha 'from Urua in pieces called "handa", varying in weight from two and a half to three pounds. They are cast in the rough shape of a St Andrew's cross, and the diagonal measurement is from fifteen to sixteen inches, while the arms are about two inches wide and half an inch thick'. Thompson contends, although he does not give any evidence, that 'the Mahandi was a form of currency from the Zambesi to Uganda and from the East to the West coasts'. It is known also from Barotseland.

The narrow *handa* is generally associated with the early Monomotapa Period and the wide *handa* belongs to a later Congo development but the distribution of the various types (Fig. 5A) does not permit of any definite conclusion as regards their origin. Professor Gregory stated: 'It seems to me improbable that negroes in East Africa should have stumbled by chance on the same pattern of ingot as that which the Phoenicians used in Cornwall; so that, whoever actually built Zimbabwe, it seems probable that there are traces of Phoenician influence on the early mining industry of Rhodesia.' Wieschoff, on the other hand, 'can see no convincing similarity between the African and extra-African specimens'. Jensen records that 'on a special kind of large stone slab, photographed by our expedition in Guragheland south of Addis Ababa one finds drawings of the mentioned moulds, which correspond exactly with those found in Southern Rhodesia', and Frobenius concluded that they originated in Cyprus.

Scrappy as the available evidence is, it all points to the conclusion that the *handa* ingot reached Southern Rhodesia from north-east Africa at the beginning of the Monomotapa period.

IRON GONGS

During Bent's excavations at the Zimbabwe 'Acropolis' he found three double iron gongs 'in the neighbourhood of the temple on the fortress' and subsequently Hall unearthed more specimens

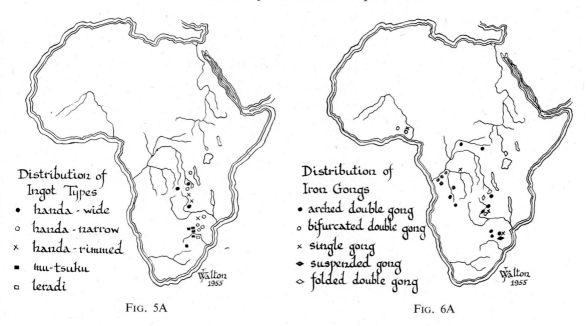

Distribution of
Ingot Types
• handa - wide
o handa - narrow
x handa - rimmed
▪ hu-tsuku
□ leradi

Walton
1955

FIG. 5A

Distribution of
Iron Gongs
• arched double gong
o bifurcated double gong
x single gong
◆ suspended gong
◇ folded double gong

Walton
1955

FIG. 6A

from Umnukwana, Zimbabwe and Dhlo Dhlo. Whenever stratigraphical horizons were recorded the gongs came from a higher level than the soapstone bowls and imported glass and china. In Enclosure 6 of the Elliptical Building an iron gong was found in association with gold crucibles, iron pincers and a soapstone amulet at a point 9 inches above a soapstone bowl but below the mould, iron hoes and assegais. In Enclosure 1 at Renders Ruins two double gongs were discovered in association with masses of iron and copper wire, hoes, axes and chisels at a level above that of a large soapstone bowl, Arabian glass, thin green glass, china and pottery with a green glaze, whilst from the outer enclosure of the Mauch Ruins Hall obtained two double iron gongs from the 'usual Kaffir debris' which had been used to fill in the enclosure. Double iron gongs have also been recorded in Southern Rhodesia from Umnukwana, where they were associated with a *handa* ingot and a soapstone bowl; from the Shamrock Mine, 25 miles from Selukwe and from Dhlo Dhlo.

These double iron gongs consist of two identical gongs linked together by an arched handle by which they were usually held in a suspended position whilst being struck (Fig. 6*a*). Each gong was made from two pieces of sheet iron welded together along a flange and having an oval cross-section. Identical gongs are widely distributed throughout the Congo basin and have been described by many observers. Stanley saw them in use at Urangi where, in February 1877, 'the great chief of Urangi made his presence known by sounding his double iron gong. This gong consisted of two large iron bell-shaped instruments, connected above by an iron handle, which, when beaten with a short stick with a ball of india-rubber at the end, produce very agreeable sounds'. Almost identical gongs were widely used until recently along the Congo from its mouth northwards almost to the source of the Ubangi as well as along the Kasai and the Kasongo (Fig. 6*b*) and an interesting illustration of such a gong in use is given in the German edition of the *Travels of P. Joanne Antonio Cavazzi in the Congo, Angola and Matamba*, published in Munich in 1694 (Fig. 6*c*). Mr Sandes, the curator of Zimbabwe, informs me that in the Cameroons these gongs are played as an orchestra in sets of ten, ranging in size from the Zimbabwe type up to gongs about 4 feet 6 inches high. They are inverted and held upright by putting a foot in the loop. His informant stated that they are no longer manufactured but that older members of the tribe knew how they were made. Of extreme interest is the double gong collected by Alfred Sharpe from Kazembe, south of

Lake Moero. This was $16\frac{1}{2}$ inches high, hammered together out of two thick sheets of iron and without a clapper.

In Barotseland double gongs of a slightly different pattern are still in use. These show the same flanged construction but each gong has its own straight handle and the two handles are welded together to give a Y-shape (Fig. 6d). The Yoruba double gongs are very similar except that the two gongs are not of the same size (Fig. 6e).

Double gongs throughout Southern Rhodesia and the Congo have always been directly associated with the rulers of great empires such as Urangi, Kazembe and Zimbabwe. Mr Frank Worthington informed Mr Sandes that in 1897 when he first interviewed Lewanika in Barotseland these gongs were used to announce meetings and to call the slaves. According to Holub the Barotse ruler maintained his own band of musicians to greet him on his arrival, to accompany his departure, and to play at the various public dances and at any ceremony or function decided upon by the chief. Among the instruments of this orchestra was 'a double gong without a clapper'. At Muene Putu Kasongo in the kingdom of Kiamvo (Kwango) a large double gong, two feet in length, was beaten to announce the death of a chief of royal blood.

A single gong, of the same construction as the double gongs but with a straight handle, was discovered, together with a striker, at Renders Ruins, Zimbabwe (Fig. 6j). Similar gongs were employed by the Barotse (Fig. 6f) and identical gongs are depicted in use on two Benin bronze plaques (Fig. 6g, h). Another quite different single gong was found at Zimbabwe by Hall, who described it as 'oblong, and has an ornament at each end made of tapered strips of iron coiled into circles, and these ornaments strongly suggest that the gong was only used when suspended' (Fig. 6i). Father Vancoillie has illustrated a gong from the Kasai district of the Belgian Congo which is used for sending messages or alarms. Although of a somewhat different shape and much larger than the Zimbabwe example, it is also suspended from two forked uprights by iron loops, one at each end, with the opening at the top.

Stratigraphical evidence shows that the arrival of these double gongs into Southern Rhodesia took place some time after the foundation of the Monomotapa Empire at the beginning of the fifteenth century. The distribution pattern (Fig. 6A) indicates that they spread from the Congo along the Kasai to Kazembe and thence southwards to Zimbabwe. The ruling Kazembe at the time of Sharpe's visit stated that his ancestors came from Mwato Yanwo on the Kasai. Significant in this connection is the statement by Hall and Neal that: 'There appears to have been two races of conquerors styled Abolosi: one of these, it is believed, was the Cazembe of the present Northern Rhodesia, who, according to Diego de Conto (Diogo do Couto), devastated the country of Sofala, and entering into Monomotapa, entrenched themselves and conquered the country.' This took place about A.D. 1560, a date which agrees well with the stratigraphical evidence, and supports the suggestion that the peoples of Kazembe introduced the iron gongs into Southern Rhodesia.* They continued in use at Dhlo Dhlo until after A.D. 1700 and in Barotseland and the Congo even up to the present time.

Most of the material culture discussed belongs to the early Monomotapa Period and had its origin in north-east Africa. The iron gongs show a very different influence and it remains to consider what other cultural traits can be associated with the iron gongs and a West African origin. The ceremonial axe-head found at Khami and the multi-barbed bronze spear heads from Zimbabwe have associations with the Congo but their occurrence is unrelated to any dateable objects. Fluted-neck pottery from Khami and Barotseland does, however, show distinct affinities with metal powder flasks from Benin and the peculiar fluting and tiered-construction of this pottery suggests that it was derived from a metal model (Fig. 7).

---

* This is doubted by Ian Cunnison, who contends that the first eastward migration of a Lunda Kazembe took place about 1740 A.D. (*Man*, 157, 1955).

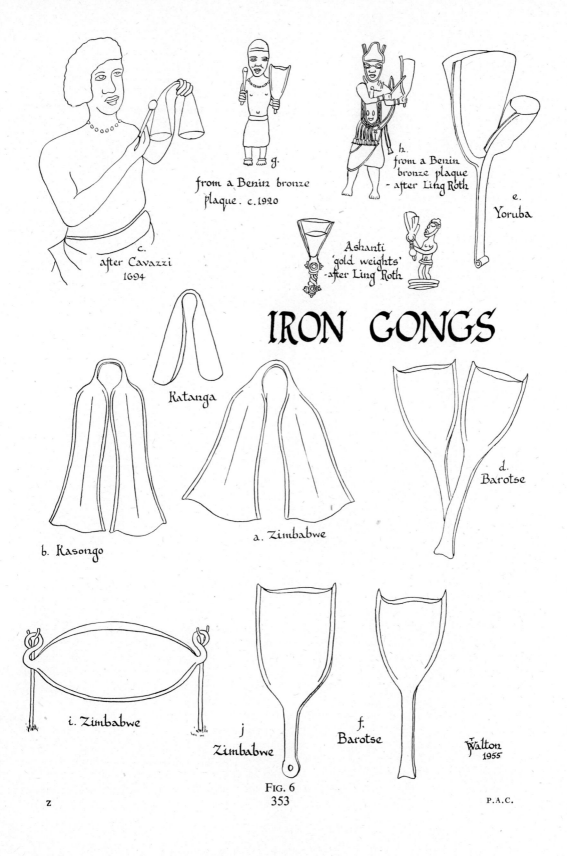

from a Benin bronze
plaque. c.1920

g.

h.
from a Benin
bronze plaque
- after Ling Roth

c.
after Cavazzi
1694

Ashanti
'gold weights'
- after Ling Roth

e.
Yoruba

IRON GONGS

Katanga

b. Kasongo

a. Zimbabwe

d.
Barotse

i. Zimbabwe

j.
Zimbabwe

f.
Barotse

Walton
1955

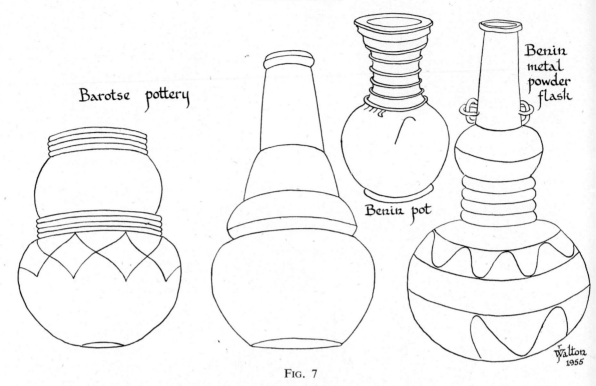

Barotse pottery

Benin pot

Benin metal powder flask

Walton 1955

FIG. 7

CONCLUSIONS

All the objects discussed have been recovered from horizons either contemporaneous with or subsequent to the imported glass and china of thirteenth to fourteenth century date. This suggests that the culture which they represent reached Southern Rhodesia about A.D. 1400 and continued, as the Dhlo Dhlo evidence indicates, to after A.D. 1700. This is the period of the Monomotapa Empire and it seems reasonable, therefore, to associate these objects with the founders of that empire. Soapstone bowls, chevron and dentelle wall patterns, *handa* ingots, monoliths and Class C pottery are normally found together in a limited number of what were obviously centres of importance and no doubt the headquarters of major chiefs. Their regional distribution is restricted to the eastern part of Rhodesia with the exception of Dhlo Dhlo. At the latter site these objects are somewhat rare and probably represent a late westward migration of Monomotapa people influenced by the later Kazembe peoples.

In time, in distribution, and in their limited occurrence at major sites the objects under discussion all conform to the historical empire of Monomotapa. The general distribution of these cultural features points to an origin from the vicinity of the Great Lakes and still further back in southern Abyssinia and there are many points of resemblance between the ruling Hima-Tusi groups of the inter-lacustrine Bantu, the Gala and associated peoples of southern Abyssinia, and the Monomotapa people. Early writers on Monomotapa all speak of the ruling tribe as being men 'of great stature' with light-coloured skins who were proud in their bearing and greatly respected by those peoples with whom they came in contact.

All along the eastern Monomotapa migration route are found survivals of an early civilization traditionally ascribed to a people from the north. The Uashin Gishu stone buildings, roads, terraces and irrigation works, referred to by Huntingford as the Azanian Culture, are attributed to a tall, red-skinned, bearded people who came from the north and whom Hungtingford connects with the Gala. This culture is more closely linked, however, with that of Inyanga rather than Zimbabwe. A number of earthworks in the area east of Lake Albert are attributed to the Bachwezi, a tall, fair, Hamitic people from the north who established an empire in Uganda. The stature and light-coloured skins of these invaders from the north were their most striking features and Margaret Trowell records that the Hima 'in height surpass by far all the eastern Hamites of the north-east and also the northern Nilotes, who are the tallest negroes. The impression of abnormal tallness of Hima-Tusi men is emphasized by their leanness and fine bone-structure'. The Karanga were also described as 'strong, light and agile'. 'The colour of the skin (of the Hima) is reddish-brown and generally lighter than that of the negro.'

The Hima peoples of Uganda show very similar physical characteristics to the founders of a number of empires from the Great Lakes down to the eastern part of Southern Rhodesia but they are also physically and culturally closely linked with certain Gala peoples and it is generally assumed that the Hima migrated to the northern half of the Lakes plateau during the first centuries of the present millenium, bringing with them the long lyre-horned cattle depicted on the Zimbabwe soapstone bowls.

Wieschoff, by a comparative study of Monomotapa kingship traits with their parallels in other parts of Africa, has also established a close similarity between Monomotapa, Hima and Gala cultures and Meinhof has suggested that these Hamitic peoples were the actual carriers of the Bantu language and that they were the founders not only of the Monomotapa empire but also of the East African Lake states.

Physical and cultural anthropology, linguistics, and tribal histories all support the present study of Monomotapa material in tracing its origin to the Hima and so to the Gala and neighbouring peoples in southern Abyssinia. Archaeological evidence from Southern Rhodesian sites indicates that this culture first reached Zimbabwe at the end of the fourteenth or the very beginning of the fifteenth century. Other writers have sought a Hima or Gala origin for the Zimbabwe culture, notably Wainwright, who placed the Gala migration as early as A.D. 900. He associated the earliest Zimbabwe buildings with the Gala and, on very slender and unsatisfactory linguistic grounds, he attributed the Monomotapa culture to this early time, a thesis which is not supported by the available evidence and which was strongly refuted by Huntingford and Schofield.

The Monomotapa culture of Southern Rhodesia, represented by massive girdle walls, conical towers, Class C pottery, monoliths, soapstone bowls and other associated objects, may be said with considerable evidence to have been brought to Southern Rhodesia by peoples of Hima-Gala origin about A.D. 1400. The Inyanga culture, which is linked with Uashin-Gishu, can also be traced back to a closely allied people.

Although the Monomotapa culture was introduced by the Hima peoples other influences are also evident, represented particularly by the double gongs which had their origin in the Congo and spread eastwards along the Kasai to Kazembe. These do not occur in the lower Monomotapa levels and they were introduced at a subsequent date by the Kazembe people about A.D. 1560.

The elaborate culture of the Monomotapa period thus represents two distinct elements; an earlier Monomotapa culture, represented by the soapstone bowls, soapstone birds, Class C pottery, monoliths and *handa* ingots, which reached Southern Rhodesia about A.D. 1400 and originated among the Hima-Gala peoples of southern Abyssinia; and a later Kazembe influence, represented mainly by the double gongs, which had a West African origin and spread to Southern Rhodesia about A.D. 1560.

ACKNOWLEDGEMENTS

In preparing this paper I owe much to Mr Roger Summers of the National Museum, Bulawayo, to Mr R. F. M. Immelman and Mr O. H. Spohr of Cape Town University, to Mr J. F. Schofield, to Miss E. M. Shaw of the South African Museum and to Mr R. S. Sandes, the curator of Zimbabwe.

Section Three

BIBLIOGRAPHY

Andrews, Edward M., 'The "Webster" Ruin in Southern Rhodesia, Africa', *Smithsonian Misc. Coll.*, 50, 1907, pp. 35–47.

Axelson, Eric, *South-East Africa 1488–1530*, 1940.

Bent, J. Theodore, *The Ruined Cities of Mashonaland*, 3rd Ed., 1902.

Cameron, V. L., *Across Africa*, 1877.

Caton-Thompson, G., *The Zimbabwe Culture*, 1931.

Cole, Sonia, *The Prehistory of East Africa*, 1954.

Dicke, B. H., 'The Lightning Bird and other Analogies and Traditions Connecting the Bantu with the Zimbabwe Ruins', *S. Afr. Jnl. Sci.*, XXVIII, 1931, pp. 505–11.

Finch, E. M., 'Pit People of the Inyanga Downs', *Proc. Rhod. Sci. Ass.*, XLII, 1949, pp. 47–51.

Frobenius, L., *Erythräa*, 1931.

Hall, R. N., *Great Zimbabwe*, 1905.

Hall, R. N., *Prehistoric Rhodesia*, 1909.

Hall, R. N. and W. G. Neal, *The Ancient Ruins of Rhodesia*, 2nd Ed., 1904.

Holub, E., *Sieben Jahre in Sud-Africa*, 1881.

Jensen, A. E., *Man*, 150, 1952.

Jensen, A. E., 'Simbabwe und die Megalithkultur', *Paideuma*, 1939, pp. 101–20.

Jensen, A. E. 'Das Gada-System der Konso und die Alterklassen-Systeme der Niloten', *Ethnos*, 19, 1954, pp. 1–23.

Livingstone, D., *Last Journals*, 1874.

MacIver, D. R., *Mediaeval Rhodesia*, 1906.

Masey, F. A., 'Zimbabwe: An Architect's Notes', *Proc. Rhod. Sci. Ass.*, 1911, pp. 37–56.

Posselt, W., 'Under the Mashona Kings', *Sunday Times*, Johannesburg, August 17, 1924, and 'The Early Days in Mashonaland and a Visit to the Zimbabwe Ruins', *NADA*, 1924, pp. 70–6.

Sandes, S. D., Letter to the author dated June 20, 1955.

Schofield, J. F., *Primitive Pottery*, 1948.

Schofield, J. F., 'A Survey of the Recent Prehistory of Southern Rhodesia', *S. Afr. Jnl. Sci.*, XXXVIII, 1942, pp. 81–111.

Stanley, H. M., *Through the Dark Continent*.

Stayt, H. A., *The Bavenda*, 1931.

Stead, W. H., 'Succeeding to the Name Mandeya', *NADA*, 1946, pp. 11–12.

Summers, Roger, 'Iron Age Cultures in Southern Rhodesia', *S. Afr. Jnl. Sci.*, 1950, pp. 95–107.

Thompson, Louis, 'Ingots of Native Manufacture', *NADA*, 1949, pp. 7–19.

Trowell, M. and Wachsmann, K. P., *Tribal Crafts of Uganda*, 1953.

Vancoillie, G., 'Recueil de Signaux Claniques ou Kumbu des Tribus Mbagani et du Kasai', *African Studies*, 8, 1949, pp. 33–45.

Wainwright, G. A., 'The Founders of the Zimbabwe Civilization', *Man*, XLIX, 1949, pp. 62–6.

Walton, James, 'The Soapstone Birds of Zimbabwe', *S. Afr. Arch. Bull.*, X, 1955, pp. 78–84.

Walton, James, 'Iron Gongs from Central Africa', *Man*, LV, 1955, pp. 20–3.

52

Excavations at Khami Ruins, Matabeleland

by K. R. ROBINSON

DURING the last nine years the Commission for the Preservation of Natural and Historical Monuments and Relics of Southern Rhodesia has undertaken a series of excavations at Khami Ruins. It is proposed first to give a short account of the recent archaeology of the Khami Ruins area based on work done, and then to describe briefly a few of the important excavations.

The only recorded excavation done in the ruins previously was a somewhat superficial trench dug through a hut-site by MacIver about 1904. Before that date digging had occurred, mainly for the purpose of finding gold. Fortunately the gold proved to be sparse and the early diggers soon transferred their attention elsewhere.

DESCRIPTION OF SITE

The Khami Ruins are located about 13 miles west of Bulawayo in the vicinity of the Municipal Dam. The largest and most important buildings—which number eight—are scattered over an area of approximately one square mile in extent near the dam outlet on the west bank of the Khami River. Outside this area there are, however, a considerable number of minor ruins to the distance of five or six miles from the main group.

The country is very broken and heavily bushed, small rocky granite kopjes and knolls occur in great profusion, and through this jumble of rock and vegetation the Khami river has cut a deep gorge. Rising in the Matopo Hills and flowing in a northerly direction the Khami eventually joins the Gwaai river, a tributary of the Zambezi. The stretch of river known as the Khami Gorge extends from a point about a quarter of a mile below the dam outlet downstream about half a mile. It contains a series of rocky pools which usually hold water all year round. This almost permanent water supply, in an area normally semi-arid, was undoubtedly a source of attraction to both men and animals, particularly those tribes who lived largely by hunting. Purely agricultural people would tend to avoid the area as suitable land for cultivation is very limited. Grazing is fairly good —the Mopane and other bush providing feed when the grass is scarce—but it is probable that large herds of big game, particularly buffalo and elephant, accompanied by carnivora, made the herding of cattle precarious. It is of interest to note on Stanford's Map of Mashonaland and Matabeleland, London, 1880, that Khami Ruins and vicinity is marked 'King's Preserve'. Mr C. K. Cooke of Khami Dam has informed me that local natives have stated that Lobengula had police in the area who kept out intruders. A certain amount of game still survives, bird life in particular is extremely rich and varied.

EARLY SETTLEMENTS

The makers of the Wilton microliths were the last of the Stone Age hunting peoples to occupy the Khami Valley, and they may well have been driven out by the arrival of the first of the metal-working groups to enter the district. These latter practised what I have termed the Leopard's Kopje Culture from the hill situated about a mile north-east of the Hill Ruin, where the typical

357

pottery was first noted. It is probable that this name will eventually be replaced by another, but it is convenient for the time being.

The Leopard's Kopje people built rough stone walls which often closed gaps between kopjes thus forming protected areas which were used for village sites and cattle kraals. In other districts similar walls at times enclose large tracts of country, but at Khami they are limited in extent, and the population appears to have been small. The huts were sited round the edges of the enclosed areas, and it is probable that livestock was kraaled in the central space at night. Cattle were kept and agriculture was practised in patches of good soil near kopjes. Both iron and copper were used, the former being smelted in small clay furnaces. It is probable, however, that metal was in short supply. Small rings of iron and copper measuring not more than 10 mm. in diameter were popular as ornaments; iron hoes were made and also arrow-heads. Pottery was abundant and varied,* and has affinities with material from the Limpopo valley sites and with Class R_I. It closely resembles the Hillside pottery described by Schofield (1948) and may be identical. The pot forms comprise shallow and deep bowls, the former with inturning rims, shouldered pots, beakers and carinated vessels. The decoration may be incised or stamped. The clay is nearly always full of quartz fragments, but the finish is often of a high standard.

Clay figurines were a strong feature of this culture, and they may represent cattle or human beings. The latter sometimes take the form of women with large buttocks, legs outstretched and body bent backwards.

Glass beads do not occur in large numbers, and they may be absent or rare at some sites. Owing to the difficulty in obtaining them we have not yet a very extensive collection, but it is safe to say that they differ from the Khami Ruins series and appear to be related to the early beads of Bambandyanalo and to some extent Zimbabwe.

So far there is no evidence of contact between the builders of the platforms and enclosures which comprise the Khami Ruins, and the less ambitious wall-builders from Leopard's Kopje, and it will be shown that the living sites of the latter occur stratigraphically below the walls and rubbish heaps of the former.

The Khami Ruins and Culture

The stone walls, which are the most obvious feature of the ruins today, follow the Zimbabwe traditions of dressed granite blocks laid in courses without mortar. The predominant type of wall is the platform retaining wall, which, in fact, is often nothing more than a facing of dressed blocks built against a mass of stone filling. Free-standing independent walls are rare, and they are usually confined to the enclosures which frequently occur attached to hut platforms or adjacent to them. Schofield (1942) regards these as cattle pens, and there can be no doubt that he is correct as drains invariably pierce the base of the walls of these places, nor do they show any evidence of human occupation.

So far as Khami is concerned platforms appear to have been preferred to enclosures as living sites from the beginning. From time to time the original platforms were enlarged and heightened, and, as a rule, the old occupation levels were swept clean before building again over them. There were, however, exceptions to this rule.

The most usual type of building is composed of one or more hut-platforms varying in diameter from about 40 to 60 feet, raised above the surrounding ground level anything from 6 to 20 feet. In the latter instance the retaining walls are stepped back in terrace form. There is often a passage entrance, use having been made of space between platforms, but in the case of elaborate passages blocks of masonry were sometimes built specially to act as one of the passage walls. It is often noticeable in the lesser ruins that walling does not continue completely round the platform, and its protective value seems doubtful.

* In order to avoid confusion the pottery classification advocated by Schofield has been adhered to.

Excavations at Khami Ruins, Matabeleland

We shall see later that wood and daga were as important items in construction as stone, and there is evidence to show that a good deal of stone walling was originally hidden by a coating of thick daga plaster, this does not apply to the main outer walls however. Decoration is predominantly chequer pattern, other patterns existed but are now destroyed.

It has been stated that the most important buildings are located in the vicinity of the river below the Khami Dam, of these what is known as the Hill Ruin takes precedence. It consists of a terraced hill built in the form of three platforms A, B and C, one above the other like giant steps, situated on the edge of the cliffs overlooking the gorge of the Khami river. The hill-top is accessible by means of a main entrance passage located to the north-west, or by a hidden passage, recently discovered, which leads up from Platform Ba. On the hill-top (Plat. C) are the remains of dwellings which, judged by their form and plan, were occupied by a person of rank. Finds of an unusual nature tend to confirm this view.

Only a small portion of the population lived on the stone-walled platforms, many more dwelt in huts, mainly west of the Hill Ruin, where walling was absent or very slight. The material culture associated with these huts is identical with that of the main ruins. It is true to say, however, that imported china, gold, and the more ceremonial native pottery has not been recovered from these more humble dwellings. In short the Hill Ruin probably represents the residence of a powerful chief, and the buildings in its vicinity may have been occupied by members of his family or various functionaries attached to his court, while the common people lived outside the walls.

Metal work was carried on at some of these more humble sites, but this was confined to such crafts as copper bead making, wire drawing, etc.; of iron smelting there is no evidence within the ruin field. Other occupations were: carving in ivory, weaving cloth, and probably the manufacture of shell beads.

Pottery at Khami is very plentiful and belongs almost without exception to that type of ware placed by Miss Caton-Thompson in Class D at Zimbabwe, and by Schofield in Class R_3. Its chief characteristic is the lavish use of contrasting colours worked in geometric designs forming bands and panels round the body or neck of the pot. Decorated and undecorated vertical, concave, or bowl-shaped necks are a feature. Some of these necks are fluted. Accompanying this polychrome ware is a large quantity of undecorated ware which comprises globular or sub-spherical pots with short vertical or slightly flared necks and rolled rims. These latter usually have the same finish as the decorated pots, i.e. they are burnished with graphite.

Extensive middens occur all over the ruin field, particularly on the slopes east of the Hill Ruin. None of these deposits are of greater thickness than 4 feet. In addition to sherds and other odds and ends, all the middens contain large quantities of bone, mainly, if not entirely, derived from game animals. The bone itself is bleached white, and is normally quite sound. Undoubtedly hunting formed an important part of the economy at Khami. On the other hand querns are rather scarce and rarely display signs of long or hard usage.

To end this short description it may be mentioned that the only date known with certainty is that of the final destruction by the impis of Zwangendaba which occurred about A.D. 1830. These warriors are said to have driven out the people of Mambo; this refers to the powerful Rozwi rule of pre-Nguni times when the paramount chief was known as Mambo. This title is still used throughout Mashonaland for important chiefs, and is known across the Zambezi. It would appear that formerly its use was restricted to rulers of considerable importance such as the Munumutapa or successful rivals.

EXCAVATIONS

Within the ruin field a total of 29 recorded excavations have been completed. Something has been learnt from all of these, but only the more important can be mentioned here.

NO.1 SECTION E 19

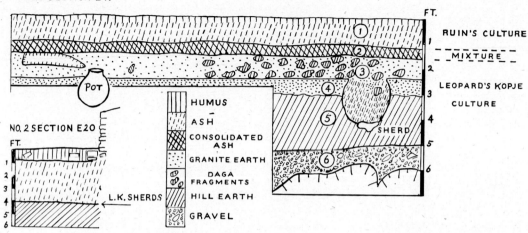

FIG. 1

1. *Trench East of Cross Ruin: Excavations Nos. 19 and 20*

A trench taken to bedrock in a level piece of ground about 30 yards east of the Cross Ruin (No. 2 Ruin) gave the following information (Fig. 1, No. 1):

(1) 0–12 inches   Grey ashy midden containing R_3 sherds and glass beads of the Khami Ruins Culture.

(2) 12–17 inches   Hard ash layer containing quartz pebbles sherds of R_3 ware mixed with a few sherds of Leopard's Kopje type. Bone fragments bleached but sound.

(3) 17–29 inches   Compacted granitic earth containing fragments of hut daga, L.K. sherds only, bone fragments mineralized, brown in colour. Evidence of erosion on surface of this layer.

(4) 29–35 inches   Tramped earth floor containing L.K. sherds, small rings of copper, corroded iron fragments, and a few altered glass beads unlike those from layer (1). A complete pot was embedded in the floor, and there was also a small excavation in the form of a storage pit dug through the floor to a depth of 2 feet. The latter was filled with ash and a few sherds.

(5) 35–59 inches   Ochreous granitic sand, sterile.

(6) 59–72 inches   Quartz gravel containing developed Rhodesian Still Bay or Magosian in the upper few inches. Below was bedrock.

This section proves an occupation of the area by Leopard's Kopje people prior to the accumulation of the ash midden (1) assignable to the Khami Ruins period, and suggests that the earlier occupation site had been abandoned for some time before reoccupation took place.

A pit sunk at the base of the lowest retaining wall bounding Platform Ca of the Hill Ruin showed that the wall had its foundation course resting on a ruin-period midden over 3 feet in thickness which had accumulated on hill earth. In the upper few inches of the latter were recovered Leopard's Kopje sherds (Fig. 1, No. 2). Odd sherds of Leopard's Kopje ware have been recorded from bedrock on Platform B, and in the hut CbI on Platform C.

2. *Platform Ba: Excavations Nos. 17a and 17b*

Two trenches were sunk to bedrock with the purpose of studying the construction of the plat-

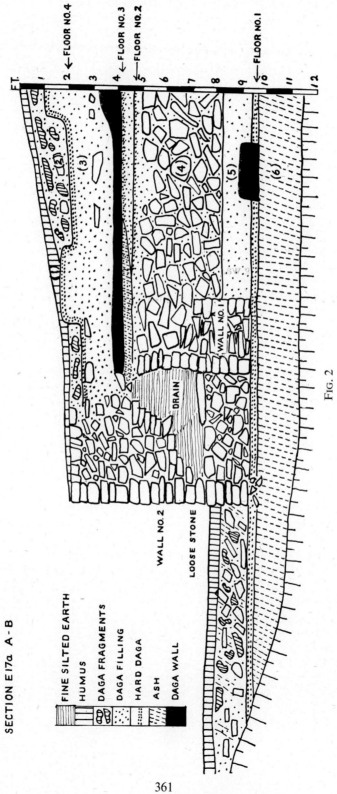

FIG. 2

form. The first of these, 17*a* (Fig. 2), was planned to cut the retaining wall of Platform Ba, although the wall face was not demolished. The layers from the top down were as follows:

(1) Humic earth.
(2) Broken hut daga, charcoal, ash. A destruction layer.
(3) Stratified daga filling with Floors II, III, IV.
(4) Stone filling.
(5) Daga filling and Floor I with associated wall (No. 1).
(6) Ash midden on bedrock. Dried grass roots in surface.

The sequence of events appears to have been as follows:

(*a*) The accumulation of midden on bedrock. Midden actually extends below Platform Ca of the Hill Ruin, and is therefore one of the earliest middens on the hill. The presence of grass roots indicate that it was finally covered by vegetation.

(*b*) Floor I laid down on midden, wall No. 1 built in Floor I. The latter in the section has the appearance of a free-standing wall. Floor I provided evidence of occupation in the form of daga walls, and associated finds.

(*c*) Area south of wall No. 1, i.e. on Floor I, filled in first with daga then with stones. Wall partially demolished, stone filling carried over it and present retaining wall begun. Drain constructed.

(*d*) Floor II laid down on stone filling.

(*e*) Platform further heightened by living Floors III and IV.

(*f*) Floor IV covered by debris derived from destroyed buildings.

The second trench 17*b* bisected wall No. 1 again. An almost identical series of layers were exposed, but the destruction layer was confined to a small area at the southern end of the excavation which does not appear in the section. Wall No. 1 here continues over a large boulder, and has become the retaining wall of a platform over which was built the hut selected by MacIver for his trench (Ba1). At the south end of the excavation a second hut, Ba2, was cut into, its foundations are partly built over a destruction layer and it belongs to the final phase of the platform. The first hut, Ba1, is also late. It is built on the remains of an earlier daga structure—possibly a hut but the evidence has been obscured by MacIver's trench—the foundations of which rest directly on a daga floor covering the stone filling behind wall No. 1. It appears to have existed during the occupation of Floor II when the upper part of wall No. 1 was plastered and a daga wall or projection was built against it, and may, perhaps, be as old as the original platform bounded by wall No. 1 and therefore be of the same date as Floor I.

Thus three definite stages in the occupation of the site are represented:

(*a*) That represented by the midden (Layer 6) which is probably connected with the first walling on the hill above.

(*b*) Floor I and associated walling, i.e. wall No. 1.

(*c*) Filling in with stone and subsequent heightening and enlargement of platform, and the building of the present retaining wall.

Finds were few, but beads and sherds occurred throughout. The following facts were noted:

(*a*) At least one sherd of Leopard's Kopje ware was recovered from bedrock mixed with Khami Ruins ware (R_3).

(*b*) Polychrome decoration occurred throughout.

(*c*) In the midden (Layer 6) all designs were incised on the pot before burning, but above this level they were frequently engraved after burning.

(*d*) Typical Khami series beads occurred throughout, but there was a preponderance of minute beads in the midden.

(*e*) Pellets of gold occurred at all levels, but they were rare.

(*f*) No imported china was recovered. At other excavations at Khami Nankin china has only been recovered from the most recent floors.

3. *Excavation of Hut Cb1 and Passage, Hill Ruin, Excavation Nos. I to II*

During 1947 a buried hut of unusual form was located in a central position on Platform Cb, Hill Ruin. Clearance of the hut disclosed a passage, 134 feet in length, leading up to it from Platform Ba, a rise of 28 feet.

The hut is semicircular in form. The west walls, which form an arc measuring 20 feet across the chord, are substantially constructed of daga faced with stone over which was laid daga plaster. The east wall, the chord of the arc, consists of a small platform (Cd2) specially built for the purpose, also constructed of daga, stone and plaster. This platform is actually an extension of the east wall of the passage, the latter entering the hut from the south. The entrance was constricted to a width of 2 feet 6 inches by pole and daga walls which projected outwards from the passage walls. Parallel to the east wall, and 4 feet from it, is a daga kerb which supported four wooden posts; thus there was a continuation of the passage across the hut terminating in a second entrance to the north. The walls average 5 feet in height, and were surmounted by a very solid rim of daga much damaged during the destruction of the building. In the hut floor were ten post holes containing the charred remains of posts, these, added to the four in the daga kerb, seven spaced along the east wall, and two at each end of the west walls, make a total of twenty-three posts in the hut. This may be compared with the lack of post holes in normal huts at Khami. Outside the hut, round the western perimeter, are spaced three radial walls of stone, originally daga plastered, forming two unequal compartments formerly closed by a girdle wall of daga. Three broad steps of daga covered stone lead over the central radial wall. Within the southern compartment was discovered a circular stone lined hole, 24 inches in diameter at the top tapering regularly to a depth of 60 inches. This was filled with fine ashy silt, and presumably acted as a drain. Two similar holes were located built in Cd2 near its edge. Such drains are a common feature at Khami, usually in the vicinity of huts. Their use as latrines has been suggested.

The deposit which filled the hut before excavation was composed as follows:

Black humic earth	9 to 12 inches average thickness
Thick daga slabs with pole marks	6 to 9 inches average thickness
Grey to white ash, charcoal, flat granite slabs	30 to 36 inches average thickness
Sooty deposit on floor	1 inch average thickness

A trench across the hut floor disclosed eight successive daga floors to a depth of 6 feet, the first of which was laid on bedrock. Only the two most recent of these floors were associated with the hut. Excavations in Cd2 produced the remains of charred roof timbers embedded along a portion of its edge.

Finds from within and immediately outside the building include two small carved lions of ivory, a set of ivory divining dice, and a hoard of bronze and iron weapons. The latter may have affinities with the ancestral spears of the Venda.

The stone walls of the passage leading to the hut were originally lined with wooden posts set at intervals of from 2 to 3 feet. In some instances the posts were built into niches. The walls were plastered with daga after the posts had been placed in position. The lower section of the passage is entered from Platform Ba, and from there the passage rises in a spiral manner, with a level stretch in the middle, to the hill summit. Over the lower section, apparently partially supported by the passage roof, there was a hut-like structure the remains of which may still be seen on Platform Ca. The middle section widens considerably forming a kind of room, while in the east wall of the upper section is a recessed chamber, originally separated from the passage by a daga wall with an entrance.

Section Three

The deposit which filled the passage before excavation was composed of the following layers:

Black humic earth	12 inches average thickness
Fallen stones	36 inches average thickness
Daga slabs with pole marks	12 inches average thickness
Ash and charred posts	24 inches average thickness

The above varied to some extent, but only in total thickness, not in the nature of the layers.

Finds from the passage included polychrome pottery, glass, shell and gold beads, and the calcined remains of an elephant's tusk from the chamber in the upper passage.

The evidence suggests that a roof of thick daga, supported by woodwork, extended over both the hut Cb1 and the passage. Hence the daga slabs which occurred in hut and passage, the numerous posts, and the peculiarly substantial walls of the hut. Excavations in the passage floor have shown that the upper passage was built over the remains of earlier structures, perhaps an earlier passage.

I think it is safe to conclude that we are dealing with the private quarters of a chief within which were kept objects of a sacred or ritual nature, while the main entrance situated on the western side of the hill led direct to the living huts.

The evidence of destruction by fire is clear in hut and passage, and in every structure on the hill.

CONCLUSIONS

There appears to be no reason to doubt the local belief that Khami was one of the towns built and occupied during the period of Rozwi dominion.

There is no evidence of a break in the occupation of the buildings indicating that the site was abandoned and re-occupied by people of a different ethnic group. The pottery is virtually the same from the beginning to the end of the ruin period, i.e. polychrome band and panel ware.

With regard to the daga roofed hut and passage, I do not believe these features were peculiar to Khami, and we must look for the remains of similar structures at other sites. The danger of fire must have been constant at such centres as Khami, and it would be natural to protect buildings which housed sacred objects. There is also the possibility, emphasized in the histories of the Venda (Warmelo, 1940), that the chief or Mambo remained hidden from his people and was regarded as semi-divine.

A tradition that the dwelling of Mambo was made entirely of daga is clearly indicated by information obtained from the Rozwi of Bikita, and Makalanga of Bulilima district. All these informants were referring to the paramount Rozwi Chiefs, the last of whom was skinned alive by the Swazi early in the nineteenth century.

Unfortunately up to now no dating evidence has been obtained but I think it is fairly safe to regard Khami and Dhlo Dhlo as belonging to the same period, basing one's conclusions on the similarity of the pottery and beads plus structural details of the buildings. The pots from the lower occupation levels at Dhlo Dhlo (Caton-Thompson, 1931) require some explanation however; their relationship with the polychrome ware at that site is not clear.

Looking at the question from a different angle, it is known with certainty that Khami was occupied by the Rozwi as late as the beginning of the nineteenth century. Examinations of the middens has shown that none exceed 4 feet in thickness, the deposits are very little consolidated, and the bone contained in them is remarkably well preserved. While recognizing that these factors provide no proof of date, they certainly hint at a not very remote origin for the Khami Ruins, and a period of occupation which is unlikely to have exceeded a hundred years or so. This brings us to the beginning of the eighteenth or the end of the seventeenth century. The fact that Nankin china has only been recovered from the most recent levels at Khami suggests that this site is earlier than Dhlo Dhlo, but imports of any kind are rare at Khami and may well have been treasured for generations.

Excavations at Khami Ruins, Matabeleland

ACKNOWLEDGEMENT

My thanks are due to the Matabeleland branch of the Rhodesian School Exploration Society for assistance with the survey of the Hill Ruin.

SUMMARY

1. An occupation of the Khami Ruins area by a metal-using people antedating the ruin period has been proved. This earlier culture, known as Leopard's Kopje Culture, possesses beads and pottery which have affinities with material from Bambandyanalo in the Limpopo valley, and perhaps with the culture associated with the lower levels at Zimbabwe.
2. The hut-platform type of architecture was dominant throughout the ruin period. Platforms were enlarged and heightened from time to time, but there is no evidence of a break in the occupation, or change in culture.
3. Pottery and beads show only minor changes in the ruin deposits.
4. Gold occurs in small quantities at all levels.
5. Imported wares have been recovered from the most recent levels only.
6. The Hill Ruin was probably the residence of a chief, and was accessible by means of two entrance passages; (a) the main entrance on the west side of the hill leading to living huts, and (b) a hidden and winding passage leading up from Platform Ba to a semicircular hut on the hill-top. Both passage and hut appear to have been roofed with daga supported on a wooden framework.
7. The use of daga as roofing may have been a protection against fire of structures used to house sacred objects, and which may also have formed the hidden dwelling of the chief or Mambo.
8. Khami was one of the towns built and occupied by the Rozwi under their paramount chief or Mambo.
9. Dating evidence is lacking, but it is probable that Khami and Dhlo Dhlo belong to the same period, i.e. seventeenth century or later. The destruction of Khami occurred about A.D. 1830 and was due to the invasion of Zwangendaba and his impis.

REFERENCES

Caton-Thompson, G. (1948), *Zimbabwe Culture*, Clarendon Press, Oxford.
MacIver, R. (1906), *Mediaeval Rhodesia*, Macmillan.
Schofield, J. F. (1948), *Primitive Pottery*, S. A. Arch. Soc. Handbook No. 3, Cape Town.
Schofield, J. F. (1942), 'A Survey of the Recent Prehistory of Southern Rhodesia', *S.A.J.Sci.*, XXXVIII.
Summers, R. (1950), 'Iron Age Cultures in Southern Rhodesia', *S.A.J.Sci.*
Warmelo, N. J. van (1940), *The Copper Miners of Musina and the Early History of the Zoutpansberg*, Government Printer, Pretoria.

53

The Origins of the Stone Architecture of Zimbabwe

by A. WHITTY

IN the course of the survey work which I have been carrying out at Zimbabwe I have had an opportunity to study in some detail the architectural characteristics which are to be found in the stone-work. I will start with a brief summary of these characteristics.

The buildings consist of coursed dry-stone work, mostly walls, but with certain other constructions. No wall is straight for sufficient length to justify any belief in the intention of the builders to make it so, nor, similarly, is any curve truly circular or regular in form. Many walls have a marked batter. There are no right-angles and very few angular corners. Nothing appears to have been deliberately levelled. A large part of the walling has been so arranged as to defy any reasonable interpretation in terms of the functions of the various enclosures it forms. Even those enclosures for which a tentative function may be adduced are so often inconsistent with each other in some major respect that their classification becomes virtually impossible. Thus, a statement of the architectural characteristics must be confined, if it is not to beg the question of function, to points of building technique and convention.

The main classifiable characteristics may therefore be summarized as follows:

1. The walling throughout demonstrates an evident ignorance of the principle of bonding. Such bonding as there is appears to be fortuitous.
2. Intersecting walls are not bonded together, one always having been built against the other.
3. Most walls have rounded ends. Entrances are normally between two opposing round-ended walls.
4. Many entrance ways are provided with small buttresses or bastions against the internal wall each side of the opening.
5. There are numerous examples of a type of construction known as a 'platform', consisting of what appears to be a raised dais, supported by retaining walls.
6. The western face of the Acropolis hill has been re-formed into a complex of apparently unplanned terraces sustained by retaining walls, of which the western wall of the Acropolis itself appears to be the crowning feature.
7. The girdle wall of the Elliptical Building appears to have no characteristic which is not represented elsewhere in the ruins, apart from its great size, its excellence of workmanship and the quality of its decorative treatment.
8. In a number of cases the rounded walls, where forming entrances, are linked by a few foundation courses, sometimes recessed to form steps.
9. There are two conical towers in the Elliptical Building, and a number of smaller objects in other places which appear to have some basic resemblance to them.
10. The area enclosed by at least one of the valley ruins has been found to be covered by a layer of daga cement, normally lapping against the bottom courses of the walls.

11. In the ends of many rounded walls where they form entrances, or in their attached bastions, are roughly V-shaped vertical grooves.
12. Where walls end square on plan, they are normally shown to have once abutted some object which has since disappeared.
13. There is a small number of openings having lintels, with the walling carried over them. These lintels consisted either of wooden poles or of rough slabs of stone, usually slate.
14. The decorations in stonework are principally to be found on the Elliptical Building, the most significant being the double chevron pattern on the outside of the main wall. The top of the larger conical tower is reported once to have been decorated with a dentelle pattern.

The summary which I have given is necessarily brief, but covers the main characteristics by which the stonework may be recognized. These characteristics are not incidental to the architecture; they are the main contents of it.

An examination of them shows that apart from the decorative treatment and possibly the conical towers there is nothing here which can clearly be ascribed to an exotic influence. The techniques, so far as they go, are consistent and clearly defined. They appear to be peculiar to Zimbabwe and its satellite sites.

It has been shown by Miss Caton-Thompson and others that a number of occupations of the site have brought about changes in the form which the enclosures took, particularly a late occupation which produced connecting walls over older hut sites. Such additions, although they show a difference of approach to function, produced nothing fundamentally new in building technique.

We are therefore faced with a highly specialized architecture which consists, as it stands, of a *fait accompli* for which some sort of evolutionary background must be found.

It may be argued in favour of an exotic origin for the ruins, that the nature of the material has had a determinative effect upon the form of the architecture, or that an architecture based on primitive imitation is likely to be widely divergent from its original. It is my opinion that neither of these arguments, nor a combination of them, is sufficient to account for the consistent, developed and crystallized nature of the Zimbabwe stonework.

In view of this opinion, I am putting forward a hypothesis which consists in the supposition that the architecture which we see is indigenous, so far as its origins are concerned. I am unable to prove that this is so in the manner which an archaeologist would require. The architectural forms which I shall call in evidence are open to differences of interpretation. On the other hand, the arguments which lend support to my own interpretation of the ruins are, I feel, sufficiently convincing to provide a sound basis for further investigation. My contention, therefore, is that the form and the technique of the building work is consistent with an entirely primitive system which did not borrow from outside until after it had hardened into an unalterable tradition.

Miss Caton-Thompson has expressed an opinion that the perfected building at Zimbabwe stands at the beginning of a sequence and not at the end. She adds: 'The time scale in Rhodesia's case leads, I believe, away from the best towards deterioration and not from immaturity to maturity.'

I take it, therefore, that Miss Caton-Thompson saw nothing in the course of her investigations at Zimbabwe or at other sites from which a growth of the culture from immaturity to maturity could be inferred. The problem of the architecture, as I see it, is that either it was imported in a mature state or else the tradition grew up locally, leaving little or no trace of its growth. In view of the difficulty of finding any source from which a mature tradition may have been derived, I believe that the latter supposition is correct. The fact that it left little or no trace of evidence acceptable to archaeology, is my justification for this somewhat circuitous approach to the problem. The origid of the architectural tradition with its clearly defined peculiarities may well never be proved, but an approach to it can be made by a study of those special building techniques and conventions which characterize its maturity.

Section Three

I will now discuss the classified characteristics which I have previously summarized.

1. *Ignorance of the principle of bonding.* This is obvious to anyone who looks at the walling. It has no evidential value in relation to the origin of the architecture, except to emphasize its primitive nature.

2. *Lack of bonding between intersecting walls.* The same argument might be applied to this characteristic, except for the existence of a very marked similarity between the placing of a wall against a natural boulder and the placing of it against another wall. Many examples of both may be seen on the Acropolis (Fig. 1).

It is reasonable to assume that before any stone building work had been carried out at Zimbabwe, the boulder formation of the hill top was very much as it is today. A people using the site as a place of refuge would have found certain defects in the position. It is evident that somebody not only found those defects, but remedied them. One such defect was that the approaches to the stronghold were too easy of access. The simplest way of rectifying this was to place a mass of material in the gaps between the boulders. Merely to pile up rubble in order to achieve this end would have had a deterrent effect only upon a determined enemy. It is by no means unreasonable to suggest that over a period of time, the value of producing a wall with a comparatively vertical face, comparable to that of the existing boulders, would have been realized. It is a big step from collecting a pile of rubble to building a wall.

The latter process requires the orderly arrangement of selected material. The abundance of stone, together with its local characteristic of splitting off from its parent body in layers, would have made this step easier. The unscalable nature of the many great boulders on the site provided an obvious model for imitation. In view of these facts, a development of technique from rubble piling into walling is not improbable. The character of the walling and the technique of abutting a wall against a boulder, another wall, or some other object, is entirely consistent with the supposition that the process was developed from the necessity of performing this defensive function (Fig. 2).

Such a conclusion, based on supposition, does not stand on its own.

3. *Rounded Entrances.* The practice of building entrances in the form of gaps between two opposing round-ended walls is fundamental to Zimbabwe architecture. The similarity in form between such an entrance and a way into an enclosure formed by boulders is very marked. If the boulder site was occupied as a defensive position before building work started, then it is possible that the occupants thought of an entrance only in terms of a narrow gap between two rounded boulders, and that this conception persisted when it came to constructing an artificial entrance.

It has been suggested that the rounded entrance is derived from hut architecture, where rounded forms are fundamental. A hut entrance is, however, based upon a frame construction basically vertical in conception. If the design were in fact transferred from hut architecture, it is hard to see, once the principle had been established, why it went no further. Apart from the development of vertical grooves at entrances, which may possibly be accounted for on these grounds, there is nothing else at Zimbabwe to lend support to this argument. It is simpler and more reasonable to suggest that the rounded entrance way was derived from the imitation of gaps between boulders.

This conclusion, again based on supposition, does not stand on its own.

4. *Bastions at entrances.* The natural approaches to the Cleft Rock Enclosure and to the Balcony Enclosure on the Acropolis (Fig. 3) are artificially narrowed at strategic points by means of bastions similar in type to those found inside the entrance ways of the Elliptical Building and many of the Valley ruins. In all cases the bastions have the effect of constricting the entrance, either by making it narrower or longer, an obvious advantage from the point of view of defence. It is therefore not impossible that the general practice of placing bastions on the inside of entrance ways was derived from the tactical desirability of placing them on the inside of natural entrances to the rock enclosures on the Acropolis (Fig. 6).

This conclusion, also, is based on supposition and cannot stand on its own.

368

FIG. 1. Wall in gap between two boulders, in Balcony Enclosure, Acropolis
Photographs by Roger Fairlie, in collaboration with the author

Natural Platform PB (largely   Artificial Platform PD, with Covered
screened by walling)   Passage below and to left
FIG. 2. View of the central part of the Acropolis from the main wall above the Western
Entrance

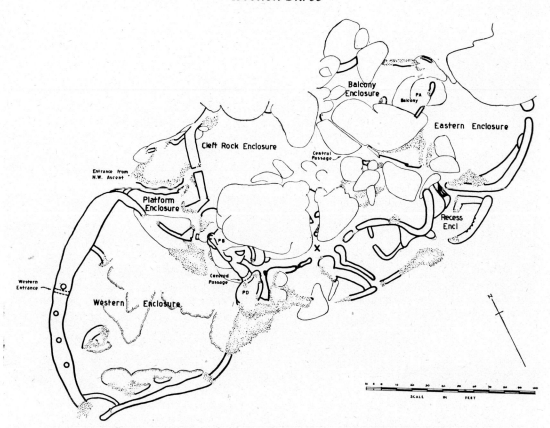

Fig. 3. Great Zimbabwe. Plan of the central enclosures of the Acropolis

5. *Platforms*. The natural rock enclosures on the Acropolis are so formed that observation of the approaches from the entrances is considerably restricted. There is easy access from each enclosure to a natural rock platform from which a wide field of view is possible (Fig. 3, PA and PB and Fig. 2). These platforms are crowned in each case with a length of protective walling on the outer edge. It is not unreasonable, by virtue of their similarity to the artificial platforms in the Valley and elsewhere, to deduce that the latter were derived from the former.

This conclusion was arrived at by R. N. Hall who believed that the function of the platform was connected with the ritual of the two 'Temples' on the Acropolis and the Elliptical 'Temple'. It is questionable whether these Temples existed at the time when the natural platforms were first used, and I would prefer to suggest that they were originally observation posts. Miss Caton-Thompson drew attention to the fact that in the Maund Ruins they appear to overlook the entrance to enclosures. The motive for their artificial construction in the valley is obscure and I shall return to it when discussing the conical towers. Their suggested derivation, however, is not unreasonable.

The four tentative conclusions which I have given for the derivation of walling, rounded entrances, bastions and platforms are, when considered individually, of little value. Considered together they are of more interest. They all four point to a derivation of forms or techniques, principally concerned with defence, from the same small area of the Acropolis, that is, the rock enclosures. More significant is the possibility that all four features are derived from an imitation of the natural rocks amongst which they were evolved. If these conclusions are provisionally accepted there is one clear inference to be drawn. That is, that the original builders were concerned in their own minds not so much with the building of walls, bastions or parapets, but with the building of rocks. The form which their constructions assumed, not only among the boulders of the kopje, but over the whole area of the ruins is strongly suggestive of this. The extremely primitive nature of the architecture, which I summarized earlier, has little in it which does not fall into place in a process of architectural development in which the conception of a wall in a generalized sense was absent from the minds of its builders. Reference to the ground plans of the Philip's Ruins and the Outspan Ruins (Figs. 4 and 5) will indicate more clearly than any words the mental conception of building which I have described.

If, as I have indicated, a wall, bastion or parapet was merely considered as an extension of existing rock, the forms which these functional objects took are not in any way surprising. They are, in fact, closely related in form to the natural boulders. This relationship between form and function which may reasonably be expected in the creative work of primitive people is strengthened in this case by the identity of material in both natural and artificial examples of the useful object. A mental conception of building of this type would impose very severe limitations upon formal and technical development. It is my contention that the architecture which we see at Zimbabwe may reasonably be explained as the inevitable result of such limitations.

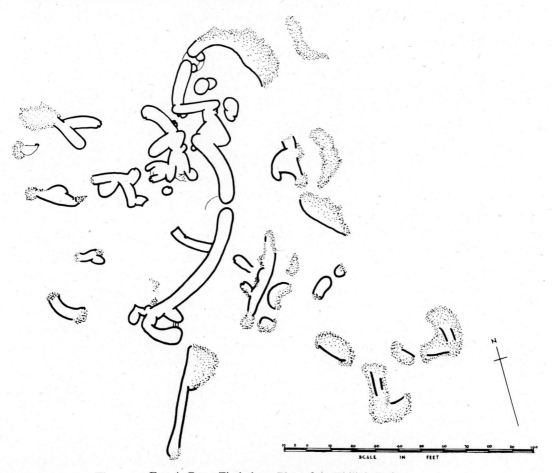

FIG. 4. Great Zimbabwe. Plan of the Philip's Ruins

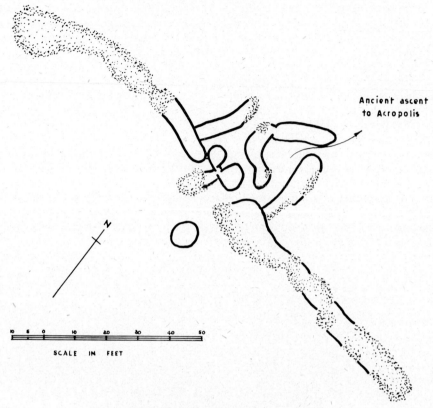

Fɪɢ. 5. Great Zimbabwe. Plan of Outspan Ruins

6. *The Terraced Enclosures*. When it became necessary to expand the building work outside the immediate area of the rock enclosures, the freedom in design which this offered was already shackled by an established custom of form and technique. A wall, in terms of this custom, naturally and inevitably abutted a boulder (which might be in the form of another wall or a natural boulder) or itself ended in the form of a rounded boulder. The practical need for walling to return inward against the side of the hill, in order to form enclosures, would have entrenched this custom still further. I would therefore sum up the attitude of mind which created this form of art as that which could utilize the plastic quality of an artificial boulder, while at the same time retaining most of its visual characteristics, in order to extend what had proved to be a satisfactory environment (Fig. 2).

7. *The girdle wall of the Elliptical Building*. This construction is generally agreed to be the most remarkable object of the ruins. Its mere size is overwhelming and the excellence of the workmanship is obvious. Nevertheless, it shows very marked evidence of the limitations which I have outlined. Its shape is irregular and its thickness varies considerably. Apart from the recessed steps, to which I shall refer later, the entrances appear to be no further developed in form than many other smaller examples on the Acropolis and elsewhere.

A peculiarity for which an explanation is needed is the so-called 'gap' near the northern extremity of the building. The two ends of the wall which form this gap approach each other at an angle which precludes the possibility that they could ever have been part of a continuous curve. Hall reports that the foundation courses of the western part meet the foundation courses of the

372

eastern part at an oblique angle. The upper parts of both walls were so ruinous as to form a gap from ground level upwards. It is suggested that the gap was the result of a rebuilding and shortening of a previous wall which had originally taken a wider sweep, and was merely a mis-joint. This is a mistake which I cannot imagine even the most thoughtless workmen making and is inconsistent with their evident skill in building their walls along the most tortuous lines when occasion demanded it. The explanation is also unsatisfactory because no join or mend, which must have accompanied such an alteration is visible at any point on the existing wall. The skill which would have been required to carry out such a work without visible sign would, I think, have been quite out of proportion with the general standard of the work.

A simpler account of the gap is that it is the remains of an intentional angular joint in which the two walls were not bonded together. The architectural convention that a wall either finished with a rounded end or abutted against another wall or boulder sufficiently accounts for the circumstances. If the eastern section had finished, or rather started, in a rounded end, and the western had abutted the side of it, the present state of the wall could be reasonably explained and the technique of the junction would be entirely in keeping with the normal practice. The use of this technique in the case of walls of this very considerable height would account for their collapse at this point.

8. *The Recessed Linking courses across Thresholds.* This feature is particularly well represented in the North Entrance of the Elliptical Building. The use of stone thresholds, whether recessed to form steps or not, need not surprise us. Any entrance is subject to heavy wear, and a little experience of building on the steep sides of the Acropolis would show the desirability both for providing against this and for retaining the higher level inside the enclosure at the point of entry from below. In order to account for this difference in height, steps of some sort would be necessary. If these steps projected outwards from the threshold, they would, by such projection, increase the difference in height to be taken up. It is logical, therefore, that they should occupy the area covered by the thickness of the wall, that is, the threshold itself. Such steps could be set into the threshold by means of stopping off the lower courses of the wall where they ran into the opening. The process which was used, however, was to continue these courses across the opening, at the same time sweeping them back in an inward curve, each course setting back further than the one below it. This method avoids any angular treatment of the stonework and is entirely consistent with the curvilinear usage which persists throughout the building work. So far as I am able to see it is the only method of forming threshold steps which obviates the necessity either of abruptly stopping some of the stone courses against nothing or of forming angular set backs, techniques which the builders evidently abhorred. There are two examples of recessed steps on the Acropolis, in each case the entrance having been subsequently sealed off by a later superimposed wall.

9. *The Conical Towers.* The derivation and purpose of this form of construction has been the subject of a great deal of speculation. I am unable to account for it in terms of an early functional requirement. One theory as to its origin is that it was an imitation of a minaret, similar to that on the Malindi Mosque at Zanzibar, known through contact with the coast. The fact that the summit of the larger tower was decorated is a strong indication of some form of exotic influence. Both this fact and the comparatively symmetrical shape of the tower itself, show a tendency to break away from the architectural tradition which characterizes the remainder of the buildings. Whatever its origin, it seems that the purpose of this construction must have been of a religious or politico-religious nature. For this reason it is unlikely that it is a development of a functional requirement. I would suggest, however, that if the early Acropolis dwellers had regarded the enormous boulders which formed their fortress as the abode of a protective spirit, their expansion into the valley area may well have been accompanied by the necessity of providing such spiritual accommodation on the new site. (Compare Figs. 7 and 8 which show the relationship between Tower and Platform in natural form and artificial form.)

So great must have been the influence of rock upon these peoples' existence that the possibility of an indigenous origin for the form of the tower must not be ruled out. Such a possibility gives

FIG. 7. The Balcony, from the Eastern Enclosure (Acropolis)

FIG. 6. Approach to Cleft Rock Enclosure from point X (Fig. 1)

Fig. 8. The Conical Tower and Platform (*right*) in the Elliptical Building

added support to my earlier suggestion that another specialized form of boulder, the original plat-form, was also artificially constructed on those sites which did not naturally possess it. It may be of some significance that not only the Conical Towers but the Platform which Miss Caton-Thompson dismantled in the Maund, were constructed with a rock filling.

10. *The Daga Cement Pavements.* The purpose of these pavements was probably to provide a firm, dry terrain in areas where the natural earth was liable to flooding or saturation. I am unable to find evidence of the use of this material for this purpose on the Acropolis, and its derivation may be ascribed to a response to a late functional requirement which appeared after building methods had crystallized into a firm tradition. An exotic origin seems unlikely. The nature of the material is so removed from that of rock, and so closely allied to that of the mud plaster generally used on hut walls and floors, that an adaptation from this source is most probable. I would emphasize that in my opinion this adaptation is not evidence of any integration of the separate conceptions of hut architecture and stone building.

11. *Vertical grooves in entrance ways.* It is noticeable that this characteristic is comparatively rare on the Acropolis. I consider that its origin probably lies in an adaptation from hut architec-ture. The grooves may have been used in two ways. Either they could house a number of horizontal stones or timbers so as to form a removable barricade, or else they could be used as slots into which door jambs were fitted. A light wooden framework tied to one jamb may have acted as a gate, which could be secured by being tied to the opposite jamb. Such a feature is consistent with a domestic rather than a defensive purpose, and lines up in this respect with the siting of the valley ruins.

If this conclusion is correct, it constitutes the only valid argument I am able to see in favour of any sort of association of ideas between stone building and hut architecture. The general absence of evidence that the technique and design of huts had any effect on the development of the stone architecture is one of the remarkable features of Zimbabwe.

12. *Square-ended walls.* The fact that square-ended walls once radiated from now vanished huts has been clearly demonstrated by Miss Caton-Thompson. I have found no evidence to sug-gest that such wall terminations were ever used in any other circumstances. The derivation is clearly connected with a strong tendency to build walls against something. The association of rocks and huts constituted a traditional environment which I believe was imitated on those sites where natural boulders were not available.

13. *Lintelled Openings.* It was stated by Bent that the then ruinous entrances to the Elliptical Building showed evidence of once having been provided with wooden lintels which carried the upper part of the wall continuously over them. The Western entrance to the Acropolis has been restored with stone lintels but was probably built originally with wooden beams, which are also known to have been used elsewhere, notably over a drain in the Elliptical Building.

The Covered Passage in the Acropolis has stone lintel slabs and is placed between the walling adjacent to a natural Platform (PB) and what appears to be an artificial platform (PD) (see Fig. 3 and Fig. 6). The opening is about 2 feet wide. Had the walls of this opening been carried up without the covering it would have been a simple matter to step across from one platform structure to the other. The process of laying stone slabs across the gap is, in my opinion, such an elementary step that it is not inconsistent with the mentality which may be inferred from the other work of the builders. It is noticeable that lintelled entrances, as such, are only recorded in positions where access from one side of the entrance to the other, on top of the wall, would appear to have been desirable. The walling on either side of the Covered Passage shows evidence of more than one stage in the building work. The height of the first stage coincides with that of the lintel.

The conception of a lintelled opening is universal, and therefore the possibility of exotic origin cannot be excluded. On the other hand, the method of carrying it out at Zimbabwe, over rounded wall ends, is highly suggestive of local inventiveness resulting from functional requirements. This is not unlikely in view of the fact that every known lintelled entrace at Zimbabwe can just as easily be regarded as a bridge, a very elementary conception, as a tunnel in the stone work. It is noticeable that no lintelled opening has door-jamb grooves. This is a further indication that the builders regarded their lintels as bridges rather than as doors in the stone walling.

14. *Decorative work.* The decorative patterns formed in stonework almost certainly originated from foreign sources. The most distinctive pattern, the chevron, has been found built in stone work in a similar manner as far afield as Ghirza in Tripolitania, and has been identified in general with Arab decorative work.

The appearance of this type of work at Zimbabwe and its further elaboration at other sites is a clear indication of exotic influence. This form of decoration is common over a very wide field and it would be ridiculous to suggest that it arose spontaneously at Zimbabwe. The association of stone pattern work with more generalized conceptions of building, as embodied in the girdle wall and the tower, is entirely logical. Decorative designs may be carried in the form of portable objects without the necessity of actual contact with the source from which they were derived. This is in marked contrast to building technique, which must be functionally understood, and which would therefore require such direct contact.

I have now discussed each of the architectural characteristics which I previously outlined. I am open to the criticism firstly that my method of approach is too speculative to be of value, and secondly that I have produced no evidence that the building work on the Acropolis was anterior to that in the valley, and therefore, that I have proved nothing. I submit, however, that the course of events which I have outlined consists of an entirely reasonable hypothesis which basically explains the facts and which may open the way to further investigation. Such investigation may be able to confirm or reject my hypothesis by methods which are outside my own field.

I shall finish by summarizing the conclusions which I feel may be drawn from this analysis of the architecture.

1. The characteristic architectural techniques and forms are so consistent and clearly defined as to presuppose an early period of formulation, development and crystallization.
2. The characteristics are generally peculiar to Zimbabwe and its satellite sites and cannot be accounted as originating from any culture within possible reach of the builders.
3. At a period before any building had been done, the Acropolis site must have provided a place of refuge of such excellence as, on this quality alone, to account for the original occupation of the area.
4. It is evident that the defensive potentialities of the site were, in fact, exploited by building work.
5. The form which the architecture assumed is consistent with a conception of building which understood its stone structures as artificial extensions to, or imitations of, natural rock, and not as walls in any generalized sense.
6. This primitive response to a small number of functional requirements in the exploitation of the Acropolis site is a sufficient cause for the emergence of the basic architectural characteristics of the ruins.
7. These characteristics survived as a controlling influence over the architecture after the time when a more generalized conception of a wall had become evident.
8. Exotic influence can be seen operating only upon the matured form of the architecture.
9. The architecture remained from first to last essentially primitive, and its matured development consisted principally of spatial extensions and embellishments of the original forms from which it arose.

The overall picture is that the Zimbabwe tradition of architecture began among the boulders of the Acropolis, where its simple techniques served a strictly functional purpose; that at an early time the creative impulse which caused it died; and that it grew only in extent and not in quality, eventually turning into the monstrous architectural curiosity which we see today.

54

Industria iberomauritánica en el Sudeste de España

par L. PERICOT GARCIA

EL caso de la llamada cultura iberomauritánica es uno de los más curiosos de nuestra Prehistoria. Tal cultura surgió de los estudios de los prehistoriadores franceses que trabajaban sobre el Paleolítico del Africa menor. En ésta, durante los tiempos más avanzados del Paleolítico superior se desarrolló una cultura muy peculiar que recibió el nombre de Capsiense, mientras una forma en cierto modo marginal del mismo, aparecía en la zona costera desde Túnez hasta el Atlántico. La estación de La Mouillah, cerca de Marnia en la frontera argelino-marroquí, fué la primera que se dió a conocer y por esto tal variante cultural es denominada por algunos, *muillense*. La característica principal de la misma es el predominio de una punta de dorso rebajado, pequeña y algo semilunar. El resto del material lo constituyen hojas, raspadores, puntas triangulares, perforadores, piezas con muesca, microlitos geométricos y microburiles, además de piezas de hueso.

El que esta industria fuera denominada iberomauritánica se debió a la convicción de Pallary de que entre el material que L. Siret recogía en el Sudeste de España y el que por su parte descubria como perteneciente a la nueva industria existía un innegable parecido.

Tras haberse definido así, se produjo una reacción, contraria a admitir relaciones entre España y Africa durante el Paleolítico superior, y se afirmó la incorrección del nombre dado a dicha industria. Todos pensamos que hacía falta hallar un nombre mejor y muchos pensamos en el de Oramiense. En el II Congreso Pan-africano de Prehistoria, celebrado en Argel, esta denominación fué también rechazada.

Pues bien, hoy, tras conocer algunos materiales del Sur de España, que me eran desconocidos *de visu*, creo que tal vez la denominación dada por Pallary no sea tan desacertada como se opinó y propongo que sea mantenida hasta que nuevos estudios hagan modificar de manera segura este punto de vista.

En efecto, entre los materiales de la colección Siret que se guardan en el Museo Arqueológico Nacional de Madrid y que ahora, por primera vez han sido expuestos, se encuentran interesantes series de las cuevas de las provincias de Murcia y Almería. Procedentes de la cueva de Zájara, hay varias piezas de silex cuyo caracter africano es indudable. Entre ellas una punta de clara técnica iberomauritánica. Su forma, ligeramente curvada, y su retoque dorsal, podrían hacerla confundir con una de las infinitas puntas que los yacimientos iberomauritánicos como la *Cueva de las Palomas* en Taforalt, por ejemplo, nos proporcionan. En cambio se diferencia claramente de las puntas epigravetienses que hemos señalado reiteradamente en el Este y Sur de España. No hay entre ellas confusión posible.

Este indicio, que dada la escasez de prospecciones modernas en el Sudeste de España, es suficiente para esperar otros descubrimientos análogos, nos mueve a sospechar que en algún momento del Paleolítico existió un contacto entre los creadores de la cultura iberomauritánica en Africa y las tierras españolas.

Industria iberomauritánica en el Sudeste de España

Es este un problema más a añadir a los que ofrece la disputada cuestión del paso del estrecho de Gibraltar por los paleolíticos, en cuya discusión estoy enzarzado con mi querido amigo y contradictor el profesor Balout, que lamento no se halle hoy entre nosotros.

[RÉSUMÉ]

Ce fut Pallary qui baptisa du nom d'Ibéromaurusien le faciès littoral du Capsien. Il croyait à une relation entre cette industrie et la culture que Siret découvrait dans le Sud-Est de l'Espagne. Une réaction postérieur affirme qu'entre le Nord de l'Afrique et l'Espagne il n'y eut de possible contact dans le Paléolithique superieur et même dans l'Epipaléothique. Dès lors, on devait substituer par les dénominations de mouilléenne ou oranienne celle d'ibéromaurusienne. Mais les collections ramassées par Louis Siret dans les grottes des provinces d'Almería et Murcia sont exposées maintenant dans le Musée Archéologique National de Madrid. Une pointe à dos abattu de la grotte de la Zájara, qui n'a rien en commun avec les pointes de l'Epigravetien espagnol, rassemble le type ibéromaurusien et confirme l'opinion que cette industrie est passée en Espagne et que la vieille dénomination peut-être est correcte.

55

The Evidence of South Arabian Palaeoliths in the Question of Pleistocene Land Connection with Africa

by G. CATON-THOMPSON

I wish briefly to examine the existing, and admittedly imperfect, evidence concerning the hypothesis of a Pleistocene land-connection between South-West Arabia and Africa. Was South Arabia a cul-de-sac or a bridge?

First I shall sketch the nature of the Palaeolithic evidence from South Arabia bearing on this problem; are the Stone-Age cultures found there, individually or successively, related to those on the African side of Bab-el-Mandeb Straits and East Africa in general?

Secondly I shall examine such facts as are known about a drop of sea-level which, on the Admiralty Chart of the existing sea-bed, would be needed to establish such a land-bridge. Faunal and botanical distributions need also to be examined, but this cannot be considered here.

The South Arabian Palaeoliths upon which my comments are based, were collected towards the interior western borders of the Hadramaut. It is now a rainless land of elevated desert plateaux, deeply entrenched by a few major valleys of impressive size, and innumerable short, steep, minor ones draining into them. The exposed rock is Nubian Sandstone overlain by Eocene cherty limestones rising in precipitous cliffs nearly 1,000 feet above valley bottoms. There is, therefore, an abundance of material available for tool-making, weathered or *in situ*.

The striking feature in all valleys is a deposit of fine-grained silty sand; it covers the valley floors and the base of the cliffs: it is ubiquitous on the high plateaux in wind-sheltered spots. It is largely an aeolian deposit, but clay streaks and pebbly bands prove water-action in addition. It is not known, even approximately, what the total depth of these silty infillings are in the valleys, or if they are a homogeneous deposit, which I greatly doubt. Even modest exposures are not plentiful; but they exist, in places where ancient stream-beds have ploughed through the silt. Fifteen-metre high banks of silt were the deepest we saw. In one case this silt—Aeolian Silt as I call it—was underlain by coarse gravels.

Our task—subsidiary to the main purpose of the expedition which was pre-Islamic dating—was, if possible, to ascertain the age of the Aeolian Silt, or failing that, to settle the age of the stream-beds which had cut into it.

The Wadi Amd, where our work partly lay, is a major valley. The silt-covered floor is over a mile wide. A narrow stream-bed hugs one side and provides deep exposures of it in the banks. This stream-bed had a history of its own, after the silt was ceasing, or had ceased to form. Palaeoliths are rare in it: but it yielded 17 artefacts. Gravel terraces of the later stream at 10, 5 and 3 m. also yielded 47 palaeoliths. The 10 m. terrace rests against the Aeolian Silt.

For the present purpose it suffices to summarize the main characteristics of these successive groups, because they share the same basic features and are clearly a continuous cultural series. Illustrated details may be found in *Proceedings of the Prehistoric Society*, Vol. XIX, pt. 2, 1953, pp. 189–218.

Chert or cherty limestone pebbles was the raw material. Neither available quartzitic sandstone nor obsidian from about 80 km. away was used. There was no selection of better quality chert, also available. Split pebbles, mainly spherical, or larger cobbles, with a minimum of flaking are predominant. A flat base was knocked up in one or more blows and flakes removed semi-peripherally, leaving cortex on the reverse. More elaborately and rarely the whole surface was flaked from various directions and intersecting edges provide a standard chopping-tool.

Flat cobbles were split longways also, usually without further evidence of intention. The flakes, though mainly primary, with cortex dorsals, exhibit marginal nibbling, some doubtless abrasional, but not altogether. Platforms are normally plain, and inclined at a moderate angle; retouch is very rare: where it exists, as in a thick flake worked into a side chopper, it is of the resolved, deeply-bitten, unsystematic type. In sum, the *in situ* series both in the Aeolian Silt and the later Gravels is undifferentiated and primitive. The silt series comes from between 5 and 6 m. below the surface, except a polyhedric chopping-tool near the surface: they are the oldest artefacts found, and are contemporary with the approaching end of the great depositional Aeolian Silt period, whatever age that may be. No fauna was found apart from molluscs of no significance.

The next geological event was erosional—the cutting of the narrow spate-bed through the silt. In time this stream bed became choked with coarse gravels to a depth of 10 m. This level survives as a fragmentary terrace. It yielded 33 palaeoliths. Judged on condition and probability some of the implements are doubtless derived from the Silt epoch. But in the 10 m. collection it is possible to detect, I think, a techno-typological advance in certain specimens, the condition of which augments the probability of their being later. Chopping-tools continue, also split pebbles; but the later-looking elements include a humpy prepared core, a double-ended core, an oval flake from a prepared core, and an end-scraper on oval bulbar flake with two patinas due to natural causes.

Subsequent stages of degradation left two lower terraces at 5 and 3 m. from which were collected 14 artefacts of the same general type. These 64 pieces *in situ* represent for the time being all we know of the earliest yet-discovered culture in South Arabia. They prove that Aeolian Silt deposition continued, as in India, into the later Pleistocene. The Wadi Amd series ends with a few pieces picked up on the surface of the Aeolian Silt, including one or two more developed specimens.

Now 64 artefacts are quite insufficient to form a basis for conclusions concerning them; and I therefore propose to use the supplementary evidence of surface palaeoliths before I indicate what, in my opinion, those conclusions are.

We brought home only a small sample of these surface finds—about 200—because circumstances made it impossible to remove more. But these 200, selected as typical, represent a very small fraction of those handled, examined and returned to their find-spot. They were not sporadic finds, but definite groups congregated at closely delimited spots, each far distant from the last, for I wished to test the possibility of local variations. But over a length of about 150 km. there was no variety: a deadly uniformity reigned everywhere: and though one or two features not found *in situ* suggest some techno-typological advance, these are hardly enough to make a stir in the evidently prolonged stagnation of Palaeolithic life in inland South Arabia. One site was of particular significance in this respect, for it comprised the scree slopes of a steep, short, ravine, still locally famed for its deep pools fed from a cliff spring. In such a rare and favoured spot, still green with water-plants, one might expect a congregation of successive industries. But this was not so. Patina alone provided hints that time elapsed while the artefacts accumulated. They are, however, of one, perpetuated culture, though inclusive of a handful of more interesting pieces. One of these is semi-bifaced. It is an elongated side-chopper, fashioned from a thick flake or split pebble by partial resolved flaking on both faces: cortex remains on butt and tip. Another is a miniature triangular core which, together with two miniature flake tools suggest a later period.

Other surface groups include, as usual, numerous chopping-tools or choppers: two spindle-shaped cores introduce a new type; and miniature flakes with or without steep marginal retouch echo the ravine collection. Of exceptional interest here is a symmetrical triangular core of fair competence of workmanship and normal size. Its apex displays the special fashioning called in Egypt the 'tortoise-point', which occurs also in the Somaliland Still Bay. Out of 106 flakes, 49 have plain platforms, 35 of which are high-angled; 14 are right-angled, 10 only facetted, and these include the miniatures. Another 13 are cortex-platformed, the remainder adiagnostic (21); pseudo-facetted (10); reworked (3).

Surveying the material both *in situ* and surface as a whole, it seems evident that we are dealing with one homogeneous culture, continuous throughout a great length of time, though within its own very narrow limits it was not altogether devoid of development. Whether this way of doing things went on till the end of the Palaeolithic is problematic. We saw nothing to suggest the contrary. The first certainty of eventual change and obvious proof of African contacts comes in the Mesolithic or perhaps Neolithic: it is witnessed by a little group of trihedral or bihedral borers from the South coast. These include one classic example of that very specialized tool, the 'pressure-flaked' trihedral rod of the Faiyum Neolithic, found also in the Doian Industry of Somalia.

The age of the Aeolian Silt and Gravel Terraces, and the affinities of the culture found in them, supplemented by the surface groups, remains to be considered, though only tentatively. I remember always that my evidence was gathered from one relatively small part of a huge country.

For African affinities one looks, naturally, to that area which includes the Horn of Africa. The physical and climatic characteristics of that region are, broadly, not dissimilar to those of South-West Arabia; the needs of life in both are sufficiently identical to create no obvious reason why their respective Palaeolithic histories should deviate from each other had they been in contact. But deviate they apparently did. On the African side, from Kenya to Somalia and the Sudan, the hand-axe tradition is strongly entrenched. No hand-axes as far as I know have come from South Arabia. One, it is true, exceptional enough to prove the rule, was found about 800 miles to the North—in other words half as much nearer the great hand-axe region along the Syrio-Arabian borders, from which it may be a stray.

Nor do I think our Arabian material can be readily equated with the Levalloisian of the African side, for comparison with even the more undifferentiated Lower Levalloisian breaks down at too many points, such as types and proportions of prepared cores, and resultant flakes and platform characters, to make it likely that they were connected by the hypothetical land-bridge.

In East Africa, as a whole, a Still Bay Culture succeeds the Levalloisian; a Magosian the Still Bay. Neither is apparent in South Arabia. On the contrary it displays the characteristics of a veritable cul-de-sac, primitive, stagnant, static.

It may be wondered if the inland locality of our finds and its distance from the coastal south-west corner accounts for this. I put this question to Professor Albright, since the Wendell Phillips Expedition was nearer the crucial area. He wrote back that in spite of all search virtually no trace of flint artefacts was found. That, of course, cannot be conclusive, but it is a pointer.

As for the Aeolian Silt, my search for parallels in structure and composition led me eventually to North-West India, where, in common with the intervening countries, a similar deposit is widespread. These deposits, from Arabia to India, seem to be monsoon precipitations of dust storms. That some of them at least are of later Pleistocene age was demonstrated by Elinor Gardner and myself in South-West Arabia, and by de Terra and Paterson 4 years earlier in the Potwar region of North-West India. It is, in fact, in the Soan Pebble Culture discovered by them in and under the Potwar Loessic Silt, that I see nearer affinities with the Arabian material than anything I know of in Africa. I am well aware that this raises distributional problems, in view of the presence in India, along with the Soan Pebble Culture, of hand-axes and cleavers, as well as Victoria West cores, presumably all, ultimately, of African origin. There is no hope of resolving the problems raised by this pattern until the approaches to India from the West and North-West in the Palaeolithic become known. Meanwhile I imagine that the Pebble Cultures, wherever found, must be regarded as the basic Stone Age Culture which, to a greater or lesser extent, and at different speeds and periods, become gradually absorbed, as technological relics, into more advanced industries. I have little

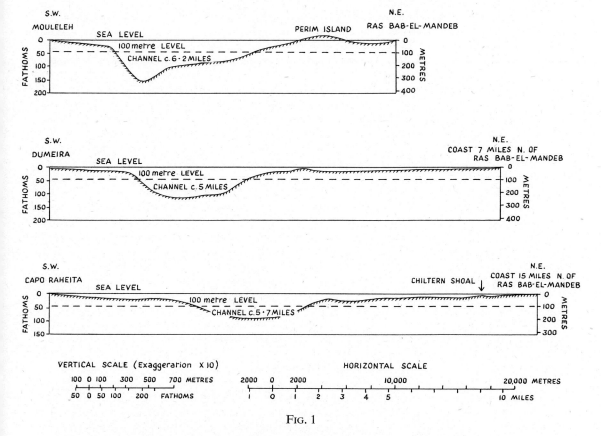

FIG. 1

doubt that the unknown, underlying levels of the Aeolian Silt in South Arabia will provide us some day with the ancestral Pebble Culture of that region.

To assign a date to the top metres of that silt and its contained artefacts is only a guess. One can safely state that they mark the end of a Major Depositional Epoch; but whether that epoch is to be equated with the Kanjeran-Gamblian Interpluvial of Kenya remains open. There exists no geological guidance as yet as to how major monsoonal epochs should be classified climatically. In India de Terra assigned the Potwar Loessic Silt to the Third of Four Himalayan glaciations. But Paterson, working in the same region, favoured a Third Interglacial age, which, perhaps is the more probable.

All things considered, I suggest that the static, crude culture of South-West Arabia, as we know it, gives no support to the view that a land-bridge made intercommunication with East Africa possible. If it had existed, surely some reflection of that vigorous succession of East African cultures would exist on the Asiatic side? All we have, in fact, is the 'tortoise-point' trimming, and that, in isolation, seems insufficient.

Yet Africa *is* very near. The Bab-el-Mandeb Straits are at present only 14½ miles at their narrowest, with Perim Island as a stepping-stone. The Admiralty Chart of 1950 shows the Rift origin of the Straits, with precipitous contours of the sea-beds falling suddenly from 20 or 30 fathoms to 100 or more in the main channel. Thus a fluctuation in sea-level needs to be substantial to effect a dry passage. In the Mediterranean we recall the pre-Flandrian regression of − 100 m.; but little or nothing is known about Red Sea regressions. At Zeila, on the Gulf of Aden, in British

Section Three

Somaliland, Dr Desmond Clark has called our attention to evidence of a drop of about 89 m. which, for sufficient reasons, he is inclined to synchronize with the Mediterranean regression. To gauge the effect of such a fall of sea-level on the hypothetical land-bridge, I have had constructed through the kindness of J. B. Mitchell, Lecturer in the Geography School, Cambridge University three cross-sections at and near the Straits of Bab-el-Mandeb (Fig. 1). These three incorporate the shallowest passages on the Admiralty Chart. The vertical scale is 10 times the horizontal. Fathoms are marked up one side, metres the other.

To give the -89 m. at Zeila a good clearance, and to conform to the Mediterranean regression in the Upper Pleistocene, the -100 m. level has been ruled in dash-lines. Section 1 shows that at this level the deep-water channel is reduced to 6·2 miles wide and 225 m. deep. In section 2 the deep-water channel is 5 miles wide and 150 m. deep. In section 3, the most northerly one, about 15 miles north of Ras Bab-el-Mandeb, the deep-water channel is 5·7 miles wide and 100 m. deep. Following these very interesting results, which certainly encourage the idea that a width of deep water of a mere 5 miles might not be beyond the capacity of Palaeolithic man to negotiate, I sought such information as I could get about currents. *The Red Sea and Gulf of Aden Pilot*, 1944, states that from June to September during the South-West monsoon, water runs out of the Red Sea, and from November to April during the North-East monsoon runs in. The currents are very variable and set approximately in the direction of the wind: they attain 40 miles a day in the main strait; but in the Little Strait—between Perim Island and the Arabian shore—the currents are very strong and dangerous. Given the increased intensity of the monsoons, which is witnessed in Palaeolithic times by the Aeolian Silt deposits, and given the narrowness of the open channel on the -100 m. figures quoted, one may also speculate upon the probable difficulties which might be encountered in the passage. All this opens out a fascinating field for comprehensive research, involving several sciences, biological as well as physiographical, which it would be richly worth while for an active prehistorian to undertake.

Meanwhile I reiterate that the Palaeolithic evidence from South Arabia, in isolation from many other considerations, such as earth movements, etc., seems to be definitely against any connection with East Africa after, or during, hand-axe times, let us say—tentatively correlating Pluvials and low sea-levels—the Kanjeran Pluvial. If a Pebble Culture reached Arabia from Africa during the preceding Pluvial of East Africa, the Kamasian, it would not be surprising.

56

Earliest Use of Fire

by KENNETH P. OAKLEY

IN 1925 Professor Raymond Dart received pieces of bone breccia collected by Mr W. I. Eitzman of Pietersburg at limeworks in the Makapansgat Valley near Potgietersrus in the Transvaal. As some of the fragments of bone had a charred appearance, Professor Dart suspected that this was a cave deposit containing hearths of Early Man. Some of the blackened fragments were submitted for analysis to Dr James Moir of the Government Chemical Laboratories and to Dr F. W. Fox of the South African Institute for Medical Research. Acid residues of this material contained black particles which by means of transformation into carbon dioxide were proved to be free carbon. This was apparently confirmation that the blackness of the bone fragments was due to charring.

Some twenty years later, fossil bones of *Australopithecus* were discovered in blocks of what appeared to be the same breccia at the Makapan Limeworks. As no stone implements or remains of Man were found in the deposit, Professor Dart concluded that the Makapan species of *Australopithecus* had been a fire-user and he accordingly described it under the name *A. prometheus*. Examination of blocks of the breccia had also revealed patches of glass-like material which appeared to support the idea that it contained evidence of fire (Dart, 1952, p. 97), but subsequently this turned out to be collophane (amorphous calcium phosphate) having no connection with burning.

The discovery of pebble-tools in the 200-foot terrace of the Vaal, and of '*Telanthropus*' in the Australopithecine breccia at Swartkrans led recently to a re-opening of the question whether any evidence of fire in the Makapan Breccia could legitimately be used as evidence that *Australopithecus* was a fire-user.

Analysis of samples of the Australopithecine breccia collected by the author in 1953 failed to confirm the presence of free carbon. Indeed, the blackness of the bone fragments in all the specimens which he collected proved to be due to oxides of iron and manganese. The possibility that some of the crackled and distorted bone fragments in the Australopithecine breccia have been calcined (i.e. burnt to the extent of losing the free carbon) has been considered, but must be dismissed. Bones which have been calcined have a lower fluorine content than uncalcined bones from the same bed, whereas the crackled bones from the Makapan breccia have the same fluorine content as others in the bed. The pattern of crackling in the bones is due, in the writer's opinion, to calcite mineralization.

The possibility that the carbon in the samples tested by Moir and Fox was introduced by a blasting charge has to be borne in mind. Until the free carbon can be detected in samples of the Australopithecine breccias collected under test conditions it would seem best to regard the case for *Australopithecus* being a fire-user as non-proven. Even if the association of the Australopithecine remains with traces of fire were beyond all doubt, the possibility that the fire was of natural origin or due to contemporary human pebble-tool makers would still have to be considered.

The oldest undoubted evidence of the use of fire in Africa comes from the Cave of Hearths at 4,950 feet above sea-level in the Makapansgat Valley, where Professor C. van Riet Lowe found a hand-axe industry of the Final Acheulian stage in association with a layer of ashes (Lowe 1938, 1954, 1955). At first it appeared to the excavators that this 'Basal Hearth' included four feet of pure ash, resting on a floor of white stalagmite ('Basal Dripstone'). This unique occurrence suggested that when man first entered the cave it had a clean white floor, and that on this he had proceeded to burn fires continuously until ashes had accumulated to a depth of several feet. But further examination combined with chemical analysis established that, excluding the top few inches of true hearth, this ash consisted of calcined bat-guano (Oakley, 1954). Evidently, after the formation of the stalagmite floor, under wettish conditions, the cave became dry and was frequented by bats whose excreta accumulated on the cave floor to a considerable depth in the course of many centuries. Later, when the side of the cave nearest the valley had been breached by erosion or a cliff-fall, man began to use it as a shelter and laid or lit fires on the floor which then consisted mainly of dry bat-guano. This material burns like peat. One may presume that it became accidentally ignited by the fires of the hand-axe people. Once ignited, aided by draughts through fissures in the rock behind, it would have gone on burning slowly for a long period—until the whole mass was completely calcined. I estimate that the four feet of ash in the 'Basal Hearth' may represent more than 12 feet of original guano.

There are ashes of human fires at ten levels in the Cave of Hearths, ranging in date from Final Acheulian to Iron Age. It is remarkable that this rock-shelter should have been used as a site of human occupation on and off from the end of the Acheulian times until shortly before the coming of Europeans, and yet no cave in this valley or elsewhere in Africa is known to have been occupied by man *before* the Final Acheulian stage.

There are Upper Acheulian occupation layers in the Montagu Cave (*c*. 1,300 feet above sea-level) in the Cape Province, and these too contained traces of fire (Goodwin, 1929, p. 13). Dr Desmond Clark has informed me that charred wood occurred also on the Final Acheulian 'floors' of the open site at Kalambo Falls.

It may be significant that the oldest acceptable evidence of the use of fire in Africa occurs on the same cultural horizon as the earliest undoubted occupation of caves. Although cave deposits antedating those in the Cave of Hearths are known to occur in the Makapansgat Valley, none has yielded so far any unquestionable evidence of human occupation. Yet it may be inferred that pre-Acheulian, and Early or Middle Acheulian tool-makers frequented the district, for their artifacts occur abundantly in the basal gravel of the low terrace exposed in the banks of the Rooispruit, west of Potgietersrus.

To account for these facts I tentatively put forward the hypothesis that man did not regularly occupy caves before he had domesticated fire as a protection against carnivores, and that in Africa this did not occur before the stage of Late Acheulian culture.

In Asia and Europe there is evidence of the use of fire earlier than in Africa: at Choukoutien (inter-Mindel or Mindel-Riss?); Torralba in Spain (M. Acheulian); Hoxne in Suffolk (M. Acheulian), and at a number of Upper Acheulian sites, including La Cotte de St Brelade in Jersey, the Tabun Cave and La Grotte d'Oumn-Quatafa in Palestine, and the rock-shelter of Jerf Ajla near Palmyra in Syria, recently excavated by Professor C. S. Coon. Apart from Choukoutien, there is no unquestionable evidence of the use of caves in Eurasia before the Riss I glaciation, following the time of Middle Acheulian culture.

REFERENCES

Dart, R. A. (1925), 'A Note on Makapansgat: a Site of Early Human Occupation', *S. Afr. J. Sci.*, 22, 454.
Dart, R. A. (1952), 'Faunal and Climatic Fluctuations in Makapansgat Valley: their Relation to the Geological Age and Promethean Status of *Australopithecus*', *Proc. First Pan-African Cong. Prehist.* (1947), 96–106.
Goodwin, A. J. H. (1929), 'The Montagu Cave', *Ann. S. Afr. Mus.*, 24, 1–16.
Van Riet Lowe, C. (1938), 'The Makapan Caves, an Archaeological Note', *S. Afr. J. Sci.*, 35, 371–81.
Van Riet Lowe, C. (1954), 'The Cave of Hearths', *S. Afr. Arch. Bull.*, 33, 25–9.
Van Riet Lowe, C. (1955), 'The Cave of Hearths', *S. Afr. Arch. Bull.*, 38, 61.
Oakley, K. P. (1954), 'Evidence of Fire in South African Cave Deposits', *Nature*, 174, 261.

57
Beitrag zur Vorgeschichte von Südwestafrika

von G. J. FOCK

Die prähistorische Forschung in Südwestafrika steht noch ganz in ihren Anfängen und es liegen so wenige Veröffentlichungen vor, daß noch vor wenigen Jahren Prof. Goodwin SWA als 'The Unknown' bezeichnen konnte.

Wohl aber haben die Felszeichnungen — vor allen Dingen im Brandberg — durch die Arbeiten von Leo Frobenius, Herbert Kühn, Hugo Obermaier und zuletzt von Abbé Breuil weit über Afrika hinaus Aufsehen erregt. Die Erforschung der Steinwerkzeuge steht dagegen noch ganz in den Anfängen. Vor rund 30 Jahren schrieb der Wiener Forscher Viktor Lebzelter seine *Vorgeschichte von Süd- und Südwestafrika*, in der er seine Beobachtungen während einer kurzen Reise durch das Land darlegte. Es war ein erster Überblick, aber nicht viel mehr. Inzwischen ist die Forschung in den Nachbargebieten stürmisch weitergeschritten. In SWA aber stagnierte sie mehr als zwei Jahrzehnte und erst in den letzten Jahren finden wir wieder Prähistoriker am Werk, die allerdings auch nur einiges Material herausgreifen können, das ihnen auf kurzen Reisen auffällt, oder ihnen zugeschickt wird, denn sie stammen nicht aus dem Lande, das bisher noch keine eigene Forschungsstelle besitzt. Außer von Abbé Breuil liegen bislang Berichte über SWA Funde vor von B. D. Malan, dem jetzigen Direktor des Archaeological Survey der Union von Südafrika, R. Mason und J. Rudner (Kapstadt). Wertvolle Hinweise verdanken wir den Windhoeker Geologen Dr Martin und dem verstorbenen Dr Korn.

SWA ist ungemein reich an Fundstellen und wer ein etwas geschultes Auge hat, dem erscheint das Land mit Steinwerkzeugen besät. Allein das Windhoeker Museum besitzt Funde von über 500 Stellen aus dem ganzen Lande, die meist von interessierten Laien aufgesammelt wurden. Ausgrabungen sind, bis auf einige Probegrabungen, die Dr Martin auf Veranlassung des Abbé Breuil durchführte, bisher nicht gemacht worden. Eine dieser Untersuchungen in der Philipphöhle bei Ameib im Erongogebirge ermöglichte den ersten C14 Test in SWA der das Alter der Smithfield A Kultur hier mit rund 3500 Jahren bestimmte.

Wenn auch die systematischen Grabungen fehlen, so ermöglichen doch die vielen Oberflächenfunde die Aufstellung eines vorläufigen Gerüsts aus dem hervorgeht:

1. daß in SWA bis jetzt mit Ausnahme der ältesten Perioden alle Kulturgruppen, die wir aus Südafrika kennen, vertreten sind;

2. daß anscheinend durch die Mitte des Landes, etwa entlang des Wendekreises, eine Kulturgrenze zu verlaufen scheint, u. zw. so, daß die südlichen Funde den südafrikanischen näher stehen, während Funde nördlich dieser Grenze gewisse Beziehungen zu Rhodesien und Angola aufweisen.

In SWA kennen wir bisher zwei Gebiete, die für die künftige Forschung von besonderer Bedeutung sein werden und die bis heute schon wertvolle Funde erbracht haben. Es sind dies einmal der Fischfluß mit seinen Terrassen, denen wir reiche altsteinzeitliche Funde verdanken und das Brandbergmassiv mit seiner weiteren Umgebung, vor allen Dingen den Terrassen des Ugab mit ihren dicken Ablagerungen von Kalaharisanden und dem Uisrivier. Auf die letztere Landschaft beziehen sich meine Beobachtungen.

Section Three

Der Gebirgsstock des Brandberges am Rande der Namibwüste gelegen umfaßt ein Gebiet von etwa 400 Quadratmeilen, er liegt im heutigen (Okombahe) Dama-Reservat und stellt völkerkundlich ein noch wenig erforschtes Rückzugsgebiet dar. Weit über SWA hinaus ist der Brandberg bekannt geworden durch die vielen Felszeichnungen, die sich bis in Höhenlagen von 2000 m. ü.d.M. befinden. Nach Beobachtungen von Abbé Breuil, R. Mason und J. Rudner (der erst im Juni 1955 im Brandberg gearbeitet hat) sind im eigentlichen Gebirge hauptsächlich die jüngeren Kulturen mit Steingeräten, Felsbildern und Töpferei vertreten. (Wenn Rudner und Mason die Ansicht vertreten, daß es sich hauptsächlich um Hottentottenkultur handle, so stimme ich insofern mit ihnen überein, als es sich um junge Siedlungsreste handelt. Ethnologisch möchte ich sie aber als Dama ansehen.)

Siedlungsplätze mit Steinkreisen, also wohl Hüttenresten, sind vielfach gefunden worden, so von Abbé Breuil in der Tsisabschlucht, von Mason in höheren Lagen. Andere sind von der Westseite des Gebirges bekannt und ich selbst fand an der Südseite eine Siedlung mit 20 Steinkreisen und wahrscheinlich einer Grabanlage. Dieser letztere Komplex gehört nach Ausweis der zahlreichen Steinwerkzeuge einem frühen Smithfield A an.

Funde der Chelles-Acheul Kulturen sind bisher nur im Vorland des Gebirges beobachtet worden, so z.B. an einer Stelle cca. 2 Meilen südlich vom Eingang zur Tsisabschlucht, wo auf einem größeren Areal Werkzeuge und Abschläge vom frühen Acheul bis zur Spätsteinzeit in großer Zahl zu finden sind. Vorwiegend ist es eine Abschlagkultur, allerdings kommen auch gute Faustkeile von Chelles-Acheul III vor. Das Material ist hauptsächlich Diorit und wenig gerollt. Einige Stücke zeigen einen prächtigen Wüstenlack. Auffällig ist es, daß die älteren Werkzeuge oft eine Kalkkruste besitzen, also ausgewittert sind. Aber auch an anderen Stellen des Brandbergvorlandes sind Fundes der jüngeren Acheulkulturen in großer Zahl nachgewiesen, wie überhaupt das obere Acheul in ganz SWA gefunden worden ist.

Von besonderem Interesse dürften die Terrassen des Uis Riviers für die künftige Forschung sein. Hier hatte schon 1937 Mrs Bowler-Kelley einige Aufsammlungen machen können, die sie als grobes Acheul III und IV ansah und R. Mason bestätigte 1954 ihre Beobachtungen (*SA Arch. Bulletin*, March 1955). Es handelt sich da um eine grobe Abschlagkultur, die der Victoria West Industrie Südafrikas verwandt zu sein scheint.

Die Minensiedlung Uis liegt etwa 12 Meilen vom Südostrand des Brandberges entfernt. Die Schotter der Seitenriviere wurden in früheren Jahren von der Zinnmine ausgebeutet und in diesen durchwühlten Schottern kann man noch tausende von Artefakten finden, Werkzeuge, die dem Acheul III und IV angehören. Auch *in situ* konnte ich einige Geräte der Victoria West Technik bergen. Die Schotter haben folgendes Profil:

5.   0–10 cm.   sandiger Kies
4.   10–40   mittelgrobe Schotter mit venig Sand
3.   40–60   sandige Schotter
2.   60–240   grobe Schotter bis Kopfgröße
1. 240–260   Mergel. Der Fels dürfte nicht viel tiefer liegen, da er in 5 m. Entfernung bei 240 erreicht wurde

Eine Trennung der Schichten durch Verkalkungszonen konnte nicht festgestellt werden. Dies Profil zeigt nun, daß diese Schotter in einer Zeit starker Wasserführung aufgebaut wurden. Nach oben werden diese Schotter kleiner und immer mehr mit Sand durchsetzt, was auf ein Nachlassen der Wasserführung hindeutet. Die stärkere Durchsetzung der Schotter mit Sand in Schicht 3 in Stärke von 20 cm. deutet wohl auf eine vorübergehende kürzere Trockenperiode hin. Die erwähnten Geräte stammen aus dieser Schotterwand, doch sind es zu wenige, um eine genaue Trennung nach Acheul III und IV durchzuführen. Aus den Schottern, aber leider nicht *in situ* gefunden, stammt ein Acheul III Faustkeil. Die Funde aus diesen Schottern sind leicht zu erkennen, da sie meist eine graue Färbung besitzen im Gegensatz zu den Oberflächenfunden, die eine rötliche Verwitterungsschicht haben. Das Material ist meist Quarzit und Dolorit. Die Funde sind wenig gerollt.

Nach den Beobachtungen von Dr Martin gehören diese Schotter in das Kanjeran Pluvial.

Ein anderes Profil stammt von der Siedlung Uis selbst. Hier wurde hinter dem Kraftwerk ein kleiner Graben ausgehoben, der allerdings nur 60 cm. tief war und an einigen Stellen den Fels erreichte :

3.   0–10 cm. Oberflächenschutt
2. 10–40 cm. Schotter in Kalk eingebettet
1. 40–60 cm. Verwitterungsschicht und Fels

Aus den verkalkten Schottern stammen einige wenige Geräte :

1 großer, unfertiger Faustkeil, bei dem nur die Spitze bearbeitet ist
1 hochrückiges Kernstück
3 Seitenschaber aus dicken Abschlägen mit facettierter Schlagfläche
1 stark gerollter Hohl- und Seitenschaber.

Im Vergleich mit der Funden aus der zuerst erwähnten Fundstelle machen diese Geräte einen gedrungenen und plumpen Eindruck. Soweit die Funde *in situ*, die Reste des oberen Acheul ergaben.

Auf den Terrassen, also danach wohl zeitlich jünger, liegen Werkzeuge in großer Zahl. Es konnten verschiedene Fundstellen unterschieden werden, die jedoch alle etwa 8 bis 10. m über dem heutigen Flußtal liegen und danach der gleichen Terrasse zugerechnet werden können. Bemerkenswert war besonders eine Fundstelle, die sich durch Deckkalk von der Umgebung unterschied, der sich in einer Breite von cca. 20 m. einen Hang entlang erstreckte. Die hier gemachten Funde sind aus Dolorit mit einer rötlichen Verwitterungsrinde, die Geräte sind wenig gerollt aber stärker angewittert. Es konnten folgende Typen beobachtet werden :

1. Der Pick. Er ist von beiden Seiten bearbeitet und zwar meist aus einem mehr oder weniger vierkantigem Geröll. Die Spitze ist an einer Seite gut ausgearbeitet. Andere Picks sind lang und besitzen 3 Flächen und die Spitze ist an beiden Enden herausgearbeitet. Eine weitere Art des Pick entspricht etwa dem 'Tumbien' wie ihn Clark in seinen *Stone Age Cultures of Northern Rhodesia*, Plate 9, Nr. 6 abbildet.
2. Faustkeile.
3. Rundschaber aus Kernstücken.
4. Haven (Chopper).
5. Große Klingenabschläge, die als Schaber benutzt worden sind.
6. Hohlschaber.
7. Hahnenkämme.
8. Schlagsteine.
   Spalter fehlen.

Bei den Abschlagstücken ist es bemerkenswert, daß *bloc en bloc* Technik mit einem Abschlagswinkel von durchschnittlich 108 Grad zusammen mit Levallois Technik neben einander vorkommen. In einigen Fällen wurden alte Acheul Abschläge gefunden, die zu Seitenschabern nachgearbeitet worden waren.

Alle diese Funde können wir aus der geologischen Lagerung schlecht datieren. Sie liegen z. Tl. auf den Schottern, in denen sich oberes Acheul befindet, sind also jünger als dieses. Aber mehr läßt sich auch nicht sagen. Ein Unterschied auf Grund der Patinierung ist nicht festzustellen.

Beim Vergleichen der Uiser Funde zeigen sich die nächsten Parallelen im Sangoan aus Rhodesien und Angola. Leider sind sie zahlenmäßig bisher zu gering um eine typologische Unterteilung zu ermöglichen. Es ist aber zu erwarten, daß spätere Aufschlüsse der Mine auch eine Stratigraphie für das Sangoan und jüngere Funde liefern. Vorläufig möchte ich die Uiser

Stücke als ein älteres Sangoan ansehen. In diesem Zusammenhang sei bemerkt, daß J. Rudner im Juni 1955 an der Westseite des Brandberges ein, wie er glaubt jüngeres, Sangoan fand.

Auf der Farm Kanona am Erongo konnte ich vor längerer Zeit Sangoan feststellen.

Leider sind dieses bisher alles Oberflächenfunde und erst Funde aus gesicherten Schichten können weitere Einzelheiten über das Sangoan in SWA aussagen. Auf alle Fälle ist jetzt schon erwiesen, daß Sangoankultur auch in SWA vorkommt. Damit erweitert sich das Verbreitungsgebiet dieser Kultur um ein beträchtliches nach Westen und schließt somit eine Lücke, die nach den neuesten Funden von Dr O. Davies im Namaqualand und im Gebiet der Oranjemündung noch bestand. Ob die Uiser Funde an das Sangoan von Rhodesien oder Angola anzuschließen sind, muß die weitere Forschung ergeben.

LITERATURNACHWEIS

Lebzelter, Viktor, *Vorgeschichte von Süd- und Südwestafrika*, Leipzig, 1930.
  Geologische Rundschau, 1950.
  S. Afr. Archaeolog. Bulletin.
  S. Afr. Journal of Science.
Jones, Neville, *The Prehistory of Southern Rhodesia*, 1949.
Clark, J. D., *The Stone Age Cultures of Northern Rhodesia*, 1950.
Leakey, L. S. B., *Tentative Study of the Pleistocene Climatic Changes and Stone Age Culture Sequence in North-Eastern Angola*, 1949.
Breuil, Abbé and Jean Janmart, *Les limons et graviers de l'Angola du Nord-Est et leur contenu archéologique*, 1950.
Bowler-Kelly, A., *A preliminary Report on a Tour of Archaeological Enquiry in the northern Districts of S.W.A.* Manuscript, 1937.

58

Two New Egyptian Cultures

by I. RIZKANA

PREHISTORIC research in Egypt was devoted in the last five years to two places, Heliopolis and Wadi Digla. Both of them lie in the area which connects Lower and Upper Egypt.

They are so far but cemeteries, the settlements of which are still being traced.

PERIOD	NORTHERN EGYPT	SOUTHERN EGYPT	APPROX. DATE
Dynastic	1st. Dynasty	1st. Dynasty	
		Pre-Thinite	3000 B.C.
	Maadi South and Heliopolis	Gerzah	
PREDYNASTIC	Maadi North	Amrah	4000 B.C.
	Helwan B (Omari B)	Badari	
	Fayyum "B"		5000 B.C.
	Merimdet Bani-Salamah		
NEOLITHIC	Fayyum "A"	Tasa	
	Helwan A (Omari A)		6000 B.C.

A. Darout,

FIG. 1. Succession of Neolithic and Predynastic Cultures

391

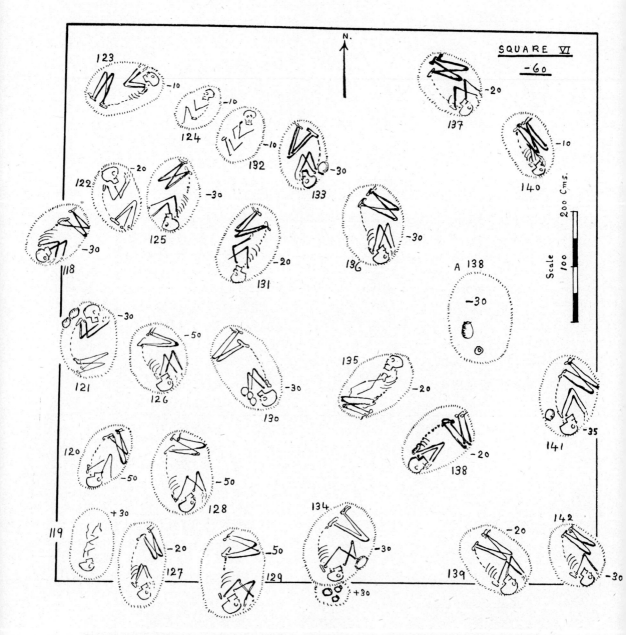

Fig. 2. A specimen square showing body attitude, direction of head and face, and depth of pits. The level of the burials is 60 cm. below surface; the depth of pits is between 10 and 15 cm. under this level

Two New Egyptian Cultures

The two sites belong to the last phase of Egyptian Prehistory which we call Chalcolithic or Predynastic or Pre-Thinite.

Heliopolis was discovered in 1950, and an area of about 1,000 square metres was excavated in the same year. About 100 human graves and 3 animal burials were found.

Wadi Digla was discovered in 1952; the whole area excavated covers about 5,000 square metres. In this area 468 human graves and 14 animal burials were found (Fig. 2).

The burials are found at depths ranging between 50 and 80 centimetres in the virgin soil. They are simple hollows, round or oval in shape. In these hollows the dead used to be buried in the usual contracted position of the Egyptian cemeteries of that period. In a few cases, however, the bodies were placed in a semi-extended position on the back, with the face upwards or placed with the chest and face downwards.

Some of the objects were buried with the dead, especially pottery vessels. It is supposed that these objects were put with the dead because they believed in the immortality of the soul, and the need for food and drink in afterlife.

The animals were buried each in a grave of its own. It is probable that the gazelles were killed before burial by making an incision in the neck. This shows that the gazelles were intentionally sacrificed before the burial. It is worthy of note that all the gazelles, except one, were buried with their heads towards the south, and six of them have pots with them.

The dog also was buried in a grave of its own with its head towards the south, and with it was placed a pot.

This means that the same system of human burials was followed in the animal burials either in the direction of the head or the putting of pottery in the grave.

The general conclusion is that this new discovery has added a link to the chain of predynastic sites in Egypt, and thrown more light on the cultural history of Egypt. This shows that the Egyptian civilization of historic Egypt did not appear suddenly or belong to a foreign race as some writers tried to prove. We have here two sites separated from each other by about 20 miles but with the same standard of culture both in the material finds and the funeral rites.

REFERENCES

1. Amer, M. and I. Rizkana, 'Excavations in Wadi Digla. First Season Report (1951–1952)', *Bulletin of the Faculty of Arts, University of Cairo*, XV, (I), May 1953.
2. Amer, M. and I. Rizkana, 'Excavations in Wadi Digla, Second Season Report (1953)', ibid. (II), December 1953.
3. Rizkana, I., 'Centres of Settlement in Prehistoric Egypt in the Area between Helwan and Heliopolis', *Bull. Inst. du Désert*, II, No. 2, 1952, pp. 1–15.

59

On the Origin of some Zimbabwe Beads

by W. G. N. VAN DER SLEEN

LAST year I had the opportunity of collecting a few hundred beads on the N.W. beaches of Zanzibar. Later I visited the Museums at Zanzibar, Dar-es-Salaam and had a discussion with Dr Kirkman at Gedi. Collections from Sofala, Kilwa, Tongoni, etc., together with Dr Kirkman's results, gave me a very thorough idea of the beads that had been brought to East Africa before the advent of the Portuguese.

It struck me at once that these beads are quite different from nearly everything I had seen and collected during a trip from the Cape to the Congo and back. A search through European Museums and literature showed me that the Zanzibar beads occur in several places in India and Pakistan and in large numbers in stone-slab graves in Sumatra and Java, the Carnelian beads even in China. This gives me the impression that the Zanzibar beads had better be called Indian-Ocean beads, as they must have been the trading material used by the Junks and Dhows that used the trade-winds for their marvellous trips between China and Sofala between the seventh or eighth and the twelfth to fourteenth centuries.

Now for the Zimbabwe beads. Most archaeologists will agree that the greater part, especially the smaller beads, are not to be distinguished from the Venetian beads that found their way *via* Flanders and Portugal to the East African coast at the beginning of the sixteenth century. These small, regular beads are not found on the East African sites. There are, however, also a comparatively small number of larger beads that have been found at Zimbabwe and other Southern-Rhodesian ruins and many of these are the same types as the Indian-Ocean beads. A very good example of these beads is to be found in the Salisbury Museum. There hangs a string of 20 to 30 beads. They are globular and about half-an-inch in diameter. They must have been made by winding thin glass strips around a wire, strips or molten rods, that must have had a diameter of one or two millimetres. The beads in the Salisbury Museum are greenish or bluish, but there are also black and greyish-white ones. Miss Caton-Thompson depicted one in her famous book as No. 5c in the colour plate.

I hope soon to be able to give a complete summary of the Indian-Ocean beads. I can tell already that they differ from most Egyptian beads and have nothing to do either with the European beads of the fifth to tenth centuries.

Are we going to find out that Zimbabwe was built under the eyes of Persian sailors from Shiraz or the land of the Sabaeans?*

---

* Since I wrote the above lines, the Indian-Ocean, or better Trade-Wind beads were found in Mapungubwe (Northern Transvaal) and in the Malay States. I could prove that nearly all these beads were fabricated in India, the older, wound types already in Roman times and the later drawn ones from the 8th to the 16th century. A short note about these beads was printed in *Man* of February, 1956.

60

Note sur l'Ibéromaurusien

par E. G. GOBERT

LE 2° Congrès panafricain de Préhistoire, tenu à Alger en Octobre 1952, a demandé par l'organe de son comité à ceux de ses membres qui résident en Afrique du Nord de se concerter en vue de décider si les industries de lamelles des régions littorales du Moghreb, connues jusqu'ici sous le nom d'Ibéromaurusien, devaient conserver cette désignation ou prendre toute autre qui paraîtrait mieux appropriée.

L'opinion des collègues consultés demeure en faveur de la conservation du terme d'Ibéromaurusien crée par Paul Pallary pour désigner l'industrie des lamelles de l'abri de la Mouillah, que nous savons aujourd'hui répandue depuis le Maroc atlantique jusqu'a la Cyrénaïque, sous divers faciès.

Ce terme a le privilège de l'antériorité et d'un déjà long usage. Les mémoires généraux sur la préhistoire de l'Afrique du Nord, qu'ils soient déjà publiés comme le manuel de Mlle H. Alimen, ou déjà imprimés mais non encore distribués comme ceux de R. Vaufrey et de L. Balout, emploient, font exclusivement usage du mot Ibéromaurusien. L'abandonner aujourd'hui créerait une confusion regrettable.

Les réserves qui avaient été précédemment énoncées sur la légitimité de l'expression choisie, ou plutôt forgée par P. Pallary, reposaient sur la hardiesse du rapprochement qu'il avait cru pouvoir faire entre l'industrie de la Mouillah et certaines industries espagnoles. Nous ne pouvons pas aujourd'hui assurer qu'il n'y ait aucun lien d'aucune sorte entre quelques cultures de la péninsule et du Moghreb. Renoncer à Ibéromaurusien serait peut-être nous exposer à le regretter plus tard, lorsque ces cultures et leurs rapports seront mieux connus.

61

Archaeology in Southern Rhodesia, 1900 – 1955

by ROGER SUMMERS

IN many ways Southern Rhodesia is a most fortunate country archaeologically. We possess rich cultural deposits especially of the Middle and Later Stone Age, an impressive number of stone monuments which point the way to Iron Age sites and a magnificent series of painted rocks and shelters. Added to this the development of the country has been at a speed which has enabled archaeological exploration to take place steadily, and finally research has proceeded at so sedate a pace that it has been possible to assimilate its results without suffering that mental indigestion so liable to attack workers in more crowded fields.

Until very recently our archaeologically-minded population was exceedingly small and the general absence of a 'leisured class' has kept down the numbers of amateurs. Before 1936 there was no full-time archaeologist in either of the Colony's museums and the total number of original publications on all branches of archaeology was very small—apart from Neville Jones's *Stone Age in Rhodesia* published in 1926 all books on Rhodesian archaeology dealt with a handful of 'ruins' —and in order to gain some insight into our prehistory it was necessary to explore the recesses of a number of journals several of which catered for many other interests besides archaeology.

In 1936 Neville Jones was appointed to a Keepership in the National Museum and from then until he retired in 1947 he devoted his whole research effort to the elucidation of the Stone Age sequence in Matabeleland. For financial reasons he was compelled to limit his work to a comparatively small area but he worked it thoroughly and by 1947 had succeeded in establishing a cultural and climatic succession.

Until 1946 there were never more than half-a-dozen local people taking an active interest in Rhodesian archaeology, and at times this number dwindled almost to vanishing point but on other occasions—especially during the visit of the British Association expeditions in 1929 and the Frobenius expedition in 1928–30—local interest was temporarily stimulated. In 1946 however the Monuments Commission appointed a whole-time Inspector of Monuments and chose Keith Radcliffe-Robinson for this office. He already had a local reputation as a careful excavator and sound observer and so was well fitted for a task which included not only the care and oversight of National Monuments but also the discovery and investigation of new archaeological sites during his tours of inspection.

In a paper of this nature one cannot mention every single worker in the field but it would be presenting an incomplete picture not to mention two more Southern Rhodesians who during the past 10 years have been especially active colleagues.

Mrs Goodall, although best known for her studies in rock art, has also been very active in ceramic studies and much that I have to say on this score is based on her fieldwork.

Unlike the other workers, Cranmer Cooke is not professionally a prehistorian but whenever opportunity offers undertakes fieldwork and has published some important material. Even greater than his direct services to prehistory are those which he gives indirectly as Honorary Secretary of our Monuments Commission, in which post he followed Jones in 1951. Without careful administration half the value of archaeology is lost and accordingly Cooke's office work is of the greatest value to us all.

In taking Jones's place in the Museum in 1947 I was most happily placed to obtain the maximum amount of help from all my colleagues, amateur and professional. I very soon realized that little was to be gained by merely following up Jones's Stone Age work and accordingly determined to apply my research effort to the Rhodesian Iron Age leaving Stone Age studies to other hands.

At the same time as the Monuments Commission commenced what was in effect an archaeological survey of its territory, there was a great influx of immigrants largely of British origin and the number of people interested in archaeology increased considerably, the foundation of an Archaeological Society in South Africa providing a welcome bond between such newly arrived amateurs and the established local prehistorians. Partly as a result of this influx of new Rhodesians, our museums began receiving a flood of enquiries about matters archaeological and collecting from surface sites became more common. We therefore amassed a great quantity of somewhat scrappy information most of which was recorded, so far as the National Museum was concerned, on a card index of archaeological sites. Much of this information and material would have been completely useless had it not been preceded by intensive excavation work but when considered in conjunction with the intensive studies it can be fitted into place and enables us to study Rhodesian cultures in space as well as time.

Jones's work in Matabeleland has now been related to the Northern Rhodesian sequence by Clark whose book, in conjunction with Jones's *Prehistory of Southern Rhodesia* provides the basis for local Stone Age studies. Caton-Thompson's *Zimbabwe Culture* is of course the classic work for the local Iron Age but Jones's and Schofield's work at Mapungubwe and unpublished material (now being prepared for the press) from Khami and Inyanga also provide the background to extensive collections, especially of pottery from Iron Age contexts.

Thus it is that Southern Rhodesian archaeological research has passed through three distinct phases—the first, straight-forward collecting, unselective because uniformed: then intensive research in very restricted areas: finally extensive collecting and minor excavation work spread all over our area and interpreted in the light of the earlier intensive work. To my mind this is the correct way to investigate the prehistory of a region but nobody in Southern Rhodesia can claim credit for such superb planning—it just happened, mainly because until recently we have been too poor to arrange things differently.

At present there is an interplay between intensive and extensive work and that will continue but we are now in a position to commence a fourth phase, that of synthesizing our results in order to obtain some idea of what was happening before the dawn of history and as the Southern Rhodesian contribution to such a Pan-African synthesis I now offer for your consideration some distribution maps.

Plotting

When she was working on *The Zimbabwe Culture* twenty-five years ago Miss Caton-Thompson was greatly handicapped by a lack of topographical maps but this defect has now been remedied and there exist fair 1/1,000,000 topographical and geological maps of the country. A series of larger scale maps 1/100,000 is now being prepared from air photographs and when this series is completed it will enable sites to be plotted with far greater accuracy than before.

Unknown Areas (Map 1)

Compared with more densely settled areas Southern Rhodesia is archaeologically speaking still very imperfectly explored. About one quarter of the country is totally unknown archaeologically and much else has received but sporadic attention.

Of the totally unknown areas that on the west, Area (i), is semi-desert and unlikely to yield

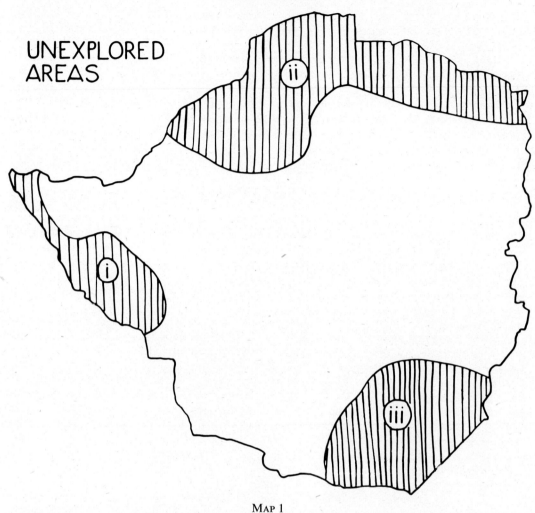

UNEXPLORED
AREAS

MAP 1

much information. The part of Area (ii) lying west of the Hunyani river also seems unlikely to yield anything very interesting for reconnaissances in its vicinity have disclosed very few sites of archaeological interest in country similar to that of our unknown area. East of the Hunyani how-ever there lies the country traditionally associated with Monomotapa and it is certain that much of interest exists there. The areas adjoining Area (iii) also contain much of interest and so this unknown area too is likely to yield important sites.

It is worth noting that the 'unknown areas', which covered nearly three-quarters of our country when this survey was started in 1947, are steadily shrinking: the eastern part of Area (ii) is now being opened up to European settlement and information is just beginning to come in whilst the building of a railway through Area (iii) promises to open it up shortly.

EARLIER STONE AGE (Map 2) (26 sites)

This map indicates the paucity of our evidence relating to this period. At one time a number of hand axes were classified as ESA but later were found to be Sangoan when larger assemblages were examined.

RHODESIAN SANGOAN (Map 3) (34 sites)

On Clark's distribution map (1950, p. 62) all Southern Rhodesian sites are shown as Bembesi variant but recent examination of the Mondoro material and some recently excavated sites in Inyanga shows that some of our material may well be classified as Zambezi and Luangwa variants.

MIDDLE STONE AGE (Map 4) (61 sites)

No attempt has been made to distinguish on this map between Rhodesian Still Bay and proto-Still Bay, indeed they sometimes appear in stratified succession on the same site. Whereas ESA and Rhodesian Still Bay occurrences can be recognized by small assemblages or even single tools, it requires a fair-sized assemblage to enable one to identify a Magosian site. Failure to make a full collection has probably restricted the number of known Magosian sites and it is just possible that some sites credited to Still Bay should in fact be Magosian. The distribution pattern of both cultures seems to be the same and sites tend to lie above the 4,000 foot contour. Exploration in the

EARLIER
STONE AGE

Fresh Artefacts ■
Rolled ·· □

MAP 2

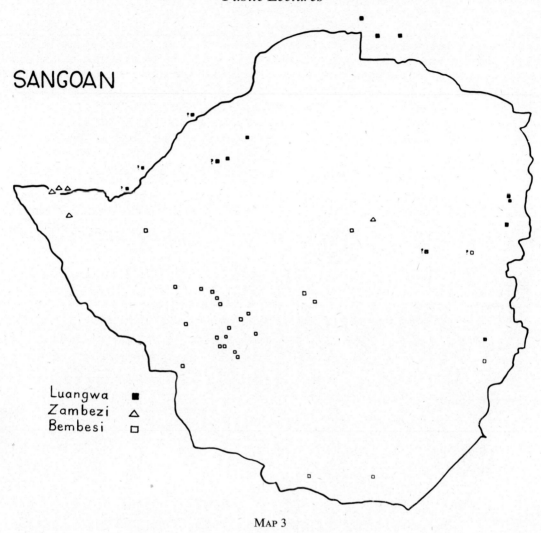

SANGOAN

Luangwa ■
Zambezi △
Bembesi □

MAP 3

lower country has not progressed so far as on the high veld, but MSA seems to be much more restricted in low-lying areas than higher.

LATER STONE AGE (Map 5) (41 sites)

Until 1950 all Later Stone Age sites in Southern Rhodesia were classified as Rhodesian Wilton, the material on which Goodwin based his note on the possible Rhodesian origin of the Smithfield N being held in suspense (Goodwin, 1934). Since Clark's publication of Nachikufu it has been necessary to re-examine some of our opinions and it is also possible to fit the suspended material into its place.

Three of the LSA sites in the eastern parts of the country contained ground stone axes (Fupi (2), Inyanga/Nyabongwe, Nyazongo (12)). The occurrence of ground stone axes—easily recognizable artefacts—has therefore been plotted and with a few exceptions has a markedly eastward distribution: the exceptions, some of which come from Wilton sites cannot be ignored and it would seem that in Southern Rhodesia these artefacts form part of the normal Wilton equipment.

There are LSA sites in the eastern parts of Southern Rhodesia, three of which have been carefully excavated by Robinson (1952, 1955), which do not contain any ground stone axes and which have none of the other characteristic Nachikufu tools.

It appears therefore that Rhodesian Wilton, which has a westerly distribution in Northern Rhodesia, occurs far and wide over the Southern Rhodesian watershed and plateau. On the other hand it seems likely that there are indications of Nachikufu occurrences in Mashonaland.

POTTERY

Bambata Ware (Map 6) (3 sites)

This is a very distinctive ware, characterized by deeply channelled decoration, crenellated rims and, occasionally, spouts. It is a fine thin ware, rather sandy in fabric and, although well-fired, is rather friable. Ever since it was first described (Schofield, 1940) fieldworkers have been searching

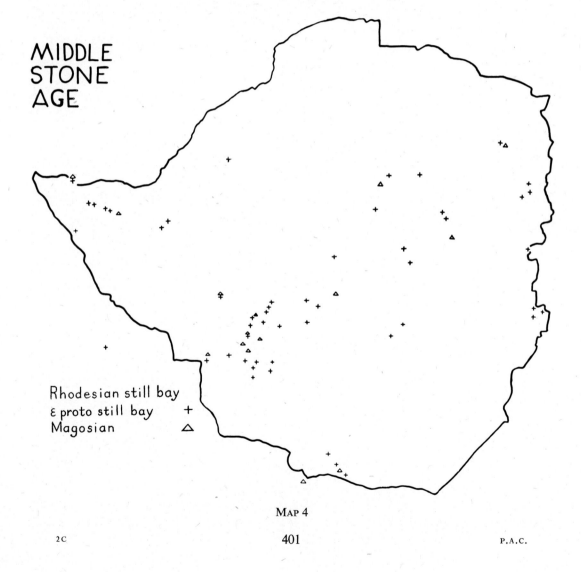

MAP 4

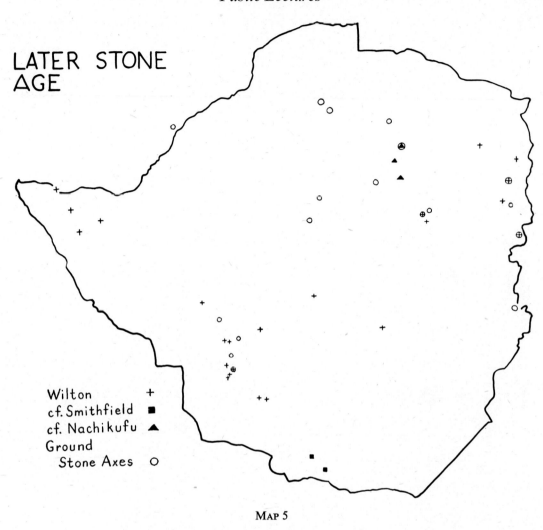

LATER STONE
AGE

Wilton   +
cf. Smithfield   ■
cf. Nachikufu   ▲
Ground
    Stone Axes   ○

MAP 5

for it in an area which has many pottery sites but despite this only five sites are known and we may therefore conclude that it has a restricted distribution, which may be discontinuous, within the borders of Southern Rhodesia.

It appears to be the earliest of local pottery and Schofield (1947) has suggested that it may be Hottentot.

POTTERY

Stamped Wares (Map 7) (48 sites)

These wares belong to the earliest phase of the Rhodesian Iron Age (Summers, 1950) and have been much studied recently. The common characteristics of these wares is decoration impressed with a square-toothed comb or stamp. It is the most evenly fired of all Rhodesian wares having a fine even red colour and burned right through. Its shapes and decoration are very satisfying— well-proportioned beakers, graceful bowls and pots with sharply carinated profiles: decoration is always limited to neck and rim or to the edge of bowls. Very occasionally one finds some graphite ornament but this is unusual except amongst bowls.

Associated with this ware are figurines of cattle, sheep and stylized human females.

Gokomere and Ziwa Wares are very similar in appearance and seem to have an easterly distribution—Gokomere throughout Mashonaland and Ziwa mainly concentrated in the valleys of rivers belonging to the Mazoe System. On the other hand Leopard's Kopje Ware, which we have reason to think may be somewhat later than the other two, seems to be concentrated on each side of the Matabeleland watershed.

The association of these wares with native gold mining has been noted and it is of interest to record that these wares have been found in or near ancient workings in 17 cases (Gokomere 7, Ziwa 4, Leopard's Kopje 6). As the filling of ancient workings was normally 'put through the mill' by miners anxious to extract everything from their mines the known associations are likely to be few in number when compared with the total amount of such occurrences now irretrievably lost.

BAMBATA WARE

MAP 6

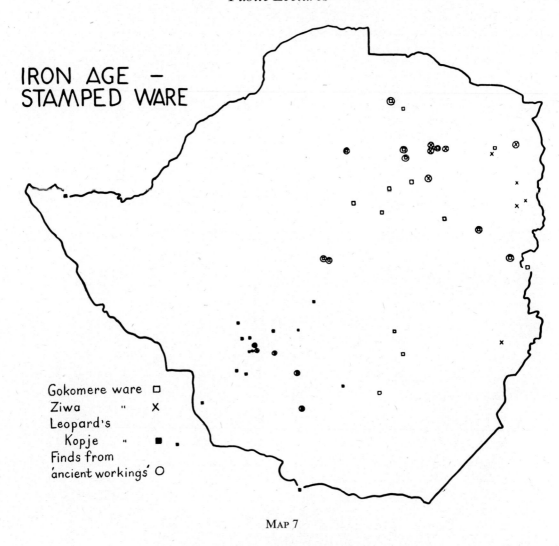

IRON AGE –
STAMPED WARE

Gokomere ware □
Ziwa   "   X
Leopard's
   Kopje   "   ■ .
Finds from
'ancient workings' O

Map 7

RHODESIAN RUINS (Map 8) (about 120 sites)

It was the need to plot these monuments that led me to undertake this survey and preliminary results have been published with a gazetteer (Summers, 1953). The published map is however a crude one as all ruins irrespective of date, cultural association or size are shown there. In 1950 I published a similar map which attempted to differentiate between architectural techniques of stonework, but subsequent work showed that this criterion merely differentiated between building materials and was devoid of cultural significance.

On this map I have endeavoured to distinguish between buildings with rough stonework, associated with Stamped Ware, and those better-built structures which are associated with a group of quite different types of pottery. Ruins which are obviously recent—known to have been built during the tribal wars which so greatly troubled the country in the nineteenth century—have been omitted and so have a number of very small places whose inclusion would have unduly complicated the map without altering the pattern.

Even so this map does not provide a clear enough picture of the complexity of our ruin pattern. It has been suggested by the Rev. H. von Sicard that an analysis of styles of wall decoration might be useful and this has now been plotted (map not reproduced). Herring-bone pattern (26 sites) is as widely distributed as the ruins themselves, chevron pattern (9 sites) tended towards an easterly distribution but the most distinctive distribution was that of chequer pattern (24 sites). With two exceptions this pattern is confined to the S.W. corner of the country and covers much the same area as Mapungubwe pottery (Map 10) although no association has yet been proved; there is however an even closer connection between the distribution of chequer pattern and that of gold objects found in hoards and burials (Map 9).

ANCIENT WORKINGS (Map 9) (about 200 mines, 18 hoards, etc.)

This is the name given to all pre-European mines whatever their age. Some may be of very considerable antiquity but some were worked until the 1870's when F. C. Selous saw some still in production. The large majority were open workings using very primitive mining techniques—far

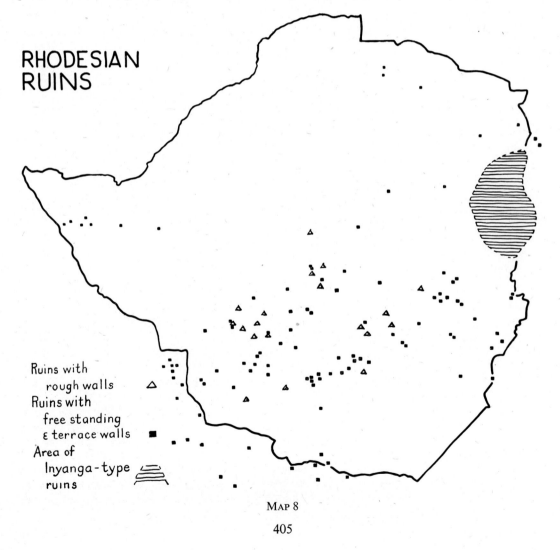

RHODESIAN
RUINS

Ruins with
    rough walls   △
Ruins with
    free standing
    ε terrace walls ■
Area of
    Inyanga-type
    ruins

MAP 8

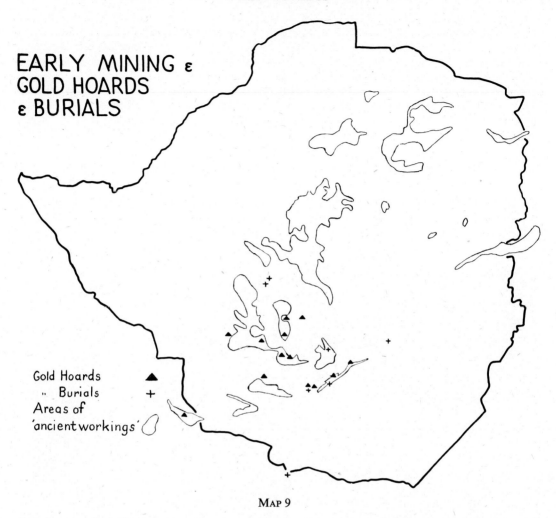

EARLY MINING ε
GOLD HOARDS
ε BURIALS

Gold Hoards ▲
" Burials +
Areas of
'ancient workings'

MAP 9

less advanced than those of the Near East in the third millenium B.C. or Europe in the Late Bronze Age.

A distribution map has already been published (Summers, 1950, Fig. 3) but it is known to be sadly incomplete. We possess information relating to some 200 early mines but it has been estimated that there were probably some 7,000 pre-European gold mines and several hundred for copper in Southern Rhodesia, so that no small scale map could possibly show all the sites (Mennell and Summers, 1955).

The map however shows the areas in which these workings cluster. These include all the Southern Rhodesian and Tati 'gold belts' with the exception of those at Fort Victoria and at Felixburg (both of whose ores are of low grade). Copper was mined in the Gwelo and Sinoia 'gold belts' and also in the Sabi valley.

Ruins with chequer-patterned walls and hoards of gold are associated with native tradition with the Rozwi, a people whose cultural connections all point Congowards. Their own legends, however, all refer to an immediate origin south of Rhodesia and these stories find confirmation in our maps.

Whereas all other maps are based on rigidly archaeological evidence, the distribution of gold hoards and burials is almost entirely drawn from Hall and Neal's *Ancient Ruins of Rhodesia* for, with the exception of Mapungubwe and Khami, all gold burials and hoards have been robbed and the contents are no longer traceable. In building up my original Ruin map I had occasion to use Hall and Neal extensively and was surprised to find that when they were dealing with facts they were passably accurate—their fantastic interpretations and Hall's intemperate criticism of Randall-MacIver have tended to obscure the value of their recording—consequently I feel that their evidence as summarized on this map may be accepted.

POTTERY

Mapungubwe and Ribbed Wares (Map 10) (10 and 6 sites respectively)

Mapungubwe wares are extremely handsome, that which Schofield called M 1 being quite the finest of local ceramics, smallish pots and very flat, sharply carinated dishes are common and decoration based on a triangular motif is incised with a sureness of hand and eye which it is hard to

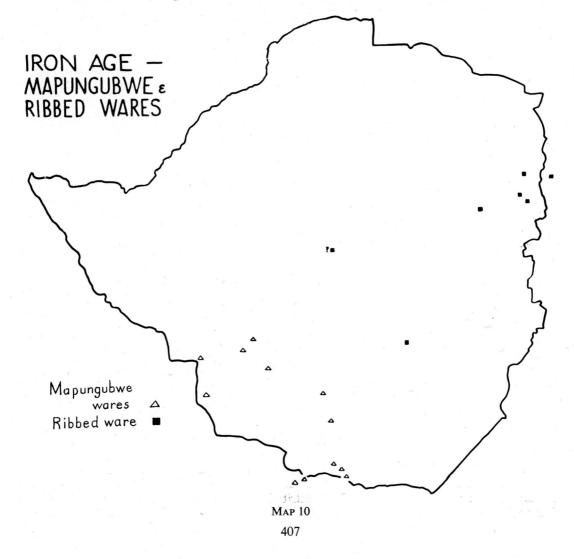

IRON AGE —
MAPUNGUBWE ε
RIBBED WARES

Mapungubwe
wares △
Ribbed ware ■

MAP 10

parallel in African potting. To an English eye it partakes of the quality of Glastonbury ware, possibly because both are so obviously ceramic copies of wooden prototypes. This fine ware is somewhat more restricted in distribution than its companion rougher ware which Schofield called M 2 and associated with a lower social grade than the users of the lovely M 1 ware.

Ribbed Ware was described long ago by Miss Caton-Thompson, who included it in her Class B 1. Apart from ribs, which have been applied to the pot and which project some 5 mm. from the general surface, the ware is undecorated. It is however often burnished, usually with graphite.

Despite the smaller number of sites these wares are distinctive and are frequently referred to Museums by amateur collectors, their distribution is therefore well known. We have some reason for thinking that they are approximately contemporary and their markedly N.E. and S.W. distribution is of some significance.

Mapungubwe wares closely resemble modern Lunda and Luba wares in Northern Rhodesia which are themselves derived from a source in the Upper Congo Basin. Ribbed Ware has some modern parallels in Bemba and Chewa ceramics in North Eastern Rhodesia but the most interesting archaeological parallel is from the Mosque site at Gedi near Mombasa (Kirkman, 1954). These distant connections may help to explain the Southern Rhodesian distribution.

Portuguese Occupation (Map 11) (12 sites)

The Portuguese occupation of 'Monomotapa' is testified by innumerable literary references and requires no confirmation for its general acceptance. When however we come to details archaeology can offer some help in solving some problems.

The distribution of Portuguese forts and trading posts is restricted to the N.E. corner of the country as is to be expected from a European culture which entered Rhodesia by way of the Zambezi valley. They are confined by a frontier which runs roughly on the lines of the Sanyati and Umfuli and Sabi rivers. That this frontier was probably a real one is confirmed by the distribution of chequer-patterned walls and of gold burials which all chronological evidence suggests are contemporary with the Portuguese occupation (*c.* 1580–*c.* 1700). The frontier as it probably was in the time of Antonia Fernandes' journeys (1512–14) has been drawn partly from literary sources and partly from information collected from present day Africans by Mr J. Blake-Thompson. Its confirmation from independent archaeological work is striking.

Many of the Portuguese records mention the difficulties in obtaining gold from 'Monomotapa' and explain this by referring to the state of war existing on the western borders of Monomotapa: presumably therefore the cultural boundary implicit in some of the Rhodesian Iron Age maps marked a political frontier in the sixteenth and seventeenth centuries although this cannot be confirmed from the maps of the period, most of which seem to have been based on secondary sources.

The relics found west of the frontier are both of them religious—a Goanese ivory carving of Our Lady and a gold *bractea* probably of Mozambique work depicting the Sacred Heart with pelicans—and may denote some missionary activity of which we possess no literary record. They may however be objects looted during the Rozwi raids at the end of the seventeenth century when, as we know from written evidence, the Portuguese were compelled to withdraw from some of their more westerly posts.

Conclusions

Although the maps set before you summarize information from about six hundred sites, about half of which have been subjected to competent archaeological scrutiny, the conclusions one may draw are somewhat limited.

Two distinct distribution patterns were obvious: a division of the country in N.E. and S.W. zones and on the other hand a fairly uniform distribution in high veld areas (above 4,000 feet). It is less obvious, on an outline map, that sites tend to be more numerous in areas drained by rivers

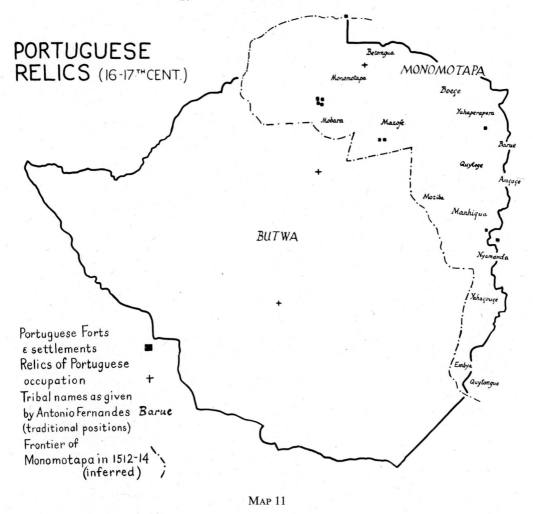

PORTUGUESE RELICS (16-17TH CENT.)

Betongua

Monomotapa

MONOMOTAPA

Boeçe

Mobara

Mazoe

Yahaperapera

Barue

Quyteye

Amçoçe

Moziba

Manhiqua

BUTWA

Nyamanda

Yahaçouçe

Embya

Quytongue

Portuguese Forts
ε settlements
Relics of Portuguese
occupation
Tribal names as given
by Antonio Fernandes *Barue*
(traditional positions)
Frontier of
Monomotapa in 1512-14
(inferred)

MAP 11

belonging to the Gwaai, Mazoe, Lundi and Umzwingwane-Shashi river systems. It may well be that more intensive searching will reveal more sites in the other river basins but they have not been neglected in the past and I feel that we are justified in examining prehistoric human geography in the light of what is now known.

To the west and south-west of Southern Rhodesia is a great steppe and semi-desert belt stretching from our border to the Atlantic. Today this area is sparsely inhabited and, except during pluvials, it must always have provided a barrier to human movement. On the eastern border lie the Inyangani and Chimanimani Mountains, with the Mozambique Plain further eastward still, much of this plain is very low-lying and the swamps of the Zambezi delta and the Pungwe Flats present barriers which restrict movement to a comparatively narrow corridor immediately east of the mountains. Thus movement across Southern Africa almost inevitably means a more or less north-south movement across Southern Rhodesia.

The dual distribution of the Sangoan (Map 3) is paralleled in Northern Rhodesia and implies movements *via* the upper Zambezi and Luangwa valleys respectively. The spread of the Bembesi or southern watershed variant over so large an area of Southern Rhodesia would seem to be due to the 'grain' of the country running in a south-easterly direction and the comparative absence of the Luangwa Variant seems due to the same cause.

Much the same explanation can be advanced for the less obvious duality of the Later Stone Age distribution (Map 5) and that of Stamped Ware (Map 7) although in the latter case there appear to be complicating factors.

The Middle Stone Age Cultures appear to have a 'High Veld' distribution—only 17 sites out of 63 being below 4,000 feet—and there seem to be significant differences in equipment between the cultures in the two Rhodesias. Nowhere in Southern Rhodesia is there any known section showing an evolution of MSA from Sangoan nor is there any obvious relationship between MSA and earlier cultures such as Clark has found at Kalambo Falls nor is there any culture really comparable to the Fauresmith in our country. It seems therefore that in Southern Rhodesia the MSA cultures were, in the first instance, a foreign intrusion.

Culturally, therefore, the Zambezi seems to be a barrier between two MSA sub-cultures and from Map 4 I feel inclined to look to the rivers of the Mazoe system as providing the corridor by which MSA cultures entered Southern Rhodesia and to trace their derivation from East Africa *via* Lake Nyasa and the Shire river. A movement from the N.E. to S.W. is also more in line with climatic probabilities than one in the opposite direction.

When we pass beyond the bounds of the Stone Age, Southern Rhodesia is, alas, *sui generis*. Consequently, I have gone beyond my country's political boundaries in my plotting. To make the problem more difficult, distribution maps relating to our Iron Age have far more detail and are more complicated than the earlier ones so without work elsewhere one's conclusions have something of the quality of guesswork.

The distribution of Stamped Ware (Map 7) shows that Ziwa Ware is almost entirely confined to the Mazoe basin but that its distribution is confused with that of Gokomere Ware. There may thus be a difference in age between the two. Leopard's Kopje Ware seems to have a Gwaai basin distribution but it could equally well have been derived from the Limpopo area *via* the Umzingwani river. Since these wares are associated with early mining, distribution is affected by geology as well as geography but I would like to draw attention to the close similarity of the distribution patterns for Leopard's Kopje Ware (Map 7), gold hoards and burials (Map 9) chequer-pattern walling (not mapped) and Mapungubwe Wares (Map 10): since Leopard's Kopje and Mapungubwe Wares rarely occur together and as the former is never associated with either ruins or worked gold the coincidence is probably significant and I am inclined to think that Leopard's Kopje Ware may have come from the South.

The Ruin distribution (Map 8) is even more complex than that of the pre-Ruin Stamped Ware. Here we suffer from too much superficial information and insufficient archaeological detail, so pending further excavation I do not propose to attempt an analysis of the map. Mapungubwe ware (Map 10) would seem to have an Umzingwane-Shashi distribution and to have come up from the south but, pending more information from Bechuanaland, how, if at all, it is related to the technically similar Lunda-Luba pottery of Northern Rhodesia, is more than we can say. On the other hand, Ribbed Ware (Caton-Thompson's Zimbabwe B 1) has an eastward distribution which may connect it *via* the Shire route to East Africa, certainly almost identical ware has recently been found at Gedi on the East Coast.

Fascinating though it would be to consider the possibility of Gallas from Gedi making Ribbed Ware on the Inyanga terraces such speculations are inadmissible nor alas can we entertain any but the most general ideas about the cultural antecedents of the Rhodesian Iron Age until we have similar maps for surrounding territories.

Although the simplest way to obtain such a series of maps is to have a fully staffed archaeological survey we need not wait for such organizations before beginning our work. The information which I have summarized on these maps has partly been collected in the course of Museum and Monuments Commission fieldwork but a very considerable amount has come merely by extracting information from Museum Collections and Catalogues. Such mapping arises from field archaeology of the simplest variety—observation and surface collecting. In the collection of such information amateurs, even children, have a large part to play and by enlisting their help we professionals can obtain a great deal of information which would otherwise be denied to us.

REFERENCES

Caton-Thompson, G. (1931), *The Zimbabwe Culture*, Oxford.

Clark, J. D. (1950), *Stone Age Cultures of Northern Rhodesia*, Cape Town.

Goodwin, A. J. H. (1934), 'The Rhodesian Origin of certain Smithfield "N" elements', *Proc. Rhod. Sci. Assn.*, 34.

Hall, R. N. and W. G. Neal (1903), *The Ancient Ruins of Rhodesia*, London.

Jones, Neville (1926), *The Stone Age in Rhodesia*, Oxford.

Jones, Neville (1948), *The Prehistory of Southern Rhodesia*, Cambridge.

Kirkman, J. (1954), *The Arab City of Gedi*, Oxford.

Mennell, F. P. and R. Summers (1955), *The Ancient Workings of Southern Rhodesia*, Occ. Pap. Nat. Mus. S. Rhod., No. 20.

Robinson, K. R. (1952), 'Excavations in two Rock-Shelters near the Ruzawi River', *S. Afr. Arch. Bull.*, 7, p. 108.

Robinson, K. R. (1955), Contribution to *Inyanga* (publication pending).

Schofield, J. F. (1940), 'Pottery from Bambata Cave', *Proc. Rhod. Sci. Assn.*

Schofield, J. F. (1947), *Primitive Pottery*, Cape Town.

Summers, R. (1950), 'Iron Age Cultures in Southern Rhodesia', *S. Afr. Jnl. Sci.*, 47.

Summers, R. (1953), *Rhodesian Ruins*, Occ. Pap. Nat. Mus. S. Rhod., No. 17.

62

A Review of Prehistoric Research in Northern Rhodesia and Nyasaland

by J. D. CLARK

THERE is still a tendency among our friends living south of the Zambezi to refer to the lands beyond that river as 'the Black North'. Such a term is used to emphasize not only the preponderance in numbers of the indigenous population over the European but also to stress the fact that these countries, Northern Rhodesia and Nyasaland, are still in many ways much of an enigma to the more civilized south, and still, even though in practice it be nothing more than a romantic fantasy, preserve something of the spirit of adventure and surprise that lay behind the well-known description of Africa as 'the dark continent'. Those of us who live in these northern territories know that they are not so black as they are painted and in fact the light has begun to pour through in many directions spotlighting certain parts as if it were shining through the holes in a vegetable colander, while leaving other parts still dimly lit or dark to try to live up to the reputation of the old unchanging Africa of pre-European days.

Our knowledge of the prehistoric past of these territories is in exactly this state. In a few areas where reasonably intensive research work has been carried out we have been able to obtain not a little information concerning the cultures that existed there but the great part of the country is still practically or entirely unknown and remains a blank on the distribution maps. Admittedly these blanks are slowly being filled and eventually will disappear but in the meantime they are very apparent and must not be overlooked.

Compared with other parts of the continent—South Africa, North-West Africa or Egypt—prehistoric research in Northern Rhodesia was very late in starting, while in Nyasaland a systematic research programme has still to be put into effect. Middle Stone Age implements had been collected at the Victoria Falls as early as 1905 and in that year the late Professor Balfour found one of the first hand-axes. The first excavation in a cave was carried out in 1924 at Mumbwa, 150 miles west of Lusaka, by F. B. Macrae, a graduate of the School of Archaeology and Anthropology at Cambridge. In 1929 the late Dr Neville Jones and Mr A. L. Armstrong investigated the old Zambezi Gravels lying above the gorges south of the Victoria Falls and put forward evidence to show that they were not all of the same age. In the same year also an Italian Expedition under Commander Attilio Gatti and having Professor Dart as a member further excavated the Mumbwa Caves and investigated several other sites in the southern half of Northern Rhodesia. In 1938 the Rhodes-Livingstone Museum, which had come into being two years before, began its programme of systematic research and with the formation of the National Monuments Commission in 1948, many additional facilities have become available so that we may now look back upon a fair degree of successful fieldwork and forward to an active field and laboratory programme for many years to come. Most of the collections that have been made in Northern Rhodesia are housed in the Rhodes-Livingstone Museum and, other than study collections, have not been sent elsewhere, so that it is possible to obtain a fairly clear picture of the particular cultures that exist here.

Prehistoric Research in Northern Rhodesia and Nyasaland

Nyasaland has not been so fortunate as it has, as yet, no museum to undertake research and no active fieldworkers. Such knowledge as we possess of the prehistory of the Protectorate is derived from three independent workers. In the 1920's and 30's Dr F. Dixey was Director of the Geological Survey and determined the age and succession of the Rift faulting and the different episodes in the formation of Lake Nyasa. In the course of this investigation he discovered certain Lower, Middle and Upper Pleistocene lake deposits on the north Nyasa plain and from some of them recovered a Middle Pleistocene fauna and some tools made on pebbles. In the 1930's Rodney C. Wood collected from a number of localities mainly in northern Nyasaland and obtained evidence of the presence of a late phase of the Sangoan Culture together with not a little Late Stone Age material. In 1950 I was invited by the Nyasaland Government to investigate certain rock painting sites in the central and northern parts of the territory. Paintings were traced in several shelters and excavations were made in two of them with interesting results which indicate that the Late Stone Age culture of these parts of Nyasaland was the same as that in the northern half of Northern Rhodesia—the Nachikufan. As yet, however, too little is known about the Protectorate—the whole of the south is a blank—for it to be of any value to produce distribution maps of the finds that have already been made. But sufficient is known to be able to say that the cultural succession is the same as that found in Northern Rhodesia, though local variations are met with, as might be expected. The bulk of the collections made by Mr Rodney Wood as well as our own are housed in the Rhodes-Livingstone Museum. Such then, briefly, is the present position in regard to the practical application of prehistoric research in the two countries. Let us now examine the approach to the problem and the results so far obtained.

It has always been a disadvantage that we in Africa tend to work in a number of almost watertight compartments the boundaries of which are the artificial political boundaries created during the nineteenth century. More often than not these boundaries take no regard of the natural ecological or geographical divisions of the continent, but we must always bear in mind that regional variation in our prehistoric cultures tends to follow the natural divisions of environment and knows no artificial boundary such as restricts us today. As far as Northern Rhodesia and Nyasaland are concerned we know not a little about some of our neighbours—Southern Rhodesia, Bechuanaland (though this has not yet been published) and the Katanga—but in so far as the other neighbouring countries are concerned we are less fortunate and adequate information is still awaited in so far as Angola, southern Tanganyika and Mozambique are concerned. These countries are still largely unknown from the point of view of the prehistorian and for all we know may prove to be of paramount importance in elucidating the origins, diffusion and trend of development of already known cultures, so that lack of knowledge of these areas must slow down correlation work between Rhodesia and other territories where research programmes are already established. It is to be hoped that this Congress may be instrumental in persuading the authorities concerned to start to fill these blanks on the prehistoric map.

The interpretation of the stratigraphical and climatic succession is of course the basis for the relative chronology of the Stone Age in Northern Rhodesia and investigations to this end have been carried out in the Upper Zambezi by Dixey, Cooke and Clark, in the Middle Zambezi by Bond and Clark, and again by Clark and others in other river valleys. The stratigraphical succession shows a very uniform pattern—an initial period of valley-cutting followed by a series of high level terraces, the lower ones containing the Earlier Stone Age complex; followed again by deep down cutting and the aggradation of thick sediments containing the Middle Stone Age cultures and lastly minor cycles of erosion and aggradation of lesser intensity contemporary with the transitional industries and the Later Stone Age. This general pattern is remarkably uniform except where special features, rock barriers or river capture, for example, have caused a local divergence from the sequence.

Also, as far as is known, Northern Rhodesia was affected very little, if at all, by the earth movements in the unstable area of the Great Rift Valley during the Pleistocene, though in immediately

413

pre-Pleistocene times warping is believed to have caused a deviation of the courses of some of our major rivers. The geological evidence may be interpreted, therefore, very largely in terms of climatic fluctuations with little or none of the complications resultant upon earth movement, which have to be taken into account in any study of the East African area. Thus we are able to show three major wet periods of long duration, each capable of subdivision, separated by drier phases when in some areas wind-blown sands were deposited or redistributed. These major wet periods or 'pluvials' were succeeded by two further wet phases of lesser intensity.

Within this basic and essential framework of stratigraphy and relative chronology, however, it is very important to develop an ecological and geographical approach if we are to get at the *raison d'être* for parallel culture patterns, change and distribution. To understand the Northern Rhodesian and Nyasaland cultures, the regional variants and lacunae, therefore, it is necessary to know the geographical and ecological background throughout the Pleistocene and early Recent times. For primitive man the environment in which he lives has unquestionably been the most important factor determining his form of culture and although Stone Age man succeeded at a very early time in mastering his raw materials and in getting the better of his environment, it was only by adapting his way of life to the prevailing ecological conditions that he was able to establish himself and furthermore to maintain himself in spite of climatic change and all that goes with this. The aim of our research in recent years has, therefore, been directed towards first establishing the chronological and climatic succession and then to interpreting the cultures in the light of the ecological setting in so far as this can be determined.

Northern Rhodesia and Nyasaland lie approximately in the south-centre of the Central African plateau—that vast, undulating, ancient surface which fills the greater part of the sub-continent and which was probably the place where man as a tool-making animal originated. Due to the Rift movements Nyasaland shows a topographical diversity from high mountain plateau, 8,000 or more feet high, to dry lowlands only a little above sea level. The greater part of Northern Rhodesia is flat rolling country some 4–5,000 feet above sea level with occasional altitudes of some 6,000 feet or more. Over much of the country the undulating plateau surface is broken by hills and valleys which develop into areas of broken country such as for example the Muchinga Escarpment bordering the western edge of the Luangwa valley. Four large rivers have cut into the plateau surface and the Zambezi with its two main tributaries the Kafue and the Luangwa, as well as the Luapula River in the north, have eroded their valleys to depths of approximately 1,000 feet or more below the plateau surface. In the north are the impressive Rift Valley lakes of Tanganyika, Mweru and a little over the north-eastern border Lake Rukwa, while in the east the natural boundary is Lake Nyasa. These geographical features have influenced the movements of peoples across the plateau, making movement from the northwest and west, as well as from and to the south, the easiest way of entering or leaving the country.

Most of the country is well-wooded even to the crests of the highest hills with woodland species, while in the north are found occasional patches of thick evergreen forest which are believed to be remnants of a once more extensive afforestation. In the southwestern part the solid geology is obscured by the Kalahari Sands, the earliest accumulation of which in our area dates to the dry period at the end of the Tertiary. These sands are on an average 100 feet thick and support an economically valuable open forest of hard woods. Since over wide areas they cover the underlying rocks, stone as a form of raw material for making implements hardly exists there. As a result there can be little doubt that wood and bone and their by-products were more extensively used in these sand areas. Eastward and northward these Kalahari Sand forests give place to the more normal *Brachystegia* woodland relieved by wide, shallow, grass-filled and swampy depressions—the *dambos*. In the major river valleys the vegetation is usually much more open, being the home of the 'Mopane' often mixed with thorn bush. The valleys must thus have formed ready-made highways for movements of people across the more thickly-forested plateau country. Sometimes in the valleys and on the plateau occur extensive areas of grassland such as that in the middle Kafue in which still live large herds of game and in the west also on the Zambezi/Congo divide. Sometimes these areas are swampy or contain seasonal or permanent lakes. The largest of these, Lake Bangweulu, is about 3,000 square miles in area.

The vegetation types are of course dependent firstly upon the rainfall distribution and then to a lesser extent on the geological and geographical features, especially altitude. These last two factors have remained virtually stable here since the beginning of the Pleistocene but the rainfall as we have seen has fluctuated. There can be little doubt that the present climatic regimen of dry winter seasons and wet summer seasons existed also throughout the Pleistocene, but the amount of rain that fell was at times less and at others more than at present, with no doubt also sometimes a more extended period of summer rains.

The present distribution of rainfall compiled by J. H. Chaplin ['On Some Aspects of Rainfall in Northern Rhodesia', *N. Rhodesia Journal*, II, No. 6, pp. 16–23] (Fig. 1) shows that the areas receiving the lowest annual rainfall are in the south and southeast, in particular the large river valleys: these receive something in the nature of 25 to 30 inches; while most of the rest of the plateau enjoys a rainfall of from 35 to 45 inches. Intensity is increased over Lake Bangweulu and on the Zambezi/Congo watershed as also along the Muchinga Escarpment to 50 inches or more.

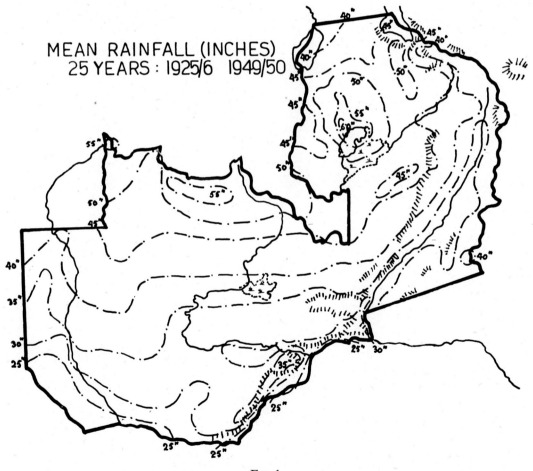

MEAN RAINFALL (INCHES)
25 YEARS: 1925/6 1949/50

FIG. 1

415

The next map, also compiled by J. H. Chaplin (Fig. 2), shows the percentage increase and decrease in the rainfall trend over the past 30 years. From it can be seen how there has been an increase in the average rainfall from the south and east up the Kafue basin and from Nyasaland across the Luangwa. There has been a corresponding decrease in the Upper Zambezi Valley in Barotseland, on the Zambezi/Congo watershed and down the Luapula Valley.

It would of course be highly dangerous to postulate from this map, based upon such a short period of observations, any uneven change in the rainfall distribution in Northern Rhodesia. So many different factors are involved and if carried to a logical conclusion we should reach absurdity in that at the one extreme we should postulate intense wet and at the other intense dry conditions. It might however indicate the trend of minor climatic fluctuations and in fact there does appear to be some measure of agreement with the inferred vegetation changes as I shall show shortly.

For the next three distribution maps showing the vegetation I am much indebted to Dr H. Wild, the Senior Botanist in the Southern Rhodesia Department of Botany and Plant Pathology who has kindly compiled them at my request. These maps have been based on Trapnell's soil and vegetation distribution maps and on the rainfall map. They have of necessity been made very simple to allow the maximum margin for errors and to show the major vegetation divisions only. The three maps show the present vegetation cover, and what this cover is likely to have been under

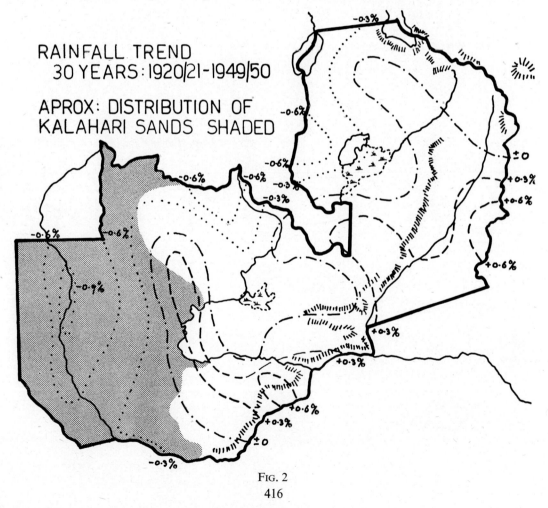

FIG. 2

416

conditions of 20 inches more and 20 inches less annual rainfall. The differential trends in rainfall changes after overall differences of 20 inches have been postulated cannot be foreseen so it has been assumed in drawing out these maps that the change was an even one.

The present-day distribution (Fig. 3) shows Kalahari Sand forest in the south-west alternating with grassland at higher elevations and in the more swampy areas. Most of the remainder of the plateau is covered by *Isoberlinia-Brachystegia* woodland, with grassland round the main swampy depressions and the Luapula. In the main river valleys it can be seen how the mopane/acacia bush predominates. The evergreen forest remnants are too small to show except in the north-east on the slopes of the Nyika Plateau and Mafingi Mountain. However, much of the Copper Belt and the Mwinilunga area is marginal and not too far off true forest.

In the 20 inch increase map (Fig. 4) a conservative view has been taken of good forest conditions and it may well have been that these were more extensive in the Northern Province. The essential point, however, is that Northern Rhodesia would have been directly linked with huge forests spreading continuously into Angola, the Belgian Congo and southern Tanganyika. The changes in flood plain grassland have been gauged in accordance with the topographical features and it can be seen how much of west and central Barotseland would be under grass and the grasslands round the swamp areas of Lukanga, Bangweulu, the Chambezi headwaters and the Luapula would have greatly increased. The *Isoberlinia-Brachystegia* woodland would have covered most of the country and filled the river valleys, while the Kalahari Sand forests would be restricted more to the higher regions of the centre and east of Barotseland. Such a rainfall distribution would mean therefore that hunters and foodgatherers would be more likely to restrict their activities to the more open southern and eastern half of the territory.

Turning now to the distribution map for a rainfall of 20 inches less than at present (Fig. 5) we are struck immediately by the enormous spread of the mopane/acacia type flora. The *Isoberlinia-Brachystegia*-type woodland is restricted to the Tanganyika Plateau and the Zambezi/Congo Watershed. The Kalahari Sand flora is greatly extended and the grassland and swamps disappear. Of interest also is the spread of semi-desert conditions into the Zambezi, Kafue, Lower Luangwa and Luano valleys. Such a vegetation pattern suggests that man would on the one hand have moved out on to parts of the plateau which he was unlikely to have favoured under 'pluvial' conditions, and on the other that he would have hugged the large river valleys where permanent or semi-permanent water could still be found.

It is very important to bear in mind such changes in environment when we consider the distribution of our prehistoric cultures.

In regard to these distribution maps I must stress again that much of Northern Rhodesia still remains unknown prehistorically, simply because no work has yet been done there. Such large areas as most of Barotseland, the Upper Kafue, and much of the Northern Province for example are as yet quite untouched. Year by year however these unknown areas are gradually becoming smaller and smaller so that eventually we trust that our distribution maps will be more accurate indicators of the occupation pattern during the Quaternary. Already they serve a very useful purpose and show where the greatest concentration of population is likely to be found, as well as how the changes in environment affected the population pattern.

The earliest culture of which we have any evidence is the Pre-Chelles-Acheul (Fig. 6) and it is found in the high-level terraces of the rivers—the Older Gravels complex as we call it. No Australopithecine deposits or remains are known as yet from Central Africa. It is possible that some of the fossil material from Leba on the southern Angola plateau may be of this age—that is, Final Kageran or later—but this has not yet been proved. The uppermost terraces of the Older Gravels have so far proved sterile, but the lower ones have yielded pebble tools often embedded in an ironstone matrix—ferricrete.

Good collections in Northern Rhodesia have come from the Zambezi near Livingstone, the Kalomo and Ngwesi gravels, while other more doubtful occurrences exist in other parts as the

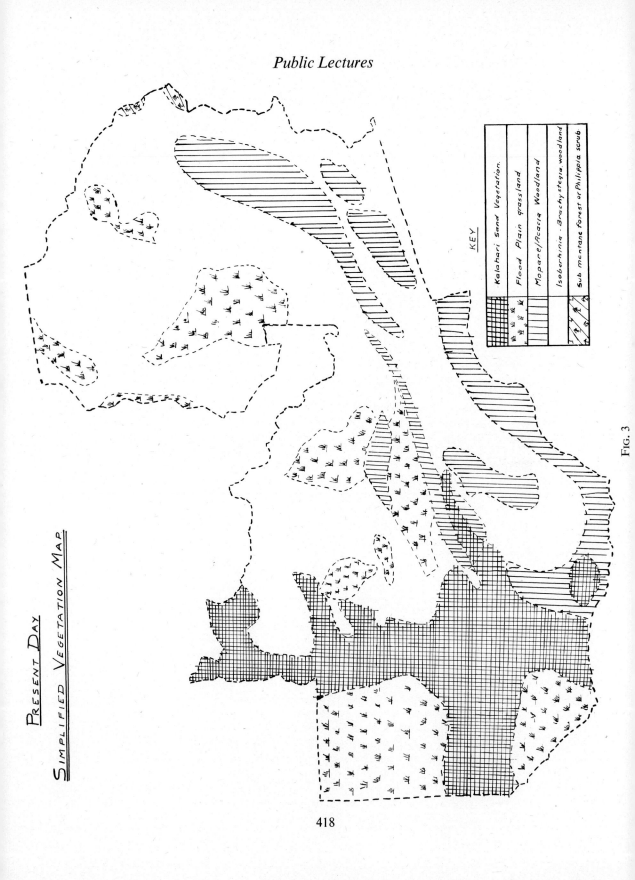

PRESENT DAY

SIMPLIFIED VEGETATION MAP

KEY

Kalahari Sand Vegetation.

Flood Plain grassland

Mopane/Acacia Woodland

Isoberlinia - Brachystegia woodland

Sub montane forest or Philippia scrub

FIG. 3

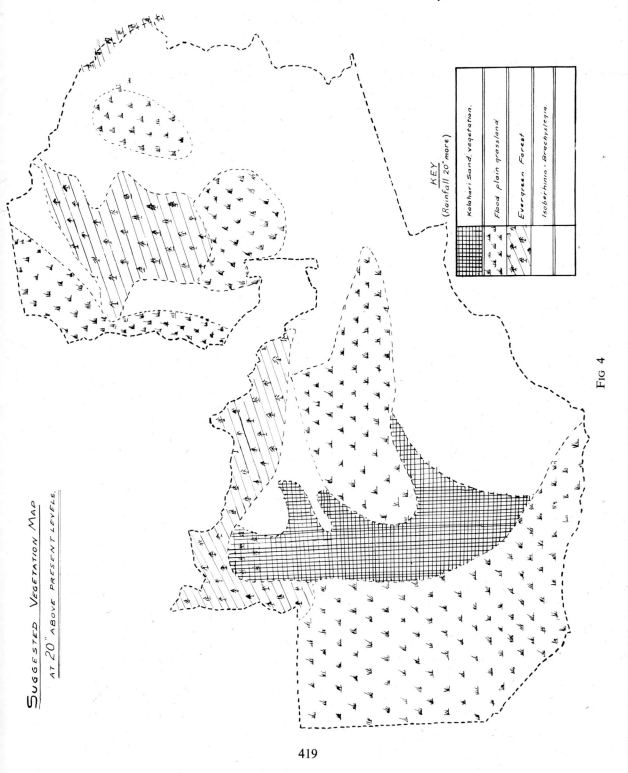

SUGGESTED VEGETATION MAP
AT 20" ABOVE PRESENT LEVELS.

KEY
(Rainfall 20" more)

Kalahari Sand. vegetation.
Flood plain grassland
Evergreen Forest
Isoberlinia - Brachystegia.

FIG 4

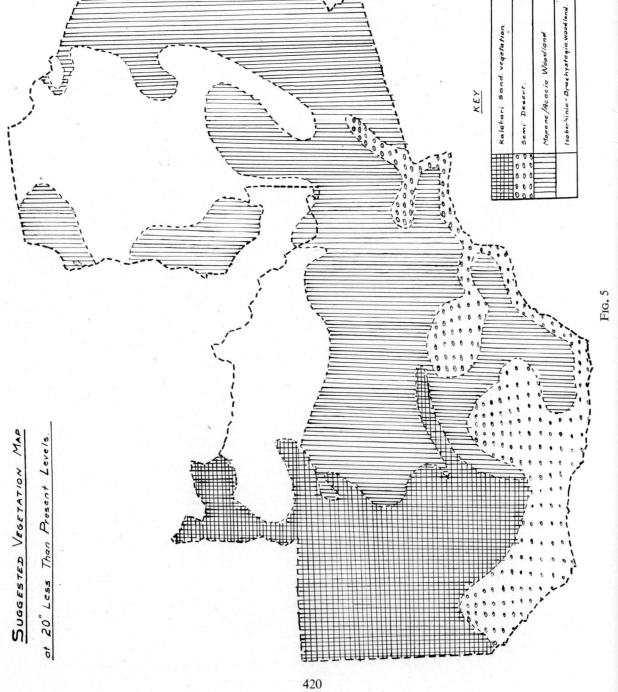

SUGGESTED VEGETATION MAP at 20" Less Than Present Levels

KEY

Kalahari Sand. vegetation.
Semi Desert.
Mopane/Acacia Woodland.
Isoberlinia - Brachystegia.Woodland.

FIG. 5

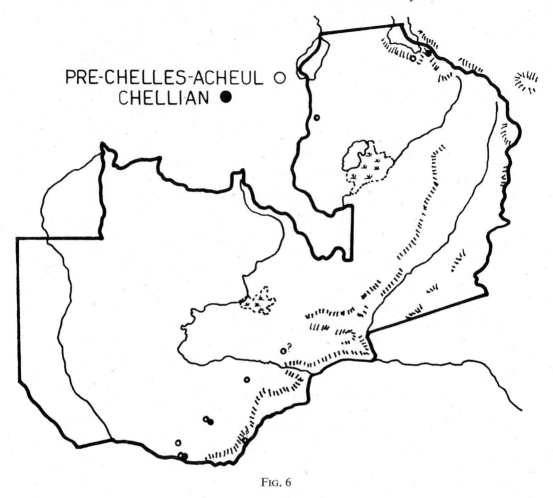

PRE-CHELLES-ACHEUL ○
CHELLIAN ●

FIG. 6

distribution map shows. The industries appear to be confined to the river valleys and the grass-covered plateau areas. Where pebbles are the predominant raw material tools of both Oldowan and Kafuan type are found. Where a material such as tabular chalcedony or chert was used, often struck from outcrops and necessitating a modified technical approach (as for example in the Upper Zambezi Valley) then quite a number of implements are made on flakes and are, in fact, flake tools. No subdivision into Kafuan and Oldowan industries is possible and the assemblages must be dated by the most advanced forms present, i.e. the Oldowan. We have not as yet, therefore, any human industry that dates to a time earlier than the beginning of the Kamasian Pluvial, though we know from other regions that Man was already present in these parts during the preceding dry Kageran/Kamasian Interpluvial.

While implements occur in sufficient profusion it is to be regretted that no faunal remains of this period are as yet known from the country. The only area where a fauna of this age occurs is in Northern Nyasaland where Dr Dixey recovered mastodon and hippo from the lacustrine Chiwondo beds. It was thought that bone-bearing and implementiferous cave breccias occurring in the Pre-Cambrian limestones near Lusaka might possibly be of Pre-Chelles-Acheul age. Excavations carried out in 1954 at one such site have shown, however, that this particular group must

421

be ascribed to the early Upper Pleistocene. The pebble tools they contain serve to demonstrate once again very satisfactorily that it is not sufficient merely because tools happen to be made on pebbles to ascribe them without the support of stratigraphical and faunal evidence to a Pre-Chelles-Acheul stage of culture. Remains of the men who made these pebble industries still elude us therefore, but there are reasonably good prospects of finding a deposit where Australopithecine or *Homo* remains may occur in one of the fissure deposits in the limestones north and south of the Kafue.

Cultural material that can be ascribed to the Chellian stage of the Chelles-Acheul is very scanty (Fig. 6). A few specimens from the Upper Zambezi were, until recently, almost the only material and even this cannot be divided stratigraphically from the latest Pebble Culture implements. Recently however a reasonably good but smaller assemblage has been recovered from a terrace at Kalomo midway between terraces yielding Pebble Culture and Acheulian implements. The climate at this time must have been definitely wet and it is probable that man preferred the drier uplands of a sub-tropical climate to be found at this time in south and east Africa. One point that should be borne in mind in connection with the Chellian in Rhodesia is that the commonest tool here, as in South Africa remained the worked pebble: the hand-axe is rare though it is the main element which distinguishes the Chellian from the earlier industries. Other tools of the Chellian stage are the polyhedral stone, worked flake and the pebble disc.

Similarly the Early and Middle stages of the Acheulian are only poorly represented stratigraphically. The best site of these times is situated in the Middle Zambezi Valley east of Chipepo's village. With the Early stage occur large and heavy hand-axes and the first cleavers, while the hand-axe and cleaver of the Middle Acheulian approximate closely to what is known as Stage III of the Acheulian or Stellenbosch in the Vaal. No living site of this or of the preceding cultures has yet been found, the implements all occurring in river gravels.

A number more Late Acheulian sites are known and several of these are also living sites, so that now, for the first time, we are able to perceive something of the manner in which the men of these times lived. Assemblages occur in the lowest terrace of the Older Gravels in the river valleys (equating with the Kanjeran or Upper Kamasian) as well as at some localities on the plateau. The most important of the assemblages from living sites comes from the Kalambo Falls on the Northern Rhodesia/Tanganyika border, from Broken Hill not many yards from where the skull and other remains of *Homo rhodesiensis* were found, from the Maramba Valley near Livingstone and from Kalomo. It is of interest to note that as with the earlier cultures the Late Acheulian appears to be restricted to two main types of country—large river valleys (which, as we have seen, in a climate similar to that pertaining today are not forested but support more open vegetation) and the open grassland and parkland of some of the higher parts of the plateau. The savannah woodland areas have as yet yielded little or nothing in the way of Chelles-Acheul material. We have reason to suppose that the climate of Northern Rhodesia during the Kanjeran was similar to that of today and drier towards the end of the 'pluvial'. This would imply that Hand-Axe Man probably preferred country which was relatively open in addition to being well watered and well stocked with game. There are indications to suggest that, in addition to hand-axes and cleavers, wooden weapons, presumably the spear, were also in use at this period. One complete wooden spear and the broken point of another are known from two Middle Pleistocene sites in western Europe and the number of small scraping tools found on our Rhodesian sites indicates that the spear was most probably in use in Central Africa also at that time. The association in Central Africa of the hand-axe and cleaver with small flake tools was very satisfactorily demonstrated from excavations carried out at Broken Hill in 1953 close to the site of the 'Bone Cave'. Here lying on the former land surface were, besides hand-axes and cleavers, numbers of small flake tools made in quartz—scrapers and chisels of various kinds—with evidence of use such as experiment shows results from working hard woods. It is important that the unquestionable association in the savannah woodland regions of Africa of these small flake tools with the Hand-Axe Culture should be appreciated, particularly as most of the earlier known sites were river gravels from which usually only the characteristic hand-axe and cleaver have been collected. The distribution of the Acheulian is shown in Fig. 7.

Contemporary in part with the Middle and Late Acheulian in our area are certain assemblages of flake tools and small choppers which have been tentatively grouped together under the term 'Hope Fountain Culture' (Fig. 7). In the time at my disposal I cannot elaborate this point, but this so-called Hope Fountain Culture now appears more likely to represent an aberrant phase of culture rather than a separate and distinct culture in itself, as the characteristic tools occur on sites ranging in date from the Pre-Chelles-Acheul to the early Middle Stone Age.

In a country such as Africa where climatic fluctuations have been so pronounced the chances of survival of the more perishable part of the equipment of prehistoric man—such as wood or fibre or even bone—are exceedingly remote. Towards the end of 1953, however, a very important site was found at the Kalambo Falls. Here in old lake beds dating either to the interpluvial or to the very beginning of the succeeding Gamblian Pluvial of Upper Pleistocene age were found final Acheulian and later camping floors in association with partially carbonized tree trunks preserved in waterlogged clays, fine silts and sands. The clays were also found to be rich in fossil pollens. The tree-trunks are provisionally identified as acacia while the pollens so far identified include over 27%

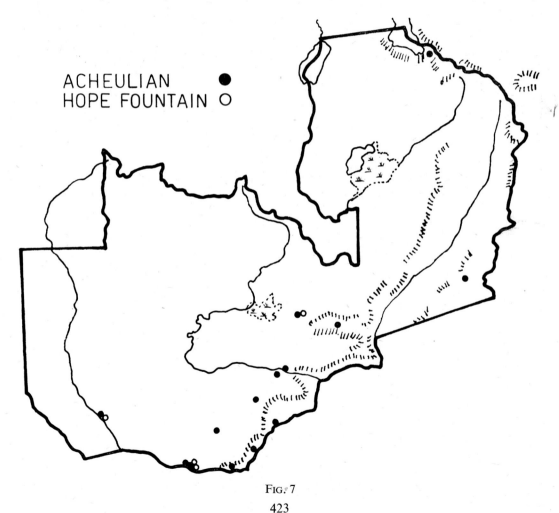

ACHEULIAN ●
HOPE FOUNTAIN ○

FIG. 7

grasses and pollen of *Cyperaceae* which indicates that the vegetation round the old Kalambo Lake was fairly open. Samples of the wood are awaiting C14 testing and may, it is hoped, give a date in terms of years for the end of the Early Stone Age in this part of Central Africa.* Furthermore, when full-scale excavations are undertaken, there is the possibility of finding preserved actual wooden implements. Already there have been recovered two pieces of wood, one a crudely pointed, stoutish fragment about 18 inches long which may have been used as a digging stake, and the other a smaller piece which appears to be the pointed end of a similar instrument. Although these wooden fragments cannot at present be accepted without reserve as undoubted implements as no clear evidence of cutting with a stone tool can be seen on them, yet the site holds out high promise of finding what, for Africa, would be a unique discovery, some of the more perishable tools of the Early Stone Age.

Stratigraphically the next cultural stage belongs to the end of the Kanjeran/Gamblian dry inter-pluvial and the beginning of the Gamblian Pluvial when the climate was again wetter. The charac-teristic culture is now the Sangoan—a culture which has its focus in the forest country of Equatoria from where its influence can be traced as far south as Bechuanaland and Natal. It seems very likely that a large part of South Central Africa was uninhabitable and therefore evacuated during the dry interpluvial as strong wind action at this time again distributed the Kalahari Sands and caused the accumulation of many feet of them in Northern Angola, the Upper Zambezi Valley and North-ern Bechuanaland. With the return of wetter climatic conditions there came back to these parts of the plateau from the north-west a people who had adapted their culture to a forest or woodland environment, and not a few of the Sangoan industries are found contained within ferricrete—a deposit associated with a rainfall of some 40 inches but with marked dry and wet seasons. The great increase in the number of Sangoan sites and their somewhat wider distribution (Fig. 8) com-pared with those of Acheulian times shows that Man had now become capable of inhabiting a woodland environment and the emphasis that is laid on woodworking tools in these industries suggests that much greater use was now made of wood and bark for tools and weapons, and also possibly that vegetable foods were assuming more importance.

At this period and almost for the first time one begins to find regional specialization and it is now possible to recognize several distinct variants of a single culture. Thus apart from the true Equatorial forms in Northern Angola and the Congo, we find such variants in N.R. as the Luangwa and Lake Tanganyika forms with their characteristic pebble 'picks' and hand-axes; the northern plateau form as illustrated by the Kalambo site almost a regional variant of the Faure-smith; the Upper Zambezi form with its Micoque-type and diminutive pointed hand-axes; the Middle Zambezi form with its pebble choppers, and south of the Zambezi the Southern Rhodesian watershed form where the pick appears to be rare and where the industries again show much in common with the Fauresmith complex of the high grasslands; and lastly the S. Rhodesian eastern mountain form where varieties of pick again occur. It seems that where the vegetation cover is thickest there the greater number of picks are to be found and we obtain the impression that many of the rough stone tools are merely the workmen's tools for producing the finished implements in some other material now vanished. The Sangoan is still largely confined to those parts of the country over which movement was relatively easy—the river valleys, wooded high veldt and the open grassland. The evidence suggests that the favourable climatic conditions which persisted during the Gamblian Pluvial did not encourage any major movement of peoples over the central plateau; rather would it seem that as the pluvial developed it had the effect of isolating the various groups with the result that the next culture stage evolving directly out of the Sangoan, the Middle Stone Age proper, shows even more local specialization with a number of Middle Stone Age variants.

In some areas the culture developed into a proto- and fully developed Still Bay—as for example in the Upper Zambezi Valley. At others—the Mumbwa Caves and Broken Hill for instance—the

* Result obtained by Dr Kulp of Columbia University gives 'more than 36,000 years before the present'.

end products of the fully developed Still Bay are rarely found and the culture seems to have persisted in its 'proto' form with little alteration. Again, notably for example round the Kafue Flats, in the Twin Rivers breccias and in the Middle Zambezi, the fully developed Still Bay point appears to be quite absent while in its place occur numbers of pebble choppers, indistinguishable from those of the Pre-Chelles-Acheul. Finally in the Luangwa Valley, and at the north end of Lake Nyasa we find apparently isolated industries which with their diminutive 'Tumbian-type' picks more closely resemble the Upper Sangoan industries of Northern Angola and the Congo.

Those grasslands where suitable raw material exists seem to have been the home of people who made the most finished end-product of the Middle Stone Age cultures—the uni- or bifacial stone lanceheads. Such are the finely made points in quartz and silcrete from Bambata in Southern Rhodesia. The variants which have remained less specialized may have remained so either by reason of partial geographical isolation, as for instance is believed to be the case in the Middle Zambezi and Luangwa Valleys; or because the end-products of these variants were made in some material other than stone, and indeed we already have some rather clumsy gouges and points of bone from Broken Hill. In fact the proto-Still Bay stone industries from the breccias at Twin Rivers and Broken Hill, both of which lie close to open woodland, must be considered to represent

SANGOAN ●

Fig. 8
425

in the main the workshop implements rather than the final end-products. Most of the stone implements are ideally suited for cutting, scraping, paring and smoothing wood and indeed not a few of the specimens, made almost invariably from quartz, show the evidence of use in one or more of these ways. Perhaps I might be allowed to digress a little here and say that wooden implements were in use at this time further south—in the Orange Free State. Some have already been found in the lowest peat layer at the Florisbad fossil spring in association with *Homo helmei* and an early Middle Stone Age industry. The spatulate ends of two broken tools suggest that they may have served as digging sticks, while a third specimen represents, I believe, the lower end of a throwing stick, very like some of the Australian throwing sticks in use today. The lowest peat at Florisbad has been dated by C14 to more than 41,000 years old. This discovery of wooden implements has suggested that excavations at some of the springs on the Northern Rhodesian plateau, round which Stone Age material is known to occur, might yield similar peats with preserved organic remains. There is not a little to indicate that the spear, probably made of wood, was the main hunting weapon in Middle Stone Age times in the sub-continent but the stone-headed club, or bolas, appears to have been an important weapon also in the savannah and more forested country, being particularly common in Northern Rhodesia, as also in Angola and the Katanga.

At this period we also obtain for the first time in Northern Rhodesia a view of the men themselves who were responsible for these early Middle Stone Age cultures. I refer to the proto-Australoid man from Broken Hill, who, although he exhibits several Neanderthal-like features, is nevertheless, especially in the limb bones, more closely allied to *Homo sapiens* as he walked upright and carried his head erect. The discovery of the Hopefield skullcap at the Cape has, as it were, vindicated Broken Hill Man and shows that he belonged to a physical type which must have been fairly widespread over the sub-continent, and moreover suggests that when the much sought after remains of Hand-axe Man of Kanjeran age are found, he will quite possibly prove to be of a form bearing resemblances to, but less specialized than Broken Hill and Hopefield.

The Distribution Map of Middle Stone Age cultures in Northern Rhodesia (Fig. 9) shows that they are more widely dispersed than any culture that has gone before, and although the earlier and later forms have not been differentiated on the map, there are indications that as the Gamblian Pluvial declined, Middle Stone Age Man tended to leave the valleys and settle on the plateau.

The periods when the most radical cultural changes took place were the times when the climate underwent a change to drier, more arid conditions. Such a change affected the whole environment —the vegetation cover, water resources, the game—and resulted in movements of peoples, culture contact, diffusion of new traits, stimulation of Man's powers of invention and the adaptation of Man's whole way of living to the new environment. Such a period had been the Kageran/Kamasian Dry when a primitive hominid first appeared as a tool-making animal; the Kanjeran/Gamblian Dry and the dry period at the end of the Upper Pleistocene when the Middle Stone Age gave place to the Later Stone Age cultures. The more we know of the transitional culture of this period—the Magosian—the more we appreciate that such a revolution did not take place in a few years but over very many centuries. Much has been said about the movement of peoples over the face of the continent and, whereas there unquestionably have been very important movements, I believe that it was the spread of new cultural traits to the sub-continent, such as the invention of the bow and arrow and the idea of hafting composite tools with gum, which was one of the chief reasons for the change from a macrolithic to a microlithic culture in Late Stone Age times. The Magosian in Central Africa shows many varied forms depending upon their stratigraphical position and the degree to which they have preserved aspects of their traditional Middle Stone Age culture. Its distribution is not particularly well-known in Northern Rhodesia (Fig. 9), due almost certainly to insufficient field work. The main number of sites are grouped around the Victoria Falls—the area most intensely investigated. But by the beginning of the Later Stone Age, some 6–8,000 years ago, the new elements had cut right across geographical and climatic barriers and the cultures of this time in South-Central Africa are broadly speaking microlithic, while in distribution they have now spread into and preferred country which probably was hitherto little occupied, that is the Muchinga Escarpment of Northern Rhodesia, the woodland of northern Nyasaland and the Zambezi/Congo Watershed.

Once again, however, we find our regional forms based essentially upon differences in environment, though these differences bear little relation to physical type and the skeletal remains found are all of Bush or Bush/Boskopoid form, with a suggestion of Pygmy and Hamitic influence in the North. There are, in the Late Stone Age, two, possibly three, broad cultural divisions—the woodland-forest culture which has been named from the type-site the Nachikufan culture; the Wilton occupying more open parkland and scrub and possibly the more Wilton-like industries of the Lake Tanganyika Basin. The two main regional divisions similarly show local divergence and specialization. The Wilton has been known longest. Besides well-made and often very small microliths and the thumbnail scraper it contains, south of the Zambezi, a variety of bone points and is associated with the well-known, naturalistic rock art. The pygmy lunates were hafted in mastic to form arrow barbs, the thumbnail scraper I believe to have been the blade of a small hand-adze. The Zambezi and the Mumbwa variants have preserved their more primitive features longer than those south of

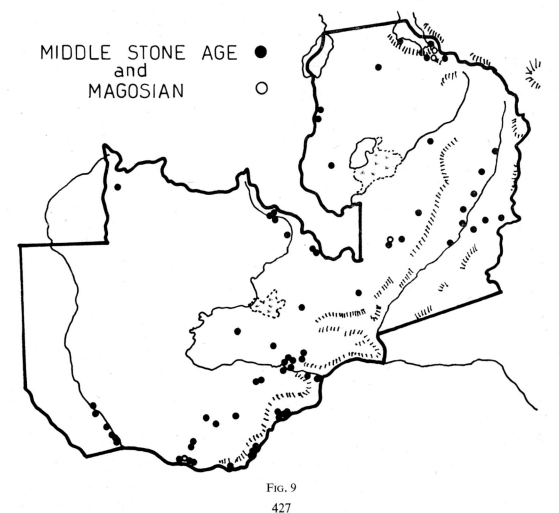

MIDDLE STONE AGE ●
and
MAGOSIAN ○

Fɪɢ. 9

427

the Zambezi and the tools are usually rather larger and less delicately made. Skin bags and ostrich egg shells for holding water must have been the more usual kind of containers. A very great deal still remains to be learned concerning these people and a critical study of their rock paintings could give much valuable information concerning their material culture, social habits, economy, magical beliefs and physical appearance.

The woodland Nachikufu culture on the other hand is represented in three well-marked stages, the earliest having been provisionally dated to approximately 4000 B.C. by C14, while in some parts the latest may not be much older than 2–300 years. The weapons of these people were the bow and arrow, both with transverse heads of stone and points of bone, the perforated stone-headed club and later the ground and polished axe. The characteristic tools were the weighted digging stick, grindstones, pestles, heavy scrapers and spokeshaves (suggesting a fairly extensive knowledge of wood-working), bone awls and polished adzes. Not a little of their food must have been derived from vegetable sources and the carbonized remains of some of these have been found. While skin receptacles no doubt were common, I believe that the adze/axe element indicates that the bark of trees was also commonly used for making into bags, rope, string and perhaps cloth. Associated also is a geometric art.

The culture occurs in three separate and distinct phases, the wide distribution of which has been proved from excavations as far apart as Central and Northern Nyasaland, the Muchingas and the Zambezi/Congo Watershed. The first phase is characterized by very small non-geometric microliths, the bored stone, and core chopping and scraping tools; the second by large triangular trapeze and U-shaped microliths and the polished axe, while the third has more Wilton-like lunates in addition to the bored stone, axes and other forms, together with pottery.

This Nachikufan culture covers the northern half of Northern Rhodesia and appears to stretch into the Katanga, Angola and Northern and Central Nyasaland, while the influence of a similar environment can be seen in the modified Wilton industries of the eastern mountain region of Southern Rhodesia and also of Mashonaland where the Wilton-type lunate occurs in association with Nachikufan-type waisted and strangulated scrapers and a local specialization a kind of lozenge- or fan-shaped thumbnail scraper.

The distribution map of these cultures (Fig. 10) shows the Wilton grouped along the Zambezi and in the south-western parts of the territory while the Nachikufan in its *Isoberlinia-Brachystegia* environment monopolizes most of the remainder of the country. The focus for settlement has now become the plateau woodland areas and it would seem that this culture had its origins somewhere to the north-west. When we look at the distribution of bored stones in the territory (Fig. 11) we see that this is approximately the same as that of the Nachikufan, especially when it is considered that from some of these sites several specimens are known. For instance at Nachikufu itself over a hundred such stones and fragments were found. The bored stone appears to have a wider distribution than the polished axe (Fig. 11), which may, it is considered, be due to the fact that it had been in use north of the Zambezi for a considerably longer time than the axe. These axes are of the kind described by Australian anthropologists as edge-ground. They are made mainly from greenstone such as diorite and also from haematite. They make their appearance with the Nachikufan II and I believe this to have been a further migration from Northern Angola or the Katanga. Believed to have been connected with the distribution of the polished axe are the grinding-groove sites (Fig. 11), almost invariably next to water on flat outcrops of sandstone or conglomerate where numbers of lenticular grinding-grooves have been worn in the rocks. These are believed to be the result of grinding polished axes. They are identical in appearance with others in the Congo and West Africa, as are they also with those from Grand Pressigny in France.

The Late Stone Age in Northern Rhodesia and Nyasaland is to be associated with a very interesting form of Rock Art. This is predominantly of a schematic nature unlike the naturalistic art of the Late Stone Age south of the Zambezi, though some naturalistic paintings occur in Northern Rhodesia also. Northern Rhodesia has yielded both paintings and engravings,

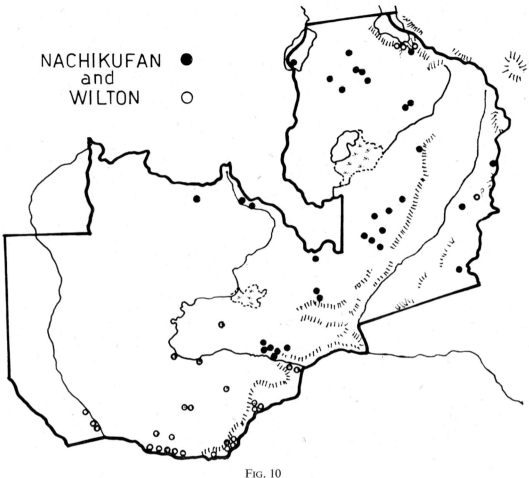

NACHIKUFAN ●
and
WILTON ○

Fig. 10

Nyasaland so far only paintings. The map shows the distribution of these as at present known (Fig. 12).

The engravings are found in the north-western parts of the country—in the area of the headwaters of the Zambezi, on the Zambezi/Congo watershed and on the east side of the Luapula Valley, south of Lake Mweru. All these groups are believed to date to the Later Stone Age and to be associated with the Nachikufan Culture. One group, that of the Chifubwa Stream Shelter (in which some of the engravings have also been painted) has been conclusively associated with a Nachikufan I industry and has also been dated by C14 to about 4000 B.C.

None of these engravings are naturalistic and only schematic motifs are represented. These take the form of ladders, parallel lines, hairpins, concentric circles, etc.; and sometimes cup markings.

There are also three groups of Iron Age engravings—near Lusaka and in the Middle Zambezi Valley where metal axes and other tools are represented, and one other interesting group of similar age with curvilinear motifs just over the north-western border in Angola. The invariable technique employed to make all these engravings was by pecking and rubbing.

The paintings are much more widely distributed and are concentrated mostly east of the

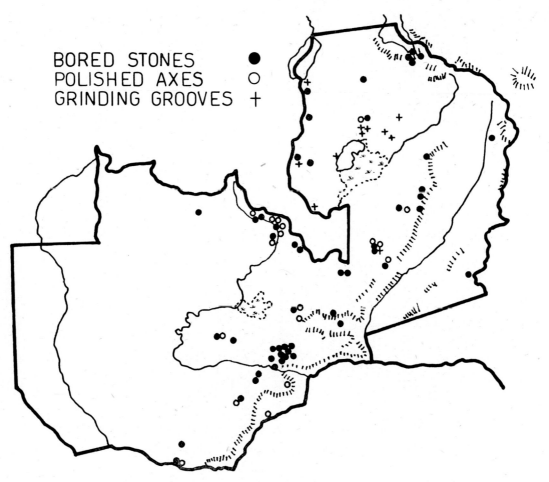

BORED STONES ●
POLISHED AXES ○
GRINDING GROOVES +

Fɪɢ. 11

Luangwa, in the Muchinga Escarpment and elsewhere in the Northern Province, in the Central Province centering round Mkushi and on the Zambezi/Congo watershed. As yet only one isolated and late occurrence west of Kalomo is known from the Southern Province. No paintings or engravings are known from Barotseland—due most probably to the fact that, being Kalahari Sand covered, the country is unsuited to this form of artistic expression. As yet, therefore (apart from the isolated instance mentioned above and those on the Zambezi/Congo watershed), not a single painting exists west of the railway line. This may in part be due to inadequate fieldwork but it is believed that it can be taken to reflect the main distribution trend of this art.

The art itself is of two forms—naturalistic and schematic. The former is by far the less common of the two. Naturalistic paintings of animals—mainly antelopes—occur north and east of Fort Jameson, at Kasama, at Nachikufu and at Na Chitalo south-east of Ndola. They are thus fairly well distributed over the area where paintings are found. In style they resemble the Central Tanganyika art groups rather than those south of the Zambezi. In two instances the naturalistic paintings are definitely earlier than the schematic motifs, at two they appear to be contemporary and at the third, Rocklands Farm near Fort Jameson, a large outline drawing of an eland is painted over faded schematic paintings. These facts coupled with the distribution of the sites at present known may indicate that the Northern Rhodesia rock art was originally naturalistic but that it later changed to a form of expression in which schematic and geometric motifs were the rule.

The schematic painting groups are many and occur equally also in central and northern Nyasaland in the Dedza, Fort Johnston and Mzimba districts. A number of superimposed styles and colours exist though the colour sequence cannot be taken to hold good throughout the territory and it is believed that the artists used whatever colours were most ready to hand in each particular locality.

In the Muchinga Escarpment area which is the best known so far and where is found Nsalu Cave containing the best group of schematic paintings, the succession of styles and colour is— yellow, reds of various kinds, red and white, white and dirty white.

These Northern Rhodesia and Nyasaland schematic art groups show exactly the same degree of physical weathering as do the naturalistic art groups to the north and south of them and there can be little or no doubt that they are contemporary and equally date to Later Stone Age times. Only the dirty white paintings which are of a crude semi-naturalistic nature are believed to be of more recent date. The distribution of these art groups, however, coincides almost exactly with the as yet known distribution of the Nachikufan north of the Zambezi, and throughout the Nachi-

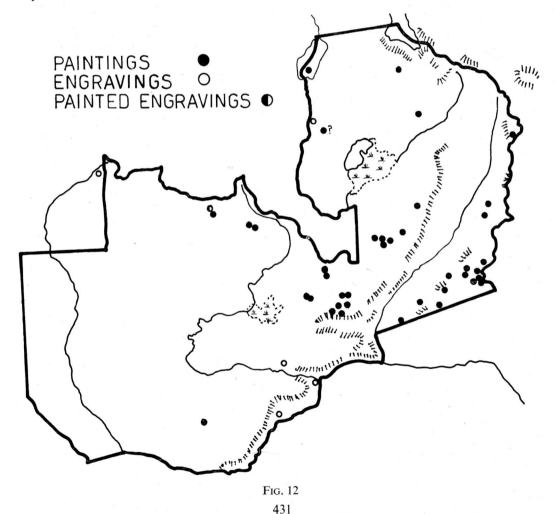

PAINTINGS ●
ENGRAVINGS ○
PAINTED ENGRAVINGS ◐

FIG. 12

kufan horizon are found crayons of red and yellow ochre and rubbed fragments together with grindstones and pestles stained with pigment. This need not, of course, imply that these were used to paint the walls of rock shelters but it is a very suggestive fact when used in support of the evidence for dating the naturalistic groups and when it is compared with the evidence from two caves where paintings extend down to a few inches above the present floor level, it assumes considerable significance.

It is intriguing to speculate why this art north of the Zambezi should assume a largely schematic nature. It has been suggested without any substantial corroborative evidence that it was due to early Arab influence, but when we consider that the painted engravings at the Chifubwa Rock Shelter have been dated by C14 to approximately 4000 B.C. it is necessary to look elsewhere for the reason behind this metamorphosis (unless of course the C14 date is not the true date). One possible reason that suggests itself is that it is the reproduction in paint on rock of an engraving technique executed on wood or bark as such a technique is likely to have been of a schematic nature due to the difficulty of producing curved lines in these media with stone tools.

In the time at my disposal I have been able to give you only the main outline of the Stone Age succession in so far as it is known in Northern Rhodesia and Nyasaland, but you will be able to follow this up if you so wish by a study of the collections themselves in the Museum. By emphasizing the environmental approach we have endeavoured to show that our Stone Age industries are not merely type-fossils liable to typological over-classification in a rigid geo-chronological framework, but that they are the handwork of Man himself and illustrate his inventiveness and adaptability and his reactions to different environments. We are unfortunate in that so much of the material culture (excepting the imperishable stone implements) is forever lost to us, but we are fortunate in that we are enabled to know more about the lives of our Late Stone Age hunters and foodgatherers by studying the remaining Northern Bushman groups. Such groups still exist in the south-west corner of Northern Rhodesia and in particular much useful information has been obtained from small groups of Hukwe Bushmen who live in the open forest and woodland of the Kalahari sand country. Not only does a technical study of these people give us a clue to the uses of some of our stone and bone implements but it also bridges a gap between the present and the past and helps us to appreciate that prehistory should be the study of Man as a living being and not purely of Man the Fossil.

63

Archaeology and Education

by MILES C. BURKITT

MY main thesis in this paper is to urge that Archaeology, more particularly perhaps in its earlier phases, is a subject peculiarly adapted for the education of both the child and the adult.

When using the term 'education', one must remember that the educationalist has three objects in view. Firstly, he is concerned with the training and disciplining of the minds of children. Just as the muscles of the young have to be trained by use, so do the 'muscles' of the mind. Secondly, there is vocational training. The young man or girl has to prepare for his or her future job and this is done partly in the school or lecture room, partly by practice and experience. With this kind of education I am not concerned in this paper. There are too few jobs available for the professional archaeologist to make it useful to run courses for those hoping for one of them. I do not think I should be far wrong if I suggested that there are not above a score of paid archaeological situations in England, and I shouldn't be surprised to learn that there were not above a couple of hundred or so all told, in the world today. Of course, this is what makes Prehistory so attractive! It is essentially a research and hobby subject of fascinating interest where the instructed amateur is well able to play a prominent part. In these days of specialization, the keen amateur is being given less and less scope. You may be a brilliant architect, but few people will recognize your work if you can't put half the alphabet after your name: and geological investigation done by someone who has not got a University or Museum post tends to be looked at askance by those who hold such situations. There are today enough trained prehistorians to keep the amateurs on the right lines, but not enough to dispense with their services. Though even in our subject, specialization is creeping in. I was somewhat shocked the other day to hear a very distinguished professor and former pupil of my own say that really an amateur should not be allowed to collect samples for the new so-called Carbon fourteen method of dating as this was essentially a job which should be reserved for the specialist! Vocational training, then, has little to do with my main thesis and in any case to my mind should not appear in any *school* curriculum, being only made available for students at a later stage. At the moment in England, there is far too great specialization at an early age. Frequently the unfortunate child is only too well aware that his whole future depends upon the next examination, and, however interested he may be in other subjects which he may come across, he must stick firmly to this particular last. Too often our education—especially in the Grammar Schools— is like a hurdle race, where the competitors must look neither to the right nor to the left; they must aim straight for the post, leaping over various examination obstacles as they appear in the way, and the one who gets there first gets the job. It has fallen to my lot to be the chairman of a County Council Awards Committee which gives away large sums of money to would-be candidates for university education. Many of them, poor dears, have thought of little but Chemistry, Physics and Mathematics since they were fourteen years old, and frankly they seem sometimes semi-human!

The third object of education with which I am specially concerned tonight is to broaden the outlook on life of the individual. And for this purpose any thinking being, or rather I should say anyone who allows himself or herself to consider the world around, his relationship to it, and to a postulated Creator, must have a few facts to go on both scientific and historic. When I was at school, for many of us anything before Roman times in England could have been summed up in the one word 'woad'. Some of us were aware that things had happened at an earlier date, especially in Greece and the Near East: that there was a story of mighty conquests to learn about and that, especially in the region of the coastline of Asia Minor, there had been people who had seriously tried to think. But even so it only went back to about 550 B.C. Before that date everything was, to say the least, dim and remote. It is not always realized how *new* is the subject of Prehistory, nor what a profound difference its study does make on a person's *Weltanschauung*. Of course I know that the Englishman John Frere was the Father of Prehistory and that he had shown as long ago as the 1790's that stone implements occurred associated with an extinct fauna and that therefore the men who made them must have been of very great antiquity, but none the less for some people the chronology of Archbishop Ussher still held sway. The world had been created in 4004 B.C. and that was that! As late as 1911, the opposition to Reid Moir's Tertiary eoliths at Ipswich was as much theological as archaeological. Of course, by then, the scientific world had accepted the great antiquity of man, but it was only after Prestwich and Evans's visit to Boucher de Perthes at Abbeville that the Royal Society in London finally accepted the evidence that man was contemporary with the laying down of the gravels of the Somme valley. As a young man, I knew Sir John Evans very well: he was one of my heroes; so while I am not old enough to remember the final pronouncement of the Royal Society, I am only one remove from it, in that I knew one of the parties very well. I was, however, at a meeting of the Geological Society in London when Sir Arthur Smith Woodward first presented to that august body an account of the paintings at Altamira! You will say that England was well behind other Continental countries at this time and that elsewhere, especially in France, much prehistoric knowledge had been acquired and absorbed. This no doubt is true, but it doesn't make any difference to my general thesis.

Let us go back for a moment to a school curriculum concerned with the training of the minds of the children. Here we must remember that we are having to deal with various age groups. In England, every child has to go to school at five years of age and, until seven, is placed in one of the Infant Classes. Here the main preoccupation is, and should always be, with reading, writing and simple arithmetic. Without these keys to knowledge, nothing further is really possible. Incidentally, it is somewhat sinister today to notice how much illiteracy there is among adults. As a Magistrate, I frequently come across cases where apparently normally intelligent witnesses cannot read the oath; and yet there are in it only three words of more than one syllable! Perhaps this is because there has been a tendency with us to replace the three R's by the three P's—painting, plasticine and puppetry! But I think this matter is being gradually dealt with at the present time. The time between the ages of seven to eleven, before the child is graded either to a Secondary Modern, a Secondary Technical or a Grammar School, is frequently a flowering period of special mental growth. Most children are naturally curious, some more than others, and so as a matter of fact are the peoples of some nations more than others. I well remember as a youngster one time when I was travelling third class in the South of France. My train arriving at Bergerac, the door was flung open and down below on the platform was a large peasant woman shaped like a cottage loaf with a beaming smile and carrying a live hen. 'Take my hen, young man,' she said, 'and put it on the rack and then help me in.' After we had disposed of the hen and she had arranged herself, she beamed at me and said: 'And what are you doing here, young man?' I replied that I was concerned with prehistory. 'Ah, yes,' she said, 'that sounds interesting. Tell me about it, young man. I have heard that in the mountains far away from here there are caves full of paintings. I would like to know about them.' I am afraid that this could very seldom happen in my own country. I cannot imagine any English countryman showing the slightest interest in anything that didn't immediately concern him. He would talk freely on politics or the price of beer, but his interest in prehistoric archaeology would be very perfunctory. Yet, as the Abbé Galliani said in the seventeenth century, man is the only animal that takes an interest in things that don't immediately concern himself, and surely it should be one of the objects of education to train the child to take up this heritage of our human kind at the time of his mind's awakening.

Archaeology and Education

Now there are various ways in which the mind can be exercised. A language other than one's own should certainly be studied. It's an education in itself to realize that there are other ways than one's own of expressing what one wishes to say. But above all one must train the sense perceptions and one must train the mind to draw logical deductions from the results obtained by the sense perceptions. This is where prehistoric archaeology seems to me to be peculiarly useful. The subject may be classed as an 'art' but its methods of investigation are purely scientific. Let us take an example. Any child can draw a picture on a piece of paper in red and when it is dry draw another over it in green; and even a C-stream child, one who is of low mental calibre, will realize when it is put to him, that the red picture was painted first *because it is underneath* the green one. And yet surely this is only an application of the geological law of succession on which the whole of geological history is built. A little later the complete law can be demonstrated by getting a layer of gravel, on which is placed a layer of clay, on which is placed a layer of sand, on which is placed a layer of mud. Then, with a penholder, all can be stirred up. Once again even the C-stream child will understand that the law of superposition is only true when you add the words 'if the levels have remained undisturbed'. A child stretches its mind best when it is fascinated by what it is learning, and there are few subjects so fascinating as prehistoric archaeology, dealing as it does with people and with the origins of things. There is hardly a child who can't be made to glow by an account of cave-hunting, and of the paintings and engravings found on the cave walls deep in the heart of a mountain. Or imagine for a moment a description of Daleau's excavation at Pair-non-Pair. Slowly the floor of the cave sinks as the layers of archaeological deposit are removed; and as the walls are thereby exposed behold they are found to be covered with engravings! But what logical deduction follows? Obviously the engravings must be older than the layers which covered them, and were therefore made by people older than those who made the industries that came to light in those covering layers.

Of course, I know that at present the school curriculum is already full up; but full up with what? I was educated at Eton many years ago, the premier school in England. Our minds were exercised by doing Latin verses and algebra. I would much rather have had my mind stretched by something more interesting and something which might have become a hobby subject, a side-line interest, when I grew up. Doing quadratic equations is certainly not a hobby subject for after life!

So far I have naturally based my argument on the country whose educational system I know best, but I venture to think that in Africa prehistoric archaeology should have a very special place. Nowadays, large areas of the continent are occupied by diverse peoples of diverse origins. If they are to live happily together and form one united loyal community they must have some bond in common that is of real importance to them all. Surely this should be the land in which they live, its past history, and thence its future well-being. Here is something which is theirs whatever their differences. Is not this a focus around which they can rally, forgetting their diverse origins and interests, in the common heritage of them all—the past history of their land? I once went to see Brother Otto at the Trappist Monastery at Mariannhill, near Durban. The monks had not long come out of silence and poor old Brother Otto had a lot to get off his chest! Indeed, he talked for five hours without stopping in a German-English that wasn't always easy to follow. In his early years in Germany, he had been an artist and his Superiors at Mariannhill set him to study the rock shelter art in the Trans Kei, because they said it was necessary to know something of the story of the past before one could deal properly with the present inhabitants of the land. I suggest that that was a right attitude and one that could be followed with advantage all over Africa wherever national education has been introduced. Incidentally, I rather wonder what has happened to that vast corpus of tracings that Brother Otto made. I have no doubt they are preserved carefully somewhere in South Africa, but I would like to suggest to any of my South African colleagues present that steps could well be taken to make them available to a wider public. Publication nowadays is not easy and the costs of coloured reproductions almost prohibitive. And yet there are wealthy people in the Union who might well put up the necessary money if they realized the interest of these things.

But it is in connection with post-school education that I am more particularly concerned—what we in England call Further Education. Naturally, at this stage, vocational courses do necessarily loom large. When all's said and done individuals have to train themselves for the job of their choice in life. But none the less, there is a place for cultural education and it is vital that this should be provided if we're not to sink into a civilization of narrow specialists. In this connection, I was interested some little time ago in my brother-in-law, an important chemical manufacturer in the Midlands, telling me that they were finding it good to have among their senior staff some people with a wider cultural background than that of the mere chemical specialist because their broader outlook did affect for good their vocational work. Now this is just where prehistory can help. To begin with it provides, as I have already said, an intellectual hobby. Democracy is asking for more pay and shorter hours, but what are people to do with their leisure? In England we do provide in innumerable evening institutes for the teaching of various kinds of craft work; it's only too easy nowadays for a youngster to practise carpentry, lampshade making, glove-making, leather work, embroidery, metal work and all sorts of things of that kind. All this is admirable, but there are people who need a more intellectual hobby subject. I have already said that prehistory *par excellence* is a subject for the amateur, but I did qualify the word amateur by putting before it the equally important word 'instructed'. A non-instructed amateur not only arrives nowhere, but can do damage to the subject and can sometimes even irreparably destroy precious evidence. The serious student need never fear that the subject is too difficult, too recondite for his capacities. He may not be able to wander freely in the realms of higher mathematics: to do that is reserved for the few, the very few—the late Bishop Barnes of Birmingham, himself a mathematician of note and a Fellow of the Royal Society, once told me that he estimated that there were only about 3 per cent of the population capable of entering into the mathematicians' world and that this 3 per cent was distributed irrespective of birth, background or training—but he will be able to understand the human problems of prehistory.

But even more important than the development of an intellectual hobby, which will be a joy for the rest of one's life, an object for travel and study and archaeological investigation, is the effect on one's own philosophy of soaking oneself in the prehistoric past. To begin with, there is the astounding antiquity of man to be remembered. Somewhere, it seems, back in Miocene times, out of certain animal 'stuff', there evolved a number of lines of development. Along one of these the evolution was not so much of the hard parts of the body as of the brain, and there developed a consciousness of self in its surroundings; or rather I should say there developed a soil in which the plant of this self-awareness in life could grow. Whether that plant is entirely part of the general evolution of the human being, or whether, as some theologians would have it, it is a gift from outside—the mistletoe growing on the apple tree—I leave it to you to determine as your particular temperaments may dictate; but the fact is that this self-consciousness can be demonstrated as existing at least 50,000 years ago, and there seems no reason to deny that it may go back infinitely further, even perhaps into Tertiary times. Before the discoveries of agriculture and the domestication of animals, primitive, hunting peoples were naturally vitally concerned with food, the daily necessity without which they must die. But we know that they were also concerned with two other great phenomena of nature, namely death and birth. There is no reason to think that when an animal dies its fellows are particularly concerned; but back in Mousterian times we have undoubted evidence that, even these strange beings, the Neanderthaloids, had thoughts about death and were concerned about it; for if they had not been so concerned why did they sometimes give the dead man or woman or child—notice that children come into this as well as adults—careful ceremonial burial? I need not remind you of the little sepulchral cave at the Chapelle aux Saintes with the buried bison's horn at the entrance and the little fireplace near the head of the body, which was buried with stone implements of the period and the bones of animals then living; nor need I remind you of La Ferrassie where adults and children are buried, this time in what had been the home site. Moreover, over the trench in which one of the children was placed was a large block of stone covered with cup markings artificially made. Examples could be multiplied, especially when we pass on into upper Palaeolithic times. But why should our forerunners in this remote past have buried some, at any rate, of their dead in this elaborate way? Surely we cannot escape the conclusion that the consciousness of death inherent in them as human beings had led them to pose to themselves the questions of why and whither? I am naturally not suggesting that Neanderthal man had evolved an elaborate conception of an afterlife, but I do suggest that the placing of tools with the body together with bones of animals good for food must have meant that he felt, even if dimly, that the being who had been alive and conscious would need them wherever he had now gone. But all this is 40,000 years and more ago, and, as I have said, it is not merely that man, the animal, is of great antiquity, but that man as a self-conscious thinking being is; and this surely puts our sense of the history of our kind into a rather thought-provoking perspective.

When we come to upper Palaeolithic man, with his wealth of industrial development and his art, we can get far more into touch with him as a human being; particularly is this so when we consider his art. I am well aware and heartily subscribe to the belief that the cave art was made for utilitarian purposes—a variety of sympathetic magic in connection with the getting hold of that prime necessity for humanity, food. But if upper Palaeolithic man in France and Northern Spain had not been of an artistic nature some other form of sympathetic magic would have been evolved, and indeed outside the areas named he did not commonly paint on and engrave the walls of deep dark caves. Moreover, I see no reason to believe that all the 'home' art (the small portable decorated objects found in the home-site deposits) necessarily had a utilitarian purpose. When you look at the little reindeer turning its head, engraved on a piece of sandy limestone from the prehistoric home of Laugerie Basse in the Dordogne, which I happen to possess, you cannot but feel that the man (or woman) who made it was indeed an artist. He knew nothing about gunpowder or T.N.T. or the splitting of the atom, but he had something which we generally consider to be indicative of a high stage of culture, namely genuine powers of observation, a delicacy of artistic appreciation and a fine skill in draughtsmanship. If you study the Aurignacian paintings at Lascaux you will be astonished at the sense of movement they display. Frankly, the first time I went there I was almost made giddy. Every animal seems to be in motion; the ponies are trotting, the oxen are pounding along, a line of stags may be swimming, and so on. But when you look more closely, while the paintings of the animals clearly indicate to what genera they must be assigned, in no case that I recall would you be able to say: 'Ah, I met that animal just before I came in here.' Now the opposite is the case at Altamira. Here everything is static, even the galloping pig seems to have been caught and frozen—it doesn't really get along. On the other hand many of the animals have their own personality. The paintings could almost be portraits! My old chief, Dr Hugo Obermaier, had his favourite bison: I had mine. I didn't like his, because I knew if I turned my back, the wicked old fellow would stick me with his horns. There was a nasty, uncertain, devilish look in his eye. My own favourite was a much more charming beast. I have not time here to argue whether the difference between Lascaux and Altamira is a difference of culture or is just due to the differing temperaments and skill of the particular artists concerned. I am prepared to assert, however, that the difference is real and is not merely subjective in myself, and that it seems to me to demonstrate up to the hilt the sensitive artistic qualities that existed among certain upper Palaeolithic peoples in certain geographical areas. As we look at these upper Palaeolithic folk and study the rise and evolution of their various cultures and, *pari passu* with that evolution, the evolution of the art cycles which were developed by them, we become aware that the rise and growth and finally death, of these cultures is analogous to the birth and growth and extinction of an individual. It is all rather like the first verse of the Book of Ecclesiastes in the Old Testament. The Hebrew word translated in our 1611 edition as 'vanity' means more nearly 'bubble'; and what really the Preacher wished to say was that humanity was like those bubbles which you see on a millrace: there are always bubbles there, yet they are never for long the same bubbles. They are always breaking yet always re-forming. You will say this is a pessimistic outlook on the cultural evolution of man, as shown by prehistoric studies. If you think of it in two dimensions, it is; but are you right to do so? Is cultural evolution only to be thought of as circular? History repeating itself? Is it not rather spiral? Is there not a third dimension to consider, tenuous, difficult to perceive, but none the less real? That is one of the fascinating problems for the prehistorian. Material progress can and sometimes does get lost. We can't make stained glass windows now as they could in the Middle Ages. But surely when we try to stand back and survey the long story of human evolution from the far-off days of prehistoric man till now, there is a progress other than the merely material; and it is that progress, spiritual if you like, which is really what is interesting.

At the end of palaeolithic times there came a revolution. I may be wrong, but I think it was one of the great crises in human history. The later discovery of metallurgy doubtless aided man's material well-being, but the development of the neolithic civilization, the result ultimately of man's finding out how to grow crops and domesticate animals, was a revolution, only comparable to the discoveries of electricity and nuclear physics. It entirely changed man's way of life. If the folk who went before can be described as our forerunners, from now onwards we can talk about our ancestors. For if your early eighteenth-century forebears could have been magic-carpeted back to neolithic times, they would have found things a bit simple on the material side indeed, but they would have soon fitted in to their hosts' way of life and outlook upon it—it would not have been essentially different from their own; whereas if they had gone back further and lived among my dear Magdalenian cave artists, they would indeed have felt themselves in another world—and even more so if Puck had taken them back to a Neanderthal settlement. I am not concerned in this paper to discuss the origin of the discovery of agriculture and the domestication of animals. I would merely say, as regards the latter, that by domestication I mean intentional breeding in captivity, not mere taming which may well have taken place in earlier periods. Nor can we argue as to whether the origin of the neolithic civilization was single or multiple, whether it took place in one area and was thence diffused to the rest of the world, or whether similar conditions in more than one area did not engender the discoveries on which it is based. It is possible to suggest that areas formerly fertile and now desert passed through an oasis stage during which man had to exercise his wits and do something about it, or go under. All these questions are of fascinating interest, as, too, are the different kinds of wild animals he used in his first domestications. It is sometimes possible through their help to determine from what direction came the new neolithic practices which 'neolithicized' a presumably mesolithic or palaeolithic area, enormously increasing the comforts of life. Again while these new discoveries made a great difference in the material prosperity of humanity it is not with this prosperity that I am concerned, and it is not merely this prosperity which makes the great gap between our forerunners and our ancestors. But it will, I hope, be interesting for a moment to consider some of the further effects of the new discoveries. First and foremost agriculture in particular demands a reasonably static existence. I know, of course, that in Northern Europe there is a stage where a little planting is done in a clearing in the forest and as soon as the ground begins to yield poorly, camp is moved and a new site selected. But at an early date in neolithic times, more particularly in the Near East, we find the development of the village, people living in one place, non-nomadic and dependent for the first time upon food production as against the mere hunting and food collecting of their predecessors. Now there are increased supplies and the possibility of storage against scarcity. It cannot have been easy for palaeolithic man to have stored food for any length of time (except perhaps for a little meat preserved in the natural 'fridges' of the ice age!) but now the growing of cereals consequent on planting and harvesting made such storage possible. As there was more food, so there were more people. Among primitive folk the Law of Malthus to a large extent holds sway. I imagine the population must have been regulated by the pressure of babies. If babies could be kept alive, they were; if they could not, well, they just died off. Now many more could be kept alive and therefore the population increased. But not every one was needed for the food production. There must have been an increase in leisure, and it is only where there is leisure that experiment and progress are possible. There is a deep truth in the remark of the old Quaker. A young man had been telling him how busy he was, that his business required this and his other activities required that, and that from morning to night, with only just enough time for sleep, he was fully occupied. At last the old Quaker looked at him and said: 'But, friend, when hast thou time to think?' Surely in a beehive it is only among the drones that any progress is possible! Doubtless I am simplifying matters, and I was certainly not there to check it all up, but I have the impression that it was only with the growth of the neolithic civilization that leisure on a large scale could be enjoyed. Of course there is never an advantage without a disadvantage. Our careful villagers have laid up large stores against the long winter, while their neighbours over the hill have used up their supplies in riotous living. The obvious result must have frequently taken place! In palaeolithic times doubtless men quarrelled. They would hardly be human if they had not. But organized attack involving organized defence would seem to have been a product of the neolithic civilization.

Yet there is something deeper still that humanity learned as a result of the new way of life, and that was how to live in close contact with one another without too many sparks flying. I always tell my students at Cambridge that I learned a great deal in the early days of the last war when the evacuation took place from London of numberless women and children, who were planted down in what were thought to be the safe localities. I was billeting officer for my own village, and I very soon learned a fact of vital significance in human history, namely that no power in heaven or hell can compel two women to agree over one frying-pan in one kitchen! In this regard is Africa any different from Europe? If in a village people steal each other's goods, borrow each other's women, kill each other freely and despise the elderly, that village will not survive! And so customs grew up, especially in the Near East, where these actions were taboo. Later, these customs became codified into laws with the growth of what can be described as an embryo form of government. But that is not all. It may be true to say that the consequence of disregarding these laws would be the extinction of the community, but that would not prevent unscrupulous people from disregarding these customs for their own ends. What sanctions could be devised to make people behave? Remember we are dealing with a period long before strong central governments with, relatively speaking, infinite powers had been evolved. It would seem that there developed among certain people of the Upper Euphrates, the Mitanni, a concept of a God of cosmic and social order. His name was Artha, and he seems to have been connected with a God of similar qualities, Varuna, who was introduced into Northern India by the first Aryan-speaking invaders. Artha, of course, was a single God because he dealt with a single subject, namely Law. Indeed, he might be considered in a sense an apotheosis of law both in nature and for man. Doubtless at the beginning each people would appropriate this concept to themselves in their own special deity; only later did the idea of a God of cosmic and social order become universalized, but none the less it is something entirely different from the nature-gods and indeed from anything that we have had to deal with previously —this growth of the idea of law and order and of the way things must be done by members of a community, lest catastrophe follow. And the old legends do suggest that catastrophe did sometimes follow. Our friends, Korah, Dathan and Co. in the Book of Numbers disobeyed and as a result the earth opened and they were swallowed up! Now this acceptance of the necessity of order in a community life involves the realization that the individual, while perhaps retaining considerable freedoms, must necessarily in many ways subordinate his own desires to the good of the whole group. We today have travelled a long way since man's first realization of these early laws of life. A neolithic settlement must indeed have been a very primitive affair, but it was the beginning of what has developed into our own civilization today, and it was profoundly different from anything that had preceded it.

Finally, there is one point which I think is interesting, though it is not entirely the result of prehistoric studies. There is no doubt that any culture, whether prehistoric or modern, in order to exist must come to terms with its surroundings. No doubt our neolithic ancestors were rather better off than our earlier forerunners, because they produced and stored food instead of merely collecting it. But there were other factors to take into account and within certain limits it is true to say that similar conditions, climatic and otherwise, engender a similar material culture to cope with them: but if that were the end we should not be able to show much progress. There is, however, another factor in the human story and that is Desire. Desire may be individual or communal. It may be a result of the individual or the group wishing to do something and it may result from envy of another contacted group, who have already made certain discoveries, tending to make life easier. But it does not follow that a people will always wish to have what other people have got. I believe it is true that the Portuguese introduced the black pig into the island of Pemba but that it has never been taken over by the populations of the mainland, why, I do not know. Perhaps they did not like the black colour! It is interesting to note even in our own day how a new discovery at first merely a plaything for the rich—wireless is a case in point—because it is desired by the mass very soon becomes available for all. In prehistoric times mankind at different periods and under different conditions developed various economies, the seal hunters of the North, the reindeer hunters of Magdalenian times, and so on. How far contact between different cultures developed new desires, which may in some cases be reflected in the material culture, is a subject which is only nowadays being considered.

I have tried to give you a few desultory notes on my thesis. I have suggested that Archaeology is fortunately not a good subject for vocational teaching, that it is an admirable and fascinating study to help to train the minds of the young, and that, in Africa, it might seem to have a very special significance. I have also urged that, as an intellectual hobby subject it reigns supreme. Anyone who has seen the flowering of archaeological research which took place in England between the wars will have no hesitation in agreeing that its charm and interest have a popular appeal. Finally, I have noted some of the ways in which I feel a study of the subject does influence our world outlook, widens it, makes us feel that we are part of a larger show, and explains to some extent how some things have come about. Of course, there are many other points that I might have raised. You would hardly expect me to deal with what has become a vast subject even in my own lifetime in the course of one short talk. But if heretofore you have not considered these matters, and if I have, even to a slight extent, aroused an interest in them, then I shall feel that this paper has not been written in vain.

As a postscript, should I be asked in conclusion what is the immediate and practical application of what I have tried to say in this paper both in Africa and in Europe, I would reply that surely as a beginning the subject should be recognized in Teacher's Training Colleges and be in their curricula. I believe the native education here is the concern of Northern Rhodesia, while the European secondary education is dealt with by the Federation. But this ought not to prove too great a difficulty. Then the Examination Syndicate of the University of Cambridge should be asked to include archaeological papers, both at ordinary and at higher levels, in their options for the School Certificate. There would be no difficulty about this I am sure. Finally, where such a thing is suitable or possible local history groups could be formed, in touch with the Rhodes-Livingstone Museum, to explore their immediate localities and to report any finds. This latter procedure, I may say, has caught on very considerably in England and has been a great success creating as it does a very great interest in their surroundings for all concerned.